Fish Habitat:
Essential Fish Habitat and Rehabilitation

Funding for the publication of this book was provided by the

U.S. Department of Commerce
National Oceanic and Atmospheric Administration
National Marine Fisheries Service
National Sea Grant College Program

Fish Habitat:
Essential Fish Habitat and Rehabilitation

Lee R. Benaka
Editor

American Fisheries Society Symposium 22

Proceedings of the Sea Grant Symposium on Fish Habitat:
"Essential Fish Habitat" and Rehabilitation
Held at Hartford, Connecticut, USA
26–27 August 1998

American Fisheries Society
Bethesda, Maryland
1999

The American Fisheries Society Symposium series is a registered serial. Suggested citation formats follow.

Entire book

Benaka, L., editor. 1999. Fish habitat: essential fish habitat and rehabilitation. American Fisheries Society, Symposium 22, Bethesda, Maryland.

Article within the book

Norse, E. A., and L. Watling. 1999. Impacts of mobile fishing gear: the biodiversity perspective. Pages 31–40 *in* L. Benaka, editor. Fish habitat: essential fish habitat and rehabilitation. American Fisheries Society, Symposium 22, Bethesda, Maryland.

Cover design by Cindy Hayter, Ohio Sea Grant. Cover photos, clockwise from lower left, courtesy of the National Oceanic and Atmospheric Administration, New Jersey Sea Grant, and Victoria O'Connell at the Alaska Department of Fish and Game. Back cover photos courtesy of Louisiana Department of Wildlife and Fisheries and Ohio Sea Grant.

Library of Congress Catalog Card Number: 98-88572
ISBN 1-888569-12-3
ISSN 0892-2284

Printed in the United States of America on acid-free paper.

American Fisheries Society
5410 Grosvenor Lane, Suite 110
Bethesda, Maryland 20814-2199
USA

DEDICATION

This book is dedicated to Nathaniel Shaw Bingham (1937–1998), in appreciation for his outstanding, long-term contributions toward saving coastal habitats and their living resources for future generations.

Contents

Part Six: Fish Habitat Rehabilitation and Socioeconomic Issues

Preface

Fish habitat management and conservation received more attention in 1998 from scientists and policy makers than possibly ever before, in large part due to the essential fish habitat (EFH) measures included in the 1996 reauthorization of the Magnuson-Stevens Fishery Conservation and Management Act. It is a tribute to the foresight of my advisors from the American Fisheries Society (AFS) and the National Sea Grant College Program that they chose fish habitat and EFH as the theme of the first-ever AFS–Sea Grant Internship.

This proceedings volume, which is based on a Sea Grant symposium on fish habitat that took place at the 1998 AFS Annual Meeting in Hartford, Connecticut, presents the findings and conclusions of scientists and policy makers who have been doing the hands-on work to create and implement the EFH policy. This volume also presents the work of Sea Grant-funded researchers who studied (and continue to study) fish habitat before it was such a "hot" topic. Fish habitat experts from Canada and Europe also contribute studies to this volume, emphasizing that although EFH may be a policy implemented by fisheries managers in the United States, sophisticated studies of habitat necessary for sustainable fisheries have been conducted in many different countries for several years. I hope that the Sea Grant fish habitat symposium and proceedings volume establish a benchmark for fish habitat policy and science in the late 1990s and help to foster future collaborations and synergism in habitat research and policy.

When my advisors and I met to discuss my program of work at the 1997 AFS Annual Meeting in Monterey, California, my knowledge of fish habitat policy and science was not quite as sophisticated as it is today. The expert advice of numerous individuals was invaluable as I organized what grew into a day-and-a-half-long symposium for the 1998 AFS Annual Meeting and managed and edited this proceedings volume.

Neither the Sea Grant fish habitat symposium nor the proceedings volume based on the symposium would have been possible without the vision and leadership of Ronald Baird, Director, National Sea Grant College Program, and Paul Brouha, former Executive Director, American Fisheries Society. In addition, the support of Rolland Schmitten, Director, National Marine Fisheries Service, was instrumental in making this book a reality. I am sincerely grateful for the decision of Paul Brouha and Ronald Baird to create an AFS–Sea Grant Internship, which has served as an invaluable professional development experience for me. I believe the internship also has helped to create stronger ties and the potential for future beneficial collaborations between the AFS and Sea Grant. My efforts in organizing the symposium and proceedings volume were directed and supervised not only by Ronald Baird and Paul Brouha, but also by my Sea Grant Advisory Panel, which included Leon Cammen, Carlos Fetterolf, Shirley Fiske, Gene Fritz, Jeffrey Reutter, Jeffrey Stephan, and Robert Stickney. I greatly appreciate my advisors' assistance in recruiting an extremely talented group of fish habitat professionals for this symposium and book and helping me through challenging times during the organization of this symposium.

I also received helpful advice during the early stages of organizing the fish habitat symposium from Mark Amaral, Brenda Baxter, Thomas Bigford, Phil Bowman, Dail Brown, Jim Burgess, Lee Crockett, Ellie Dorsey, Ron Hill, Elaine Knight, Cliff Kraft, Steve Leathery, Rick Lierd, Ron Lukens, Scott Nixon, Brenda Norcross, Stephen Phillips, William Seaman, Dianne Stephan, and Waldo Wakefield.

A handful of fish habitat experts agreed to be part of the symposium and book but for various good reasons were not able to participate in the final products. I would like to thank Nathaniel Bingham, Scott Burns, Paul Coreil, Cliff Goudey, Andy Mager, Robert McConnaughey, Roger Pugliese, Doug Rader, and Ronald Smolowitz for their enthusiasm and helpfulness.

Jeremy Collie, Robert Francis, and Jerome Hermsen made valuable presentations at the Sea Grant fish habitat symposium in Hartford that are not part of this volume, and their contributions greatly enhanced the overall quality of the symposium. Russell Brown and C. Paola Ferreri organized the well-run 1998 AFS Annual Meeting and provided me with helpful advice and support during and prior to the meeting. In addition, the six panel discussion moderators—Ronald Baird, John Musick, Ann Bucklin, Robert Stickney, Carlos Fetterolf, and Scott Holt—are to be commended for the effort they devoted to ensuring thought-provoking debates on fish habitat and essential fish habitat at the Sea Grant fish habitat symposium.

I owe a debt of gratitude to all of the authors who contributed chapters to this book. The authors agreed to tight deadlines necessitated by the timeframe of my internship and endured with good cheer my pestering regarding various deadlines. I am honored that such an illustrious group of scientists and policy makers agreed to participate in this book and generously devote their valuable time to the writing of high-quality contributions to fish habitat literature.

Each chapter in this book was examined by three different peer reviewers from a variety of natural resource agencies, institutions, and professions. The careful analysis and incisive comments of the reviewers enhanced the quality of these chapters enormously. This book truly reflects not only the experience and knowledge of each author but also the advice and insight of the following reviewers: Kenneth Able, James Acheson, Ronald Baird, Donald Baltz, Betty Beach, Thomas Bigford, Robert Bilby, James Bohnsack, Ann Bucklin, Richard Burroughs, Mark Butler, Arne Carr, Joseph Cone, Patrick Connolly, Paul Coreil, John Day, Michele Dionne, Tanya Dobrzynski, Thomas Edsall, Carlos Fetterolf, John Gannon, John Gates, Chris Glass, Merlin Gollickey, Jon Hare, Ken Heck, Scott Holt, Earl Hopper, Michael Hudgins, Mike Jepson, David Jude, Michel Kaiser, Robert Kavetsky, Grace Klein-MacPhee, Ronald Kneib, Jon Kurland, Richard Langton, Ron Lukens, Charles Manooch, James McVey, John Miller, Charles Minns, James Murray, John Musick, Dennis Nixon, Paul Parker, William Pearcy, Joseph Pelczarski, Chris Perle, Stephen Phillips, Elijah Ramsey, Peter Rubec, William Seaman, Jeffrey Stephan, Robert Stickney, Robert Stone, Gregory Stunz, Page Valentine, and Charles Wenner.

Members of the National Sea Grant Office and the Sea Grant network were instrumental in creating a graphic identity for this book and helping to plan the book's marketing strategy. Sue Borda, Cindy Hayter, James Murray, Victor Omelczenko, Jeffrey Reutter, and Ben Sherman deserve thanks for helping to ensure the success of this book.

This book would not have been published in such a professional and timely manner without the skill and diligence of the publications and marketing professionals at the AFS. I sincerely thank Terry Ames, Janet Harry, Rick Horten, Robert Kendall, Sally Kendall, Robert Rand, Beth Staehle, and Eric Wurzbacher for their patience, guidance, and assistance. In addition, I would like to thank the entire professional staff of the AFS, especially Betsy Fritz, Jennifer Gallivan, Karen Maggi, Kristin Merriman-Clarke, and Elizabeth Rockman for helping to make my internship a pleasant and rewarding experience.

Finally, I wish to recognize my professors in the Marine Affairs Department at the University of Rhode Island, including Richard Burroughs, Christopher Dyer, Lawrence Juda, and Dennis Nixon, who provided me with the knowledge and skills necessary to carry out the responsibilities of this internship. And last but certainly not least, I thank Danielle Feuillan for her support.

Lee R. Benaka
Editor

Introduction

Lee R. Benaka

Sea Grant Intern, American Fisheries Society
5410 Grosvenor Lane, Suite 110, Bethesda, Maryland 20814-2199, USA

In October 1996, the U.S. Congress reauthorized the Magnuson-Stevens Fishery Conservation and Management Act through the Sustainable Fisheries Act (SFA). The SFA included unprecedented conservation measures that had been long-sought by members of the American Fisheries Society (AFS), the National Sea Grant College Program, fishing industry groups, nongovernmental conservation organizations, and federal and state agencies. Bycatch reduction and overfishing provisions and a redefinition of optimum yield were among the innovations introduced into the SFA. Also new to the SFA were essential fish habitat (EFH) provisions, which required all fishery management councils by October 1998 to amend their fishery management plans (covering over 600 stocks) to identify, for each species, the essential fish habitat which are "those waters and substrate necessary for fish for spawning, feeding or growth to maturity." Threats to habitat from fishing and nonfishing activities, as well as steps necessary to ameliorate those threats, also had to be identified by October 1998.

The EFH policy created a great deal of work for people in 1998. Managers and biologists at the National Marine Fisheries Service (NMFS) devoted a great deal of resources to support the fishery management councils and to ensure EFH rules were scientifically sound. Interest groups that never before had paid much attention to fish habitat began to learn all they could about habitat policy. Fish habitat scientists employed by universities and state agencies received more invitations to serve on advisory committees and speak at conferences than ever before.

Based on the amount of activity related to EFH that would be occurring in 1998, especially as the October 1998 deadline for EFH identification approached, leaders within the AFS, Sea Grant, and other National Oceanic and Atmospheric Administration agencies decided that fish habitat research in general, and the EFH policy in particular, was worthy of a joint AFS—Sea Grant symposium and a proceedings volume. This volume contains the proceedings of the August 1998 symposium "Fish Habitat: Essential Fish Habitat and Rehabilitation," which was held in Hartford, Connecticut. It presents the findings and conclusions of scientists and policy makers who have been doing the hands-on work to implement EFH policy and Sea Grant-funded researchers who studied (and continue to study) fish habitat before it was such a "hot" topic.

The outline of this book generally follows the symposium's structure. The book opens with perspectives on the EFH policy from federal, environmental, fishing industry, and fishery management council perspectives. These perspectives are not meant to be all-encompassing but rather individual perspectives from various entities that have helped to craft and carry out the EFH policy. The following section deals with the complex issue of EFH identification, looking at two species in particular and examining sampling methods and remote-sensing techniques related to EFH. Fishing impacts and nonfishing impacts to fish habitat make up the next two sections, which includes two substantial papers commissioned by the AFS on fishing impacts to habitat. The fifth section focuses on Great Lakes fish habitat rehabilitation, and the sixth section presents research on marine fish habitat by leading scientists. Finally, I recap points made at six symposium panel discussions and suggest future habitat policy and research directions.

As I write this introduction, the fishery management councils have five months remaining to amend all of their fishery management plans to include EFH provisions. Some people observing or participating in this EFH process have wondered, will the fish habitat provisions introduced in the 1996 Sustainable Fisheries Act make a difference for fisheries, or will they just create another level of paper to be pushed, more piles of studies, and little concrete action or visible improvement? It seems that interagency and intersector collaboration is the key to successful fish habitat policy. If agencies such as the National Marine Fisheries Service, Sea Grant, the National Ocean Service, and the U.S. Fish and Wildlife Service; nongovernmental organizations such as the AFS; the fishing industry; and the environmental community can act together and communicate effectively, EFH policy has a great chance of success. On a more practical level, it must be recognized that additional resources in the form of research dollars and bodies will need to be devoted to the enormous task of understanding and safeguarding fish habitat.

Foreword

RONALD C. BAIRD

National Sea Grant College Program
National Oceanic and Atmospheric Administration
1315 East-West Highway, SSMC-3, Room 11716
Silver Spring, Maryland 20910, USA

When Paul Brouha and I agreed to sponsor a fellowship between the National Oceanic and Atmospheric Administration (NOAA)'s Sea Grant Program and the American Fisheries Society (AFS), the intent was to ask the recipient to organize a symposium at the 1998 AFS Annual Meeting and to help edit a proceedings volume. Lee Benaka, this volume's editor, is the first AFS/Sea Grant Fellow. Paul and I also agreed that one of the most important issues in contemporary fisheries science is essential fish habitat (EFH). With encouragement from Rolland Schmitten, Director of NOAA's National Marine Fisheries Service, we decided to focus our first symposium on EFH, and this volume is a tribute to the many individual contributors and the hard work of Lee Benaka.

Concerning habitat, it is my contention that by enacting the EFH provisions in the Sustainable Fisheries Act of 1996, Congress has taken a quantum leap in legislative approaches to the management of coastal marine environments. To understand why this is the case, we need to examine the provisions of the law itself.

In October 1996, the U.S. Congress enacted The Sustainable Fisheries Act (P.L. 104-297), which amended the Magnuson Fishery Conservation and Management Act of 1976 (P.L. 94-265) (Magnuson Act) to add EFH provisions to the management and conservation clauses of the Magnuson Act. These new provisions require NOAA to facilitate the long-term protection of EFH, which has been defined as "those waters and substrates necessary to fish for spawning, breeding, feeding, or growth to maturity." In addition, EFH has been defined to include the associated physical, chemical, and biological properties that are used by fish and are necessary to support a managed level of fish biomass production.

The amended Magnuson Act mandates the sustainability of fishery resource production. The word "sustainability" implies an indefinite time frame, and the Magnuson Act's emphasis on production will require integrated management approaches to marine resources in which the integrity and function of ecological systems that support fish production are considered among competing multiple uses for a given habitat. Satisfying the requirements of the amended Magnuson Act involves ecosystem-based approaches to resource management and provides a means for defining acceptable ecosystem states for management purposes, that is, states that ensure a given level of production of fish biomass for managed species. Such an approach requires fisheries management for the first time to consider marine environments in a holistic context with sufficient dimensionality and geographic extent to preserve system functionality for fish production while also addressing multiple-use issues.

It is through this emphasis on habitat in a broad sense that the U.S. Congress has transformed the 1976 Magnuson Act into one of the most significant pieces of environmental legislation to emerge since the 1972 amendments to the federal Water Pollution Control Act (P.L. 92-500), more popularly known as the Clean Water Act. Focus on the production function of fish population dynamics introduces not only ecosystem-based management (preservation of function and integrity) but also integrated management (multiple use reconciliation) into the fisheries stewardship equation. The legislation moreover identifies metrics for what constitutes acceptable ecosystem states that can be expressed in the coinage of fish biomass production. This is a long way indeed from harvest-control and single-species approaches to fishery management.

Novel approaches to environmental management do not ensure success, no matter how well intentioned or reasoned those approaches might be. This certainly is the case with the amended Magnuson Act and emerging EFH policy. Integrated management approaches represent new management territory of extreme complexity, both biologically and socially. We are talking about sustainability (a very long time indeed), management of biological systems to produce "satisfactory" yields, anthropogenic impacts, and multiple use resolution. These management challenges encompass, for starters, wetlands and watersheds, pollution, eutrophication, exotic species, habitat alteration, recreational and commercial uses of habitat, and bycatch and other fishing gear effects. As if this were not enough, there are issues of multiple, overlapping agency—state jurisdictions as well as a far-from-complete understanding of how marine ecosystems work and the significance of ecosystem processes to exploited fish populations.

Indeed, the academic and fishery management communities, outside interest groups, and federal agencies have only recently begun to realize the implications of EFH. The implications of EFH also are not widely appreciated by the public at large. What is clear is that the management of marine fisheries can now include a staggering array of considerations affecting virtually every natural and anthropogenic impact on marine environments and every part of society involved in marine resource utilization. The challenges of EFH to our management agencies and society in general are immense. We will be faced for a long time with many contentious issues, challenges in the courts, and policy adjustments in response to new knowledge.

However, the message inherent in this symposium is not one of pessimism or impossibility. The EFH provisions represent a magnificent opportunity to take marine resource management to an exciting next level. We can continue to build on the accomplishments realized under the Clean Water Act of 1972 by, as authors Merion Chertow and Daniel Esty suggest, thinking ecologically. Thinking ecologically means thinking how the next generation of environmental policy can yield greater benefits at reasonable costs to society and then seeking realistic, practical, science-based policy solutions to specific habitat issues. This is the critical dimension of our challenge.

This volume, sponsored by the American Fisheries Society and NOAA (Sea Grant and the NMFS), represents the tentative first steps in setting a national agenda on EFH that could determine in large measure the tempo and mode of this country's evolution toward the integrated management of coastal and marine environments. Transitioning to EFH approaches to fisheries management is a monumental task but a necessary step on the road to sustainable aquatic ecosystems and fisheries resources.

Symbols and Abbreviations

The following symbols and abbreviations may be found in this book without definition. Also undefined are standard mathematical and statistical symbols given in most dictionaries.

A	ampere	i.e.	(id est) that is
AC	alternating current	IU	international unit
Bq	becquerel	J	joule
C	coulomb	K	Kelvin (degrees above absolute zero)
°C	degrees Celsius	k	kilo (10^3, as a prefix)
cal	calorie	kg	kilogram
cd	candela	km	kilometer
cm	centimeter	l	levorotatory
Co.	Company	L	levo (as a prefix)
Corp.	Corporation	L	liter (0.264 gal, 1.06 qt)
cov	covariance	lb	pound (0.454 kg, 454g)
DC	direct current; District of Columbia	lm	lumen
D	dextro (as a prefix)	log	logarithm
d	day	Ltd.	Limited
d	dextrorotatory	M	mega (10^6, as a prefix); molar (as a suffix or by itself)
df	degrees of freedom		
dL	deciliter	m	meter (as a suffix or by itself); milli (10^{-3}, as a prefix)
E	east		
E	expected value	mi	mile (1.61 km)
e	base of natural logarithm (2.71828…)	min	minute
e.g.	(exempli gratia) for example	mol	mole
eq	equivalent	N	normal (for chemistry); north (for geography); newton
et al.	(et alii) and others		
etc.	et cetera	N	sample size
eV	electron volt	NS	not significant
F	filial generation; Farad	n	ploidy; nanno (10^{-9}, as a prefix)
°F	degrees Fahrenheit	o	ortho (as a chemical prefix)
fc	footcandle (0.0929 lx)	oz	ounce (28.4 g)
ft	foot (30.5 cm)	P	probability
ft³/s	cubic feet per second (0.0283 m³/s)	p	para (as a chemical prefix)
g	gram	p	pico (10^{-12}, as a prefix)
G	giga (10^9, as a prefix)	Pa	pascal
gal	gallon (3.79 L)	pH	negative log of hydrogen ion activity
Gy	gray	ppm	parts per million
h	hour	qt	quart (0.946 L)
ha	hectare (2.47 acres)	R	multiple correlation or regression coefficient
hp	horsepower (746 W)		
Hz	hertz	r	simple correlation or regression coefficient
in	inch (2.54 cm)		
Inc.	Incorporated	rad	radian

S	siemens (for electrical conductance); south (for geography)	Wb	weber
		yd	yard (0.914 m, 91.4 cm)
SD	standard deviation	α	probability of type I error (false rejection of null hypothesis)
SE	standard error		
s	second	β	probability of type II error (false acceptance of null hypothesis)
T	tesla		
tris	tris(hydroxymethyl)-aminomethane (a buffer)	Ω	ohm
		m	micro (10^{-6}, as a prefix)
UK	United Kingdom	′	minute (angular)
U.S.	United States (adjective)	″	second (angular)
USA	United States of America (noun)	°	degree (temperature as a prefix, angular as a suffix)
V	volt		
V, Var	variance (population)	%	per cent (per hundred)
var	variance (sample)	‰	per mille (per thousand)
W	watt (for power); west (for geography)		

American Fisheries Society Symposium 22:1–2, 1999

Part One:
Essential Fish Habitat Perspectives

RONALD C. BAIRD

National Sea Grant College Program
National Oceanic and Atmospheric Administration
1315 East-West Highway, SSMC-3, Eleventh Floor
Silver Spring, Maryland 20910, USA

The presentations and discussions during the opening session of the Sea Grant fish habitat symposium at the 1998 Annual Meeting of the American Fisheries Society focused primarily on the critical dimensions of contemporary habitat degradation and the related policy and management issues involved in ensuring compliance with the essential fish habitat (EFH) provisions of the Sustainable Fisheries Act (SFA). It is important to note, however, that the intended purpose of the EFH provisions of the SFA is to ensure the production on a sustainable basis of harvestable products. The SFA ultimately is concerned with measurable economic benefits (derived from the removal of fish from the environment), and the SFA's habitat preservation and rehabilitation elements are intended to preserve and enhance those economic benefits. Although the SFA's EFH provisions have profound implications for the environmental protection of marine ecosystems, the SFA differs considerably in its philosophical basis from other environmental protection legislation in that the SFA implies that ecosystems are "managed" for economic purposes.

From the perspectives of the fisheries manager, environmentalist, industry representative, and scientist who make up the first section of this book, there is general agreement that habitat degradation is the most important threat to the long-term recovery and preservation of exploitable fish stocks. Degradation simply must be addressed, and in a timely fashion. The contributors point to the diversity of threats and impacts arising primarily from explosive population growth and development in coastal areas. The authors call attention to the nonfishing activities that now threaten fish stocks. Impacts from nonfishing activities occur primarily in coastal waters and estuaries, environments upon which a significant proportion of our commercial fish stocks are dependent at some stage of their lives. Specific threats cited by the authors of the following chapters include destruction of wetlands, eutrophication, harmful algal blooms, and direct degradation or alteration of the environment. Harvesting practices are also strongly implicated as contributors to degradation. Excessive bycatch, overfishing, and gear-induced habitat destruction can lead to irreversible or long-term effects due to the conversion of ecosystems to less-productive states. The authors acknowledge a fundamental relationship between quality of habitat and quality of fisheries resources.

There is general agreement among the authors that the EFH provisions are a necessary first step to habitat preservation and restoration. Previous laws have been too narrow to allow comprehensive approaches to fisheries habitat management. The real challenge is the development of public policy and suitable EFH guidelines. There promises to be considerable controversy over current interpretations of EFH policy that will create an intense political climate. Strong views are expressed in some of the following chapters that the current law and guidelines have serious problems. There is concern that the SFA contains no enforceable mechanisms for preventing nonfishing activities from degrading habitats. Minimalist approaches and political pressures are real problems here. The policy's lack of performance criteria and lack of risk-assessment measures are also noted in this section of the book. Threats need to be ranked according to scale, severity, and persistence. Some of the authors note the importance of consensus and constituency involvement and cite problems with definitions such as critical habitat, ecosystem health, sustainable abundances, and optimum yield in relation to the EFH provisions. The notion of preserves and refuges, as well as the importance of activities detrimental to fish stocks that occur in areas where fish are not abundant, must be considered. Finally, some of the authors in this section express concern that the EFH policy may be open to such broad interpretations and controversies that the resulting backlash might further "water down" the present legislation.

Overall, the EFH provisions provide for the first time the legislative framework for broad habitat considerations to be incorporated into the management of fisheries resources and by extension into the management of marine environments in general. The EFH provisions represent a profound opportunity for this nation and an equally difficult challenge. The key to success will be the development of practical, workable public policy and science-based, operationally clear guidelines formulated with broad consensus and constituency input.

American Fisheries Society Symposium 22:3–10, 1999

Essential Fish Habitat: Opportunities and Challenges for the Next Millennium

ROLLAND A. SCHMITTEN

National Oceanic and Atmospheric Administration, National Marine Fisheries Service
1315 East-West Highway, 14555 SSMC3, Silver Spring, Maryland 20910-3282, USA

Abstract.—With the passage of the Sustainable Fisheries Act in the fall of 1996, significant new opportunities and challenges exist in the United States to protect and conserve the habitat of marine, estuarine, and anadromous finfish as well as key populations of mollusks and crustaceans. As of October 1998, all federal fishery management councils (the Councils) were required to amend their fishery management plans (covering over 700 stocks) to identify, for each species, the essential fish habitat, which is "those waters and substrate necessary to fish for spawning, feeding or growth to maturity." Threats to habitat and steps necessary to ameliorate those threats also had to be identified. Information from fisheries scientists and managers throughout the country will be needed to accurately identify essential fish habitat and habitat threats and to monitor the effectiveness of protective measures that come into force once habitat has been identified as essential. My vision, which is also that of the National Oceanic and Atmospheric Administration, is no further loss of habitat quantity and quality as well as the preservation and restoration of habitat biodiversity by the year 2004. The essential fish habitat provisions of the Magnuson-Stevens Act provide an outstanding opportunity for the National Marine Fisheries Service, the Councils, and our numerous partners from every sector of society to develop new ecosystem approaches to fishery management addressing cumulative impacts to habitats in a comprehensive, effective, and efficient manner.

The world's oceans have provided fisheries resources for food and other products for all of human history and prehistory. The peoples of the world have shepherded this bounty in a sustainable way, most often by their limited numbers and limited technology, until recent history. As we approach the end of the 20th century, our capabilities for maintaining sustainability of marine resources, both in the United States and the world, are put to the test. We are challenged to develop new and innovative ways to transition our management approaches to sustainable fisheries for the next millennium by eliminating overfishing, protecting and restoring fish habitat, reducing waste (bycatch) or indiscriminate practices resulting in waste, and applying ecosystem principles to fisheries management. The National Marine Fisheries Service (NMFS), part of the National Oceanic and Atmospheric Administration in the U.S. Department of Commerce, is poised to meet these challenges to assure healthy stocks of marine, estuarine, and anadromous fisheries resources for the foreseeable future.

This paper focuses on a part of sustainability that has taken on renewed significance: the importance of sustainable fish habitat for restoring and maintaining healthy fish stocks. First we must establish the context in which sustainable capture fisheries can be attainable—most importantly by eliminating overfishing, reducing the ecosystem disruption caused by excessive bycatch, and, in this proper context, protecting and restoring aquatic habitat.

Status of U.S. Fisheries Resources

Marine fishery resources the world over are under intensive pressure from fishing (Botsford et al. 1997; FAO 1997a; Garcia and Newton 1997). The Food and Agriculture Organization (FAO) of the United Nations reported a world marine fisheries catch of around 84 million metric tons for 1995, the most recent year for which data are available (FAO 1997a, 1997b). The FAO also indicated that the majority of stocks harvested from the wild may be classified as fully or overexploited. There is a growing consensus that the major sources of pressure on fishery sustainability come from overcapacity of the harvesting industry, habitat loss, and open-access policies. These are challenges where new approaches are called for and where the NMFS is responding. For capture fisheries in the United States, overcapacity is one of the most important factors threatening the long-term viability of exploited fish stocks and the fisheries that depend upon them. Unpublicized, in most cases, is the loss and degradation of habitat from uncontrolled population growth and pollution in coastal watersheds worldwide. These cultural activities most certainly reduce the vitality of fisheries stocks. Most of these impacts are local and regional; for wide-ranging species the impact may be global. The threats to our fish habitat are not unlike the proverbial Chinese execution: death by a thousand cuts.

Bycatch from commercial fisheries confounds our management as well as habitat- and biodiversity-protection efforts. Each year, world commercial marine fisheries result in about 27 million metric tons of discards with about 77 million metric tons of catch landed. Thus, about one-quarter of the catch may be discarded (Alverson et al. 1994; Alverson 1998). The highest U.S. ratios of discarded-to-retained catch are in the southeast shrimp trawl fisheries (averaging about 4 kg of finfish to 1 kg of shrimp [NMFS 1998]), although this bycatch is steadily declining with the development and increased use of bycatch-reduction devices. Impacts on nontarget species seem to vary widely, for example, heavy shrimping bycatch that includes red snapper *Lutjanus campechanus* may seriously diminish snapper stocks yet may not have a direct effect on other species such as spot *Leiostomus xanthurus*. Yellowtail flounder *Pleuronectes ferrugineus* in New England are so severely depleted that their take as bycatch seriously impedes the stock's recovery. We have similar problems in other regions of the United States. We have yet to fully understand how bycatch may impact long-term sustainability of the ecosystem, biodiversity, and nontarget species (e.g., see UASGCP 1996.) The full impact of bycatch on the ecosystems that support sustainable fisheries and diverse habitats needed for healthy fish populations is still to be determined.

Our most recent assessments of the 727 species managed under federal fishery management plans indicate that 86 species are listed as overfished, 183 species are listed as not overfished, and 10 species are considered to be approaching an overfished condition (NMFS 1997). For 448 species, the status relative to overfishing is unknown (NMFS 1997.) Despite an apparent stable trend in catch levels over recent years, a large number of our world and national fish stocks are in decline, with many currently overfished. As a regulatory agency, NMFS has traditionally focused on overfishing issues, overcapitalization, and rebuilding stocks. We are now equally committed to the preservation of habitat, the life-support systems for our fisheries bounty. This habitat is under intense pressure.

Stewardship of Fisheries Resources

In 1996, the U.S. Congress acknowledged the state of decline of world and U.S. fisheries and the importance of habitat by enacting historic legislation that called for bold new actions. The Sustainable Fisheries Act (16 U.S.C. 1801 et seq) amended the Fishery Conservation and Management Act of 1976, which established jurisdiction over marine fisheries resources in the 200-mi U.S. exclusive economic zone (EEZ). The Sustainable Fisheries Act (SFA) is implemented by the Secretary of Commerce through the National Marine Fisheries Service. Of key importance are eight regional fishery management councils (the Councils) that are responsible for fishery management plans for each of the managed fishery stocks. Council members are a cross section of stakeholders and experts nominated by governors of the coastal states in each region and appointed by the Secretary of Commerce (the Secretary). The SFA requires that managers use the best scientific information as the basis for management actions.

These new mandates have redefined the conservation and management goals for the living marine resources within the EEZ. In the SFA, Congress declared that we must take action now to ensure that the nation realizes the full benefits from its fishery resources. The new amendments emphasize the importance of sustainability of the nation's fisheries and establish a new standard by requiring that fisheries be managed at maximum sustainable levels and that new approaches be taken in habitat conservation.

The SFA requires that all overfished stocks must be rebuilt to a sustainable level as soon as possible but within 10 years. The SFA also requires the establishment of new national standard guidelines as guiding principals for the management of the nation's fisheries. These standards include requirements that overfishing be halted (probably the most groundbreaking new standard), that all fishery management programs take into consideration effects on fishing communities, that bycatch be reduced, and that safety of life at sea be promoted. In addition, the SFA introduces a requirement to protect marine ecosystems while striving to achieve the greatest overall benefit to the nation. This ecosystem-protection requirement is reflected in new provisions for the identification and conservation of essential fish habitat.

Essential Fish Habitat

Given this context, a key element in moving toward sustainable fisheries is the identification, conservation, and restoration of fish habitat. Healthy habitat is a basic requirement for the reproduction, growth, migration, and livelihood of sustainable fishery stocks (e.g., see Peters and Cross 1992; Stroud 1992; Langton et al. 1996; NMFS 1996). New tools are needed to protect and conserve the living environment of marine, estuarine, and anadromous finfish, mollusks, and crustaceans.

The renaissance in the NMFS habitat program began in the fall of 1996 with the development of the National Habitat Plan and the passage of the Sustainable Fisheries Act. The SFA offers significant new opportunities and challenges to protect and conserve the habitat of marine, estuarine, and anadromous finfish as well as key populations of mollusks and crustaceans. As of October 1998, all federal fishery management councils (and NMFS, in the case of three Secretarial plans for highly migratory species) were required to amend their 39 fishery management plans to identify and describe the essential fish habitat (EFH) for more than 700 federally managed fishery stocks. Threats to habitat and steps necessary to ameliorate those threats also had to be identified. The U.S. Congress defined essential fish habitat as "those waters and substrate necessary to fish for spawning, breeding, feeding or growth to maturity" (USDOC 1996:6). Historically, fishery management plans have focused on allowable catch levels and types of fishing gear and limitations on fishing effort. Before the SFA, the Secretary, NMFS, and the Councils had little authority to substantially influence the quality and quantity of habitat necessary for sustainable fisheries.

The new essential fish habitat mandate promises to change fishery management and the way society thinks about living marine resources. Habitat considerations are now a key part of fishery management decisions. In addition, fish habitat now enjoys greater recognition in all state and federal actions that may adversely affect our oceans, estuaries, and rivers.

The SFA requires that essential fish habitat be identified and described for each federally managed species. The identification must include descriptive information on the geographic range of EFH for all life stages along with maps of EFH for life stages over appropriate time and space scales. Habitat requirements must also be identified, described, and mapped for all life stages of each species. The task of determining species distributions by life stage and characterizing associated habitats will be a major accomplishment of and continuing challenge for NMFS and Council experts. Much of this distributional and habitat information has been brought together for the first time using geographic information system technology and will provide an important tool for fisheries resource management. The EFH designations are intended to be as specific as possible depending upon availability of data.

Managing Threats to Essential Fish Habitat

A key element in the essential fish habitat process is the identification of existing and potential threats to habitat as well as the conservation and enhancement measures necessary to eliminate or minimize those threats. The destruction and degradation of aquatic habitats essential for sustainable fish populations is a growing concern. Approximately 60% of the world's population lives within 60 km of the coast (Kennish 1998). Population density along the U.S. coasts is currently four times the national average, and urban growth and development continues to expand in coastal areas. Such pressures on coastal areas inevitably lead to more pollution and threats to habitat. The nature and extent of particular threats to fish habitat will vary by region and usually depend on habitat type, exposure, and other environmental variables (Sindermann 1996; Kennish 1998). The most common threats to habitat can be categorized as (1) physical habitat destruction, alteration, blockage, and fragmentation; (2) inadequate water quality and quantity; (3) eutrophication and hypoxia, which are integral aspects of water quality and quantity; and (4) introduction of exotic species. The following paragraphs highlight several examples of altered environmental conditions that are reducing the viability of aquatic habitats.

About three-quarters of the nation's commercial fish landings are composed of species that depend on estuaries for reproduction, nursery areas, food production, or migration (Chambers 1992).

Viable estuaries, in turn, usually depend on healthy and abundant wetlands, both emergent and submerged (NRC 1995a). The most recent estimate of emergent wetland losses in the coterminous United States is around 40,486 ha/year (USEPA 1998). Since colonial times, the coterminous United States has lost approximately one-half of its original wetlands. Although these figures include many freshwater wetlands not utilized by federally managed species, the loss of important wetland habitat used by such species is significant. According to our most recent calculations, commercial marine fisheries contributed US$21.0 billion in value added to our gross national product in 1996, and U.S. consumers spent a net amount of $41.2 billion on fishery products that same year (USDOC 1997a). Further contributions to our economy come from recreational fisheries, and recent recreational fisheries surveys have calculated that saltwater anglers spent $8.1 billion in 1996 (USDOI/DOC 1997). A significant portion of marine recreational species also depend on estuaries and wetlands for some portion of their life cycles. Saving and restoring wetlands must be a high priority of our essential fish habitat activities.

There is a worldwide increase in the frequency and extent of harmful algal blooms that have significant lethal and sublethal effects on coastal fish populations (Burkholder 1998). Recent examples include a serious outbreak of *Pfiesteria* and *Pfiesteria*-like episodes during the summer of 1997 in Chesapeake Bay, which had a substantial impact on the regional fishing industry. Although there have been suggestions that coastal development and nonpoint-source pollution may be responsible for the increased frequency of harmful blooms, the linkages, if any, are poorly understood. Our habitat management strategies must necessarily address the implications of the growing prevalence of marine microorganisms that are harmful to finfish, shellfish, and humans.

Seasonally severe and persistent hypoxia has been documented for an enormous area (some 16,000–18,000 km^2, known as the "dead zone") of the Louisiana continental shelf, apparently driven by excessive nutrients from riverine sources. The oxygen-stressed bottom community is characterized by significant reductions in biodiversity. This large hypoxic area is located in the center of our extensive Gulf of Mexico shrimp fisheries. Effects of hypoxia on fishery resources include direct mortality, altered migration, reduction in suitable habitats,

changes in food resources, increased susceptibility to predation, and disruption of life cycles including aspects of spawning and recruitment (Atwood et al. 1994). Increasing trends of hypoxia in coastal waters around the world have been documented (Diaz and Rosenberg 1995). The decline and in some cases collapse of finfish and benthic invertebrate fisheries in Scandinavia and northern Europe has been partly attributable to hypoxia in open-shelf systems (Baden et al. 1990). Control of nutrient input into coastal waters must be a high priority in our efforts to protect essential fish habitat.

The invasion of exotic species into domestic waters and the subsequent displacement of native species has become a growing problem, as the continuing battle with the zebra mussel *Dreissena polymorpha* will attest. Recent studies have characterized San Francisco Bay as the most invaded estuary in the world (e.g., Cohen and Carlton 1998). A large amount of exotic species dominate many habitats of the San Francisco Bay and Delta system in terms of number of species, number of individuals, and biomass. The rate of invasion appears to be accelerating (Cohen and Carlton 1998). Exotic-species control efforts are essential to preclude introductions of exotic species that can alter the basic ecological balance of our coastal and anadromous fish habitats.

A Focus on Impacts from Fishing Activities

The SFA places particular importance on minimizing, to the extent practicable, the adverse effects of fishing on essential fish habitat. This will be a particularly challenging issue for NMFS, the Councils, and the commercial fishing industry. Changes in natural marine communities are an inevitable result of harvesting marine organisms with any gear type. A growing number of scientific studies indicate that repeated fishing effort using certain types of fishing gear over certain types of fish habitat can result in significant habitat alteration or destruction (Dayton et al. 1995; Auster and Langton 1999, this volume). The Councils must determine the extent to which the use of particular fishing gear in certain areas (and perhaps at certain times) is adversely affecting essential fish habitat. The Councils must also consider whether proposed management measures (such as limiting or prohibiting certain gear types, time and area closures, harvest limits, and the establishment of harvest refugia) are feasible considering the long- and short-term costs and benefits to the fishing industry and the habitat. These decisions will be key in protecting important parts of essential fish habitat.

Conservation of Fish Habitat

Once the EFH amendments to the federal fishery management plans are approved by the Secretary of Commerce, substantial new provisions for habitat protection will go into effect. Any federal agency that undertakes actions that may adversely affect essential fish habitat must consult with NMFS to determine the effects of such actions on both the habitat and the managed species. In addition, NMFS must recommend to federal and state agencies necessary steps to avoid, minimize, or offset any adverse effects of agency activities to EFH (50 CFR Part 600, Subpart J and K).

Opportunities and Challenges

The National Marine Fisheries Service can go to a new plateau for building sustainable fisheries by taking advantage of the opportunities afforded by the SFA and meeting the challenges to accomplish the ambitious agenda put forth. Habitat conservation is a key part of our sustainable fisheries policy. To accomplish this, I have a vision to ensure that fish habitat is sustainable and that the NMFS and its partners take advantage of opportunities and meet this challenge. This vision is delineated in the following sections.

Stop the Loss of Habitat and Restore Degraded Habitats

We must eliminate overfishing as soon as possible but at least by 2004 to ensure the capacity of fish populations to maintain themselves. We must also ensure sustainable fisheries by stopping the destruction and degradation of the places fish require to live, migrate, and reproduce. The Clinton Administration's Wetland Plan of 1993 established a goal for no overall net loss of wetlands with the long-term goal of increasing the quality and quantity of the nation's wetlands resource base (WHOEP 1993). Accomplishing this goal will be a major advance toward habitat sustainability. Success will require significant initiatives in wetland restoration and creation such as the recent restoration efforts of the

NMFS in Louisiana, which have added thousands of hectares to our wetland inventory. My vision is full implementation of the essential fish habitat provisions of the SFA coupled with an aggressive program of habitat restoration that could eliminate all essential habitat loss due to human activities within the next five years (see USDOC 1997b.)

Use an Ecosystem Approach

Traditional approaches to fisheries management have focused on single species. Although we have often been aware that single-species fish populations are integral parts of communities and ecosystems as a whole, our laws and management regimes constrained us to a narrow, single-species focus. A transition to sustainable fisheries will require new ecosystem perspectives (see Christensen et al. 1996; Mooney 1998). A recent study demonstrated that over the past 45 years, although probably longer, we have been "fishing down the marine food web" with lower trophic-level animals making up progressively increasing proportions of the global fisheries catch (Pauly et al. 1998). Clearly, global marine ecosystems are being altered in a profound way. With the passage of the SFA, Congress acknowledged that ecosystem principles must be incorporated into fisheries conservation and management activities. A key action in response to the SFA's mandate has been the establishment of a Fisheries Ecosystem Management Advisory Panel, which was scheduled to make recommendations in fall 1998 to the Secretary of Commerce and Congress on the application of ecosystem principles to sustainable fisheries. The essential fish habitat provisions of the SFA are a basic element in our new ecosystem-management approaches to fisheries management. I consider this new philosophical direction to be a most important part of our transition to sustainable fisheries.

Maintain Biodiversity

The preservation of biodiversity and biological integrity is the most central element of an ecosystem approach. The U.S. Environmental Protection Agency listed the loss of biodiversity as one of four great risks to natural ecology and human well-being (USEPA 1990). However, marine ecosystems in general have received little attention in studies of biodiversity and conservation in comparison to terrestrial ecosystems (NRC 1995b). For example, little is known about the organisms in coral reefs other than corals or reef fishes, although this habitat type hosts a high level of biodiversity (Thomas 1993). Irish and Norse (1996) stated that only 5% of all contributions in a leading conservation journal were marine in focus. I am committed to a consistent, far-reaching program to address marine biodiversity as part of our essential fish habitat, protected-species, bycatch-reduction, and stock-enhancement activities. In particular, over the next five years we must characterize on a regional basis the biodiversity of all of our essential fish habitat and associated fish communities and track our progress in preserving and restoring basic biological attributes.

Appropriately Use the Precautionary Principle in the Face of Scientific Uncertainty

We will never accomplish the transition to sustainable capture fisheries unless we adopt risk-averse management approaches in situations where we do not fully understand the ecological consequences of all of our management options (e.g., see Garcia 1994; Dayton 1998). This concept applies both to the regulation of harvest by the commercial and recreational fishing community and to those cultural and economic activities that may compromise the sustainability of fish habitat. With policies developed under the SFA, we can apply precautionary approaches in managing essential fish habitat through strategies that:

1. encourage managers to designate fish habitat as essential when faced with scientific uncertainty;
2. include historic and degraded habitat, with certain considerations, to provide the basis for the restoration of habitats and, eventually, more sustainable fish populations; and
3. apply ecosystem principles that will lead to new linkages between human activities, fish habitat, and fish populations both in subsequent actions by the fishery management councils and in consultations with federal and state agencies.

An old saw from early environmental debates in the 1970s, usually invoked as a plea when popular policies and programs that might compromise aquatic habitats were moving forward, was that "fish don't vote." Application of a measured precautionary approach will result in a shift of the burden of proof from nonvoting fish to those who may be infringing on fish habitat (see Dayton 1998.)

Build Partnerships for Success

Reportedly, the Fuegian language of the natives of Tierra del Fuego contains the word mamihlapinatapai, which means "looking at each other hoping that either will offer to do something that both parties desire but are unwilling to do" (Poundstone 1992). Too often, when we get stakeholders together to resolve competing interests, our desired collective outcomes are compatible, but all parties are frozen in inflexible negotiating positions and resolution is difficult. When I survey the continuing conflict that we have among interested parties that frequently gather in confrontational regulatory and administrative situations over fishery and fishery habitat issues, I am convinced that we can build better links, that is, partnerships, with state and local groups and public and private organizations to head off conflicts and avoid mamihlapinatapai.

Just as important is fostering a national commitment through partnering agreements to gather information and develop policies toward protecting the ecological resources that sustain our fisheries bounty. To succeed in the successful identification and conservation of essential fish habitat, the NMFS will be developing a close working relationship with states, tribes, and other groups throughout the fisheries and nonfisheries communities. We should make a special attempt to work with nonfisheries communities as their cooperation is vital to habitat protection and restoration. Much of the essential fish habitat of concern is in state coastal waters, estuaries, and rivers, and we must partner with states and local interests in the collection and sharing of information as well as the implementation of appropriate management measures.

The protection of habitat will require a much better understanding of the relationship between human activities and habitat viability, as well as the link between habitat health and sustainable fisheries populations. We must partner closely with academia (providing the necessary encouragement and support) to obtain information on life histories of fish populations, the complexities of habitats for all life stages throughout their range, the connection between environmental stresses and habitat, and other key puzzles. We are already developing partnerships with other federal agencies, many of which conduct activities that may affect essential fish habitat. Finally, we are working closely with professional societies and special-interest groups.

A Vision for the Next Millennium

My vision for sustainable fisheries for the next millennium is both simple and complex. The simple part is that we have, for the most part, the tools to do what we have to do, at least in U.S. waters, to transition to both sustainable fisheries catches and habitat. We have the legislative authority and indeed the mandate under the SFA to stop overfishing, minimize impacts to our fishing communities, stabilize our fishery ecosystems, and conserve and restore habitat. Working through this transition to sustainable fisheries will not be easy. People, many of whom are citizens of the United States and are not part of the fishing community, will need to adjust their cultural and economic practices.

The protection of essential fish habitat constitutes the complex aspect of my vision. Our stewardship of the sea and its resources depends more and more on our stewardship of the land. Stewardship of our land is appropriated among many authorities and constituents. This is where new partnerships, better education and outreach, and innovative approaches are necessary to establish the collective will of the nation to protect our fisheries resources. We in the federal government are doing our part by implementing, for instance, the Vice-President's Clean Water Action Plan (USEPA 1998). But the real impact must come from ground-level commitment at the state and local level to protect our sustainable fisheries heritage.

I am convinced that we will achieve sustainable fisheries and protect and restore the habitat upon which those fisheries depend as we go in to the next millennium. In doing so, we will be heeding the counsel of the late Nat Bingham, a close friend of mine for many years and to whom this volume is dedicated, who summed it up quite crisply: "It's the habitat, stupid!"

References

Alverson, D. 1998. Discarding practices and unobserved fishing mortality in marine fisheries: an update. Washington Sea Grant College Program, WSG 98–06, Seattle.

Alverson, D., M. Freeberg, S. Murawski, and J. Pope. 1994. A global assessment of fisheries bycatch and discards. Food and Agriculture Organization Fisheries Technical Paper 339. Rome, Italy.

Atwood, D. K., A. Bratkovitch, M. Gallagher, and G. L. Hitchcock, editors. 1994. Dedicated Issue on NOAA's Nutrient Enhanced Coastal Ocean Productivity Study. Estuaries 17(4).

Auster, P. J., and R. W. Langton. 1999. The effects of fishing on fish habitat. Pages 150–187 in L. R. Benaka, editor. Fish habitat: essential fish habitat and rehabilitation. American Fisheries Society, Symposium 22, Bethesda, Maryland.

Baden, S. P., L. O. Loo, L. Pihl, and R. Rosenberg. 1990. Effects of eutrophication on benthic communities including fish: Swedish West Coast. Ambio 19:113–122.

Botsford, L. W., J. C. Castilla, and C. H. Peterson. 1997. The management of fisheries and marine ecosystems. Science 277:509–515.

Burkholder, J. M. 1998. Implications of harmful microalgae and heterotrophic dinoflagellates in management of sustainable marine fisheries. Ecological Applications. 8(1)Supplement:S37–S62.

Chambers, J. R. 1992. Coastal degradation and fishery declines in the U.S. Pages 45–51 in R. H. Stroud, editor. Stemming the tide of coastal fish habitat loss. National Coalition for Marine Conservation, Savannah, Georgia.

Christensen, N., and 12 coauthors. 1996. The report of the Ecological Society of America Committee on the Scientific Basis for Ecosystem Management. Ecological Applications 6(3):665–691.

Cohen, A. N., and J. T. Carlton. 1998. Accelerating invasion rate in a highly invaded estuary. Science 279:555–558.

Dayton, P. K. 1998. Reversal of the burden of proof in fisheries management. Science 279:821.

Dayton, P. K., S. F. Thrush, M. T. Agardy, and R. J. Hofman. 1995. Environmental effects of marine fishing. Aquatic Conservation: Marine and Freshwater Ecosystems 5:205–232.

Diaz, R. J., and R. Rosenberg. 1995. Marine benthic hypoxia: a review of its ecological effects and the behavioural responses of benthic macrofauna. Oceanography and Marine Biology: An Annual Review 33:245–303.

FAO (Food, and Agriculture Organization). 1997a. Review of the state of world fishery resources: marine fisheries. FAO Fisheries Circular 920, Rome, Italy.

FAO (Food, and Agriculture Organization). 1997b. The state of world fisheries and aquaculture: 1996. FAO, Rome, Italy.

Garcia, S. M. 1994. The precautionary principle: its implications in capture fisheries management. Ocean and Coastal Management 22:99–125.

Garcia, S. M., and C. Newton. 1997. Current situation, trends, and prospects in world capture fisheries. Pages 3–27 in E. L. Pikitch, D. D. Huppert, and M. P. Sissenwine, editors. Global trends: fisheries management. American Fisheries Society, Symposium 20, Bethesda, Maryland.

Irish, K. E., and E. A. Norse. 1996. Scant emphasis on marine biodiversity in conservation biology. Conservation Biology 10(2):680.

Kennish, M. J. 1998. Pollution impacts on marine biotic communities. CRC Press, Boca Raton, Florida.

Langton, R. W., R. S. Steneck, V. Gotceitas, F. Juanes, and P. Lawton. 1996. The interface between fisheries research and habitat management. North American Journal of Fisheries Management 16:1–7.

Mooney, H. A., editor. 1998. Ecosystem management for sustainable fisheries. Ecological Applications 8(1)Supplement.

NMFS (National Marine Fisheries Service). 1996. Our living ocean. Report on the status of U.S. living marine resources, 1995. U.S. Department of Commerce, National Oceanic and Atmospheric Administration Technical Memorandum, NMFS-F/SPO-19. Washington, D.C.

NMFS (National Marine Fisheries Service). 1997. Status of fisheries of the United States. Report to Congress. NMFS, Silver Spring, Maryland.

NMFS (National Marine Fisheries Service). 1998. Southeastern United States Shrimp Trawl Bycatch Program: report to Congress. NMFS, Silver Spring, Maryland.

NRC (National Research Council). 1995a. Wetlands: characteristics and boundaries. National Academy Press, Washington, D.C.

NRC (National Research Council). 1995b. Understanding marine biodiversity. National Academy Press, Washington, D.C.

Pauly, D., V. Christensen, J. Dalsgaard, R. Froese, and F. Torres, Jr. 1998. Fishing down marine food webs. Science 279:860–863.

Peters, D. S., and F. A. Cross. 1992. What is coastal fish habitat? Pages 17–22 in R. H. Stroud, editor. Stemming the tide of coastal fish habitat loss. National Coalition for Marine Conservation, Savannah, Georgia.

Poundstone, W. 1992. Prisoner's dilemma. Doubleday, New York.

Sindermann, C. J. 1996. Ocean pollution: effects on living resources and humans. CRC Press, Boca Raton, Florida.

Stroud, R. H., editor. 1992. Stemming the tide of coastal fish habitat loss. National Coalition for Marine Conservation, Savannah, Georgia.

Thomas, J. D. 1993. Biological monitoring and tropical biodiversity in marine environments: a critique with recommendations and comments on the use of amphipods as bioindicators. Journal of Natural History 27:795–806.

UASGCP (University of Alaska Sea Grant College Program). 1996. Solving bycatch. Report 96-03. UASGCP, Fairbanks.

USDOC (U.S. Department of Commerce). 1996. Magnuson-Stevens Fishery Conservation and Management Act as amended through October 11, 1996. National Oceanic and Atmospheric Administration Technical Memorandum NMFS-F/SPO-23.

USDOC (U.S. Department of Commerce). 1997a. Fisheries of the United States. Current Fishery Statistics No. 9600, USDOC, Washington, D.C.

USDOC (U.S. Department of Commerce). 1997b. Implementation plan for the Code of Conduct for Responsible Fisheries. USDOC, Washington, D.C.

USDOI/DOC (U.S. Department of the Interior, U.S. Fish and Wildlife Service and U.S. Department of Commerce, Bureau of the Census). 1997. 1996 National Survey of Fishing, Hunting and Wildlife-Associated Recreation. USDOI/DOC, Washington, D.C.

USEPA (U.S. Environmental Protection Agency). 1990. Reducing risk: setting priorities and strategies for environmental protection. SAB-EC-90–021. USEPA, Washington, D.C.

USEPA (U.S. Environmental Protection Agency). 1998. Clean Water Action Plan: restoring & protecting America's waters. EPA-840-R-98–001, USEPA, Washington, D.C.

WHOEP (White House Office on Environmental Policy). 1993. Protecting America's wetlands: a fair, flexible and effective approach. The White House, Washington, D.C.

American Fisheries Society Symposium 22:11–22, 1999

An Environmentalist's Perspective on Essential Fish Habitat

Cynthia M. Sarthou

Campaign Director, Gulf Restoration Network
Post Office Box 2245, New Orleans, Louisiana 70176, USA

Abstract.—It cannot be denied that habitat is essential to healthy fish populations. A significant number of fish species in the Gulf of Mexico and around the country depends on estuaries during some stage of their life cycles. Despite this fact, fish habitats are increasingly destroyed and degraded by pollution, dredging, freshwater influx, and other human activities. If healthy fish populations are to be maintained, threats to fish habitat must be addressed. However, traditional management practices have neglected and continue to ignore threats to important fish habitat. The essential fish habitat (EFH) provisions of the 1996 Magnuson-Stevens Fishery Conservation and Management Act (Magnuson-Stevens Act) present an unprecedented opportunity to develop habitat-based management approaches to protect and restore important fish habitats in the ocean and in vital estuarine areas. This is not to say the EFH provisions of the Magnuson-Stevens Act are a panacea for habitat protection. For example, there is no enforceable mechanism for preventing activities that destroy areas of EFH. Nonetheless, the EFH provisions of the Magnuson-Stevens Act can go far in achieving the intended results if the National Marine Fisheries Service (NMFS) promulgates guidelines requiring ecosystem-based management, if regional EFH amendments go beyond minimalist requirements to address threats to habitat through comprehensive habitat management plans, and if regional fishery management councils become important players in the host of federal decisions that affect fish habitat. The NMFS and the regional fishery management councils must be required to take full advantage of this unique opportunity.

Coastal waters and their adjacent wetlands provide essential habitat for the nation's fisheries resources. Seventy-five percent of recreationally and commercially exploited marine fish species depend on coastal waters, particularly estuaries, during some stage of their life cycle (Chambers 1992). Despite this dependence, coastal habitats important to fisheries are increasingly destroyed or degraded by physical alteration, pollution, freshwater influx, nutrient enrichment, and other human activities. The cumulative degradation and loss of this habitat has a significant adverse effect on marine fish populations.

Habitat protection generally has not been included in traditional fisheries management, which has focused on fishing activities. Moreover, the leadership of the National Marine Fisheries Service (NMFS), the federal agency that manages our nation's marine fisheries, has failed to aggressively support its own habitat protection programs. The essential fish habitat (EFH) provisions of the Magnuson-Stevens Fishery Conservation and Management Act (Magnuson-Stevens Act) signal an acknowledgment of the importance of habitat and present an unprecedented opportunity to develop habitat-based fishery management systems—approaches that incorporate conservation, protection, and restoration of essential habitats as key objectives of any effective natural resource management program. However, the opportunity presented by the Magnuson-Stevens Act will be realized only through careful creation of a strong NMFS habitat protection program and full implementation of the EFH provisions by the regional fishery management councils (Councils) and the NMFS. Our nation's fisheries and beleaguered marine ecosystems can be "rebuilt" only if strong and meaningful efforts at habitat protection are fully integrated within the NMFS's and the Councils' fishery management programs. Without a significant commitment to habitat protection by Congress and at the highest levels within the NMFS, the continuing loss and degradation of habitat may result in irreversible damage to our nation's fisheries resources.

The Importance of and Threats to Our Fisheries Resources

Oceans cover nearly three-fourths of our planet. They are a vast and irreplaceable resource, a treasure for current and future generations of humankind. Oceans harbor a bewildering array of life forms, and the health of those oceans and the ecosystems they support is important to the stability of all life on our planet. The health of marine ecosystems has a profound effect on such things as the world's oxygen supply and atmospheric stability (Safina 1992).

The fish and other forms of marine life that are produced in the oceans also provide food for billions of people, and marine ecosystem functions sustain human life in ways just now beginning to be discovered (Kiraly et al. 1998).

Marine fisheries represent a significant part of our national economic and recreational resources. In 1991, the commercial catch (at dockside) was valued by the NMFS at US$4 billion. However, the total economic impact of the nation's commercial fisheries has been estimated at $50 billion, although fishermen assert that when appropriate multipliers are applied, estimates of the economic impact of commercial fishing are much higher. The Sport Fishing Institute in 1994 estimated that sportfishing generated $15 billion in economic activity per year in the early 1990s (Fedler and Nickum 1994). Together, marine fish and invertebrates generate $65 billion in economic impact per year. It is evident, however, that these fisheries could provide much greater value to the nation if they were rebuilt. It is estimated that U.S. marine fishery populations have declined to about 20% of their former abundance (J. R. Chambers, Living Oceans Program, unpublished data). In 1994, American consumers spent $41.2 billion on seafood products, with $34.4 billion being spent on domestic seafood (Safina 1994). Finally, a significant number of Americans pursue various forms of recreational activity such as scuba diving and snorkeling that are dependent upon healthy ecosystems and contribute significant sums to the economies of many coastal communities.

Although there have been some management successes in the United States since the enactment of the Magnuson Fishery Conservation and Management Act in 1976, such as the substantial recovery of king mackerel *Scomberomorus cavalla* stocks in the Gulf of Mexico, many fish stocks exhibit a pattern of decline in population. In its 1997 "Report to Congress on the Status of Fisheries in the United States," the NMFS reviewed 727 marine species under federal management in the nation's 200-mi exclusive economic zone (EEZ). Of the 279 species for which sufficient data were found to determine status, 86 species were listed as "overfished," and 10 species were listed as approaching an overfished condition (NOAA 1997). Although the major causes of fishery population declines have been attributed to overfishing, there is evidence that many fish populations dependent upon coastal waters are being equally affected by cumulative habitat degradation and loss (Chambers 1992).

It is ironic that the ecological productivity and broad appeal of coastal waters are creating conditions that are contributing to habitat degradation. Today, more than one-half of the U.S. population lives in coastal counties, and coastal areas continue to be among the most rapidly growing areas. It is predicted that by the year 2010, more than 75% of the U.S. population will reside within 50 mi of a coast (Morton 1997).

Historically, population growth and associated landward human activities were seen as separate from the ocean or of environmental insignificance in the face of the sea's vastness. We have learned, however, that human development and ocean health are interconnected. Kiraly et al. (1998:C-2) found that:

"Research and experience have shown that the bounty of the ocean is not limitless. Increasing population and the accompanying expansion of human activities have the capacity to diminish the ocean's productivity in numerous ways. The ocean's living resources and the benefits derived from them are threatened by fisheries operations, chemical pollution and eutrophication, alteration of physical habitat, and invasions by exotic species. Looming on the horizon are new threats caused by ozone depletion and human-induced climate change, whose potential negative impacts on whole ecosystems add further to the impact of already existing threats caused by other human activities."

Coastal habitat protection is too often lost in the nation's race to develop the coasts for agriculture, energy, recreational development, and urban projects.

As coastal populations grow, so does the stress placed on marine environments. The most significant human-induced stresses on habitat are depletion and alteration of freshwater flows, alteration of physical habitats, introduction of toxic contaminants, and overenrichment of nutrients (Chambers, unpublished data). So significant are these problems that the U.S. Congress, in its report entitled "Coastal Waters in Jeopardy: Reversing the Decline and Protecting America's Coastal Resources" (U.S. Congress 1989), acknowledged that:

"The continuing damage to coastal resources from pollution, development, and natural forces raises serious doubts about the ability of our estuaries, bays and near coastal waters to survive these stresses. If we fail to act and if current trends continue unabated, what is now a serious, widespread collection of problems may coalesce into a national crisis by early in the next century."

Participants in a national symposium entitled "Stemming the Tide of Coastal Fish Habitat Loss" held in Baltimore, Maryland in 1991 similarly concluded that "the increasing loss of fish habitat…is the single largest long-term threat to the future viability of the marine fisheries of the United States" (Hinman and Safina 1992). A review of the present state of our coastal waters, wetlands, coral reefs, and the Gulf of Mexico indicates that prediction of a coming national crisis may soon become a reality.

Coastal Waters

Despite the value of coastal waters for both human and fish populations, and the existence of laws intended to protect coastal waters, there is increasing evidence that many coastal waters continue to be degraded. According to the 1994 National Water Quality Inventory, 44% of U.S. estuarine waters are not supporting their designated uses, meaning that they are neither fishable nor swimmable (Ehler et al. 1998). A 1994 survey of 78% of the estuarine waters of the United States similarly found that 37% of the assessed waters were impaired (USEPA 1995).

Water quality in coastal areas has deteriorated to such an extent that on any given day, one-third of the shellfish harvesting areas of the United States are closed (Chambers, unpublished data). Other areas, although open to harvesting, are subject to fish consumption advisories. From 1958 to the present, productive shellfish growing waters of Maine have experienced dinoflagellate blooms responsible for paralytic shellfish poisoning, often necessitating closures in some areas. Dinoflagellate blooms are affecting all productive shellfishing waters of the nation at an increasing rate (Chambers, unpublished data). In addition, nutrient overenrichment is believed primarily responsible for the loss of native sea grasses in Chesapeake Bay, an important habitat for juvenile fish and shellfish. Finally, outbreaks of *Pfiesteria piscidia* have been reported in coastal North Carolina and Maryland and have been associated with major fish kills in those areas (USEPA 1997; Ehler et al. 1998).

Degraded water quality has resulted in serious reductions in Chesapeake Bay oyster harvests. It is estimated that oyster harvests decreased from 32 million pounds in 1959 to 4 million pounds in 1989. Quahog (hard clam) catches in Rhode Island have also declined.

Quahog production in 1985 was 4.2 million pounds (in weight of meat), valued at $15 million. In 1994, production had declined by over 50% to 1.6 million pounds, valued at $7.6 million (Morton 1997).

The causes of declines in water quality are clear. Urbanization and increasing population growth have increased the amount of pollution entering coastal waters and estuaries. Increasing populations use greater amounts of toxic chemicals, pesticides, herbicides, pathogens, nutrients, and other pollutants, and discharge those pollutants into the environment. Significant amounts of these contaminants eventually enter local waterways, streams, rivers, and, eventually, our coastal waters. To accommodate expanding populations, communities radically alter land uses, replacing natural areas with impermeable surfaces, such as roads and buildings, which do not allow absorption of rainwater. As a result, runoff rates are increased, leading to increased erosion. Moreover, the contaminants carried by stormwater degrade the quality of our coastal waters (Morton 1997; Ehler et al. 1998).

Toxic chemicals, pesticides, herbicides, and pathogens entering coastal waters have been shown to directly affect reproductive success, growth, and survival of some fish. Exposure of fish to contaminants can cause failure of egg development, interfere with time of spawning, result in production of deformed offspring, and cause alteration of genes and the immune system (Chambers, unpublished data). Sediment and nutrient loading associated with runoff also increase turbidity and light attenuation, thereby killing submerged aquatic vegetation. Thus, only 10% of the sea grass beds that once existed still exist today (USEPA 1997; Ehler et al. 1998). Finally, as urbanization and inland activities increase, so do the volumes of municipal and industrial waste discharged into local waterways. These discharges, in turn, can result in degradation of fisheries habitat, including a reduction in the value of estuaries and wetlands (Ehler et al. 1998).

Wetlands

Coastal wetlands and estuaries rank among the most productive of ecosystems. Wetlands, which include salt marshes, sea grass beds, and mangroves, provide critical functions as the sources of nutrients for nearshore production, as filters for land runoff, and as stabilizers for coastal lands (Kiraly et al. 1998). Estuarine wetlands are essential habitat for saltwater fish and are beneficial to freshwater fish. Through nutrient cycling, wetlands promote the growth of the smallest organisms in the aquatic food chain, which are then eaten by larger organisms and then by fish. These primary production and predation processes work especially well where water is sheltered, shallow, and rich with nutrients (W. M. Kier Associates 1998). Estuarine wetland areas also provide valuable spawning and nursery grounds for fish and shellfish (Chambers, unpublished data).

Approximately 75% (Chambers 1992) of commercially valuable fish and shellfish landings, and 80 and 90%, respectively (USDOC 1992a,1992b) of all recreationally valuable fish and shellfish landings in the United States use estuaries for some stage of their life cycles, often the early critical stages of life. For example, biologists have determined that shrimp larvae are carried by currents to estuarine wetlands. Without wetlands, many fish and shellfish simply cannot survive.

Despite the demonstrated importance of wetlands to fish and shellfish populations, the wetlands of the United States are disappearing at an alarming rate (W. M. Kier Associates 1998). Since the 1700s, the 48 contiguous states have lost over half of their original wetlands (Watzin and Gosselink 1992). In 1995, there were 100.9 million acres of wetlands remaining in the conterminous United States, representing a loss of 54% (more than 117 million acres) since the 1700s. Only 5.2 million acres of those existing wetlands in 1995 were intertidal wetlands. Estuarine vegetated wetlands made up 89% of total estuarine wetland acreage, totaling 4.6 million acres. Nonvegetated estuarine and marine wetlands composed 11%, or 577,100 acres, of all remaining intertidal wetlands (USFWS 1995). The U.S. Fish and Wildlife Service estimated that 372,300 acres of estuarine vegetated wetlands were lost from the mid-1950s to the mid-1970s. Between 1974 and 1983, another 70,799 acres were lost at a rate of 17,900 per year. In addition, 310,000 acres were lost from 1982 to 1992 at an estimated rate of 31,000 acres per year. These loss estimates do not include sea grass beds or low-salinity wetlands adjacent to saline marshes or riverine systems, which together constitute a large proportion (85%) of the wetlands important to living marine resources (Chambers, unpublished data). Although the rate at which we continue to lose vital coastal and estuarine wetlands appears to be slowing, the conversion of wetland areas for agriculture, forestry, residential and commercial construction, and hydromodification continues at a rapid pace, which has a significant impact on the availability of wetlands acreage (USDA 1995; Kiraly et al. 1998).

Coral Reefs

Approximately 10,465 mi^2 of coral reefs fall within U.S. jurisdiction (Miller and Crosby 1998). These corals are home to numerous coral-dependent species of commercially valuable fish under federal management and untold numbers of species of little commercial but significant ecosystem value. Coral reefs also provide critical protection to shorelines.

Shallow-water coral health and cover has declined over the last two decades. This decline is largely attributable to human influences, including siltation, pollution, physical damage, dredging, overfishing, and destructive fishing practices. The last decade has also seen an "alarming increase in coral diseases, with growing evidence that susceptibility to disease is in part linked to human-induced stresses" (Kiraly et al. 1998).

The Gulf of Mexico: A Region in Crisis

Coastal water quality degradation, wetlands loss, and decline in coral reef health are prime indicators that society's demands on our coastal areas are exceeding the capacity of coastal areas to satisfy those demands while simultaneously supporting healthy sustainable marine ecosystems and fish populations dependent upon them. When discussed in a regional context, the full ecological and economic ramifications of the continuing human-induced stress on the marine environment and ecosystems becomes clear.

The Gulf of Mexico is home to some of the most productive fisheries in the United States and is responsible for a significant proportion of the marine commercial and recreational landings in the United States. In 1989, commercial shrimp landings in the Gulf were valued at $374 million, and menhaden landings were valued at $52 million. In 1992, 5 of the top 10 commercial fishing ports in the United States, as measured by volume of catches, were located in the Gulf; recreational fishermen took 16 million fishing trips and caught 132 million fish in the Gulf; 1,200 fish processors and wholesalers employed roughly 12,500 workers; and over 25,000 vessels called the Gulf of Mexico home (Weber 1995). In 1996, $300 million were generated from oysters landed in the Gulf of Mexico (GOMP 1997). The Gulf is also home to a healthy tourism industry. For example, approximately 25 million people visit Florida beaches each year, spending as much as $25 billion (Weber 1995).

Nowhere in the nation is the link between estuarine habitat and fish production more obvious than in the Gulf of Mexico. The NMFS estimates that 95% of all commercially and recreationally valuable fish in the region are estuarine dependent, spending some stage of their life cycles in coastal wetlands (USEPA 1995). Historically, the estuarine-dependent nature of these fish posed no problem for the region. The Gulf is home to 31 major estuaries that include 55% of the coastal marshes in the lower 48 states (Weber 1995). The coastal wetlands of Louisiana alone comprise 41% of the total coastal wetlands of the United States (Turner 1990). The Gulf is also home to the most extensive mangrove forests in the United States (Weber 1995).

Over the last several decades, however, the Gulf coast has become home to growing numbers of people. The population of the Gulf coast has more than doubled since 1960. Although the coastal counties account for only 17% of the total land area of the Gulf coast states, the population of those counties increased from 7.4 million in 1960 to 14.7 million in 1988. The National Oceanic and Atmospheric Administration (NOAA) has projected that the Gulf's coastal population will increase by another 22% by the year 2010, increasing population density in Gulf counties to approximately 227 people per square mile. The greatest growth is expected in the coastal counties of western Florida and Texas (Weber 1995).

This growth in population has brought with it land development and agricultural activity resulting in increasing destruction and degradation of Gulf estuaries. Development has resulted in conversion of more and more coastal areas to residences, shopping malls, industrial parks, and casinos. Between 1970 and 1989, Gulf coastal counties issued 2.5 million residential construction permits, including permits for 1.4 million single-family homes and nearly 1 million apartment buildings with five or more units, as well as 143,000 nonresidential construction permits. The Gulf coast also accounts for 18 million agricultural acres—more agricultural acreage than any other area of the country. Much of this acreage consists of converted forests and wetlands (Weber 1995).

The Gulf region has lost more wetland acreage than any other region of the country and continues to lose wetlands in an amount equal to approximately 51% of the national total loss of wetlands (USFWS 1995). Alabama, Florida, Mississippi, and Texas have lost extensive coastal wetlands, but the greatest wetland losses in the Gulf have been shouldered by the state of Louisiana. Between 1978 and 1990, Louisiana lost on average 37.8 mi^2 of wetlands annually (Martin et al. 1996). It is expected that Louisiana will lose another 1 million acres of valuable wetlands in the next 50 years. However, wetlands are not the only habitat being lost in the Gulf. Large areas of submerged aquatic vegetation, including sea grasses, mangroves, and emergent marshes are disappearing. For example, by 1981, Tampa Bay had lost 81% of its sea grasses (Lewis et al. 1985) and 44% of its emergent marsh and mangrove habitats to coastal development (Lewis and Lewis 1978), and it is estimated that by 1992, Galveston Bay had lost 95% of its former sea grass meadows.

Water quality in the Gulf also has suffered as a result of anthropogenic changes. Levels of nutrients, introduced into estuaries via urban stormwater, sewage treatment plants, atmospheric deposition, agricultural runoff, and boater discharges, have increased dramatically. Additionally, the amount of nitrogen and phosphorus entering the Gulf via the Mississippi and Atachfalaya rivers doubled between 1950 and 1995. Present nitrogen and phosphorous loadings are largely attributable to agricultural runoff from throughout the Mississippi River basin.

Excessive levels of nutrients entering the Gulf foster algae blooms that in turn result in depletion of oxygen levels. In 1994 such an algae bloom resulted in a fish kill of approximately 200,000 fish in coastal Louisiana (Martin et al. 1996). Increases in nutrient levels also have resulted in the formation of a major hypoxic area, commonly referred to as the Dead Zone, which forms each summer at the mouth of the Mississippi River off the coast of Louisiana and Texas. Over the past several years the area has measured between 6,000 and 7,000 square miles. This area significantly disturbs benthic communities, killing all marine life unable to exit the area (Rabalais et al. 1995). The formation of smaller dead zones has been reported in Mobile Bay, Florida Bay, and other coastal areas in the Gulf region. Unprecedented red tides have also occurred along the Gulf coast in recent years. One such incident along the Texas shore claimed 14 million fish. In 1996, 149 manatees died in Tampa Bay after exposure to a toxic red tide that remained behind the barrier islands well into the spring migrating season (Morton 1997).

In 1991, over 52% of the 9 million acres approved for shellfish growing in the Gulf of Mexico were restricted (USDOC 1991). As of 1995, a majority of the shellfish-growing waters of the Gulf continued to be under regulatory control for harvest (GOMP 1997). The largest single causes for shellfish area closures are septic system failure and urban runoff. Under such circumstances, a 65% reduction in landings in the period from 1985 to 1989 is far from surprising (Weber 1995).

As population and development have increased, and as water quality and estuarine habitat have decreased, commercial fish landings in the Gulf have also decreased. Commercial fishery landings have declined 26% since 1978, with annual landed values, measured in constant 1987 dollars, decreasing by $240 million or 31% (Chambers, unpublished data). In 1992, the Gulf yielded 1.4 billion pounds of fish and shellfish, in contrast to 1980 yields of 2.0 billion pounds. Oyster harvests in the Gulf have also declined. In 1985, 26 million pounds of oysters were landed by Gulf fishermen. In 1992, only 12 million pounds of oysters were landed (Weber 1995). Landings of Gulf of Mexico pink shrimp, which are dependent upon the sea grass nursery areas of south Florida, are at an all-time low (Chambers, unpublished data).

Under these circumstances, reduction in fishing effort will do little to rectify most of the declining landings faced by the Gulf's fishing communities. Sustainable management of shrimp, oysters, and other estuarine-dependent fish requires management regimes that address the root cause of the declines in these marine fish populations—the continuing loss of important estuarine habitats. However, to date, the NMFS and the Gulf of Mexico Fishery Management Council have been virtually powerless to stem the growing environmental crisis in the marine environment, focusing instead almost exclusively on methods to decrease fishing effort.

The Role of Federal Fisheries Management

Although the threat posed by overexploitation of fisheries resources is real, the previous discussion of human-induced stresses illustrates that overfishing is not the only serious threat to fisheries. This section examines efforts of the NMFS to address the degradation of fish habitat. It is important to note that a variety of federal, state, and local agencies have jurisdiction over land-use planning and actions affecting fish habitat. However, the NMFS has the undisputed responsibility to conserve (and promote the utilization of) our nation's marine fisheries and has had ample justification to aggressively pursue fisheries habitat protection. Despite this charge to conserve marine fisheries, attempts by the NMFS to address habitat concerns have largely been ineffective. Historically, lack of aggressive leadership and funding has severely hampered the efforts of the

NMFS to address habitat issues. The sheer level of development (approximately 20,000 permits per year) has overwhelmed the small number of professionals within the NMFS habitat program, hampering completion of thorough assessments of potential development-related impacts to habitat. Moreover, the absence of a "veto" over extremely damaging projects has seriously limited the NMFS's ability to protect habitat. The following subsections describe recommendations made regarding the NMFS and habitat conservation in the late 1980s and early 1990s, the response of the U.S. Congress to those recommendations, and recent efforts by NMFS to conserve essential fish habitat.

Recommendations of the Late 1980s and Early 1990s

In 1989 the U.S. Congress acknowledged the accumulating evidence of the decline in environmental quality of the nation's estuaries and coastal waters, the decline in coastal productivity as habitats disappear, and the existence of serious doubts about the ability of our estuaries, bays, and near-coastal waters to adequately function under these stresses (U.S. Congress 1989). The need for creation of a broad and enforceable mandate for fish habitat and conservation and the need for strong leadership and increased funding within the NMFS for habitat conservation was recognized. In fact, these issues became the subject of numerous recommendations for change to the existing federal fisheries management system (Hinman and Safina 1992; NFWF 1992). The specific recommendations for change voiced by the varying interests, and particularly the similarity of the proposed changes, present a valuable context within which to evaluate current legislative changes to federal fisheries management.

In 1991, participants in a national symposium on coastal fish habitat conservation entitled "Stemming the Tide of Coastal Fish Habitat Loss" made the following recommendations regarding changes in policy and organizational framework needed for federal stewardship of living marine resources (Hinman and Safina 1992):

1. Create high-level habitat program leadership in the NMFS and NOAA with increased regulatory authority.
2. Increase funding for federal habitat programs sufficiently to fulfill the NMFS essential habitat conservation and stewardship mission.

3. Amend the Magnuson Fishery Conservation and Management Act to include habitat conservation as a national standard for guiding management, giving the NMFS regulatory authority over projects that could severely damage fishery-supporting habitat and requiring the NMFS to ensure that all federal actions be consistent with the objectives of approved fishery resource management plans.

That same year, the National Fish and Wildlife Foundation produced a similar set of recommendations (NFWF 1992):

1. The NMFS should (1) establish a formal National Habitat Protection Program, (2) develop specific national and regional strategies to guide the National Habitat Protection Program, and (3) set goals, objectives, and specific program and funding levels for all involved NMFS elements.
2. Funding levels for the NMFS should be significantly increased to allow adequate staffing and funding of the NMFS's National Habitat Protection Program.
3. The Magnuson Act should be amended to improve the accountability of other federal agencies to the NMFS trust authority. Such amendments should require federal agencies to consider the impact of their actions on fisheries under federal management and to compensate for the adverse effects of activities that demonstrably affect species under federal fisheries management. The Magnuson Act also should be amended to empower the NMFS to force agencies to change actions that affect federally managed fisheries before the actions can proceed and to revise federal water project management and water allocation policy to protect and improve freshwater supplies to fish-supporting habitats.

In 1994, in a joint report entitled "Marine Fishery Habitat Protection," the Institute for Fisheries Resources, the East Coast Fisheries Federation, and the Pacific Coast Federation of Fishermen's Associations likewise advocated that (Institute for Fisheries Resources 1994):

1. Congress strengthen the NMFS's stewardship authority by giving the agency the power to modify actions that would damage important fishery habitats, and provide full funding for the staff and resources needed by the NMFS to carry out its fish habitat protection mandate.

2. The Secretary of Commerce require the NMFS to provide strong national leadership for the protection of fish habitats by (1) creating a National Habitat Protection Program, (2) directing that the NMFS treat the protection of fish stocks and the protection of habitats as the agency's primary and co-equal missions, and (3) directing the NOAA to provide real resource stewardship by focusing its coastal environmental quality-related programs on supporting habitat protection objectives through research, monitoring, synthesis, and management activities.

Finally, in 1994, the National Academy of Science (NAS) published recommendations to improve fisheries management, recommending that the NMFS and the regional fishery management councils be empowered to protect habitat needed to sustain fishery resources (NAS 1994). More specifically, the NAS concluded that "a more proactive means of preserving habitat important to fishes is needed that can prevent incremental losses of these habitats by a multitude of little changes" (NAS 1994:30).

Sustainable Fisheries Act

The call for change in the existing federal fisheries management program for too long went unheeded. Only in 1994, with the publication of the NAS recommendations, did the hue and cry for recognition of the need for, and elevation of, habitat protection result in any legislative change in the NMFS management authority and structure. The result was passage by Congress of the essential fish habitat provisions of the 1996 reauthorization of the Magnuson-Stevens Fishery Conservation and Management Act (Magnuson-Stevens Act) (16 U.S.C. § 1801 et seq., as amended 1996), also referred to as the Sustainable Fisheries Act.

Many have hailed the EFH provisions of the Magnuson-Stevens Act as "setting the stage for turning the product of a failed management system into healthy, productive, and sustainable fisheries" and as " ensur[ing] the conservation and management of essential fish habitats once…designated" (Kiraly et al. 1998:C-25, C-31). However, the changes mandated by the Magnuson-Stevens Act are far from a panacea for the ills that plague fisheries managers seeking to address habitat concerns. The EFH provisions of the Magnuson-Stevens Act do signal a much-needed emphasis on habitat protection. The

Magnuson-Stevens Act's EFH provisions legislatively acknowledge that habitat loss has resulted in a diminished capacity to support existing fishing levels and that a national program is needed "to promote the protection of essential fish habitat" (16 U.S.C. § 1801[b][7]). In fact, within the Magnuson-Stevens Act Congress specifically finds that (16 U.S.C. §1801[a][9]):

"One of the greatest long-term threats to the viability of commercial and recreational fisheries is the continuing loss of marine, estuarine, and other aquatic habitats. Habitat considerations should receive increased attention for the conservation and management of fishery resources of the United States."

However, the Magnuson-Stevens Act fails to authorize the NMFS to effectively protect habitat.

The Magnuson-Stevens Act requires that each fishery management plan (FMP) developed by a regional fishery management council describe and identify essential fish habitat for the fishery based on guidelines established by the Secretary of Commerce (the Secretary), minimize to the extent practicable adverse effects on habitats caused by fishing, and identify other actions to encourage the conservation and enhancement of such habitat (16 U.S.C. § 1853[7]). The Magnuson-Stevens Act also requires that the Secretary (16 U.S.C § 1855 [b][1]):

1. establish by regulation guidelines to assist Councils in the description and identification of EFH and in the consideration of actions to ensure the conservation and enhancement of such habitat;
2. assist in the actual identification of EFH, the adverse impacts on that habitat, and the actions that should be considered to ensure the conservation and enhancement of that habitat;
3. review programs administered by the Department [of Commerce] to ensure that relevant programs further the conservation and enhancement of EFH; and
4. coordinate with and provide information to other federal agencies to further the conservation and enhancement of EFH.

Councils are authorized to present to the Secretary and to any federal or state agency comments regarding any activity that is likely to substantially affect the EFH of any fishery resource under its authority. In response to a Council's comments, the Secretary is required to recommend actions that can be taken to conserve the habitat to any federal or state agency pursuing the activity of concern (16 U.S.C. § 1855[3][4]). Finally, the Magnuson-Stevens Act requires that federal agencies consult with the Secretary with respect to any action that may adversely affect essential fish habitat. If during consultation the NMFS provides recommendations for changes in a project necessary to protect EFH, the federal agency must respond in writing to the NMFS. If the federal agency disagrees with NMFS recommendations, the agency must "explain the reasons for not following the recommendations" (16 U.S.C. § 1855[4][B]). Although the NMFS has the right to invoke expanded consultation, the federal agency ultimately remains free to reject the NMFS and Council recommendations for disapproval of, or changes to, a project or permit.

Most federal agencies are involved in coastal land-use decisions that impact fisheries habitat. Input by the National Marine Fisheries Service into these decisions remains limited. The Magnuson-Stevens Act requires only that federal agencies consult with the NMFS on projects that could impact EFH by submitting a completed EFH assessment to the NMFS for review. The NMFS is then given the option of concurring with the assessment, commenting on the assessment, recommending measures for conservation, or, if the NMFS believes that substantial adverse impacts to EFH may result or that additional analysis is required, initiating expanded consultation. In the end, the result is the same: the federal agency to which the comments are submitted merely has the "responsibility" to respond in writing before the final approval of the action. If the federal agency fails to adopt the NMFS's conservation recommendations, the agency need only explain its reasons. Although actions inconsistent with the NMFS's recommendations can be elevated to the Assistant Secretary of Commerce level, there is no requirement that agencies modify projects or otherwise comply with the NMFS's recommendations before proceeding with the project.

Thus, in enacting the Magnuson-Stevens Act, Congress ignored the recommendations of the Institute for Fisheries Resources, the National Academy of Sciences, a national symposium on coastal fish habitat conservation, and the National Fish and

Wildlife Foundation that NMFS be given the authority to force other federal agencies to modify actions that adversely impact EFH. Federal agencies such as the U.S. Army Corps of Engineers and the U.S. Minerals Management Service remain free to ignore recommendations of the NMFS and the Councils no matter how great an impact their projects may have on EFH. Historically, fish habitat protection has not ranked as a priority with other federal agencies, and written expressions of concern by the NMFS and the Councils regarding the adverse impacts of other federal agencies' activities on fish habitat have, in all but a very few cases, been relatively ineffective. There is no reason to believe that this will change.

In the end, the strength of the Magnuson-Stevens Act is that it now properly acknowledges the fundamental relationship between the health of our fisheries and the health of their habitats, as well as the need for an ecosystem approach to the management of our fisheries. This recognition holds promise for the course of future fisheries management. One of the Magnuson-Stevens Act's main weaknesses lies in its failure to empower the NMFS to "ensure the conservation and management" of EFH in any context other than those impacts on habitat associated with fishing practices. The Magnuson-Stevens Act does not give the NMFS authority to require other federal agencies to take action to protect habitat designated as EFH. In fact, the Magnuson-Stevens Act fails to elevate habitat conservation to the level of a national standard.

The very best that the NMFS can do under the Magnuson-Stevens Act is to work with federal and state agencies to develop binding agreements to protect EFH. Interagency memoranda of understanding (MOUs) may provide a possible mechanism to elevate fish habitat protection to an appropriate level and to require agency accountability (R. M. Fujita, Environmental Defense Fund, unpublished data). Nonetheless, MOUs cannot take the place of the "veto" authority needed by NMFS.

The National Marine Fisheries Service Commitment to Habitat Protection

An additional concern with the EFH provisions of the Magnuson-Stevens Act relates to the NMFS's commitment to habitat protection in the face of political pressure. As is the case with any piece of legislation, the effectiveness of the EFH provisions in achieving their intended purpose relies upon the interpretation of those provisions adopted by the NMFS in its regulations. An Interim Final Rule (IFR) to implement the EFH provisions of the Magnuson-Stevens Act was issued by NMFS on 17 December 1997 (62 Federal Register 66531–66559) and became effective on 20 January 1998. The IFR was, and continues to be, the subject of intense objection by nonfishing industry interests, including utilities and timber and mining interests. Accordingly, it is unclear at this time whether the NMFS will succumb to those interests and issue a Final Rule that is significantly different from the IFR. The environmental community has worked diligently to ensure that the Final Rule is not a weakened version of the IFR, and formal comments on the IFR submitted by representatives of the environmental community to NMFS are outlined in this section.

The IFR is largely consistent with the spirit and letter of the Magnuson-Stevens Act, as well as its legislative history. The IFR provides a useful guide to the Councils and the NMFS for the identification and protection of essential fish habitat in a broad ecosystem context. For example, the IFR makes clear that EFH is identifiable in state waters and that identification of the prey of managed species and the habitats of that prey is required to address broader ecosystem concerns. The IFR also encourages consideration of the use of no-take marine protected areas as management tools for protecting habitat and habitat function.

This is not to say that the NMFS's interpretation of the Magnuson-Stevens Act, as reflected by the IFR, is without weakness. The Magnuson-Stevens Act clearly mandates that the Councils and the Secretary should take action to address any adverse impact to fish habitat (16 U.S.C. §1853[a][7]). The IFR only requires that "identifiable" adverse impacts of fishing practices should be demonstrated before protective action can be taken, defining "identifiable" as "both more than minimal and not temporary in nature" (62 Fed. Reg. 66538). The preamble to the IFR states that this requirement is not intended to "raise the threshold of damage from fishing impacts higher than that intended in the statute." However, the requirement inevitably does raise the threshold of damage. By its definition of "identifiable," the NMFS limits the full scope of protections that are afforded by the EFH mandate, including protections from "minimal" and "temporary" but nonetheless harmful adverse impacts. In effect, the IFR modifies the Congressional intent of the EFH provision (Marine Fish Conservation Network, unpublished data).

Additionally, the Magnuson-Stevens Act clearly defines EFH in terms of life history characteristics, specifically stating that "'essential fish habitat' means those waters and substrate necessary to fish for spawning, feeding, breeding, and growth to maturity" (16 U.S.C. 1802[10]). Nevertheless, within the IFR, the NMFS defines EFH merely in terms of productivity. In the end, the redefinition of EFH invites leniency in interpretation and may result in the exclusion from EFH designation of habitats necessary to fish for the life history characteristics outlined by the statute. Habitat must be interpreted broadly to mean the habitat required to support managed species and the ecosystems of which they are a part. Each individual species has a habitat that it needs to live and reproduce and depends on a community of other species for food and survival. The dynamic interactions of these species and their overlapping mosaic of habitats constitute an ecosystem. The NMFS regulations must recognize the importance of conserving entire habitats and communities. Recognition of this fact is critical to the recovery of individual species and the ecosystem functions the species provide (Fujita, unpublished data). Thus, unless scientific information dictates that certain areas are not necessary to support the life history characteristics of a species, the habitat required to support managed species and the ecosystems of which they are a part should be designated as EFH (Marine Fish Conservation Network, unpublished data). A definition of EFH based on productivity, rather than broader life history requirements, will inevitably substantially weaken EFH protection.

The Magnuson-Stevens Act places no geographic or political limitation on the NMFS's or the Councils' abilities to identify or designate EFH beyond the United States' 200-mi exclusive economic zone. However, the IFR does impose such a limitation when it specifies that habitats found beyond the borders of the 200-mi EEZ cannot be designated as EFH (Section 600.805[b][2]). The exclusion of habitat beyond the EEZ from designation as EFH is illogical. The IFR allows Councils to "describe, identify, and protect habitats of managed species" in international waters or waters of another nation, thereby recognizing that the range of a species may extend beyond the artificial, political boundaries of "federal" waters. Accordingly, there is no reason why EFH identification should not apply beyond the borders of the EEZ. At a minimum, identification and designation of EFH, whether inside or outside of the 200-mi EEZ, should be appropriate for species under U.S. jurisdiction and whose migratory range is beyond the EEZ (Marine Fish Conservation Network, unpublished data).

Additional concerns with the IFR relate to the NMFS's failure to provide sufficient guidance to Council and NMFS staff to ensure effective implementation of the Magnuson-Stevens Act. For example, the IFR fails to specify performance criteria to define the success (or failure) of mitigation measures or monitoring procedures designed to determine whether projections of impacts on habitat are correct. No longer can the NMFS rely on promises to mitigate or projections that do not anticipate significant impacts associated with a project or activity. State and federal agencies must be held accountable. The most effective mechanism for ensuring accountability is through specification of performance criteria (Fujita, unpublished data). Performance criteria should be based on key indicators of habitat quality such as habitat diversity, fish density, fish survival rates, and the degree to which natural processes that maintain the habitat remain intact. Monitoring targeted to the assessment of the performance criteria could then be required. Finally, adaptive management should be used to respond to monitoring data and performance criteria (Fujita, unpublished data).

Finally, the IFR requires that all threats to EFH and the actions to address those threats be listed in fishery management plans. The IFR implies that once threats are identified, the NMFS and Councils will take steps to implement actions to address threats to EFH and consult with agencies on all projects that substantially impact EFH. Such an expectation is unrealistic, requiring a workload for the NMFS, the Councils, and other federal agencies that far exceeds existing capabilities. Threats to EFH are numerous and require detailed assessments of potential impacts. To facilitate real action to protect and restore EFH, threats need to be ranked and addressed in order of their importance. Formal ecological risk assessment, management, and identification have not been possible given the relatively short time frame for preparing EFH-related fishery management plan amendments. Nonetheless, a systematic approach to the ranking of threats should be applied. According to a National Research Council (National Academy of Sciences) report, threats can be ranked according to their geographic extent, severity, and longevity. Priority should be given to threats that potentially affect large areas of EFH; that are severe (e.g., cause direct mortality or destroy EFH); that can persist for a long period of time; and that are essentially irreversible (Fujita, unpublished data). Guidelines for how to react to threats of varying degrees of seriousness, for which the course of action may be clear or uncertain, would be helpful. For example, if the nature of the threat is relatively well characterized (e.g., dumping of toxic dredge material), and if the course of action to address the threat is quite clear (prevent dumping), then immediate action would be warranted. Very serious threats should merit action even if the course of action or the exact nature of the threat is uncertain (Fujita, unpublished data).

If the Final Rule were to eliminate the weaknesses discussed above, NMFS would:

- begin to set the stage for full and effective implementation of the EFH mandate in the Magnuson-Stevens Act,
- provide many of the tools necessary to implement ecosystem-based management that ensures effective conservation of EFH, and
- enable some fishery and ecosystem recovery.

Absent these changes, the NMFS may succeed in diluting the potential for change embodied in the new provisions and weaken any potential for habitat protection created by the Magnuson-Stevens Act. Nonetheless, the IFR is moderately successful at interjecting ecosystem considerations into fishery management. Moreover, the IFR introduces much-needed improvements to the NMFS fisheries management system and implements changes that will further the protection of habitats critical to maintenance of healthy fish populations.

The greatest concerns that remain lie not with the Magnuson-Stevens Act or the NMFS's implementation of the provisions of the Magnuson-Stevens Act, but (1) with the continuing failure of Congress to adequately fund the NMFS, particularly the habitat aspects of its program, and (2) the absence of strong leadership within the NMFS regarding habitat protection. Shortages in funding have plagued the NMFS habitat protection program since its inception. Despite the overwhelming agreement among fisheries managers, scientists, and the conservation community regarding the need for significant increases in funding for full staffing and support of the habitat protection program, Congress remains reluctant to provide those funds. Even in the face of Congressionally mandated requirements for immediate action set forth in the Magnuson-Stevens Act, Congress has failed to provide the funding neces-

sary to support full implementation of the Act. Absent adequate funding it is doubtful that full and timely implementation of the EFH provisions of the Magnuson-Stevens Act will occur. Although the NMFS and Councils may successfully meet the requirements that EFH and the threats to EFH be identified, effective action to stem the tide of habitat destruction will not occur absent a substantial increase in available funding. Much-needed scientific research aimed at a better understanding of various habitats and their importance to various fish species will not occur. Moreover, the rate of development in coastal communities will continue to overwhelm the abilities of the NMFS and Councils to adequately assess and comment on the impacts of proposed development on EFH. Accordingly, unless Congress makes the needed financial commitment, the effectiveness of the EFH provisions in ensuring the conservation of EFH will be minimal, the loss and degradation of EFH will continue at current rates, and our fisheries will continue to decline.

Conclusion

Habitat degradation and loss threaten the integrity of our marine ecosystems. An understanding of the danger of habitat degradation to marine fisheries spurred Congress to enact the EFH provisions of the Magnuson-Stevens Act. The provisions bring a much-needed acknowledgment of the importance of fisheries habitat and the need for a national program to conserve that habitat. However, the Magnuson-Stevens Act fails to address a critical problem facing federal fisheries managers, namely, federal managers' lack of authority to require other federal agencies to incorporate necessary habitat conservation measures into projects under their control. Additionally, without Congressional appropriation of sufficient funding for full implementation of the Magnuson-Stevens Act, efforts at habitat conservation will continue to be ineffectual.

Acknowledgments

I thank Katherine L. Smith, a student at Tulane University, for donating her time to assist me in researching this paper. I would also like to thank James Chambers, Tanya Dobrzynski, Rod Fujita, Ken Hinman, Suzanne Iudicello, and Tom Okey for the documents and information they provided.

References

Chambers, J. R. 1992. Coastal degradation and fishery declines in the U.S. Pages 45–51 in R. H. Stroud, editor. Stemming the tide of coastal fish habitat loss. National Coalition for Marine Conservation, Savannah, Georgia.

Ehler, C., and nine coauthors. 1998. Perspectives on marine environmental quality. Pages E-1–E-17 in Year of the ocean: discussion papers. National Oceanic and Atmospheric Administration, Washington, D.C.

Fedler, A. J., and D. M. Nickum. 1994. The 1991 economic impact of sport fishing in the United States. Sport Fishing Institute, Washington, D.C.

GOMP (Gulf of Mexico Program [U. S. Environmental Protection Agency]). 1997. Shareholder report. EPA 855-R-97-003. U.S. EPA, Stennis Center, Mississippi.

Hinman K., and C. Safina. 1992. Summary and recommendations. Pages 245–249 in R. H. Stroud, editor. Stemming the tide of coastal fish habitat loss. National Coalition for Marine Conservation, Savannah, Georgia.

Institute for Fisheries Resources. 1994. Marine fishery habitat protection: a report to the United States Congress and the Secretary of Commerce. Institute for Fisheries Resources, Sausalito, California.

Kiraly, S. J., and fourteen coauthors. 1998. Ensuring the sustainability of ocean living resources quality. Pages C1– C34 in Year of the ocean: discussion papers. National Oceanic and Atmospheric Administration, Washington, D.C.

Lewis, R. R., M. J. Durako, M. D. Moffler, and R. C. Phillips. 1985. Seagrass meadows of Tampa Bay: a review. Pages 210–246 in S. F. Treat, J. L. Simon, R. R. Lewis III, and R. L. Whitman, Jr., editors. Proceedings of the Tampa Bay area scientific information symposium. Burgess Publishing, Minneapolis, Minnesota.

Lewis, R. R., and C. S. Lewis. 1978. Colonial bird use and plant succession on dredged material islands in Florida. volume II. Patterns of vegetation succession. Environmental Effects Laboratory, U.S. Army Corps of Engineers, Waterways Experiment Station, Vicksburg, Mississippi.

Martin, D. M., T. Morton, T. Dobrzynski, and B. Valentine. 1996. Estuaries on the edge: the vital link between land and sea. American Oceans Campaign, Washington, D.C.

Miller, S. L., and Crosby, M. P. 1998. The extent and condition of U.S. coral reefs. In State of the coast report. National Ocean and Atmospheric Administration, Silver Spring, Maryland.

Morton, T. 1997. Draining to the ocean: the effects of stormwater pollution on coastal waters. American Oceans Campaign, Washington D.C.

NAS (National Academy of Sciences). 1994. Improving the management of U.S. marine fisheries. National Academy Press, Washington, D.C.

NFWF (National Fish, and Wildlife Foundation). 1992. FY 1993 fisheries and wildlife assessment, U.S. Department of Commerce, National Oceanic and Atmospheric Administration. NFWF, Washington, D.C.

NOAA (National Oceanic, and Atmospheric Administration). 1997. Report to Congress on the status of fisheries in the United States. Washington, D.C.

Rabalais, N. N., R. E. Turner, and W. J. Wiseman, Jr. 1995. Hypoxia in the northern Gulf of Mexico: past, present and future. In Proceedings of the first Gulf of Mexico hypoxia management conference. EPA-55-R-97-001. U.S. Environmental Protection Agency, Stennis Center, Mississippi.

Safina, C. 1992. A primer on conserving marine resources, 2nd edition. National Audubon Society Living Oceans Program, New York City.

Safina, C. 1994. Where have all the fishes gone. Issues in Science and Technology 37-43.

Turner, R. E. 1990. Landscape development and coastal wetland losses in the northern Gulf of Mexico. American Zoology 30:89–105.

U.S. Congress. 1989. Coastal waters in jeopardy: reversing the decline and protecting America's coastal resources. Merchant Marine and Fisheries Committee, U.S. House of Representatives, U.S. Congress, Washington, D.C.

USDA (U.S. Department of Agriculture). 1995. National resources inventory summary. National Resource Conservation Service, USDA, Washington, D.C.

USDOC (U.S. Department of Commerce). 1991. The 1990 national shellfish register of classified estuarine waters. USDOC, National Oceanic and Atmospheric Administration, Washington, D.C.

USDOC (U.S. Department of Commerce). 1992a. Marine recreational fishery statistics survey, Atlantic and Gulf coasts, 1990-1991. Current Fishery Statistics No. 9204. USDOC, National Oceanic and Atmospheric Administration, National Marine Fisheries Service, Washington, D.C.

USDOC (U.S. Department of Commerce). 1992b. Marine recreational fishery statistics survey, Pacific coast, 1987-1989. Current Fishery Statistics No. 9205. USDOC, National Oceanic and Atmospheric Administration, National Marine Fisheries Service, Washington, D.C.

USEPA (U.S. Environmental Protection Agency). 1995. Wetlands fact sheet number 2. USEPA, Washington, D.C.

USFWS (U.S. Fish and Wildlife Service). 1995. Report to Congress: status and trends of wetlands in the conterminous United States. USFWS, U.S. Department of the Interior, Washington, D.C.

Watzin, M. C., and J. G. Gosselink. 1992. The fragile fringe: coastal wetlands of the continental United States. Louisiana Sea Grant College Program/U.S. Fish and Wildlife Service/National Oceanic and Atmospheric Administration, Baton Rouge.

Weber, M. 1995. Gulf of Mexico states. Pages 35–59 in State of the coasts: a state-by-state analysis of the vital link between healthy coasts and a healthy economy. Coast Alliance, Washington, D.C.

W. M. Kier Associates. 1998. Fisheries, wetlands and jobs. Clean Water Network, Washington, D.C.

American Fisheries Society Symposium 22:23–30, 1999

Conserving Fish Habitat from the Seafood Perspective

RICHARD E. GUTTING, JR.

National Fisheries Institute
1901 North Fort Myer Drive, Suite 700, Arlington, Virginia 22209, USA

Abstract.—Food production in the United States from ocean fisheries is leveling off after impressive growth in the 1970s and 1980s. Fishery officials project further gains through more effective regulation of harvests and reduced discarding of catch. In the longer term, however, the most important opportunity to boost production involves rehabilitating fishery habitats that have been damaged or lost because of poor management. Many thousand tons of additional seafood production can be "unlocked" for fishermen and consumers if habitats are restored. Changes in 1996 to the Magnuson-Stevens Fishery Conservation and Management Act (the Magnuson-Stevens Act) call for the mapping of these habitats and the inclusion of habitat concerns in fishery management planning. These new requirements, if properly implemented, will help focus the attention of fishermen and seafood consumers on what is being lost and what needs to be done to restore productivity. Although these requirements are a good first step, the rules and guidance for the new essential fish habitat (EFH) provisions are fundamentally flawed. For example, the rules to implement EFH provisions muddle the Magnuson-Stevens Act's definition of EFH with numerous references to prey species and vague ecological ideas. Especially troubling is the introduction by the National Marine Fisheries Service through the rules of the concept of "contribution to a healthy ecosystem" as an apparent standard for delineating necessary amounts of EFH. In addition, it is important to remember that competition among fishing fleets is fierce, and the promise of these new habitat requirements could be lost if habitat concerns become enmeshed in the ongoing political battles for harvest allocations.

The fishermen gave him a special standing to demand a response from political leaders...the fishermen gave environmentalism its human face.—Cronin and Kennedy (1997)

The fisheries of the United States (called the "giant protein factories" of the United States by H. L. Mencken) produce more than 10 billion pounds of fish and shellfish each year (NOAA 1997). The portion of the annual harvest sold for food generates more than US$3.5 billion for commercial fishermen and their families. And by the time this food reaches consumers, it is worth more than $40 billion.

Some 250,000 Americans depend upon commercial fishing for their livelihood. These fishermen and their fleet of 100,000 fishing vessels have been joined in recent years by a growing number of farmers who are pioneering the production of food in coastal waters through aquaculture. The many suppliers and coastal communities supporting these fishermen and farmers generate additional revenues to our economy. This renewable flow of wealth from the sea contributes significantly to the nutritional well-being of Americans. Scientists have widely acknowledged that seafood contributes to nutritious meals and good health (Lands 1986; Nettleton 1986; Nettleton 1987; Simopoulos and Robinson 1998). In 1997, Americans ate an average of about 15 lb of seafood each (NOAA 1997).

This chapter describes the need to protect fish habitat, which is the cornerstone of seafood productivity. After describing past efforts to protect fish habitat, including the leadership role that fishermen and the seafood industry have taken in these efforts, this chapter describes the essential fish habitat (EFH) provisions of the 1996 Magnuson-Stevens Fishery Conservation and Management Act (the Magnuson-Stevens Act), focusing on troubling language found in the Interim Final Rule to implement the EFH provisions. Finally, this chapter suggests practical steps to take to ensure that the EFH policy accomplishes its basic goals as outlined in the Magnuson-Stevens Act.

The Need to Protect Fish Habitat

Not only are U.S. fisheries valuable in economic and human terms, they are sustainable and have been producing food for centuries. However, ensuring that fisheries remain productive is a challenging but critical objective. In recent years, fishery managers have made substantial efforts to restrict harvests. Much less effort has been devoted to protecting the habitats upon which fisheries depend. Unless these habitats are protected, fishery management will fail, and food will be lost.

Habitat losses are painfully evident in many parts of the country. Nearshore waters in many states, for example, are closed to fishing, especially shellfishing, because of poor water quality, which is caused by polluted runoffs from rural and urban areas and the continuing discharge of poorly treated sewage (Chambers 1992). The physical alteration and destruction of habitats also threaten seafood production. For example, wetlands, which provide critical habitat during the life cycles of most commercially important fish, are being lost at alarming rates (USFWS 1997). (However, the average annual net loss of wetlands appears to be slowing.) Likewise, scallop dredging and bottom trawling have altered the biological and physical characteristics of the seafloor, which may have significant consequences for fishery productivity (Auster and Langton 1999, this volume).

In recent years, the growing number and severity of harmful algal blooms have been of particular concern to fishermen and the seafood industry (USDOI 1997). Scientists speculate that excessive nutrient loads, particularly nitrogen and phosphorous, may be a contributing factor to the blooms (NOAA 1998). These blooms have hurt the scallop fishery off Long Island and salmon aquaculture operations in the Pacific Northwest and have closed down other shellfish fisheries throughout the United States. In addition, harmful algal blooms have had a significant impact on coastal fisheries resources and some marine mammals (Burkholder 1998). According to some estimates, cutbacks in production resulting from harmful algal blooms may have cost seafood firms in excess of tens of millions of dollars in lost revenue per year (Anderson et al. 1993).

Although habitat loss and coastal degradation affect vacationers, homeowners, and resort operators, commercial fishermen (and the fish and shellfish resources themselves) are the primary victims. When habitat is lost, fishery productivity declines. When water quality deteriorates due to pollution, fishing grounds are restricted or closed. The results are lost revenue for fishermen, fish processors, distributors, restaurants, and retailers, and, ultimately, a loss of food for Americans.

But there are other losses to consider—losses due to "food scares" resulting from polluted coastal waters. Consumers become frightened when they hear about fish contaminated by polychlorinated biphenyls (PCBs), *Pfiesteria*, or mercury on the nightly news, or when they see sensational pictures in their morning newspapers of fish neatly garnished with hypodermic needles through their gills. If consumers are unnecessarily frightened, it is the seafood community and consumers who suffer from lost sales and food that cannot be sold.

Sensational and unbalanced media stories confound the efforts of environmental groups and the seafood community to protect fish habitats. Closing fisheries because of pollution protects consumers from contamination, but such activities have not convinced enough of the public or Congress to take true remedial action. Citing statistics about lost seafood jobs and revenue and degraded fish habitat and water quality only goes so far. It seems that the contamination of an estuary is only of passing interest to those living at a distance from it—particularly if the body of water is closed to fishing and no seafood is being produced.

Few Americans understand how much seafood production is being lost and what this means to the health and well-being of their families. Unless the public understands why seafood production is important, the marine environment, seafood firms, and consumers will lose. If parents understood that their children need seafood for development, and if older people knew that seafood was important for their health, threats to seafood production would be far more significant to the public. Developing a strong message that seafood is important could help build public support for protecting fishery habitats.

Past Efforts to Protect Habitat

Despite many different federal and state regulatory programs and land-use planning efforts aimed at preventing the destruction of fish habitats, population growth and coastal development have continued to degrade these habitats. For example, before the 1996 Magnuson-Stevens Fishery Conservation and Management Act, the National Marine Fisheries Service (NMFS) fulfilled its responsibilities to protect fish habitat through consultations with other federal agencies under various federal statutes including the Clean Water Act (33 USC 1251–1387), the Federal Power Act (16 USC 791a-828c), the Fish and Wildlife Coordination Act (16 USC 661–666c), the National Environmental Policy Act (42 USC 4321–4347), the Outer Continental Shelf Lands Act (43 USC 1331–1356), and the Safe Drinking Water Act (42 USC 300f-300j). These laws, however, do not specify what fish habitat information is important to consider in project planning, and the NMFS was given little or no guidance by Congress as to what information or recommendations should be provided to other agencies. Indeed, in many instances, the NMFS was under no obligation to make recommendations regarding various federal activities that might affect fisheries.

This is not to say that before 1996, NMFS comments were ineffective in protecting fisheries habitat. For example, in early 1993, NMFS comments contributed to the withdrawal of an application to construct a 3,160-acre impoundment on a brackish marsh complex in Louisiana, as well as to the determination that additional studies were needed before the U.S. Army Corps of Engineers' Alaska District could authorize modification of its permit to allow for construction of a new oil pipeline (NMFS 1994). Although such comments sometimes proved to protect fish habitat, the NMFS's effectiveness was limited by the large number of actions that had to be addressed on a case-by-case basis.

Various sectors of the commercial fishing and seafood industries have long realized that healthy fish habitats are the key to sustainable and large catches, and the fishing and seafood communities have taken many actions during the 1970s, 1980s, and 1990s to protect fish habitat. These actions generally fall into three categories: (1) taking direct and private actions to conserve fish habitat, (2) filing lawsuits, and (3) lobbying members of Congress and other politicians for changes in laws and policies. The direct and private activities of the commercial fishing and seafood industries to protect fish habitat are too numerous to list here but include the work of Trident, Icicle, and Unisea Seafoods to clean up solid waste and fuel storage waste on the Pribilof Islands off the coast of Alaska (Matsen 1996). The Maine Sardine Council in association with other local fishing, conservation, and natural resource management organizations sponsored a project in 1997 in which lobstermen used a sampling and interviewing protocol to determine the extent of recent and historical Atlantic herring *Clupea harengus* spawning in central Maine (C. Brehme, Island Institute, unpublished data). Also in Maine, fisherman Ted Ames interviewed New England groundfishermen in the early 1990s to construct a preliminary map of inshore cod *Gadus morhua* and haddock *Melanogrammus aeglefinus* spawning grounds (Waterman 1997). Commercial fishermen have also actively participated in habitat restoration efforts in Louisiana, in part through leadership in the Coalition to Restore Coastal Louisiana, which in 1996 was chaired by commercial shrimper Donald Lirette (Holley 1996). Lobbying actions have included efforts by fishermen including Frank Martins, Zeke Grader, and Nat Bingham to establish California's Salmon Stamp program in 1978, which charges trollers fees for habitat projects that help rebuild salmon stocks (Kronman 1998).

Surprisingly, fishery agencies such as the NMFS had few comprehensive regulatory tools to protect fish habitats before 1996 because no comprehensive law existed that required federal agencies to prevent threats to fish habitat in the course of their activities (Ballweber and Jackson 1996). Instead, for decades, various state and federal environmental agencies pursued different regulatory strategies to restrict pollution, conserve estuaries, and restore waters to a "fishable" condition. These efforts occurred without a clear understanding of which areas or habitats were most important to maintaining healthy levels of food production. Moreover, although the vital linkage between fish habitat quality and fishery production has been exhaustively described in qualitative terms in the ecological literature (see Pierce 1991), the quantitative relationship between loss of a particular habitat and a specific level of fish production has not been made by fishery managers. Indeed, a very small percentage of the NMFS budget was allocated to protecting and enhancing habitats in the 1980s and early 1990s, resulting in the creation of a NMFS "Habitat Protection Budget Initiative" in 1994 (NMFS 1994).

Essential Fish Habitat Regulations

The lack of comprehensive regulatory focus on fish habitat changed as a result of the essential fish habitat provisions enacted as part of the 1996 Magnuson-Stevens Fishery Conservation and Management Act (Public Law 104–297). These new provisions:

- integrated efforts to conserve habitat into the fishery management process of the Magnuson-Stevens Act;
- required every fishery management plan to identify the habitat needed to sustain each federally managed fishery; and
- provided federal fishery managers with substantial input regarding how the activities of state and federal agencies will be carried out.

The enactment of the EFH provisions was a major priority for commercial fishermen and seafood processors. Now, for the first time, each fishery management plan must identify the essential fish habitat of the fishery, the activities adversely impacting this habitat, and the actions needed to ensure that this habitat is conserved or enhanced. Federal agencies, in turn, must consult with fishery managers when their activities might adversely affect the habitat identified in a plan and must respond in writing to NMFS recommendations concerning their activities.

These new requirements did not grant the regional fishery management councils "predominate management authority" over the geographic areas to be identified as essential fish habitat. Instead, the purpose of the EFH regulations was to identify important habitat for each fishery to provide other agencies "with the information on which to base decisions on actions that have the potential to effect that habitat" (U.S. Congress 1995). In December 1997, NMFS issued guidelines to implement the EFH provisions, and these guidelines (discussed in the following section) expanded the scope of EFH beyond the Congressional mandate and inspired negative and at times hostile reactions from some sectors of the seafood industry and other interested parties.

The Interim Final Rule

Since the passage of the 1996 Magnuson-Stevens Fishery Conservation and Management Act, the NMFS has repeatedly consulted with interested parties concerning how best to implement the EFH provisions. On 19 December 1997, the NMFS issued an interim final rule (IFR) to implement the EFH provisions; this rule presently governs how the EFH provisions are to be interpreted by the regional fishery management councils and the Secretary of Commerce (NMFS 1997). Despite the commendable efforts of the NMFS to involve all interested parties, the IFR is fundamentally flawed. As a result, the IFR's far-reaching mandate—which encourages ecosystem approaches that lack the full support of the seafood industry and other interested parties—the efforts of fishermen and the seafood industry to protect essential fish habitats and their own livelihoods have been jeopardized.

Scope

A comparison of concepts and definitions found in the 1996 Magnuson-Stevens Fishery Conservation and Management Act and the IFR demonstrates the IFR's excessive scope and mandates. For example, the Magnuson-Stevens Act defines essential fish habitat in Section 3(10) as "those waters and substrate necessary to fish for spawning, breeding, or growth to maturity." The IFR's guidance regarding how essential fish habitat is to be described and identified in fishery management plans, however, is muddled through the introduction of "prey species" as fish for which essential fish habitat must be identified (62 FR 66541). That is, the opening paragraphs of the IFR state that fishery management plans (FMPs) must describe and identify the essential fish habitat for "managed species" (62 FR 66531). These managed species are distinguished at several points in the rules from other species, such as the prey species of managed species (62 FR 66534). The rules, however, state that the loss of the habitat of prey species constitutes an adverse impact on the EFH of the managed species, thus effectively expanding the definition of EFH to cover the habitat of prey species as well as those species under management (62 FR 66541). This expansion of management oversight is unnecessary, confusing, and better left to the judgment of individual regional fishery management councils.

The scope of EFH to be identified and defined differs significantly between the Magnuson-Stevens Act and the IFR. According to the Magnuson-Stevens Act, fishery management plans are prepared with respect to a fishery, and the correct starting point for describing and identifying the essential fish habitat for a fishery according to Section 303(a)(7) of the Magnuson-Stevens Act is the species of fish identified in the description of the fishery under Section 303(a)(2). Under Section 303(a)(2), this description must include "the species of fish involved and their location." In addition, Section 3(13) of the Magnuson-Stevens Act defines "fishery" to mean "one or more stocks of fish which can be treated as a unit for purposes of conservation and management and which are identified on the basis of geographical, scientific, technical, recreational, and economic characteristics." Section 3(12) of the Magnuson-Stevens Act provides that the term "fish" includes marine animals and plants other than marine mammals and birds.

These definitions, together with the reference to "involved" species in Section 303(a)(2) of the Magnuson-Stevens Act, suggest that regional fishery management councils have wide discretion in determining what stocks of fish to include in the description of a fishery as outlined in Section

303(a)(2). For example, the councils appear to have latitude to include species that are prey of the species caught in the fishery, or species caught incidentally, in the description of the fishery, because both prey species and bycatch species are involved with the fishery. However, unless a species is included in the description of the FMP as described in Section 303(a)(2), its habitat should not be confused with the essential fish habitat for the fishery that is referred to in Section 303(a)(7). Of course, the councils can identify and protect habitats for species not managed under FMPs, but it is inappropriate for the interim final rule to dictate that councils should identify the habitats of major prey species.

Ecosystem Focus

The IFR also confuses the identification of essential fish habitat by introducing ecological principles that are not fully accepted by members of the seafood community into the definition of habitat. As has been stated, the IFR specifies loss of prey as an adverse impact upon essential fish habitat, which suggests that prey is a component of EFH and further expands the management concept of an ecosystem (to the chagrin of some sectors of the seafood industry). Despite a lack of consensus in the fishing community on what constitutes an ecosystem and the directive in Section 406 for a study on how ecosystem principles might be applied in the Magnuson-Stevens Act, the IFR's stated purpose is to "encourage a broader, ecosystem approach to meet the EFH requirements of the Magnuson-Stevens Act" (62 FR 66531).

Early versions of the Magnuson-Stevens Act in House and Senate bills defined EFH in terms of an "area." The concept of area was subsequently narrowed to "waters" to clarify that land areas were not included. The concept of waters was then expanded somewhat to refer to "waters and substrate," as appears in Section 3(10) of the Magnuson-Stevens Act. However, the term "waters and substrate" was not defined in the Magnuson-Stevens Act. Although the IFR does not define the term "habitat," it does define "waters" to include "aquatic areas and their associated physical, chemical, and biological properties that are used by fish" and "substrate" as "sediment, hard bottom, structures underlying the waters, and associated biological communities"(62 FR 66551). The terms "associated physical, chemical, and biological properties" and "associated biological communities" are not defined. However,

according to the technical guidance provided by the NMFS, "Biological communities could include mangroves, tidal marshes, mussel beds, cobble with attached fauna, mud and clay burrows, coral reefs, and submerged aquatic vegetation."

The preceding definitions do not agree with more commonly understood definitions. *Webster's New Collegiate Dictionary*, for example, defines "habitat" as "the place or type of site where a plant or animal naturally or normally lives and grows." In addition, *Webster's New Collegiate Dictionary* defines "water" as a liquid "occupying or flowing in a particular bed" and "substrate" as "the base on which an organism lives." Further, according to *In re Sernaker*, 707 F.2 d 989, 991 (Fed. Cir. 1983), "A substrate literally means a basis on which an organism lives, as a plant on the soil." Even the NMFS, in its rules for the Endangered Species Act, defines "critical habitat" as an "area" (50 CFR 402.02 and 424.02). Because the IFR failed to use these commonly understood terms, it confounded the task of identifying essential fish habitat.

The legislative history on essential fish habitat is sparse. At no point in this history, however, does Congress suggest that associated physical, chemical, and biological properties; associated biological communities; or ecosystem approaches should be included in the definition of either habitat or essential fish habitat. Although a few comments were made about ecosystem principles during Congressional discussions, these comments were directed toward Section 406 of the Magnuson-Stevens Act, which was added at the request of Senator Olympia Snowe (R-ME) to provide for a two-year study on how ecosystem principles might be applied in fishery management in the future (Congressional Record 1996a). The provision for this study suggests that Congress intended that ecosystem considerations should be addressed during subsequent amendments to the Magnuson-Stevens Act.

Most importantly, the IFR provides confusing guidance on the central issue of determining what habitat must be included in identifying essential fish habitat. The necessary amount of waters and substrate, which makes up the definition of essential fish habitat in Section 3(10) of the Magnuson-Stevens Act, depends upon the abundance of the species. As a general rule, the more fish there are, the more space is occupied. The missing element in the definition of essential fish habitat, therefore, is the size of the fish stock, which should be assumed in determining what waters and substrate are necessary. Considerations of fish stock size, which is related to the management concepts of optimum yield and maximum sustainable yield, are matters best left to the discretion of regional fishery management councils and not to the mandates of the IFR. The IFR defines the term "necessary" as "the habitat required to support a sustainable fishery and the managed species' contribution to a healthy ecosystem"(62 FR 66551). The reference to a healthy ecosystem implies that regional fishery management councils should consider whether a managed species is prey for marine mammals or serves other ecological functions, an admittedly bold innovation in fisheries management that is too radical for some habitat-conservation advocates in the seafood industry (62 FR 66533).

Again, with the emphasis on healthy ecosystems, the IFR introduced a new concept that is not emphasized in the Magnuson-Stevens Act's legislative history (although the concept of ecosystem health has been the subject of several scientific studies in recent years). As the House Report explains, the new habitat provisions were created to identify the habitat for each fishery "that is essential for the long-term productivity of the fishery" (U.S. Congress 1995). The IFR's definition of EFH in terms of healthy ecosystems creates an unrealistic expectation that such ecosystems should be "similar to comparable, undisturbed ecosystems with regard to...nutrient dynamics, trophic structure, species richness, stability, resilience, contamination levels, and the frequency of diseased organisms"(62 FR 66551). The preceding characteristics are ill defined and create the virtually impossible task of ensuring that EFH restores heavily fished areas of the ocean and coastal areas to an idealized, pristine state. In addition, the healthy-ecosystem concept in essence mandates a basic objective for each FMP, thus preempting the authority of the regional fishery management councils to set such objectives. Admittedly, under Section 3(28) of the Magnuson-Stevens Act, ecological factors are to be considered and the protection of the marine ecosystem is to be taken into account along with other factors when the optimum yield of a fishery is established. However, these considerations should not be, in themselves, an end result as is suggested by the IFR.

Optimum Yield

The desired long-term productivity level for a fishery is defined generally in the Magnuson-Stevens Act as the optimum yield (OY). The regional fishery management councils establish an OY for each federally managed fishery. This yield is the amount of fish "which will provide the greatest overall benefit to the Nation...taking into account the protection of marine ecosystems," according to Section 3(28) of the Magnuson-Stevens Act. Definitions of OY found in the Magnuson-Stevens Act suggest that the necessary habitat constituting EFH should be the habitat required to sustain a stock or stocks at the OY level specified in Sections 3(28) and 303(a)(3) of the Magnuson-Stevens Act. Defining EFH by referencing a fishery's optimum yield rather than healthy ecosystems is consistent with the basic structure of the Magnuson-Stevens Act, which authorizes the regional fishery management councils, not the NMFS, to determine the objectives for each FMP. Such an approach also has the advantage of focusing the habitat provisions of a plan on achieving the fundamental objective of a plan, which is to achieve and maintain the optimum yield. Depending on a particular council's management of a particular species, this OY may or may not primarily focus on maintaining healthy ecosystems, feeding mammals and birds, or fulfilling other ecological functions mentioned at various points in the rules.

The use of the concept of optimum yield rather than healthy ecosystems to guide the identification of EFH is supported through an examination of terminology. The term "essential" suggests that essential fish habitat is a subset of fish habitat. Likewise, according to the definition of optimum yield in Section 3(28), the OY of a fishery cannot exceed its maximum sustainable yield (MSY). Therefore, EFH should not exceed the waters and substrate required by the managed stocks at their level of abundance defined as the maximum sustainable yield. This level of abundance at MSY typically is lower than the level of abundance of unexploited stocks. The IFR has introduced a tension between the concept of OY in the Magnuson-Stevens Act, which emphasizes fisheries production, and the concept of healthy ecosystems, which focuses on entire fish populations and their full range of interactions. This is not to say that the IFR's focus on entire fish populations and complex ecological interactions is ignoble, but such a rapid expansion of fisheries management philosophy threatens to alienate sectors of the seafood industry that originally supported strengthening the Magnuson-Stevens Act to conserve fish habitat.

Adverse Effects

Another significant aspect of the EFH policy is the directive in Section 303(a)(7) of the Magnuson-Stevens Act that FMPs "minimize to the extent practicable adverse effects" on EFH "by fishing"(Congressional Record 1996b). The Magnuson-Stevens Act does not define what is meant by "to the extent practicable," although this phrase is used in several other sections of the Magnuson-Stevens Act, including Sections 301(a)(3) and 301(a)(5). However, in speaking about the use of this phrase in relation to a similar mandate to reduce bycatch, Representative Don Young (R-AK) noted that (Congressional Record 1996c):

"'Practicable' requires an analysis of the cost of imposing a management action; the Congress does not intend that this provision will be used to allocate among gear groups, nor impose costs on fishermen and processors that cannot be reasonably met."

The rules, however, provide that in determining what is "practicable" the councils should consider (62 FR 66553):

...whether, and to what extent, the fishing activity is adversely impacting EFH, including the fishery; the nature and extent of the adverse effect on EFH; and whether the management measures are practicable, taking into consideration the long and short-term costs as well as benefits to the fishery and its EFH, along with other appropriate factors, consistent with national standard 7.

The IFR substitutes a vague benefit–cost balancing standard for the more straightforward practicality standard in Section 303(a)(7), which is intended to prevent unreasonable costs from being imposed upon fishermen and to prevent the unwarranted restriction of fishing activity. This revision of the standard in Section 303(a)(7) could profoundly impact the livelihoods of many thousands of fishermen.

The Future

As of October 1998, all fishery management plans should have been amended to identify and describe essential fish habitat for each federally managed fishery. As of this writing, regional fishery management councils are revising their fishery management plans to meet this statutory deadline, and it remains to be seen whether the ambiguities interjected into the EFH policy by the IFR will be significant.

Thanks to Congress, however, the regional fishery management councils now have an opportunity to systematically identify the habitats needed to sustain fishery productivity and to solicit the support of the fishery community to protect these habitats. It would be unfortunate if the potential of this new program is squandered by the misguided effort of the NMFS to interject unclear ecosystem concepts into the program. It also would be disappointing if fishermen decided not to support this effort to protect habitats because the fishermen were denied the protections provided them by the Congress when it insisted that any habitat measures regarding fishing gear be "practicable." It is unfortunate that the focus of the IFR has driven a wedge between former allies in the struggle to conserve fish habitats.

In the longer term, much more needs to be done beyond fulfilling the requirements of the Magnuson-Stevens Act. Fishery scientists and the seafood industry need to engage fishermen and seafood processors in the collection and interpretation of information needed to fully identify essential fish habitats and to better define the linkage between these habitats and fish production. Some promising first steps have already been taken in this direction. (See Pederson and Hall-Arber 1999, this volume.) Such a partnership offers the best hope for future progress in protecting these habitats.

In addition, many thousands of tons of food continue to be "locked up" and unavailable for harvest because of pollution. Additional tons of food are not being produced each year because habitats have been lost. Under the 1996 Magnuson-Stevens Fishery Conservation and Management Act, the regional fishery management councils can recommend regulatory measures to minimize the impacts of fishing upon habitats. However, the councils still lack any real authority to control many other human activities, such as the disposal of wastes and coastal development, which are slowly destroying fishery productivity.

Stronger regulatory linkages need to be made by Congress between these nonfishing activities and the essential fish habitats identified by the councils. Additional resources also are needed to rehabilitate habitats that have been damaged. The ability of the seafood industry to help forge these linkages and obtain these resources depends in large measure on the success achieved by fishery scientists, the councils, the NMFS, and the seafood industry in implementing the EFH program.

References

Anderson, D. M., S. B. Galloway, and J. D. Joseph. 1993. Marine biotoxins and harmful algae: a national plan. Woods Hole Oceanographic Institution Technical Report WHOI-93-02, Woods Hole, Massachusetts.

Auster, P. J., and R. W. Langton. 1999. The effects of fishing on fish habitat. Pages 150–187 in L. R. Benaka, editor. Fish habitat: essential fish habitat and rehabilitation. American Fisheries Society, Symposium 22, Bethesda, Maryland.

Ballweber, J. A., and D. C. Jackson. 1996. Opportunities to emphasize fisheries concerns in federal agency decision-making: an introduction. Fisheries 21(4):14–19.

Burkholder, J. M. 1998. Implications of harmful microalgae and heterotrophic dinoflagellates in management of sustainable fisheries. Ecological Applications 8(1)Supplement:S37–S62.

Chambers, J. R. 1992. Coastal degradation, and fishery declines in the U. S. Pages 45–51 in R. H. Stroud, editor. Stemming the tide of coastal fish habitat loss. National Coalition for Marine Conservation, Savannah, Georgia.

Congressional Record (Sept. 18). 1996a. Sustainable Fisheries Act, Senator O. Snowe, R-ME. Pages S10825–S10826, Washington, D.C.

Congressional Record (Oct. 18). 1996b. Amendment offered by Mr. Fair to the Sustainable Fisheries Act. Representatives Fair, Young, Gilchrest, and Taugin. Pages H10223–H10228, Washington, D.C.

Congressional Record (Sept. 27). 1996c. Sustainable Fisheries Act, Representative D. Young, R-AK. Page H11437, Washington, D. C.

Cronin, J., and R. R. Kennedy, Jr. 1997. The riverkeepers: two activists fight to reclaim our environment as a basic human right. Scribner, New York City.

Holley, C. N. 1996. Coalition formed to restore estuaries. National Fisherman 77(8):14.

Kronman, M. 1998. Voices carry on. National Fisherman 79(5):24–26.

Lands, W. F. 1986. Fish and human health. Academic Press, San Diego.

Matsen, B. 1996. Cleaning up the Pribilofs. National Fisherman 76(12):10.

Nettleton, J. A. 1986. Seafood nutrition. Osprey Books, Huntington, New York.

Nettleton, J. A. 1987. Seafood and health. Osprey Books, Huntington, New York.

NMFS (National Marine Fisheries Service). 1994. Habitat protection activity report: 1991–1993. National Oceanic and Atmospheric Administration, Silver Spring, Maryland.

NMFS (National Marine Fisheries Service). 1997. Magnuson-Stevens Act provisions: essential fish habitat: interim final rule and request for comments. Federal Register [Docket 961030300-7238-04; ID 120996A]:66531-66559.

NOAA (National Oceanic, and Atmospheric Administration). 1997. Fisheries of the United States, 1996. NOAA, Silver Spring, Maryland.

NOAA (National Oceanic, and Atmospheric Administration). 1998. Year of the ocean: discussion papers. NOAA, Silver Spring, Maryland.

Pederson, J., and M. Hall-Arber. 1999. Fish habitat: a focus on New England fishermen's perspectives. Pages 188–211 in L. R. Benaka, editor. Fish habitat: essential fish habitat and rehabilitation. American Fisheries Society, Symposium 22, Bethesda, Maryland.

Pierce, J. B. 1991. Collective effects of development on the marine environment. Pages 287–298 in Oceanologica Acta, proceedings of the international colloquium on the environment of epicontinental seas.

Simopoulos, A. P., and J. Robinson. 1998. The omega plan. HarperCollins, New York City.

U.S. Congress. 1995. Fishery conservation and management amendments of 1995 (June 30, 1995). House report 104-171:30, Washington, D.C.

USDOI (U.S. Department of the Interior). 1997. National harmful algal bloom research and monitoring strategy: an initial focus on Pfiesteria, fish lesions, fish kills and public health. USDOI, Washington, D.C.

USFWS (U.S. Fish and Wildlife Service). 1997. Status and trends of wetlands in the coterminous United States. U.S. Government Printing Office, Washington, D.C.

Waterman, M. 1997. Thanks for the memories. National Fisherman 77(11):20–21.

American Fisheries Society Symposium 22:31–40, 1999
© Copyright by the American Fisheries Society 1999

Impacts of Mobile Fishing Gear: The Biodiversity Perspective

ELLIOTT A. NORSE

Marine Conservation Biology Institute
15806 NE 47th Court, Redmond, Washington 98052-5208, USA

LES WATLING

Darling Marine Center, University of Maine, Walpole, Maine 04573, USA

Abstract.— The increasing concern about impacts of bottom trawling, scallop dredging, and other mobile fishing methods has focused primarily on effects on commercial fisheries, but these fishing activities also act more broadly on benthic biological diversity. Because the seabed is erroneously envisioned as a featureless, nearly lifeless plain, impacts of commercial fishing gear have long been underestimated. Structures on and in the seabed, including biogenic structures (reef corals, kelp hold-fasts, shells, tubes, and tunnels), create a diversity of habitat patches. They provide refuges from predation and feeding places for demersal fishes and other species. Benthic structural complexity is positively correlated with species diversity and postsettlement survivorship of some commercial fishes. Mobile fishing gear disturbs the seabed, damaging benthic structures and harming structure-associated species, including commercially important fishes, although some other commercial fish species can persist where seabed structures have been removed. Bottom trawling is therefore similar to forest clear-cutting, but it is far more extensive and is converting very large areas of formerly structurally complex, biologically diverse seabed into the marine equivalent of low-diversity cattle pasture. In contrast with the U.S. National Forest Management Act, which governs use of living resources in federally owned forestlands, the 1996 Magnuson-Stevens Fishery Conservation and Management Act does not prevent ecosystem "type conversion" and ignores the need to maintain biological diversity. Preventing further loss of marine biodiversity and key fisheries will depend on our willingness to protect marine areas from effects of mobile fishing methods.

I'd like to be under the sea in an octopus' garden with you.—Beatles (rock group), "Octopus' Garden" (song)

The ocean is a desert with its life underground and the perfect disguise above.—America (rock group), "A Horse with No Name" (song)

Human activities are rapidly reducing the Earth's biological diversity (the diversity of genes, species, and ecosystems). Since Myers (1979), Lovejoy (1980), and Norse and McManus (1980) revealed that the loss of biological diversity is a massive worldwide phenomenon, especially in tropical forests, studies—including the most comprehensive biodiversity status report to date (Heywood 1995)—have found that physical destruction of ecosystems is the most pervasive cause of biodiversity loss. But such studies have focused mainly on land. In the sea, overfishing and pollution have long been considered leading threats to biodiversity, but more comprehensive examination shows that these are only two of five major threats (Norse 1993); one of the other threats is physical destruction of ecosystems. In the sea the leading cause of ecosystem destruction is use of mobile fishing gear such as bottom trawls and dredges, which smooth, crush, and up-root benthic structures (Auster and Langton 1999, this volume; Watling and Norse 1998). To help read-ers gauge the impacts of mobile fishing gear, we first discuss the importance of seabed structures and the relationship between habitat structural complexity and biodiversity. We then discuss management approaches designed to maintain and restore marine biological diversity.

People who study conservation in benthic ecosystems have much to learn from forests, which cover 38×10^6 km^2 (Perry 1994)—about 7.5% of the Earth's surface—because forests are the best-studied wildlife habitat. Many of the canonical findings in wildlife biology, conservation biology, and landscape ecology, such as the realization that island biogeography theory applies to ecosystems that have been fragmented (Terborgh 1974; Diamond 1975), have come from studies of organisms in forests. In contrast, the seafloor of the world's continental shelves, which cover 28×10^6 km^2 (Sharp 1988), is far less familiar to the human species. Indeed, even many marine scientists rarely or never see the seafloor in person. In the minds of the public, the seabed is either a lush garden or a desert, but the truth is more subtle and complex. Marine ecosystems dominated by large (>1 m), living three-dimensional structures, including kelp forests, mangrove forests, and coral reefs, are actually a very small (albeit very important) part of the marine realm (for example, coral reefs occupy only 0.6×10^6 km^2 or 0.1% of the Earth's surface [Reaka-Kudla 1997]). The rest of the seabed that the public sees consists mostly of sandy beaches and muddy plains and may appear featureless to the untrained eye. This perception is mainly a function of people's peculiar perspective; the narrow bands of sandy beaches that people visit are pounded by waves that prevent the growth of most biogenic structures (e.g., sponges, clam shells, amphipod colonies, cerianthid anemone tubes, polychaete worm tunnels, sea cucumber fecal deposits), while the vastly greater areas covered by mud (primarily silt- and clay-sized particles) are home to structures that are often too small to be resolved by cameras towed meters above the seabed. Yet, no less than on land, structures on and in the seafloor are crucial habitat features for most of the world's marine species. Coral reefs alone host 25% of the world's marine fish species (McAllister 1991).

People who study or manage species in the terrestrial realm have long known that avoiding loss of exploited wildlife populations goes beyond limiting mortality through bag, season, and size limits. It is at least as important to maintain features in the habitat such as cover and food that are essential to species' reproduction and growth. Wildlife biologists and other conservation biologists have built a substantial understanding of the three-dimensional spatial structure needed by species from leopards to spotted owls. For example, in the U.S. Pacific Northwest, structurally complex late-successional forests provide the myriad kinds of spaces—holes, cavities, chimneys, overhangs, thickets, lookout posts, and bridges—that many wildlife species need. The clearcuts and tree plantations (i.e., even-age monocultures of trees that are created after ancient forests are clear-cut) that replace them are structurally far simpler and cannot support many of the species found in ancient forests (Norse 1990).

Intuitive understanding of the importance of structural complexity underlies much of the scientific and public concern about clear-cutting, but there is also ample scientific evidence. Nearly four decades ago, MacArthur and MacArthur (1961) pointed out that songbird diversity is higher in forests that are more structurally complex. On land it is not difficult to observe the relationship between structure, which wildlife biologists call "cover," and species that need it, and studies of structure–diversity relationships are now quite sophisticated (e.g., Hansen et al. 1995). In the sea, however, scientific knowledge has depended far less on direct observation than on remote sampling (often using fishing gear) from the decks of vessels. This sampling practice has tended to limit understanding to structureformers that come up in sampling gear. Fishery biologists have long known that kelp forests, coral reefs, and rocky reefs attract many commercially important fishes and the species they eat. Yet, as Thrush et al. (1998:876) note, "Fishery models often fail to include the potential role of interactions between habitat features and the survivorship of juveniles of exploited stocks." Fishery biology (in contrast to ichthyology and benthic ecology) has been slow to appreciate the importance of small structures on the seabed as habitat and the consequences of their destruction.

The diverse smaller structures of the seabed include cobble- and pebble-sized rocks; sand ripples; thalassinid crustacean mounds; sea cucumber fecal deposits; pits left by feeding rays and crabs; sea-grass blades; the spines of living sea urchins; kelp holdfasts; sponge, sea pen, and bryozoan colonies; many kinds of tunnels; and annelid worm, amphipod crustacean, vermetid gastropod, and cerianthid anemone tubes. These structures are naturally abundant in most marine ecosystems (see synopses in Gage and Tyler 1991 and Giere 1993). Seabed structures can result from past events (e.g., cobbles deposited by melting glaciers) or from ongoing processes (e.g., reef-building by mytilid mussels and sabellariid polychaetes). Some of the most important structures occur below the sediment–water interface, riddling the seabed with a complex of tunnels and tubes (summarized in Wheatcroft et al. 1990). Other structures, ranging from polychaete worm and amphipod crustacean tubes to corals and kelps, reach millimeters to tens of meters into the water column. Although seabed structures are generally far smaller than the ones in terrestrial forests, they are at least as important as habitat features for a myriad of species, including postsettlement young of commercially important fishes. Because structural complexity is so vital in benthic ecosystems, reduction of complexity affects all aspects of benthic biological diversity, including fisheries. Of the many natural and anthropogenic factors that disturb the seabed and reduce structural complexity, the leading factor is fishing with mobile gear (Watling and Norse 1998).

Importance of Seabed Structures: A Fish-Eye View

Why is seabed structure so important? Biological activity is most pronounced at interfaces, and the interface between the water column and the seabed is no exception. The species diversity and biomass of life in the half-meter above and below the sediment–water interface are usually orders of magnitude higher than in the overlying several meters of the water column (this has long been recognized by paleontologists who study ancient benthic communities [Ausich and Bottjer 1982]). Not only does the seabed collect the rain of detrital particles from above, but it also has the three-dimensional lithic and biogenic structures that provide habitat for innumerable species. Thus, these structures—even ones as small as one or a few centimeters in size— provide cover and food for invertebrates and fishes that eat them. Virtually everybody who has watched marine animals has observed that juvenile and adult fishes, crabs, lobsters, and octopuses stay close to rocks and hide in holes or interstices between rocks when potential predators approach (Bohnsack 1991). As Ebeling and Hixon (1991) noted, without the shelter that complex structures provide, juvenile fishes are highly vulnerable to predators in both tropical and temperate reef ecosystems. Postsettlement Atlantic cod *Gadus morhua*, for example, show strongest survivorship on rugose bottoms (Gotceitas and Brown 1993). Lithic features such as boulders, rock ledges, and sand waves also play important roles in feeding. For example, juvenile red hake *Urophycis chuss* hover just downcurrent of sand wave crests, where they catch zooplankton carried by bottom currents (P. J. Auster, National Undersea Research Center for the North Atlantic and Great Lakes, personal communication), much as trout hover in the lee of sunken logs, catching stream drift. Moreover, the troughs between sand ripples and the pits dug by infaunal-feeding rays and crabs often accumulate organic material and become feeding places for detritivores and their predators. In the Gulf of Maine, areas not frequently disturbed by mobile fishing can have large numbers of redfish *Sebastes fasciatus*, each individual occupying space near the bottom of individual boulders (Auster, personal communication; L. Watling, personal observations).

In the marine realm, the relationship between habitat structural complexity and biodiversity has been best documented for fishes in coral reefs, where structures are conspicuous and direct observation is comfortable for divers. Ormond and Roberts (1997:233) noted, "There is often, for example, a striking relationship between fish species richness and habitat structural complexity or heterogeneity" and went on to note that "such a relationship is well known from terrestrial…as well as other marine studies," although this relationship might not always be strong in coral reefs. In perhaps the earliest study that quantified this relationship in the sea, Risk (1972) found higher fish species richness as coral rugosity increased. In the Tuamotu Archipelago in the South Pacific, Bell and Galzin (1984) found that slight changes in live coral cover resulted in dramatic increases in fish species diversity. Some 68% of the 115 fish species investigated were found only at sites with some live coral. Following the loss of live coral cover on the reefs of the island of Okinawa due to an outbreak of the sea star *Acanthaster planci*, Sano et al. (1984) were able to predict the subsequent loss of fish species. Some species were coral polyp feeders and so disappeared due to an absence of food, but many others declined as the structural complexity of the habitat decreased due to erosion of the dead coral substratum. There are also studies showing strong correlation between structural complexity and species recruitment, abundance, or diversity in ecosystems other than coral reefs (e.g., Hicks 1980; Connell and Jones 1991; Fernandez et al. 1993; Carr 1994; Herrnkind and Butler 1994; Szedlmayer and Able 1996).

Structural complexity provides smaller species with living space, increased food abundance, and refuge from predation (Sebens 1991). For example, Bros (1987) found that species diversity increased when artificial barnacle shells were added to a smooth surface. Presumably the increased surface area and presence of small spaces provided habitat for additional species. Lowered vulnerability to predators is another important aspect of habitat structural complexity. Prey abundance was greater in seagrass beds (Nelson 1979), worm tube aggregations (Woodin 1978), mussel clumps (Witman 1985), and algal turfs (Coull and Wells 1983; Marinelli and Coull 1987) than in less-structured bottoms when predators were present. It is now almost axiomatic that the more diverse marine habitats have higher species diversity (Sebens 1991).

The reasons why structural complexity is essential for many benthic species become clearer upon examining the relationship of organisms to the fluid dynamics just above the seabed. Most of the world's seabed consists of unconsolidated, fine, muddy sediments, where the sediment–water interface would be essentially flat but for the living things that increase structural complexity both above and below the sediment surface. Many seabed organisms are suspension feeders, orienting themselves with currents that bear food particles. Drag sharply decreases current velocities in the few centimeters above the sediment, decreasing opportunities for suspension-feeding (see reviews by Butman 1987; Snelgrove and Butman 1994). As a result, benthic organisms that raise their feeding structures even one or a few centimeters into the water column are better situated to capture plankton and detritus carried by currents. Furthermore, because the oxygen content of seawater is more than four orders of magnitude lower than that of air, respiration in and on the seabed rapidly depletes oxygen in the millimeter-to-centimeter-thick bottom boundary layer that sits just above the seabed (Jørgensen 1996), with the result that, on mud bottoms, sediment 1 cm or more below the sediment–water interface is almost always devoid of oxygen (see review by Watling 1991). Because anoxia is inimical to nearly all benthic animals, many infauna that make tunnels or tubes within the seabed generate currents that break through the bottom boundary layer, bringing the infauna oxygenated water and food particles. Other infauna and many epibiota avoid the oxygen-poor conditions of the sediment by placing their respiratory structures above the bottom boundary layer.

The structures that benthic species create increase seabed structural complexity. Many other species, including species sought as food by fishes, that do not colonize soft substrata per se live on or in these biogenic structures. For these reasons, structures—even small ones—are more important for epibiota on the seabed than on the land. Hard surfaces in the sea are generally far more densely colonized than hard surfaces on land, including rainforests, with their abundance of epiphytes and associated animals (E. A. Norse, personal observations). The diversity of benthic infauna and epibiota, therefore, provides essential habitat features including structures and food that sustain many of the world's commercial fishes (Boehlert 1996).

Changes in Species Composition at Reduced Structural Complexity

In terrestrial ecosystems, species composition is determined largely by the spatial configuration of structure-forming species; ancient coniferous forests,

tallgrass prairies, and sandy deserts have very different assemblages of species. Structures that are essential to some species are unnecessary or even disadvantageous to others; removing structures frees up resources for species that do not need structures. For example, a Pacific Northwest wildfire or logging operation that eliminates ancient western red cedars *Thuja plicata* and northern flying squirrels *Glaucomys sabrinus* creates opportunities for fireweeds *Epilobium angustifolium* and creeping voles *Microtus oregoni*. Species composition is so closely tied to structure that terrestrial wildlife biologists have long manipulated habitat structure to maximize populations of species they consider desirable, such as deer *Odocoileus* spp.

Because fishery biologists have (until very recently) been less attuned to effects of small seabed structures, habitat relationships of fishes, especially postsettlement stages, are far less known in the sea and have largely been overlooked in fishery management. However, ecological theory and ubiquitous observations both suggest that severe disturbances that remove structure from the seabed will profoundly change species composition, harming many species but favoring some others, thereby decreasing species diversity. In this regard, trawling and dredging have effects similar to organic enrichment, which reduces species diversity and produces communities comprised of large numbers of a few opportunistic species (Pearson and Rosenberg 1978). A small but growing body of studies from places where scientists have looked at effects of mobile fishing gear, including Northern Europe, Australia, New Zealand, and the Atlantic and Pacific coasts of North America, support this hypothesis.

In the North Sea, where all the large *Sabellaria spinulosa* polychaete reefs were deliberately removed, species typical of open sands now dominate and support significant flatfish fisheries (Riesen and Reise 1982). In Loch Gareloch on the Irish Sea, trawling significantly reduced populations of some infauna (e.g., the nut clam *Nucula nitidosa*), while opportunistic cirratulid and capitellid polychaetes became more abundant (Lindeboom and de Groot 1998). In northwestern Australia, Sainsbury (1987, 1988) found high-value *Lethrinus* (emperors), *Lutjanus* (snappers or seaperch), and *Epinephelus* (groupers or rockcod) dropped from 45 to 77% of the catch to 15% after trawling removed structure-forming sponges and gorgonians. At the same time, commercially less-valued species characteristic of sandy bottoms in the genera *Nemipterus* (threadfinbream) and *Saurida* (lizardfishes or grinners) became more abundant. In Hauraki Gulf, New Zealand (North Island), Thrush et al. (1998) found that areas with the least disturbance from trawling, seining, and scallop dredging had the most long-lived surface-dwelling invertebrates, the smallest proportion of opportunistic species, and the highest species diversity (using one kind of sampling gear) and highest density of large individuals and most organisms (using another type of gear). On Georges Bank off New England, Collie (1998) reported that mobile fishing gear on gravel bottoms removed the three-dimensional cover provided by epifauna, with undisturbed areas having higher abundance, biomass, and species diversity as indicated by the presence of fragile species such as sponges, nudibranchs, worms, and small fishes, while areas subjected to bottom trawling and scallop dredging were characterized by scavengers such as hermit crabs and sea stars. Finally, off the Big Sur coast of California, Engel and Kvitek (1998) found that heavily trawled areas have a low diversity of polychaete worms but large populations of an opportunistic amphinomid polychaete *Chloeia pinnata*, which the authors found to be the dominant prey item of several flatfish species. In these cases, trawling tended to eliminate competitively dominant, long-lived but disturbance-sensitive structure-forming benthic species, freeing up food and space for shorter-lived, disturbance-insensitive, opportunistic (weedy) species. In the absence of needed benthic structures or foods, groupers and cod disappear but lizardfishes and flatfishes fare better. Trawling and dredging decrease species diversity but increase populations of disturbance-tolerant benthic species and fishes that eat them, just as clear-cutting eliminates ancient forests and spotted owls and shifts production toward grasses and grazers.

Mobile Fishing Gear Effects, Type Conversion, and Sustainability

Bottom trawls and dredges used to catch benthic and demersal fishes, crabs, lobsters, shrimps, bivalves, sea urchins, and corals disturb the seabed in ways that overturn rocks, flatten sand waves, and crush, bury, and expose benthic organisms and biogenic structures (see reviews by Auster and Langton 1999 and Watling and Norse 1998). In the past, sizable structures (e.g., boulders) prevented trawling, but the advent of rockhopper and streetsweeper gear now allows trawling on virtually any kind of bottom, and fish finders and global positioning systems

allow fishers to locate good spots and relocate them accurately until the spots are no longer so good. Moreover, the progressive disappearance of high-value commercial fishes in shallow waters has pushed fishing ever deeper; Merrett and Haedrich (1997) noted that trawling occurs as deep as 2,000 m, covering a total area of approximately 2.5 km^2 during each tow. Trawlers are more powerful than in the past, and improved technologies allow trawlers to fish deeper, farther offshore, and on rougher bottoms (Mirarchi 1998). The technological and economic forces that have increased fishing power and intensity have brought unprecedented disturbance to the seabed worldwide. Ecosystems with high structural complexity are likely to change most as fishing pressure increases (Auster 1998).

The use of mobile fishing gear is now the most important source of anthropogenic disturbance of the seabed and the principal agent of disturbance (anthropogenic or natural) in deep shelf, slope, and seamount waters where disturbance frequencies are naturally low. Watling and Norse (1998) have now shown that trawling occurs on a scale that had not previously been imagined; worldwide, an area equaling about half of the continental shelf—an area twice as large as the lower 48 U.S. states combined—is trawled every year. The few specific areas for which data are available are trawled at return intervals (average time between successive disturbances) ranging from years down to months.

In gauging the impact of a disturbance, it is useful to compare its return time with the time required for succession to restore the ecosystem's original structure. Impacts are more worrisome as return intervals become a significant fraction of the time until successional climax, because these return intervals shift the successional mosaic toward one dominated by recently disturbed patches. In many forest communities, biologists know the time needed for communities to attain late-successional characteristics. Much less is known about succession in many continental shelf, slope, and seamount areas, but a very crude estimate can come from knowing the life span of key structure-forming species. This assumes that these structure-forming species can colonize recently disturbed patches; alternatively, they could require intermediate successional stages before becoming established. Pacific Northwest Douglas-fir and western hemlock communities start to develop late-successional (ancient forest) attributes at about 200 years, and the dominant structure-formers have maximum life spans of 500–1,200 years, so disturbance return times (logging rotations) of anything less than 200 years essentially eliminate late-successional forests from the landscape matrix.

Life spans of marine structure-forming species are less known than they are for forest trees, but they range from months or years to several centuries (maximum estimated longevity for ocean quahog clams *Arctica islandica* is 221 years [Kraus et al. 1989]) or even more (gorgonian corals in the genus *Primnoa* can reach 500 or perhaps even 1,500 years in age [Risk et al. 1998]). It is reasonable to assume that recovery times in benthic ecosystems range from months to millennia, typically (on the continental shelf) ranging from years to decades. Because disturbance return times are short in comparison—for example, four months on Georges Bank (Auster et al. 1996), one year in the Gulf of Maine (Auster et al. 1996), and a worldwide continental shelf average of roughly two years (Watling and Norse 1998)—mobile fishing gear often disturbs the seabed much faster than succession and other benthic processes can restore seabed structure, converting ecosystems dominated by structure-forming and structure-needing species to ecosystems dominated by other species. The terrestrial equivalent of this would be wholesale, worldwide, unplanned, and unchronicled conversion of virgin forest to cattle pasture.

In the Irish Sea, where trawling has occurred intensively, the IMPACT-II report (Lindeboom and de Groot 1998:361) stated, "The present species-poor and low biomass fauna may represent an artificial manmade community adapted to the regular fishing disturbance experienced at this site" and concluded (p. 364), "if trawling intensity remains high, these communities may never recover." Foresters call this kind of anthropogenic change "type conversion," a practice prohibited except in extraordinary circumstances under the U.S. National Forest Management Act, the federal law that governs extraction and replacement of trees on most federally owned multiple-use forestlands. Strangely enough, the Magnuson-Stevens Fishery Conservation and Management Act of 1996 (also called the Sustainable Fisheries Act) does not even address ecosystem conversion, despite the fact that mobile fishing gears are converting structurally diverse benthic ecosystems to essentially featureless plains at a rate two orders of magnitude faster than forests are being converted worldwide. Trawling and dredging could be one of the least-known factors affecting the world's biological diversity.

It has become clear in this decade that marine biodiversity is increasingly threatened (Norse 1993; Butman and Carlton 1995). At the same time, many of the world's demersal fisheries have shown alarming downward trends (FAO 1997). Although it is clear that many fish species are being caught at rates their populations cannot sustain, it is no less clear that demersal fish habitat is being stripped of its essential structural complexity. Which of these two contributing factors is more important is not yet known (Fogarty and Murawski 1998), but it is the height of folly to think that overexploitation is the only way that fishing decreases fisheries yields. It is also apparent that areas supporting some demersal fisheries, including brown shrimp *Penaeus aztecus* in the northern Gulf of Mexico and plaice *Pleuronectes platessa* in the North Sea, have been trawled for many years without marked decreases in catch after their initial conversion. These may be canonical examples of fisheries based on opportunistic, disturbance-tolerant species.

In view of the profound effects of mobile fishing gear on benthic ecosystems, it is remarkable that there is no management structure in place in the United States (or anywhere else that we know about) charged with maintaining the seabed's biological diversity. As Boehlert (1996:33) noted, "legal authority under the Magnuson Fishery Conservation and Management Act (under which fishery management plans are developed) gives no consideration to genetic, species, or ecosystem biodiversity except as it affects protected species or critical habitats." This situation remained unchanged when the Magnuson Fishery Conservation and Management Act was reauthorized as the Sustainable Fisheries Act of 1996; only habitat essential to the well-being of fishes is given consideration. Areas of the seabed where fish are likely to roam, but are not known to be essential to any life history stage, are outside the management requirements of the Sustainable Fisheries Act. Consequently, there are no provisions to limit habitat destruction and biodiversity loss anywhere that is not designated as essential fish habitat. Nobody is safeguarding the seabed from fishing.

In January 1998, 1,605 marine scientists and conservation biologists from 70 nations issued a statement called "Troubled Waters: A Call for Action" (MCBI 1998). The statement called upon citizens and governments worldwide to "Ameliorate or stop fishing methods that undermine sustainability by harming the habitats of economically valuable marine species and the species they use for food and shelter." The question that fishery biologists, fishers, conservationists, managers, legislators, and the public must ask is whether we are willing to live in a world where spotted owls, cod, and groupers become as vanishingly rare as their rugose habitats, to be superceded by cattle, plaice, and lizardfishes. To people concerned only about the gross tonnage of meat produced, such questions might not be troubling; there are almost always some organisms opportunistic enough to survive even where disturbance is severe and chronic. But to a growing number of people, including thousands of leading scientists, the loss of marine biodiversity is an appalling prospect.

Any alternative to the current approach must take legislative and management steps to both protect substantial areas of seabed from becoming structurally simplified and to restore the seabed's structure, species composition, and functioning. The actions we take ultimately hinge on whether we value the living sea as anything more than a wet, salty cattle ranch.

The difficult task of balancing short-term economic gains with maintenance of biodiversity and longer-term economic benefits involves recognizing economic behaviors of people who take wild living resources. Loggers prefer large, high-quality, high-value trees and focus their attention in forest areas having them. As Norse (1990) noted, U.S. National Parks and Wilderness Areas tend to be located in areas of low biological and economic productivity, such as scenic, craggy snow-covered mountains that lack trees sought by loggers; these areas have a low diversity of forest species. In a similar way, fishers concentrate trawling and dredging effort in certain areas (see Figure 1 in Mirarchi 1998). Some other areas (quite likely areas with the lowest habitat value for fishes) escape disturbance from fishing. However, protecting areas that nobody wants because they are biologically unproductive does little to maintain biodiversity.

Lessons Learned

Marine conservation lags behind terrestrial conservation, both in terms of what scientists know and in the creation and implementation of laws to protect resources. Lawmakers and marine fisheries managers are only now awakening to something their terrestrial counterparts have known for two decades: that human-caused disturbance is dramatically reducing biological diversity, and that to avoid undesirable losses, disturbance frequency or severity must be reduced. Although the seabed is a crucial component of the Earth's biological diversity, the prevailing marine fisheries paradigm focuses on managing populations in isolation from their environment. This paradigm has pushed populations of

many high-value fishes so far below maximum sustainable populations that the world's fish catch is increasingly comprised of low-trophic-level "baitfishes" rather than higher-trophic-level fishes (Pauly et al. 1998). Foot-dragging and "more-of-the-same" fishery legislation, management, and scientific research are a guaranteed recipe for further losses, not only of the commercial fisheries that are the focus of U.S. laws, but, more broadly, of the biological diversity that supports fisheries.

In the nearly two decades since biological diversity loss was defined as the world's premier conservation challenge, scientific and managerial advances have strengthened conservation in the terrestrial and freshwater realms. Yet the United States has no federal laws focused on maintaining biological diversity in the sea and nothing remotely approaching the multidisciplinary analysis and decision making that led to conservation of spotted owls and their Pacific Northwest ancient forest habitat. The biodiversity ethic that has become the driving force in nonmarine conservation has yet to make substantial inroads in the marine realm; marine conservation is still largely about maximizing the fish catch or preventing a few other preferred species (especially marine mammals) from harm. As the sea loses biological diversity at an accelerating rate, it is clear that a different approach is needed.

Although some die-hards will undoubtedly deny the importance of trawling and scallop dredging impacts no matter how strong the evidence is, there are fishermen—at least when they are speaking anonymously—who know what marine scientists have only recently learned, as the following quotes from Nova Scotia and New Brunswick fishermen reveal (Fuller and Cameron 1998):

"Draggers have leveled off Western Bank. During the '70s and '80s they tore all the plant life off it. This has the same effect as clearcutting." (Respondent 1)

"There used to be an awful mess of [tree-like corals] and the nets got tore to pieces. We got them pretty much cleaned up. We used to clean out the trees when hauling back the nets." (Respondent 14)

"There shouldn't be dragging, it tears the plant life off the bottom. It might take ten years to come back. You can't take a plow through a field and expect the grass to grow back right away." (Respondent 29)

"Rockhopper gear changes the bottom and gets rid of places fish can hide." And "Now they scallop 24 hours a day, all winter long. There are more boats and more power to tow with, this causes the gear to dig in better ... They drag up everything and it doesn't have a chance to come back." And "If the system were left alone, it will recover somewhat. It needs time to heal." (Respondent 3)

We believe that the United States and other nations need to make all human activities in the sea—whether shipping, oil and gas production, recreation, or fishing—compatible with maintaining and restoring biological diversity. As on land, we need intelligent, flexible, scientifically sound, and carefully monitored limits on our take of marine wildlife as well as a comprehensive system of protected areas that are managed to maintain marine biodiversity. In practical terms, that means that a substantial portion of the sea (the signers of "Troubled Waters" called for 20%) must be off-limits to any activity, including trawling and dredging, that significantly reduces biological diversity. The essential fish habitat provisions in the 1996 Magnuson-Stevens Fishery Conservation and Management Act are a step in the right direction, but unless the provisions are strengthened to address broader biodiversity needs, they are not sufficient. There need to be zones in the sea where people can fish and other zones where the marine life can recruit, grow, and spawn free from fishing pressure, just as wildlife can in terrestrial national parks.

Acknowledgments

Ideas and information for this chapter came from a workshop on "Effects of Bottom Trawling on Marine Ecosystems" held by Marine Conservation Biology Institute in June 1996 at the University of Maine's Darling Marine Center. We thank the other workshop participants: Peter Auster (University of Connecticut, USA); Jeremy Collie (University of Rhode Island, USA); Paul Dayton (Scripps Institution of Oceanography, USA); Eleanor Dorsey (Conservation Law Foundation, USA); Jonna Engel (Moss Landing Marine Laboratory, USA); Donald Gordon (Department of Fisheries and Oceans, Canada); Richard Langton (Maine Department of Marine Resources, USA); Larry Mayer (University of Maine, USA); Cynthia Pilskaln (University of Maine, USA); Ian Poiner (Commonwealth Scientific and Industrial Research Organization, Australia); Peter Schwinghamer (Department of Fisheries and Oceans, Canada); Simon Thrush (National Institute of Water and Atmospheric Research, New Zealand); Page Valentine (U.S. Geological Survey, USA); and Waldo Wakefield (Rutgers University, USA). We are grateful to the workshop's funders: the Curtis and Edith Munson Foundation, Natural Resources Defense Council, and three components of the National Oceanic and Atmospheric Administration: Auke Bay Fisheries Laboratory of the National Marine Fisheries Service, Stellwagen Bank National Marine Sanctuary, and the Office of Strategic Policy and Planning. We thank the Geraldine R. Dodge Foundation, Educational Foundation of America, Surdna Foundation, Sun Hill Foundation, David and Lucile Packard Foundation, Horizons Foundation, Pew Fellows Program in Marine Conservation, New England Biolabs, the DuPont Company, Ted Stanley, Anne Rowland, and Bert Cohn for support during the writing of this chapter. We also thank Peter Auster, Ewann Berntson, Caroline Gibson, and Lee Benaka for astute comments on various drafts. This is Marine Conservation Biology Institute contribution Number 26.

References

Ausich, W. I., and D. J. Bottjer. 1982. Tiering in suspension-feeding communities on soft substrata throughout the Phanerozoic. Science 216:173–174.

Auster, P. J. 1998. A conceptual model of the impacts of fishing gear on the integrity of fish habitat. Conservation Biology 12:1198–1203.

Auster, P. J., and eight coauthors. 1996. The impacts of mobile fishing gear on seafloor habitats in the Gulf of Maine (Northwest Atlantic): implications for conservation of fish populations. Reviews in Fisheries Science 4:185–202.

Auster, P. J., and R. W. Langton. 1999. The effects of fishing on fish habitat. Pages 150–187 in L. R. Benaka, editor. Fish habitat: essential fish habitat and rehabilitation. American Fisheries Society, Symposium 22, Bethesda, Maryland.

Bell, J. D., and R. Galzin. 1984. Influence of live coral cover on coral-reef fish communities. Marine Ecology Progress Series 15:265–274.

Boehlert, G. W. 1996. Biodiversity and the sustainability of marine fisheries. Oceanography 9:28–35.

Bohnsack, J. A. 1991. Habitat structure and the design of artificial reefs. Pages 412–426 in S. S. Bell, E. D. McCoy and H. R. Mushinsky, editors. Habitat structure: the arrangement of objects in space. Chapman and Hall, New York City.

Bros, W. E. 1987. Effects of removing or adding structure (barnacle shells) on recruitment to a fouling community in Tampa Bay, Florida. Journal of Experimental Marine Biology and Ecology 105:275–296.

Butman, C. A. 1987. Larval settlement of soft-sediment invertebrates: the spatial scales of pattern explained by active habitat selection and the emerging role of hydrodynamical processes. Oceanography and Marine Biology Annual Review 25:113–165.

Butman, C. A., and J. T. Carlton, editors. 1995. Understanding marine biodiversity: a research agenda for the nation. National Academy Press, Washington, D.C.

Carr, M. H. 1994. Effects of macroalgal dynamics on recruitment of a temperate reef fish. Ecology 75:1320–1333.

Collie, J. 1998. Studies in New England of fishing gear impacts on the sea floor. Pages 53–62 in E. M. Dorsey and J. Pederson, editors. Effects of fishing gear on the sea floor of New England. Conservation Law Foundation, Boston.

Connell, S. D., and G. P. Jones. 1991. The influence of habitat complexity on postrecruitment processes in a temperate reef fish population. Journal of Experimental Marine Biology and Ecology 151:271–294.

Coull, B. C., and J. B. J. Wells. 1983. Refuges from fish predation: experiments with phytal meiofauna from the New Zealand rocky intertidal. Ecology 64:1599–1609.

Diamond, J. M. 1975. The island dilemma: lessons of modern biogeographic studies for the design of natural preserves. Biological Conservation 7:129–146.

Ebeling, A. W., and M. A. Hixon. 1991. Tropical and temperate reef fishes: comparison of community structures. Pages 509–563 in P. F. Sale, editor. The ecology of fishes on coral reefs. Academic Press, San Diego.

Engel, J., and R. Kvitek. 1998. Impacts of otter trawling on a benthic community in Monterey Bay National Marine Sanctuary. Conservation Biology 12:1204–1214.

FAO (Food, and Agriculture Organization of the United Nations). 1997. Review of the state of the world fishery resources: marine fisheries. Fisheries circular number 920 FIRM/C920. FAO, Rome.

Fernandez, M., O. Iribarne, and D. Armstrong. 1993. Habitat selection by young-of-the-year Dungeness crab Cancer magister Dana and predation risk in intertidal habitats. Marine Ecology Progress Series 92:171–177.

Fogarty, M. J., and S. A. Murawski. 1998. Large-scale disturbance and the structure of marine systems: fishery impacts on Georges Bank. Ecological Applications 8(1)Supplement:S6–S22.

Fuller, S., and P. Cameron. 1998. Marine benthic seascapes: fishermen's perspectives. Marine Issues Committee Special Publication 3, Ecology Action Centre, Halifax, Nova Scotia.

Gage, J. D., and P. A. Tyler. 1991. Deep-sea biology, a natural history of organisms at the deep-sea floor. Cambridge University Press, New York.

Giere, O. 1993. Meiobenthology, the microscopic fauna in aquatic sediments. Springer-Verlag, New York.

Gotceitas, V., and J. A. Brown. 1993. Substrate selection by juvenile Atlantic cod (Gadus morhua): effects of predation risk. Oecologia 93:31–37.

Hansen, A. J., W. C. McComb, R. Vega, M. G. Raphael, and M. Hunter. 1995. Bird habitat relationships in natural and managed forests in the west Cascades of Oregon. Ecological Applications 5:555–569.

Herrnkind, W. F., and M. J. Butler IV. 1994. Settlement of spiny lobster, Panulirus argus (Latreille, 1804), in Florida: pattern without predictability? Crustaceana 67:46–64.

Heywood, V. H., editor. 1995. Global biodiversity assessment. Cambridge University Press, New York.

Hicks, G. R. F. 1980. Structure of phytal harpacticoid copepod assemblages and the influence of habitat complexity and turbidity. Journal of Experimental Marine Biology and Ecology 44:157–192.

Jørgensen, B. B. 1996. Material flux in the sediment. Pages 115–135 in B. B. Jorgensen and K. Richardson, editors. Eutrophication in the marine environment. Coastal and estuarine studies, volume 52. American Geophysical Union, Washington, D.C.

Kraus, M. G., B. F. Beal, and S. R. Chapman. 1989. Growth rate of Arctica islandica Linne: a comparison of wild and laboratory-reared individuals. Journal of Shellfisheries Research 8:463.

Lindeboom, H. J., and S. J. de Groot, editors. 1998. IMPACT-II. The effects of different types of fisheries on North Sea and Irish Sea benthic ecosystems. Netherlands Institute for Sea Research (NIOZ), Texel, Netherlands.

Lovejoy, T. 1980. A projection of species extinctions. Pages 328–332 in Council on Environmental Quality and U.S. Department of State. The global 2000 report to the President, volume 2, the technical report. U.S. Government Printing Office, Washington, D.C.

MacArthur, R. H., and J. W. MacArthur. 1961. On bird species diversity. Ecology 42:594–598.

Marinelli, R. L., and B. C. Coull. 1987. Structural complexity and juvenile fish predation on meiobenthos: an experimental approach. Journal of Experimental Marine Biology and Ecology 108:67–81.

McAllister, D. E. 1991. What is the status of the world's coral reef fishes? Sea Wind 5:14–18.

MCBI (Marine Conservation Biology Institute). 1998. Troubled waters: a call for action. http://www.mcbi.org/trouble1.html (accessed 3 November 1998).

Merrett, N. R., and R. L. Haedrich. 1997. Deep-sea demersal fish and fisheries. Chapman and Hall, New York.

Mirarchi, F. 1998. Bottom trawling on soft substrates. Pages 80–84 in E. M. Dorsey and J. Pederson, editors. Effects of fishing gear on the sea floor of New England. Conservation Law Foundation, Boston.

Myers, N. 1979. The sinking ark: a new look at the problem of disappearing species. Pergamon, New York City.

Nelson, W. G. 1979. Experimental studies of selective predation on amphipods: consequences for amphipod distribution and abundance. Journal of Experimental Marine Biology and Ecology 38:225–245.

Norse, E. A. 1990. Ancient forests of the Pacific Northwest. Island Press, Washington D.C.

Norse, E. A., editor. 1993. Global marine biological diversity: a strategy for building conservation into decision making. Island Press, Washington, D.C.

Norse, E. A., and R. E. McManus. 1980. Ecology and living resources: biological diversity. Pages 31–80 in Environmental quality 1980. Council on Environmental Quality, Washington D.C.

Ormond, R. F. G., and C. M. Roberts. 1997. The biodiversity of coral reef fishes. Pages 216–257 *in* R. F. G. Ormond, J. D. Gage, and M. V. Angel, editors. Marine biodiversity: patterns and processes. Cambridge University Press, Cambridge UK.

Pauly, D., V. Christensen, J. Dalsgaard, R. Froese, and F. Torres Jr. 1998. Fishing down marine food webs. Science 279:860–863.

Pearson, T. H., and R. Rosenberg. 1978. Macrobenthic succession in relation to organic enrichment and pollution of the marine environment. Oceanography and Marine Biology Annual Review 16:229–311.

Perry, D. A. 1994. Forest ecosystems. Johns Hopkins University Press, Baltimore.

Reaka-Kudla, M. 1997. The global biodiversity of coral reefs: a comparison with rain forests. Pages 83–108 *in* M. L. Reaka-Kudla, D. E. Wilson and E. O. Wilson, editors. Biodiversity II: understanding and protecting our biological resources. Joseph Henry Press, Washington, D.C.

Riesen, W., and K. Reise. 1982. Macrobenthos of the subtidal Wadden Sea: revisited after 55 years. Helgolander Meeresuntersuchungen 35:409–423.

Risk, M. J. 1972. Fish diversity on a coral reef in the Virgin Islands. Atoll Research Bulletin 153:1–6.

Risk, M. J., D. E. McAllister, and L. Behnken. 1998. Conservation of cold- and warm-water seafans: threatened ancient gorgonian groves. Sea Wind 12(1):2–21.

Sainsbury, K. J. 1987. Assessment and management of the demersal fishery on the continental shelf of northwestern Australia. Pages 465–503 *in* J. J. Polovina and S. Ralston, editors. Tropical snappers and groupers: biology and fisheries management. Westview Press, Boulder, Colorado.

Sainsbury, K. J. 1988. The ecological basis of multispecies fisheries and management of a demersal fishery in tropical Australia. Pages 349–382 *in* J. A. Gulland, editor. Fish population dynamics, 2ⁿᵈ edition. Wiley, New York.

Sano, M., M. Shimizu, and Y. Nose. 1984. Changes in structure of coral reef fish communities by destruction of hermatypic corals: observational and experimental views. Pacific Science 38:51–79.

Sebens, K. P. 1991. Habitat structure and community dynamics in marine benthic systems. Pages 199–234 *in* S. S. Bell, E. D. McCoy, and H. R. Mushinsky, editors. Habitat structure: the arrangement of objects in space. Chapman and Hall, New York.

Sharp, G. D. 1988. Fish populations and fisheries: their perturbations, natural and man-induced. Pages 155–202 *in* H. Postma and J. J. Zijlstra, editors. Continental shelves. Ecosystems of the world, volume 27. Elsevier Publishers, Amsterdam.

Snelgrove, P. A., and C. A. Butman. 1994. Animal-sediment relationships revisited: cause versus effect. Oceanography and Marine Biology Annual Review 32:111–177.

Szedlmayer, S. T., and K. W. Able. 1996. Patterns of seasonal availability and habitat use by fishes and decapod crustaceans in a southern New Jersey estuary. Estuaries 19:697–709.

Terborgh, J. 1974. Preservation of natural diversity: the problem of extinction-prone species. BioScience 24:715–722.

Thrush, S. F., and nine coauthors. 1998. Disturbance of the marine benthic habitat by commercial fishing: impacts at the scale of the fishery. Ecological Applications 8:866–879.

Watling, L. 1991. The sedimentary milieu and its consequences to resident organisms. American Zoologist 31:789–796.

Watling, L., and E. Norse. 1998. Disturbance of the seabed by mobile fishing gear: a comparison to forest clearcutting. Conservation Biology 12:1180–1197.

Wheatcroft, R. A., P. A. Jumars, C. R. Smith, and A. R. M. Nowell. 1990. A mechanistic view of the particulate biodiffusion coefficient: step lengths, rest periods, and transport directions. Journal of Marine Research 48:177–207.

Witman, J. D. 1985. Refuges, biological disturbance, and rocky subtidal community structure in New England. Ecological Monographs 55:421–455.

Woodin, S. A. 1978. Refuges, disturbance, and community structure: a marine soft-bottom example. Ecology 59:274–284.

American Fisheries Society Symposium 22:41–42, 1999

Part Two:
Essential Fish Habitat Identification

JOHN A. MUSICK

Virginia Institute of Marine Science, School of Marine Science
The College of William and Mary, Gloucester Point, Virginia 23062, USA

The fishes are the most diverse group of vertebrates on earth with some 24,000 species estimated. This great biodiversity is associated with great habitat diversity that comprises the aqueous biosphere from freshwater, to estuaries, to the coastal seas, to vast oceanic water masses.

Identification of essential fish habitat (EFH) among a multitude of environments requires a multitude of methods. In this section, five papers are presented that reflect the diversity of methods that might be employed to evaluate EFH for groups of fishes that depend on different habitats.

Thomas Minello studies habitat utilization by juvenile fishes and crustaceans in the highly productive estuaries of the northern Gulf of Mexico. Using drop nets in several different habitats, Minello analyzes animal density patterns within habitats to designate EFH. Minello concludes that all of the six habitat types he studied are likely to be essential for some fishery species. He stresses the need for additional, broader systematic sampling to define geographic differences in habitat utilization and also to examine intra-habitat variability. As a final note, Minello stresses that the identification of EFH requires an understanding of the functional relationships between species and habitat parameters.

David Packer and Tom Hoff review habitat utilization in the Middle Atlantic Bight by the summer flounder *Paralichthys dentatus*, one of the most important recreational and commercial fishes in that region. They begin with an extensive literature review of the critical habitat parameters for juvenile summer flounder. The authors have been able to glean information beyond simple preferred salinity and temperature ranges. Summer flounder has been well studied and thus information is available on the effects of temperature on growth and so forth. In addition to their literature review, Packer and Hoff analyze catch-per-unit-effort data from the National Marine Fisheries Service's (NMFS's) groundfish surveys and egg and larval surveys to provide seasonal density distribution maps over the continental shelf. In addition, they use presence–absence data from the National Oceanic and Atmospheric Administration's (NOAA's) Estuarine Living Marine Resources Program to map the utilization of estuaries by juvenile summer flounder. Packer and Hoff note that juvenile summer flounder are clearly estuarine dependent and thus estuaries should not only be identified as EFH but also as habitat areas of particular concern (HAPCs). Such HAPCs are critical to the sustained production of a species and are rare or sensitive to anthropogenic perturbations.

Anadromous fishes present problems in defining EFH different than those for marine and estuarine forms. Philip Roni and his colleagues make an important first attempt at defining EFH for four species of anadromous salmon *Oncorhynchus* spp. in the Pacific Northwest. For some of these species, EFH may include lotic spawning reaches ≥3,200 km from the ocean where they have sustained most of their growth. In addition, spawning and migration patterns may vary greatly among stocks, species, and drainages. The authors use geographic information system databases to define freshwater EFH for Pacific salmons, but they encountered difficulties with finer-scale resolution <1:100,000. The authors recommend that future efforts should focus on developing accurate seasonal salmon distribution data at a 1:24,000 scale.

Peter Rubec and his coauthors have developed habitat suitability index (HSI) models for spotted seatrout *Cynoscion nebulosus* for two estuaries on the west coast of Florida. Their results are encouraging in that models developed for Tampa Bay predicted fairly well the habitat suitability patterns for the same species measured in Charlotte Harbor. Thus, HSI models developed in one system may be useful in predicting HSI patterns in other nearby systems. Caution is advised in attempting to apply this paradigm to systems that are geographically more distant or where environmental differences among systems constrain the distribution of original environmental parameters used to develop the models. In addition, inter-area differences in biological communities (predators, competitors, etc.) may alter distribution patterns of species regardless of the environmental parameters.

Kenneth Able reviews the extensive research he has directed at the Mullica River–Great Bay National Estuarine Research Reserve in southern New Jersey. He relates this work to the four levels of information for EFH designation suggested by NMFS (described in the Minello chapter). Able notes the importance of long-term data sets in attempting to define EFH at level 1 (presence–absence) or level 2 (relative abundance). Short time series and the inherently wide year-class fluctuations exhibited by many species may confound EFH analysis. In addition, Able notes that although terrestrial habitats may be well mapped, subtidal habitats usually are not. This leads to difficulty in interpreting level-2 data with respect to EFH (if you cannot define the habitat, how can you define EFH?). Able goes on to note that more information is needed on habitat-specific behavior of fishes to determine how they use specific habitats (important for level-3 EFH definitions) and suggests that more-integrative approaches such as the use of stable isotopes or remote sensing would be of value in answering questions about habitat quality.

It should be obvious that healthy fisheries require healthy fish habitats. This tautology was largely ignored in the Magnuson Fishery Conservation and Management Act of 1976 (P.L. 94-265) but finally was recognized in the 1996 Sustainable Fisheries Act (P.L. 104-297), largely through the efforts of people like Paul Brouha (former Executive Director of the American Fisheries Society). Unfortunately, although EFH must be clearly defined in federal fishery management plans, the NMFS and the regional fishery management councils can do little more than point to the fact that given areas have been designated as EFH when agencies (e.g., the U.S. Army Corps of Engineers) that issue permits consider proposals that could impact those areas. Thus, EFH is not protected by law. In addition, in most EFH evaluations that have been done to date, virtually all of the habitat where a species is known to occur has been designated as EFH. The NMFS EFH guidelines allow for recognition of habitat areas of particular concern (as Packer and Hoff point out), but more is needed. Permitting agencies look to the NMFS and the regional fishery management councils for guidance in avoiding impacts in areas that are critical to fisheries. I believe an EFH designation system based on three principals—utilization, availability, and vulnerability—might better serve the agencies charged with permitting; such agencies, in the end, will have a great deal of influence on the protection of EFH and the fisheries supported by EFH.

The present EFH guidelines focus primarily on utilization. What is needed is a clear delineation of habitat availability (how much is there?) and habitat vulnerability (what are the odds of human perturbation?). Habitats such as estuarine tidal creeks that are heavily used by fishes, in short supply, and very vulnerable to development should rank high on the protection priority list. Conversely, other habitats like the continental shelf that have wide seasonal usage but are relatively vast in magnitude and much less likely to be heavily impacted by man should rank lower on the list.

A system of essential fish habitat classification based on these principals would be of greater value in providing guidance to agencies charged with making the difficult decisions concerning development that face us now. Such decisions will only become more difficult in the future.

American Fisheries Society Symposium 22:43–75, 1999

Nekton Densities in Shallow Estuarine Habitats of Texas and Louisiana and the Identification of Essential Fish Habitat

THOMAS J. MINELLO

National Marine Fisheries Service
Galveston Southeast Fisheries Science Center Laboratory
4700 Avenue U, Galveston, Texas 77551, USA

Abstract.—The Magnuson-Stevens Fishery Conservation and Management Act (Magnuson-Stevens Act) of 1996 requires the identification of essential fish habitat (EFH) for fishery species under federal fishery management plans (FMPs). As defined in the Magnuson-Stevens Act, EFH includes waters and substrate necessary for spawning, breeding, feeding, or growth to maturity. Without EFH, fishery species will be unable to maintain the productivity needed to support a sustainable fishery or contribute ecologically to aquatic ecosystems. The highly productive estuaries in the northern Gulf of Mexico contain many habitat types that are potentially essential for species under FMPs such as brown shrimp *Penaeus aztecus,* white shrimp *P. setiferus,* pink shrimp *P. duorarum,* gulf stone crab *Menippe adina,* red drum *Sciaenops ocellatus,* gray snapper *Lutjanus griseus,* and bluefish *Pomatomus saltatrix;* these species spend their juvenile life stages in estuarine nurseries. Estuarine habitats also may be important for prey required as forage by managed species and for other fishery species not under FMPs. My objective in this paper was to summarize information on densities of juvenile fishery species and other animals (all generally <100 mm total length) in shallow-water estuarine areas of Texas and Louisiana. I attempted to identify where these species live (delineate their habitat) and to analyze density patterns within habitats that would be useful in distinguishing EFH. My analysis was restricted to data collected with enclosure sampling techniques because these techniques have been shown to provide comparable density estimates among highly diverse shallow-water areas. Habitat types evaluated included *Spartina alterniflora* marsh edge (SAME), mixed-vegetation marsh edge, inner marsh (>5 m from open water), submerged aquatic vegetation (SAV), oyster reefs, and shallow nonvegetated bottom (SNB). Data also were categorized by season, salinity regime, estuarine system, and year of collection. Mean densities among habitat types frequently varied in relation to salinity regime, but overall, SAME was used most by brown shrimp, white shrimp, blue crab *Callinectes sapidus,* spotted seatrout *Cynoscion nebulosus,* and southern flounder *Paralichthys lethostigma.* Highest densities of pink shrimp, red drum, and sand seatrout *Cynoscion arenarius* were found in SAV. Stone crabs had highest mean densities on oyster reefs and gulf menhaden *Brevoortia patronus* on SNB. Each of the six habitat types examined ranked first or second in use by at least one of these fishery species. Thus, all of these habitat types are likely essential for some fishery species. The analysis highlighted many of the challenges confronted in determining habitat-use patterns and emphasized the need for additional systematic sampling to examine geographic variability in habitat use and to examine distribution patterns within habitats. However, in addition to analyses of intrahabitat densities, the identification of EFH requires information on functional relationships between fishery species and habitat characteristics.

Despite evidence of important ecological linkages between environmental conditions and fishery production, the management of commercial fishery resources in the United States has historically concentrated on assessing stock size and controlling fishing mortality. However, under the Magnuson-Stevens Fishery Conservation and Management Act of 1996 (Magnuson-Stevens Act), the conservation and management of fishery habitat became an important component of comprehensive fishery management programs. The Magnuson-Stevens Act directs fishery management councils and the National Marine Fisheries Service to identify essential fish habitat (EFH) for all managed fishery species and to identify adverse impacts, actions to ensure conservation and enhancement, and approaches to the restoration of EFH. Essential fish habitat is defined in the Magnuson-Stevens Act as waters and substrate necessary for spawning, breeding, feeding, or growth to maturity. Without EFH, fishery species will be unable to maintain the productivity needed to support a sustainable fishery or contribute ecologically to aquatic ecosystems (62 FR 66531) (NMFS 1997).

An organism's habitat is the place where it lives (Odum 1971; Whitaker and Levin 1975; Baltz 1990; Peters and Cross 1992; Ricklefs 1993). From this simple definition, two important concepts ensue: (1) that at any particular life stage, a species has one habitat and (2) that an organism defines its habitat by its spatial distribution. Ecologists attempt to describe the habitat of a species based on characteristics known to be ecologically meaningful; for fishery species these characteristics often include structure (e.g., vegetation type, rock outcroppings); substrate (sediment grain size, organic content); hydrodynamics (currents, tidal flooding patterns); and general hydrology (depth, temperature, salinity, turbidity). Accurately identifying the habitat for each life stage of a fishery species is a crucial first step in identifying EFH, because areas that are not habitats are not essential habitats. In addition, however, some parts of a species' habitat may not be essential for maintaining that species' productivity.

In the Gulf of Mexico, many abundant fishery species that live and spawn in coastal waters have young that migrate into estuarine nursery grounds where they grow into subadults. Habitats in estuaries are likely to contribute substantially to the productivity of these fishery species because estuarine ecosystems have some of the highest levels of primary production observed. The general link between environmental conditions in Gulf estuaries and fishery production has been recognized for some time (Gunter 1941, 1961; Hildebrand and Gunter 1953; St. Amant et al. 1962; Zein-Eldin 1963). Indeed, production of shrimp has been correlated on a large scale with the amount of coastal wetlands in the region (Turner 1977). For most species, however, specific habitats used within estuaries have not been adequately defined, and the portions of these habitats that are essential in maintaining fishery production have not been identified.

The juveniles of fishery species that use estuaries as nursery grounds are only temporary residents and transient members of estuarine communities (Deegan and Thompson 1985; Kneib 1997). These juveniles often appear to be ubiquitously distributed within estuaries, and the entire estuary might be their habitat. A habitat delineation of the entire estuary, however, does little to identify functional relationships or important interactions with habitat characteristics, and, therefore, such a delineation does little to assist us in identifying essential portions of a habitat. It is necessary to subdivide this habitat into smaller parcels (termed "intrahabitat" areas here) that have distinct features important to fishery species. We can identify these important intrahabitat areas by examining density patterns within the habitat or by examining relationships between habitat characteristics and life history functions such as growth, survival, and reproduction. Some of the most commonly examined intrahabitat areas are associated with well-recognized ecological communities within estuaries such as sea grass beds, oyster reefs, salt marshes, mangroves, tidal mudflats, and subtidal bay bottom; these community habitats are termed biotopes (Whitaker et al. 1973). The estuarine habitat of a species can also be divided into different intrahabitat areas based on other characteristics. For example, both animals and plants have different tolerances to salinities found within estuaries, and the use of the above biotopes by a fishery species can change in relation to salinity regimes (Zimmerman et al. 1990a, 1990b). Within intertidal marsh, elevation and proximity to open water also appear to affect use patterns and habitat value for some fishery species (Rozas and Reed 1993; Minello et al. 1994; Peterson and Turner 1994; Minello and Webb 1997). On nonvegetated bottom, water depth affects habitat use (Ruiz et al. 1993), and differences in sediment texture have been related to differences in shrimp (Williams 1958; Rulifson 1981) and fish (Keefe and Able 1994; Moles and Norcross 1995) distributions.

My objective in this paper is to improve our ability to delineate habitats of juvenile fishery species and other small nekton (all generally <100 mm total length or carapace width) in shallow estuarine areas of Texas and Louisiana. The density database developed for this purpose was restricted to data collected with enclosure sampling techniques because these techniques provide comparable density estimates among highly diverse biotopes (Rozas and Minello 1997). Samples were classified into six habitat types including submerged aquatic vegetation, *Spartina alterniflora* marsh edge, mixed-vegetation marsh edge, inner marsh, shallow nonvegetated bottom, and oyster reefs. Mean nekton densities were calculated for these habitat types; for fishery species, densities in different salinity regimes were also examined. On the basis of utilization patterns, I speculate on the relative importance of these intrahabitat areas and their possible designation as EFH.

Methods

Data were collected from 22 studies where enclosure samplers were used in estuarine habitats of Texas and Louisiana including published work by Zimmerman et al. (1984, 1989, 1990a, 1990b); Zimmerman and Minello (1984); Thomas et al. (1990);

Czapla (1991); Minello et al. (1991); Minello and Zimmerman (1992); Rozas and Reed (1993); Peterson and Turner (1994); Minello and Webb (1997); Rozas and Minello (in press); and unpublished study results from the Galveston Laboratory of the National Marine Fisheries Service. Over 5,000 samples were classified into the following habitat types:

- *Spartina alterniflora* marsh edge (SAME)—defined as intertidal *S. alterniflora* marsh within 5 m of open water;
- Mixed-vegetation marsh edge (MVME)—defined as above but with various other species of vegetation including *Spartina patens, Juncus roemerianus, Scirpus* spp., *Typha,* and *Distichlis spicata*;
- Inner marsh—defined as marsh more than 5 m from open water and including *S. alterniflora* or *Distichlis spicata*;
- Submerged aquatic vegetation (SAV)—including *Thalassia testudinum, Halodule wrightii, Syringodium filiforme, Halophila engelmanni,* or *Ruppia maritima*;
- Oyster reef—consisting of low intertidal areas along Confederate Reef in the Galveston Bay system of Texas;
- Shallow nonvegetated bottom (SNB)—generally restricted to water <1 m deep including creeks, ponds, shoreline, and open bay areas. Shallow nonvegetated bottom was mostly subtidal except for the shallowest areas on extreme low tides.

For each study, density data for fishes and decapod crustaceans were incorporated into the database as mean values (number per m²) after characterizing the samples by habitat type, year, season, salinity regime, and estuarine system. Size or biomass data were not included in the database. However, I have reported mean sizes for some common fishery species based on samples in the database collected in Galveston Bay. These data and published size data by Zimmerman and Minello (1984), Thomas et al. (1990), Czapla (1991), and Rozas and Minello (in press) indicate that the vast majority of organisms represented in the database were less than 100 mm in total length (TL) or carapace width (CW). Therefore, although the database included most life stages of small resident species, only the juveniles of transient fishery species were represented.

Spring samples were those samples collected in March, April, and May; summer samples were collected in June, July, and August; fall samples were collected in September, October, and November; and winter samples were collected in December, January, and February. Estuaries were divided into salinity zones based on long-term patterns in each system (Orlando et al. 1991, 1993), and these zones were defined as oligohaline (annual mean salinity between 0.5 and 5.0 parts per thousand [ppt]), mesohaline (5–18 ppt), polyhaline (18–30 ppt), and euhaline (30–40 ppt). The different estuaries sampled along the coast were consolidated into the following systems: Lower Laguna Madre (LLM); Upper Laguna Madre (ULM); Corpus Christi Bay (CCB); Redfish, Aransas, Copano, and Mesquite Bays (AB); San Antonio Bay and Espiritu Santo Bay (SAB); Matagorda Bay (MB); Galveston Bay system (GB); Terrebonne and Timbalier Bays (TB); and Barataria Bay (BB). (See Figure 1 for the locations of these systems.)

In addition to the mean density, the standard error was included in the database for the number of samples collected in a study for each habitat type, year, season, salinity regime, and estuary combination. The number of samples (N) collected and used to calculate the mean was also recorded. In addition, a location variable was included for each mean to indicate the number of different locations sampled. The difference between replicate samples at one location and sampling two locations is one of scale. If samples were separated by a distance of approximately 2 km or more, they were considered to be from different locations. The number of locations sampled for each habitat type was 184 for SAME, 132 for SAV, 183 for SNB, 61 for MVME, 22 for inner marsh, and 2 for oyster reef. The area used for the density determination (area enclosed or sampled each time the gear was deployed) and the type of gear used to collect the samples was listed in the database. The tide level at the time of sampling also was recorded because animal densities in shallow-water areas of the estuary are affected by tidal flood stage (Rozas and Minello 1997).

No formal statistical tests were used to compare means among intrahabitat areas. The mean nekton density for any area was calculated as the mean of the means included in the database for that intrahabitat area. Use of these weighted means reduced the influence of any one study on density patterns; this approach is similar to that used in a meta-analysis. The variability, or standard error (SE), presented in this chapter also was calculated using the means as observations. This variability within habitat types was often quite high because it incorporated differences related to years, seasons, salinity regimes, and estuaries. I considered

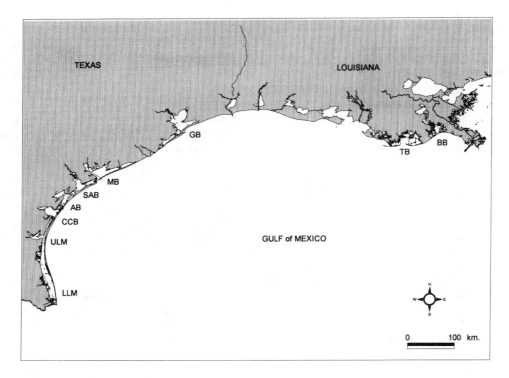

Figure 1.—Estuaries of Texas and Louisiana where data were collected on densities of fishery species and other nekton. Estuaries were consolidated into the following systems: Lower Laguna Madre (LLM); Upper Laguna Madre (ULM); Corpus Christi Bay (CCB); Redfish, Aransas, Copano, and Mesquite Bays (AB); San Antonio Bay and Espiritu Santo Bay (SAB); Matagorda Bay (MB); Galveston Bay system (GB); Terrebonne and Timbalier Bays (TB); and Barataria Bay (BB).

the use of a factorial analysis of variance (ANOVA) to partition this residual error, but the unbalanced nature of the data and the common occurrence of missing cells (treatment combinations with no data) made comparisons of main-effect means difficult (Milliken and Johnson 1984; Day and Quinn 1989). In addition, the data did not meet the ANOVA assumption of homogeneity in variances even following logarithmic transformation. If desired, limited statistical comparisons of means could be made using simple t-tests. The results of such tests should be quite conservative for the above reasons and because each mean generally represents a substantial number of samples.

Results

General Description of the Database

The database contained a total of 350 mean density values for every taxon found in each of the 5,149 samples represented. The most frequently sampled habitat types were *Spartina alterniflora* marsh edge, shallow nonvegetated bottom, and submerged aquatic vegetation (Table 1). Shallow nonvegetated bottom included creeks and ponds (samples collected within a marsh complex and surrounded by vegetation), shore (samples collected along semiprotected or exposed bay shorelines), and open water (a small number of samples collected at least 100 m from any shoreline). These nonvegetated samples were also characterized in the database on the basis of general substrate texture (mud versus sand). Submerged aquatic vegetation included four species of sea grasses and widgeongrass *Ruppia maritima*; the most frequently sampled type of SAV was shoalgrass *Halodule wrightii*. About 3% of the SAV samples were taken on areas of dredged material. The age of these beds is unknown, but they were at least five years old at the time of sampling. Mixed-vegetation marsh edge was represented by 258 samples and more than six species of marsh vegetation. Inner marsh (defined as areas more than 5 m away from open water) was vegetated by either *S. alterniflora* or *Distichlis spicata*. Oyster reefs were not well represented in the database, and data were recorded from only 16 samples (one study).

TABLE 1.—The number of mean density values and the total number of samples (in parentheses) represented in the database for each habitat type (in bold type) and each season.

Habitat type	Season				
	Spring	Summer	Fall	Winter	Total
Submerged aquatic vegetation (SAV)	**33 (469)**	**8 (192)**	**32 (367)**	**2 (60)**	**75 (1,088)**
Halodule wrightii	15 (320)	7 (184)	12 (232)	2 (60)	36 (796)
Halodule wrightii on old spoil	2 (6)	0 (0)	1 (3)	0 (0)	3 (9)
Halodule and *Ruppia*	5 (55)	0 (0)	9 (75)	0 (0)	14 (130)
Halophila engelmanni on old spoil	1 (4)	0 (0)	0 (0)	0 (0)	1 (4)
Ruppia maritima	2 (8)	1 (8)	3 (12)	0 (0)	6 (28)
Syringodium filiforme	4 (38)	0 (0)	3 (20)	0 (0)	7 (58)
Syringodium filiforme on old spoil	1 (8)	0 (0)	1 (3)	0 (0)	2 (11)
Thalassia testudinum	2 (24)	0 (0)	2 (16)	0 (0)	4 (40)
Thalassia testudinum on old spoil	1 (6)	0 (0)	1 (6)	0 (0)	2 (12)
***Spartina alterniflora* marsh edge (SAME)**	**39 (616)**	**22 (397)**	**36 (571)**	**12 (214)**	**109 (1,798)**
Mixed vegetation marsh edge (MVME)	**14 (87)**	**8 (51)**	**18 (120)**	**0 (0)**	**40 (258)**
Distichlis spicata	3 (8)	3 (21)	1 (15)	0 (0)	7 (44)
Juncus roemerianus	5 (44)	2 (9)	5 (46)	0 (0)	12 (99)
Phragmites australis	1 (1)	0 (0)	0 (0)	0 (0)	1 (1)
S. alterniflora and *Typha*	1 (4)	0 (0)	1 (4)	0 (0)	2 (8)
S. alterniflora, *Typha* and *Scirpus*	0 (0)	0 (0)	3 (12)	0 (0)	3 (12)
Scirpus maritimus	2 (14)	2 (13)	2 (11)	0 (0)	6 (38)
Scirpus spp.	1 (8)	1 (8)	1 (8)	0 (0)	3 (24)
Scirpus and Hyacinth	0 (0)	0 (0)	1 (4)	0 (0)	1 (4)
Scirpus and *S. alterniflora*	0 (0)	0 (0)	1 (4)	0 (0)	1 (4)
Spartina patens	1 (8)	0 (0)	3 (16)	0 (0)	4 (24)
Inner marsh	**5 (55)**	**4 (81)**	**4 (65)**	**1 (18)**	**14 (219)**
Distichlis spicata	1 (2)	1 (5)	0 (0)	0 (0)	2 (7)
S. alterniflora	4 (53)	3 (76)	4 (65)	1 (18)	12 (212)
Oyster reef	**0 (0)**	**1 (8)**	**0 (0)**	**1 (8)**	**2 (16)**
Shallow nonvegetated bottom	**36 (589)**	**24 (416)**	**41 (589)**	**9 (176)**	**110 (1,770)**
Creeks and ponds, mud	3 (52)	2 (24)	3 (52)	0 (0)	8 (128)
Open water, mud	0 (0)	1 (8)	0 (0)	1 (8)	2 (16)
Open water, sand	1 (24)	2 (24)	1 (16)	1 (24)	5 (88)
Shore, creeks, ponds, sandy mud	9 (286)	9 (237)	9 (221)	7 (144)	34 (888)
Shore, open water, muddy sand	1 (35)	0 (0)	1 (35)	0 (0)	2 (70)
Shore, mud	7 (36)	2 (18)	9 (52)	0 (0)	18 (106)
Shore, sandy mud	9 (114)	6 (78)	12 (170)	0 (0)	27 (362)
Shore, sand	5 (30)	2 (27)	6 (43)	0 (0)	13 (100)
Shore, muddy sand	1 (12)	0 (0)	0 (0)	0 (0)	1 (12)
Total	127 (1,816)	67 (1,145)	131 (1,712)	25 (476)	350 (5,149)

Most of the samples used in this analysis were collected in the spring and fall (68% of total), but the summer season was also well represented (Table 1). Few samples (9%) were collected during the winter, mainly because few organisms occur in these shallow-water estuarine areas during the cold months of the year. The distribution of sampling effort among seasons was similar for most habitat types. Samples in oyster reefs, however, were only collected in the summer and winter.

TABLE 2.—The number of mean density values and the total number of samples (in parentheses) represented in the database for each salinity regime and habitat type.

Summary habitat	Salinity regime				Total
	Euhaline	Polyhaline	Mesohaline	Oligohaline	
Submerged aquatic vegetation (SAV)	35 (434)	29 (606)	5 (20)	6 (28)	75 (1,088)
Spartina alterniflora marsh edge (SAME)	1 (4)	77 (1,484)	25 (291)	6 (19)	109 (1,798)
Mixed vegetation marsh edge (MVME)	0 (0)	5 (32)	17 (145)	18 (81)	40 (258)
Inner marsh	0 (0)	2 (20)	12 (199)	0 (0)	14 (219)
Oyster reef	0 (0)	2 (16)	0 (0)	0 (0)	2 (16)
Shallow nonvegetated bottom (SNB)	0 (0)	73 (1,402)	23 (268)	14 (100)	110 (1,770)
Total	36 (438)	188 (3,560)	82 (923)	44 (228)	350 (5,149)

The sampling effort represented in the database was concentrated in the polyhaline zone of estuaries, and 69% of the samples (54% of means) were collected in this salinity regime (Table 2). Mesohaline areas of estuaries were represented by 18% of the samples, while the remaining samples were split about evenly between euhaline and oligohaline areas. This distribution of sampling effort among salinity regimes was similar for most habitat types, with the important exception of SAV. Almost all SAV samples (96%) were collected in euhaline or polyhaline salinity regimes, and almost all samples in the euhaline salinity regime (prima-

rily in the Laguna Madre of South Texas) were in SAV. Submerged aquatic vegetation is common in many oligohaline and tidal freshwater areas of these estuaries, but few samples (all widgeongrass) were available from these areas.

Seven estuarine systems in Texas were represented in the database (94% of samples), as well as two systems (6% of samples) from Louisiana (Figure 1; Table 3). Within Texas, most of the samples were collected in the Galveston Bay system (74%). The south Texas coast is relatively arid, and most of the estuaries in this region have large euhaline zones; samples from the Laguna Madre and Corpus Christi

TABLE 3.—The number of mean density values and the total number of samples (in parentheses) represented in the database for each estuary, habitat type, and salinity regime. Abbreviations for habitat types are shown in Tables 1 and 2.

Estuary	Salinity regime	Habitat type						Total
		SAV	SAME	MVME	Inner marsh	Oyster	SNB	
Lower Laguna Madre (LLM)	Euhaline	29 (264)	0 (0)	0 (0)	0 (0)	0 (0)	0 (0)	29 (264)
Upper Laguna Madre (ULM)	Euhaline	6 (170)	0 (0)	0 (0)	0 (0)	0 (0)	0 (0)	6 (170)
Corpus Christi Bay (CCB)	Euhaline	0 (0)	1 (4)	0 (0)	0 (0)	0 (0)	0 (0)	1 (4)
Aransas Bay Complex (AB)	Polyhaline	2 (70)	2 (60)	0 (0)	0 (0)	0 (0)	2 (70)	6 (200)
San Antonio Bay (SAB)	Polyhaline	7 (40)	6 (36)	1 (4)	0 (0)	0 (0)	7 (40)	21 (120)
	Mesohaline	5 (20)	6 (24)	1 (4)	0 (0)	0 (0)	7 (28)	19 (76)
	Oligohaline	3 (12)	3 (12)	5 (20)	0 (0)	0 (0)	7 (32)	18 (76)
Matagorda Bay, mainly Lavaca (MB)	Polyhaline	0 (0)	6 (50)	2 (8)	0 (0)	0 (0)	5 (58)	13 (116)
	Mesohaline	0 (0)	3 (9)	8 (63)	0 (0)	0 (0)	6 (76)	17 (148)
	Oligohaline	0 (0)	2 (3)	10 (37)	0 (0)	0 (0)	3 (40)	15 (80)
Galveston Bay (GB)	Polyhaline	20 (496)	62 (1,328)	2 (20)	2 (20)	2 (16)	58 (1,224)	146 (3,104)
	Mesohaline	0 (0)	9 (192)	5 (40)	3 (24)	0 (0)	10 (164)	27 (420)
	Oligohaline	3 (16)	1 (4)	3 (24)	0 (0)	0 (0)	4 (28)	11 (72)
Terrebonne and Timbalier Bays (TB)	Mesohaline	0 (0)	7 (66)	3 (38)	9 (175)	0 (0)	0 (0)	19 (279)
Barataria Bay (BB)	Polyhaline	0 (0)	1 (10)	0 (0)	0 (0)	0 (0)	1 (10)	2 (20)
Total		75 (1,088)	109 (1,798)	40 (258)	14 (219)	2 (16)	110 (1,770)	350 (5,149)

Bay were only collected in euhaline salinity regimes and were almost exclusively from SAV. The widest salinity ranges were represented in estuaries located on the central to northern coast of Texas. Inner marsh and oyster reef samples were collected only in one or two estuarine systems.

Samples in the database were collected between the years 1982 and 1997. All years except 1992 were represented, and the distribution of samples among years was relatively even. The majority of samples (84%) in the database were collected with either a 1-m^2 or 2.6-m^2 drop sampler (Zimmerman et al. 1984). Other gear used included flumes (Peterson and Turner 1994), lift nets (Rozas and Reed 1993), and throw traps. Most samples (84%) were collected when tide levels were high and intertidal vegetation was flooded.

Especially for uncommon species, the number of means recorded in these summary data are less than the possible number of means based on sampling effort. This situation reflects a problem distinguishing between zeros and missing data. I could not always determine whether the lack of a species in a list of animals meant that it was not present in the sample or that it was not identified. In this situation, I assumed that the species was not present (zero density) if that species was identified from other samples in the study. I did not include a zero for the density of a species if it was not identified in a particular study, even though this often would have been appropriate. Therefore, the count of means for the less-common species is a minimum value. Mean densities for these species would be lower than those reported here if I had included all zeros for samples from studies where the species was not identified.

General Density Patterns in Different Habitat Types

The database included over 20,000 records of mean densities for various species collected in shallow waters of these estuaries, and these means provided general information on habitats of species and on utilization patterns within habitats (Tables 4 and 5). Decapod crustaceans were the most abundant organisms (Table 4), and 54 taxa were identified including 48 species and 6 species complexes (e.g., *Callinectes* spp.). Grass shrimps in the genus *Palaemonetes* (estuarine residents) were by far the most abundant crustaceans; this genus was collected mainly within vegetated areas. The blue crab *Callinectes sapidus* and its congeners along with

brown shrimp *Penaeus aztecus* [1] and white shrimp *P. setiferus* (also known as *Penaeus setiferus*) were also relatively abundant. Although rankings varied, these abundant crustaceans were generally dominant in vegetated areas and on shallow nonvegetated bottom (Table 6). The dominant crustaceans on oyster reefs were small resident crabs including the green porcelain crab *Petrolisthes armatus* and the xanthid crabs *Panopeus herbstii* and *Eurypanopeus depressus*. Crustacean species in the database under federal fishery management plans (FMPs) included brown shrimp, white shrimp, pink shrimp *P. duorarum* (also known as *Penaeus duorarum*), and gulf stone crab *Menippe adina*. There is also an active fishery for blue crab in Texas and Louisiana. Many of the other crustaceans in the database are prey for fishery species.

Compared with crustaceans, fishes were less abundant but more diverse; 86 species and 2 species complexes were identified in samples (Table 5). On the basis of mean density from all samples, gulf menhaden *Brevoortia patronus* was the most abundant fish in these estuaries. This species was concentrated mainly in oligohaline salinity regimes, and mean densities were highest on shallow nonvegetated bottom and in marsh edge (Table 5). The naked goby *Gobiosoma bosc* was also abundant, and this small resident fish was ubiquitous, being a dominant species in all habitat types except inner marsh (Table 6). Inner marsh was dominated by gulf killifish *Fundulus grandis*, diamond killifish *Adinia xenica*, and the sheepshead minnow *Cyprinodon variegatus* (all estuarine residents). The pinfish *Lagodon rhomboides* was a dominant species in *Spartina alterniflora* marsh edge and in SAV, and bay anchovy *Anchoa mitchilli* was dominant on oyster reefs and shallow nonvegetated bottom. Only three fish species in the database are under federal FMPs: red drum *Sciaenops ocellatus*, gray snapper *Lutjanus griseus*, and bluefish *Pomatomus saltatrix*. However, the database included information on habitat-use patterns for other fishery species of both commercial and recreational importance in the region including gulf menhaden, southern flounder *Paralichthys lethostigma*, spotted seatrout *Cynoscion nebulosus*, and sand seatrout *Cynoscion arenarius*.

---

[1] Perez Farfante and Kensley (1997) have revised the scientific names of brown shrimp, pink shrimp, and white shrimp to *Farfantepenaeus aztecus*, *F. duorarum*, and *Litopenaeus setiferus*, respectively.

TABLE 4.—Mean densities of decapod crustaceans in different habitat types including submerged aquatic vegetation (SAV), *Spartina alterniflora* marsh edge (SAME), mixed vegetation marsh edge (MVME), inner marsh, oyster reef, and shallow nonvegetated bottom (SNB). Each mean density (animals per m^2) was calculated as the mean of means in

Taxon (common name)	SAV			SAME			MVME		
	Mean	SE	Ct	Mean	SE	Ct	Mean	SE	Ct
Crustaceans	**50.216**	**8.724**	**75**	**83.540**	**6.500**	**109**	**36.037**	**5.627**	**40**
Acetes americanus			0	0.000	0.000	3			0
Alpheus heterochaelis (bigclaw snapping shrimp)	1.599	0.483	71	0.322	0.069	86	0.004	0.003	32
Ambidexter symmetricus	0.022	0.014	14			0			0
Callianassa jamaicensis (estuarine ghost shrimp)	0.057	0.000	1	0.008	0.005	17	0.000	0.000	2
Callianassa spp.			0	0.000	0.000	1	0.000	0.000	1
Callichirus major (Carolinian ghost shrimp)			0	0.000	0.000	6	0.000	0.000	2
Callinectes ornatus (shelligs)	0.013	0.013	15	0.000	0.000	15	0.000	0.000	7
Callinectes sapidus (blue crab)	5.047	1.155	67	6.239	0.746	100	2.698	0.891	40
Callinectes similis (lesser blue crab)	0.675	0.145	58	0.096	0.065	21	0.022	0.014	9
Callinectes spp.	13.746	2.614	8	3.980	1.969	8			0
Clibanarius vittatus (thinstripe hermit)	0.112	0.030	71	0.772	0.184	92	0.020	0.010	34
Dyspanopeus texana (gulf grassflat crab)	3.600	0.876	65	0.204	0.059	62	0.397	0.284	30
Eurypanopeus abbreviatus (lobate mud crab)	0.000	0.000	7	0.032	0.020	6	0.000	0.000	3
Eurypanopeus depressus (flatback mud crab)	0.009	0.009	22	0.042	0.017	56	0.000	0.000	31
Farfantepenaeus aztecus (brown shrimp)	7.341	1.026	54	7.479	0.699	104	2.598	0.574	40
Farfantepenaeus duorarum (pink shrimp)	1.563	0.702	30	1.050	0.238	73	0.498	0.296	31
Hippolyte zostericola (zostera shrimp)	6.466	1.402	68	0.724	0.597	45	0.004	0.004	30
Latreutes fucorum (slender sargassum shrimp)			0	0.020	0.000	1			0
Latreutes parvulus (sargassum shrimp)	0.013	0.013	15	0.002	0.002	19	0.000	0.000	23
Leander tenuicornis (brown grass shrimp)	0.000	0.000	8	0.001	0.001	12			0
Libinia dubia (longnose spider crab)	0.049	0.017	44	0.010	0.004	37	0.000	0.000	23
Litopenaeus setiferus (white shrimp)	0.462	0.109	74	5.528	1.019	98	1.507	0.483	37
Macrobrachium ohione (Ohio shrimp)	0.026	0.026	15	0.024	0.014	21	0.288	0.288	7
Menippe adina (gulf stone crab)	0.007	0.004	39	0.014	0.003	77	0.001	0.001	30
Ogyrides alphaerostris (estuarine longeye shrimp)	0.006	0.006	15	0.000	0.000	19	0.000	0.000	8
Pachygrapsus gracilis (dark shore crab)			0	0.011	0.011	3			0

TABLE 4. (cont.)—the database; also shown is the standard error (SE, calculated using means as observations) and the number of means (Ct = Count) used in the calculation. Data are included from all seasons, salinity regimes, estuaries, and years.

Taxon (common name)	Inner marsh			Oyster reef			SNB			Total		
	Mean	SE	Ct	Mean	SE	Ct	Mean	SE	Ct	Mean	SE	Ct
Crustaceans	**15.725**	**5.934**	**14**	**70.596**	**34.250**	**2**	**5.452**	**0.402**	**110**	**43.642**	**3.302**	**350**
Acetes americanus			0			0	0.299	0.299	3	0.150	0.150	6
Alpheus heterochaelis (bigclaw snapping shrimp)	0.000	0.000	1	3.481	2.288	2	0.019	0.004	102	0.511	0.125	294
Ambidexter symmetricus			0			0	0.000	0.000	6	0.015	0.010	20
Callianassa jamaicensis (estuarine ghost shrimp)	0.000	0.000	2			0	0.077	0.047	18	0.040	0.022	40
Callianassa spp.	0.000	0.000	1			0	0.025	0.025	2	0.010	0.010	5
Callichirus major (Carolinian ghost shrimp)	0.000	0.000	1			0	0.013	0.008	7	0.006	0.004	16
Callinectes ornatus (shelligs)			0			0	0.000	0.000	21	0.003	0.003	58
Callinectes sapidus (blue crab)	0.526	0.123	14	0.231	0.077	2	0.902	0.099	109	3.543	0.364	332
Callinectes similis (lesser blue crab)	0.000	0.000	2			0	0.105	0.053	34	0.362	0.075	124
Callinectes spp.			0			0	1.589	0.524	8	6.438	1.522	24
Clibanarius vittatus (thinstripe hermit)	0.033	0.033	3	1.212	0.904	2	0.099	0.037	108	0.299	0.059	310
Dyspanopeus texana (gulf grassflat crab)			0	0.000	0.000	2	0.031	0.013	74	1.125	0.267	233
Eurypanopeus abbreviatus (lobate mud crab)			0			0	0.000	0.000	9	0.008	0.005	25
Eurypanopeus depressus (flatback mud crab)	0.000	0.000	1	13.577	9.731	2	0.012	0.005	68	0.170	0.131	180
Farfantepenaeus aztecus (brown shrimp)	0.452	0.240	14	0.000	0.000	2	1.879	0.190	109	4.611	0.336	323
Farfantepenaeus duorarum (pink shrimp)	0.000	0.000	1	0.019	0.019	2	0.131	0.030	86	0.674	0.133	223
Hippolyte zostericola (zostera shrimp)			0			0	0.019	0.013	60	2.333	0.528	203
Latreutes fucorum (slender sargassum shrimp)			0			0			0	0.020	0.000	1
Latreutes parvulus (sargassum shrimp)			0			0	0.000	0.000	26	0.003	0.002	83
Leander tenuicornis (brown grass shrimp)			0			0	0.000	0.000	12	0.000	0.000	32
Libinia dubia (longnose spider crab)			0	0.000	0.000	2	0.000	0.000	42	0.017	0.005	148
Litopenaeus setiferus (white shrimp)	1.601	0.891	12	0.000	0.000	2	1.242	0.248	108	2.372	0.338	331
Macrobrachium ohione (Ohio shrimp)			0			0	0.000	0.000	27	0.042	0.029	70
Menippe adina (gulf stone crab)			0	1.885	0.731	2	0.002	0.001	88	0.023	0.012	236
Ogyrides alphaerostris (estuarine longeye shrimp)	0.000	0.000	1			0	0.006	0.006	26	0.004	0.003	69
Pachygrapsus gracilis (dark shore crab)			0			0	0.000	0.000	3	0.005	0.005	6

TABLE 4.—(continued).

Taxon (common name)	SAV			SAME			MVME		
	Mean	SE	Ct	Mean	SE	Ct	Mean	SE	Ct
Pagurus annulipes	0.008	0.007	25			0			0
Pagurus criniticornis	0.296	0.104	37			0			0
Pagurus impressus (dimpled hermit)	0.000	0.000	14			0			0
Pagurus longicarpus (longwrist hermit)	0.059	0.029	31	0.000	0.000	6			0
Pagurus pollicaris (flatclaw hermit)	0.018	0.014	25	0.000	0.000	9			0
Palaemonetes intermedius (brackish grass shrimp)	6.891	1.502	67	5.477	1.997	74	0.443	0.171	32
Palaemonetes paludosus (riverine grass shrimp)	0.846	0.688	15	2.705	1.991	15	0.000	0.000	7
Palaemonetes pugio (daggerblade grass shrimp)	11.637	4.005	67	58.753	5.070	96	25.655	4.903	40
Palaemonetes spp.	2.042	0.735	51	21.726	6.440	16	0.000	0.000	1
Palaemonetes transversus	0.006	0.006	15	0.000	0.000	15	0.000	0.000	7
Palaemonetes vulgaris (marsh grass shrimp)	4.181	2.965	65	3.229	0.837	73	0.105	0.068	34
Panopeus herbstii (Atlantic mud crab)	0.234	0.107	38	0.205	0.093	54	0.009	0.006	25
Panopeus turgidus (ridgeback mud crab)	0.304	0.117	65	0.026	0.015	54	0.000	0.000	30
Petrolisthes armatus (green porcelain crab)	0.015	0.012	24	0.071	0.019	29	0.000	0.000	3
Petrolisthes galathinus (banded porcelain crab)			0	0.027	0.023	33	0.003	0.003	20
Pinnixa chaetopterana (tube pea crab)	0.004	0.003	42	0.002	0.001	35	0.000	0.000	10
Pinnixa cristata			0	0.000	0.000	18			0
Pinnixa lunzi (Lunz pea crab)	0.010	0.007	17			0			0
Pinnixa retinens	0.003	0.003	35	0.000	0.000	15	0.000	0.000	7
Pinnixa spp.	0.000	0.000	8	0.000	0.000	1	0.000	0.000	1
Pinnotheres maculatus (squatter pea crab)			0	0.002	0.002	7			0
Rhithropanopeus harrisii (Harris mud crab)	0.460	0.145	44	0.723	0.193	60	0.220	0.094	36
Sesarma cinereum (squareback marsh crab)	0.000	0.000	22	0.314	0.198	61	0.062	0.036	34
Sesarma reticulatum (heavy marsh crab)	0.000	0.000	27	0.301	0.174	88	1.310	0.838	37
Sesarma spp.			0	0.120	0.097	5	2.850	2.850	2
Tozeuma carolinense (arrow shrimp)	1.641	0.474	70	0.398	0.389	58	0.003	0.003	30
Trachypenaeus constrictus (roughneck shrimp)			0	0.001	0.001	10			0
Uca spp.	0.000	0.000	26	0.476	0.209	150	0.351	0.163	99

TABLE 4.—(continued).

Taxon (common name)	Inner marsh			Oyster reef			SNB			Total		
	Mean	SE	Ct	Mean	SE	Ct	Mean	SE	Ct	Mean	SE	Ct
Pagurus annulipes			0			0			0	0.008	0.007	25
Pagurus criniticornis			0			0			0	0.296	0.104	37
Pagurus impressus (dimpled hermit)			0			0	0.028	0.028	6	0.008	0.008	20
Pagurus longicarpus (longwrist hermit)			0			0	0.038	0.030	11	0.047	0.020	48
Pagurus pollicaris (flatclaw hermit)			0	0.019	0.019	2	0.003	0.002	10	0.011	0.008	46
Palaemonetes intermedius (brackish grass shrimp)	0.250	0.050	2	0.000	0.000	2	0.034	0.013	83	3.415	0.713	260
Palaemonetes paludosus (riverine grass shrimp)			0			0	0.000	0.000	21	0.918	0.551	58
Palaemonetes pugio (daggerblade grass shrimp)	10.441	4.002	10	0.500	0.192	2	0.933	0.213	109	23.621	2.255	324
Palaemonetes spp.	0.685	0.199	5			0	0.129	0.062	18	5.028	1.432	91
Palaemonetes transversus			0			0	0.000	0.000	21	0.002	0.002	58
Palaemonetes vulgaris (marsh grass shrimp)	0.033	0.033	3	0.154	0.154	2	0.016	0.007	84	1.965	0.779	261
Panopeus herbstii (Atlantic mud crab)	0.050	0.050	2	24.596	13.904	2	0.028	0.010	61	0.391	0.221	182
Panopeus turgidus (ridgeback mud crab)			0			0	0.001	0.000	68	0.098	0.036	217
Petrolisthes armatus (green porcelain crab)			0	24.731	8.923	2	0.006	0.003	30	0.592	0.420	88
Petrolisthes galathinus (banded porcelain crab)			0			0	0.000	0.000	35	0.011	0.009	88
Pinnixa chaetopterana (tube pea crab)			0			0	0.001	0.001	44	0.002	0.001	131
Pinnixa cristata			0	0.000	0.000	2	0.005	0.004	17	0.002	0.002	37
Pinnixa lunzi (Lunz pea crab)			0			0			0	0.010	0.007	17
Pinnixa retinens			0			0	0.002	0.002	21	0.002	0.001	78
Pinnixa spp.	0.000	0.000	1			0	0.025	0.025	2	0.004	0.004	13
Pinnotheres maculatus (squatter pea crab)			0			0	0.000	0.000	7	0.001	0.001	14
Rhithropanopeus harrisii (Harris mud crab)	0.000	0.000	4			0	0.155	0.030	74	0.381	0.065	218
Sesarma cinereum (squareback marsh crab)	0.067	0.033	3			0	0.007	0.007	71	0.115	0.064	191
Sesarma reticulatum (heavy marsh crab)	1.560	0.935	5			0	0.001	0.001	97	0.326	0.139	254
Sesarma spp.	1.450	1.450	2			0	0.000	0.000	7	0.575	0.387	16
Tozeuma carolinense (arrow shrimp)			0			0	0.018	0.016	77	0.594	0.176	235
Trachypenaeus constrictus (roughneck shrimp)			0			0	0.000	0.000	10	0.001	0.001	20
Uca spp.	9.157	4.060	7	0.000	0.000	2	0.002	0.001	169	0.377	0.111	453

TABLE 5.—Mean densities of fishes in different habitat types including submerged aquatic vegetation (SAV), *Spartina alterniflora* marsh edge (SAME), mixed vegetation marsh edge (MVME), inner marsh, oyster reef, and shallow nonvegetated bottom (SNB). Each mean density (animals per m^2) was calculated as the mean of means in

Taxon (common name)	SAV			SAME			MVME		
	Mean	SE	Ct	Mean	SE	Ct	Mean	SE	Ct
Fishes	**13.996**	**1.744**	**75**	**7.712**	**0.812**	**109**	**14.889**	**3.870**	**40**
Achirus lineatus (lined sole)	0.009	0.004	48	0.018	0.004	73	0.000	0.000	31
Adinia xenica (diamond killifish)	0.008	0.005	25	0.116	0.041	84	0.134	0.057	38
Anchoa hepsetus (striped anchovy)	0.159	0.080	43	0.000	0.000	4	0.000	0.000	1
Anchoa mitchilli (bay anchovy)	0.903	0.471	70	0.257	0.128	86	1.813	0.676	37
Anguilla rostrata (American eel)			0	0.000	0.000	10	0.001	0.001	20
Archosargus probatocephalus (sheepshead)	0.027	0.014	54	0.016	0.005	74	0.005	0.004	34
Arius felis (hardhead catfish)	0.010	0.006	25	0.006	0.003	49	0.003	0.002	35
Astroscopus y-graecum (southern stargazer)	0.000	0.000	8	0.000	0.000	10	0.010	0.010	20
Bairdiella chrysoura (silver perch)	0.089	0.020	66	0.125	0.049	66	0.331	0.187	36
Bathygobius soporator (frillfin goby)			0	0.006	0.006	10	0.031	0.031	20
Brevoortia patronus (gulf menhaden)	1.447	1.262	68	0.835	0.606	76	4.967	3.833	34
Chaetodipterus faber (Atlantic spadefish)	0.000	0.000	7	0.014	0.008	36	0.000	0.000	23
Chasmodes bosquianus (striped blenny)	0.006	0.006	12	0.003	0.003	15	0.000	0.000	20
Citharichthys spilopterus (bay whiff)	0.015	0.005	56	0.007	0.003	73	0.007	0.004	36
Cynoscion arenarius (sand seatrout)	0.037	0.037	6	0.005	0.003	22	0.000	0.000	21
Cynoscion nebulosus (spotted seatrout)	0.107	0.022	52	0.204	0.028	89	0.039	0.018	38
Cynoscion nothus (silver seatrout)			0	0.000	0.000	10	0.000	0.000	20
Cyprinodon variegatus (sheepshead minnow)	0.186	0.117	44	0.202	0.077	91	1.139	0.282	40
Dasyatis sabina (Atlantic stingray)	0.000	0.000	7	0.000	0.000	10	0.000	0.000	5
Dormitator maculatus (fat sleeper)	0.013	0.013	15	0.000	0.000	21	0.012	0.010	10
Dorosoma cepedianum (gizzard shad)			0	0.000	0.000	1	0.000	0.000	2
Elops saurus (ladyfish)	0.000	0.000	22	0.002	0.002	61	0.004	0.003	31

TABLE 5.(cont.)—the database; also shown is the standard error (SE, calculated using means as observations) and the number of means (Ct = count) used in the calculation. Data are included from all seasons, salinity regimes, estuaries, and years.

Taxon (common name)	Inner marsh			Oyster reef			SNB			Total		
	Mean	SE	Ct	Mean	SE	Ct	Mean	SE	Ct	Mean	SE	Ct
Fishes	**3.538**	**0.933**	**14**	**19.019**	**14.750**	**2**	**10.048**	**2.803**	**110**	**10.511**	**1.094**	**350**
Achirus lineatus (lined sole)	0.000	0.000	1	0.000	0.000	2	0.010	0.003	91	0.011	0.002	246
Adinia xenica (diamond killifish)	0.776	0.328	13			0	0.000	0.000	86	0.102	0.026	246
Anchoa hepsetus (striped anchovy)	0.000	0.000	1			0	0.019	0.014	11	0.117	0.058	60
Anchoa mitchilli (bay anchovy)	0.000	0.000	9	8.423	8.423	2	2.371	0.529	108	1.368	0.239	312
Anguilla rostrata (American eel)			0			0	0.000	0.000	14	0.001	0.001	44
Archosargus probatocephalus (sheepshead)	0.000	0.000	6	0.019	0.019	2	0.005	0.003	88	0.013	0.004	258
Arius felis (hardhead catfish)	0.000	0.000	7			0	0.013	0.004	62	0.008	0.002	178
Astroscopus y-graecum (southern stargazer)			0			0	0.000	0.000	14	0.004	0.004	52
Bairdiella chrysoura (silver perch)	0.001	0.001	7	0.000	0.000	2	0.037	0.025	82	0.113	0.031	259
Bathygobius soporator (frillfin goby)			0			0	0.000	0.000	14	0.016	0.014	44
Brevoortia patronus (gulf menhaden)	0.100	0.100	3	0.058	0.058	2	5.608	2.698	98	3.145	1.111	281
Chaetodipterus faber (Atlantic spadefish)			0			0	0.001	0.001	43	0.005	0.003	109
Chasmodes bosquianus (striped blenny)			0	0.192	0.154	2	0.000	0.000	19	0.007	0.005	68
Citharichthys spilopterus (bay whiff)	0.000	0.000	7			0	0.022	0.004	91	0.014	0.002	263
Cynoscion arenarius (sand seatrout)	0.000	0.000	1			0	0.014	0.007	33	0.010	0.004	83
Cynoscion nebulosus (spotted seatrout)	0.010	0.008	12	0.000	0.000	2	0.034	0.005	101	0.098	0.011	294
Cynoscion nothus (silver seatrout)			0			0	0.001	0.001	14	0.000	0.000	44
Cyprinodon variegatus (sheepshead minnow)	0.728	0.312	14			0	0.060	0.044	93	0.312	0.058	282
Dasyatis sabina (Atlantic stingray)	0.000	0.000	1			0	0.006	0.004	14	0.002	0.002	37
Dormitator maculatus (fat sleeper)	0.000	0.000	5			0	0.000	0.000	24	0.004	0.003	75
Dorosoma cepedianum (gizzard shad)	0.000	0.000	1			0	0.025	0.025	2	0.008	0.008	6
Elops saurus (ladyfish)	0.100	0.000	1			0	0.076	0.070	73	0.031	0.027	188

TABLE 5.—(continued).

Taxon (common name)	SAV			SAME			MVME		
	Mean	SE	Ct	Mean	SE	Ct	Mean	SE	Ct
Etropus crossotus (fringed flounder)	0.025	0.018	6			0			0
Eucinostomus argenteus (spotfin mojarra)	0.057	0.035	65	0.006	0.002	61	0.000	0.000	33
Eucinostomus gula (silver jenny)	0.074	0.074	6	0.005	0.004	21			0
Eucinostomus lefroyi (mottled mojarra)	0.032	0.026	15	0.001	0.001	31	0.000	0.000	7
Eucinostomus melanopterus (flagfin mojarra)	0.257	0.000	1	0.023	0.016	11			0
Eucinostomus spp.	0.148	0.148	6	0.000	0.000	2	0.000	0.000	3
Evorthodus lyricus (lyre goby)	0.000	0.000	23	0.012	0.005	37	0.018	0.013	10
Fundulus grandis (gulf killifish)	0.685	0.635	31	0.396	0.096	99	0.979	0.255	40
Fundulus jenkinsi (saltmarsh topminnow)	0.000	0.000	7	0.024	0.011	13	0.034	0.020	6
Fundulus pulvereus (bayou killifish)	0.052	0.029	22	0.028	0.008	58	0.202	0.086	35
Fundulus similis (longnose killifish)	0.000	0.000	22	0.027	0.015	80	0.024	0.014	34
Gambusia affinis (western mosquitofish)	0.035	0.035	22	0.019	0.017	29	0.861	0.855	10
Gobiesox strumosus (skilletfish)	0.005	0.003	45	0.107	0.045	50	0.075	0.040	33
Gobioides broussoneti (violet goby)			0	0.011	0.009	12			0
Gobionellus boleosoma (darter goby)	1.871	0.469	68	0.914	0.311	87	0.101	0.067	39
Gobionellus oceanicus (highfin goby)	0.003	0.003	15	0.001	0.001	31	0.000	0.000	7
Gobionellus shufeldti (freshwater goby)			0	0.051	0.036	24	0.004	0.004	23
Gobiosoma bosc (naked goby)	2.015	0.614	70	2.707	0.529	94	3.993	0.868	39
Gobiosoma robustum (code goby)	1.876	0.438	68	0.063	0.049	51	0.014	0.010	30
Harengula jaguana (scaled sardine)	0.012	0.009	12			0			0
Hippocampus zosterae (dwarf seahorse)	0.078	0.020	40			0			0
Hyporhamphus unifasciatus (silverstripe halfbeak)	0.004	0.004	19	0.003	0.003	16	0.000	0.000	23
Hypsoblennius ionthas (freckled blenny)			0	0.000	0.000	1			0
Ictalurus furcatus (blue catfish)			0	0.000	0.000	10	0.003	0.003	20
Ictalurus punctatus (channel catfish)	0.000	0.000	22	0.005	0.005	21	0.000	0.000	10
Lagodon rhomboides (pinfish)	2.581	0.724	70	1.275	0.235	95	0.149	0.048	36

TABLE 5.—(continued).

Taxon (common name)	Inner marsh			Oyster reef			SNB			Total		
	Mean	SE	Ct	Mean	SE	Ct	Mean	SE	Ct	Mean	SE	Ct
Etropus crossotus (fringed flounder)			0			0	0.019	0.019	6	0.022	0.012	12
Eucinostomus argenteus (spotfin mojarra)	0.000	0.000	5	0.000	0.000	2	0.020	0.009	77	0.023	0.010	243
Eucinostomus gula (silver jenny)			0			0	0.002	0.002	27	0.011	0.008	54
Eucinostomus lefroyi (mottled mojarra)			0			0	0.006	0.005	37	0.008	0.005	90
Eucinostomus melanopterus (flagfin mojarra)			0			0	0.001	0.001	11	0.023	0.013	23
Eucinostomus spp.	0.000	0.000	2			0	0.021	0.012	10	0.048	0.039	23
Evorthodus lyricus (lyre goby)	0.026	0.011	5			0	0.000	0.000	39	0.007	0.002	114
Fundulus grandis (gulf killifish)	0.975	0.291	14	0.000	0.000	2	0.019	0.011	97	0.407	0.088	283
Fundulus jenkinsi (saltmarsh topminnow)	0.004	0.002	9			0	0.000	0.000	9	0.012	0.005	44
Fundulus pulvereus (bayou killifish)	0.136	0.054	11	0.000	0.000	2	0.001	0.001	65	0.059	0.017	193
Fundulus similis (longnose killifish)	0.059	0.030	6			0	0.001	0.000	82	0.015	0.006	224
Gambusia affinis (western mosquitofish)			0			0	0.000	0.000	37	0.101	0.088	98
Gobiesox strumosus (skilletfish)	0.000	0.000	2	3.442	2.750	2	0.034	0.024	66	0.087	0.035	198
Gobioides broussoneti (violet goby)			0			0	0.000	0.000	12	0.006	0.005	24
Gobionellus boleosoma (darter goby)	0.062	0.054	13	0.000	0.000	2	0.168	0.041	96	0.748	0.143	305
Gobionellus oceanicus (highfin goby)			0			0	0.000	0.000	36	0.001	0.001	89
Gobionellus shufeldti (freshwater goby)	0.008	0.005	5			0	0.025	0.024	24	0.026	0.014	76
Gobiosoma bosc (naked goby)	0.012	0.007	13	4.962	1.769	2	0.956	0.232	105	2.049	0.247	323
Gobiosoma robustum (code goby)			0			0	0.034	0.015	73	0.602	0.146	222
Harengula jaguana (scaled sardine)			0			0	0.009	0.009	12	0.011	0.006	24
Hippocampus zosterae (dwarf seahorse)			0			0			0	0.078	0.020	40
Hyporhamphus unifasciatus (silverstripe halfbeak)			0			0	0.001	0.001	23	0.002	0.001	81
Hypsoblennius ionthas (freckled blenny)			0	0.077	0.077	2	0.000	0.000	1	0.051	0.051	4
Ictalurus furcatus (blue catfish)			0			0	0.000	0.000	14	0.001	0.001	44
Ictalurus punctatus (channel catfish)			0			0	0.002	0.002	30	0.002	0.001	83
Lagodon rhomboides (pinfish)	0.000	0.000	11	0.308	0.308	2	0.134	0.031	100	1.023	0.184	314

TABLE 5.—(continued).

Taxon (common name)	SAV			SAME			MVME		
	Mean	SE	Ct	Mean	SE	Ct	Mean	SE	Ct
Leiostomus xanthurus (spot)	0.178	0.071	68	0.062	0.023	82	0.034	0.016	37
Lepisosteus oculatus (spotted gar)			0	0.000	0.000	10	0.000	0.000	20
Lepomis cyanellus (green sunfish)			0	0.003	0.003	9			0
Lucania parva (rainwater killifish)	0.663	0.160	60	0.543	0.246	58	1.051	0.621	17
Lutjanus griseus (gray snapper)	0.003	0.003	14	0.003	0.002	8	0.000	0.000	3
Membras martinica (rough silverside)	0.000	0.000	7	0.001	0.001	25	0.007	0.007	24
Menidia beryllina (inland silverside)	0.243	0.143	52	0.600	0.270	91	0.800	0.707	37
Menticirrhus americanus (southern kingfish)			0	0.000	0.000	5			0
Menticirrhus littoralis (gulf kingfish)			0	0.000	0.000	1	0.000	0.000	1
Microgobius gulosus (clown goby)	0.077	0.047	35	0.003	0.002	58	0.007	0.007	27
Microgobius thalassinus (green goby)	0.033	0.021	59	0.005	0.002	52	0.000	0.000	12
Micropogonias undulatus (Atlantic croaker)	0.049	0.021	59	0.024	0.011	77	0.021	0.012	35
Monacanthus hispidus (planehead filefish)			0	0.010	0.010	10	0.000	0.000	20
Mugil cephalus (striped mullet)	0.011	0.006	40	0.170	0.048	93	0.199	0.049	40
Mugil curema (white mullet)	0.003	0.003	14	0.090	0.050	6	0.200	0.000	1
Myrophis punctatus (speckled worm eel)	0.155	0.057	68	0.055	0.016	78	0.048	0.021	37
Oligoplites saurus (leatherjack)	0.000	0.000	13	0.013	0.010	15	0.000	0.000	3
Ophichthus gomesi (shrimp eel)	0.062	0.021	3	0.004	0.004	8			0
Ophidion welshi (crested cusk-eel)	0.013	0.013	8			0			0
Opsanus beta (gulf toadfish)	0.083	0.021	68	0.017	0.005	70	0.008	0.006	30
Orthopristis chrysoptera (pigfish)	0.052	0.018	65	0.020	0.007	61	0.001	0.001	30
Paralichthys albigutta (gulf flounder)	0.004	0.004	8			0			0
Paralichthys lethostigma (southern flounder)	0.013	0.007	45	0.033	0.007	85	0.023	0.010	33

TABLE 5.—(continued).

Taxon (common name)	Inner marsh			Oyster reef			SNB			Total		
	Mean	SE	Ct	Mean	SE	Ct	Mean	SE	Ct	Mean	SE	Ct
Leiostomus xanthurus (spot)	0.000	0.000	5	0.000	0.000	2	0.239	0.044	105	0.146	0.024	299
Lepisosteus oculatus (spotted gar)			0			0	0.002	0.002	14	0.001	0.001	44
Lepomis cyanellus (green sunfish)			0	0.173	0.173	2	0.000	0.000	9	0.020	0.018	20
Lucania parva (rainwater killifish)	0.018	0.009	11			0	0.013	0.009	57	0.444	0.101	203
Lutjanus griseus (gray snapper)	0.000	0.000	5			0	0.000	0.000	11	0.002	0.001	41
Membras martinica (rough silverside)	0.100	0.000	1			0	0.004	0.003	32	0.005	0.003	89
Menidia beryllina (inland silverside)	0.079	0.048	12	0.788	0.788	2	0.236	0.062	103	0.418	0.125	297
Menticirrhus americanus (southern kingfish)			0			0	0.061	0.036	5	0.030	0.020	10
Menticirrhus littoralis (gulf kingfish)	0.000	0.000	1			0	0.025	0.025	2	0.010	0.010	5
Microgobius gulosus (clown goby)			0			0	0.027	0.013	70	0.026	0.010	190
Microgobius thalassinus (green goby)	0.000	0.000	1			0	0.058	0.027	62	0.031	0.011	186
Micropogonias undulatus (Atlantic croaker)	0.000	0.000	7			0	0.092	0.022	91	0.052	0.010	269
Monacanthus hispidus (planehead filefish)			0			0	0.000	0.000	14	0.002	0.002	44
Mugil cephalus (striped mullet)	0.465	0.179	14	0.077	0.077	2	0.036	0.007	105	0.118	0.020	294
Mugil curema (white mullet)	0.100	0.000	1			0	0.018	0.018	11	0.033	0.013	33
Myrophis punctatus (speckled worm eel)	0.001	0.001	8	0.019	0.019	2	0.058	0.012	99	0.077	0.015	292
Oligoplites saurus (leatherjack)			0			0	0.010	0.008	24	0.008	0.004	55
Ophichthus gomesi (shrimp eel)			0			0	0.000	0.000	8	0.011	0.006	19
Ophidion welshi (crested cusk-eel)			0			0			0	0.013	0.013	8
Opsanus beta (gulf toadfish)			0	0.096	0.096	2	0.012	0.008	85	0.033	0.007	255
Orthopristis chrysoptera (pigfish)			0			0	0.006	0.003	75	0.022	0.006	231
Paralichthys albigutta (gulf flounder)			0			0			0	0.004	0.004	8
Paralichthys lethostigma (southern flounder)	0.000	0.000	6	0.000	0.000	2	0.023	0.004	92	0.024	0.003	263

TABLE 5.—(continued).

Taxon (common name)	SAV			SAME			MVME		
	Mean	SE	Ct	Mean	SE	Ct	Mean	SE	Ct
Poecilia latipinna (sailfin molly)	0.000	0.000	15	0.028	0.018	59	0.063	0.046	36
Pogonias cromis (black drum)	0.006	0.006	6	0.004	0.004	17	0.000	0.000	1
Pomatomus saltatrix (bluefish)			0	0.000	0.000	14			0
Pomoxis annularis (white crappie)	0.004	0.004	22	0.000	0.000	21	0.014	0.014	10
Prionotus tribulus (bighead searobin)	0.003	0.003	14	0.002	0.002	27	0.000	0.000	2
Sciaenops ocellatus (red drum)	0.096	0.054	56	0.026	0.006	82	0.010	0.006	34
Sphoeroides dorsalis (marbled puffer)			0	0.001	0.001	25			0
Sphoeroides parvus (least puffer)	0.000	0.000	30	0.009	0.004	50	0.006	0.004	32
Stellifer lanceolatus (star drum)	0.000	0.000	7	0.007	0.005	27	0.000	0.000	23
Strongylura marina (Atlantic needlefish)	0.009	0.009	23	0.021	0.010	25	0.009	0.007	27
Symphurus plagiusa (blackcheek tonguefish)	0.367	0.144	68	0.189	0.041	80	0.036	0.018	37
Syngnathus floridae (dusky pipefish)	0.007	0.005	27	0.013	0.012	33	0.003	0.002	27
Syngnathus louisianae (chain pipefish)	0.013	0.006	50	0.022	0.006	47	0.019	0.017	23
Syngnathus scovelli (gulf pipefish)	0.784	0.131	67	0.112	0.029	72	0.110	0.051	31
Syngnathus spp.	0.023	0.023	12			0			0
Synodus foetens (inshore lizardfish)	0.011	0.007	21	0.001	0.000	45	0.000	0.000	23
Trinectes maculatus (hogchoker)	0.000	0.000	7	0.000	0.000	13	0.000	0.000	3

Habitat of Fishery Species

Juvenile brown shrimp were most abundant during spring and summer, but they were also present in the fall. The mean size of brown shrimp was 28.4 mm TL (SE = 0.24), based on mean shrimp lengths in 2,858 Galveston Bay samples. Winter densities were very low, and the winter season was omitted in the analysis of distribution patterns. Brown shrimp habitat appeared to include all shallow estuarine areas examined (Table 7). This species was not recorded from oyster reefs, but only one mean value from summer (8 samples) was available for this biotope. Mean densities were highest in euhaline and polyhaline salinity regimes, but brown shrimp were also commonly found in fresher

areas of estuaries. Highest mean densities were in *Spartina alterniflora* marsh edge and submerged aquatic vegetation. Mean densities of around two animals per m^2 were also recorded for mixed-vegetation marsh edge and shallow nonvegetated bottom. Inner marsh was not used extensively by brown shrimp.

Juvenile white shrimp were most abundant in the summer and fall. The mean TL of white shrimp was 31.8 mm (SE = 0.42), based on 1,524 Galveston Bay samples. This species was also found in most intrahabitat areas examined (Table 8). However, white shrimp were concentrated in the polyhaline and mesohaline regions of the estuaries. By far, the highest mean density occurred in SAME habitat. Relatively high densities of white shrimp

TABLE 5.—(continued).

Taxon (common name)	Inner marsh			Oyster reef			SNB			Total		
	Mean	SE	Ct	Mean	SE	Ct	Mean	SE	Ct	Mean	SE	Ct
Poecilia latipinna (sailfin molly)	0.209	0.124	13			0	0.000	0.000	65	0.035	0.014	188
Pogonias cromis (black drum)	0.000	0.000	1			0	0.005	0.004	24	0.005	0.003	49
Pomatomus saltatrix (bluefish)			0			0	0.010	0.007	15	0.005	0.003	29
Pomoxis annularis (white crappie)			0			0	0.000	0.000	30	0.003	0.002	83
Prionotus tribulus (bighead searobin)	0.000	0.000	1	0.019	0.019	2	0.018	0.010	34	0.009	0.004	80
Sciaenops ocellatus (red drum)	0.000	0.000	10			0	0.029	0.007	92	0.038	0.012	274
Sphoeroides dorsalis (marbled puffer)			0			0	0.004	0.002	25	0.002	0.001	50
Sphoeroides parvus (least puffer)	0.000	0.000	2			0	0.025	0.008	66	0.012	0.003	180
Stellifer lanceolatus (star drum)			0			0	0.002	0.002	33	0.003	0.002	90
Strongylura marina (Atlantic needlefish)			0			0	0.000	0.000	35	0.009	0.003	110
Symphurus plagiusa (blackcheek tonguefish)	0.000	0.000	5	0.000	0.000	2	0.201	0.033	103	0.211	0.037	295
Syngnathus floridae (dusky pipefish)			0			0	0.001	0.001	44	0.006	0.003	131
Syngnathus louisianae (chain pipefish)			0			0	0.005	0.002	57	0.014	0.003	177
Syngnathus scovelli (gulf pipefish)	0.000	0.000	1	0.000	0.000	2	0.016	0.005	90	0.250	0.040	263
Syngnathus spp.			0			0			0	0.023	0.023	12
Synodus foetens (inshore lizardfish)			0			0	0.009	0.004	58	0.005	0.002	147
Trinectes maculatus (hogchoker)			0			0	0.003	0.002	16	0.001	0.001	39

were also collected in inner marsh, SNB, and MVME. Low mean densities were recorded for SAV, and no white shrimp were found on oyster reef.

Juvenile pink shrimp (mean TL = 19.8 mm, SE = 0.48, based on 442 Galveston Bay samples) were present mainly in the summer and fall, and this species was generally less abundant than either brown shrimp or white shrimp. Pink shrimp habitat also appeared to be more restricted than the other commercially important shrimps (Table 9). Densities were low in oligohaline areas, and no pink shrimp were found in inner marsh or on oyster reefs. Mean pink shrimp densities were highest in the polyhaline salinity regime and in SAV and marsh edge.

In recording data on the gulf stone crab, I assumed that all specimens in Texas and Louisiana were *Menippe adina*, although some crabs were reported as its congener *M. mercenaria* (the eastern Gulf species). Both juvenile and adult gulf stone crabs inhabit these estuaries, but juveniles were dominant in the samples. The mean carapace width (CW) was 26.7 mm (SE = 3.49), based on 40 Galveston Bay samples; the largest specimen was 88 mm CW. This species was found almost exclusively on oyster reefs (Table 4). The limited sampling in this biotope prevented an analysis of seasonality or an examination of distribution patterns in relation to salinity; samples

TABLE 6.—Dominant taxa collected in different estuarine habitat types. For each habitat type, the 10 most abundant decapod crustaceans and fishes are listed in rank order based on mean densities.

Rank	Submerged aquatic vegetation	Spartina alterniflora edge marsh	Mixed vegetation edge marsh	Inner marsh	Oyster reef	Shallow non-vegetated bottom
			Decapod Crustaceans			
1	Callinectes spp.	Palaemonetes pugio	Palaemonetes pugio	Uca spp.	Petrolisthes armatus	Callinectes spp.
2	Palaemonetes spp.	Palaemonetes spp.	Sesarma spp.	Palaemonetes pugio	Panopeus herbstii	Farfantepenaeus aztecus
3	Palaemonetes pugio	Farfantepenaeus aztecus	Callinectes sapidus	Sesarma spp.	Eurypanopeus depressus	Litopenaeus setiferus
4	Farfantepenaeus aztecus	Callinectes sapidus	Farfantepenaeus aztecus	Litopenaeus setiferus	Alpheus heterochaelis	Palaemonetes pugio
5	Palaemonetes intermedius	Callinectes spp.	Litopenaeus setiferus	Palaemonetes spp.	Menippe adina	Callinectes sapidus
6	Hippolyte zostericola	Litopenaeus setiferus	Uca spp.	Callinectes sapidus	Clibanarius vittatus	Palaemonetes spp.
7	Callinectes sapidus	Palaemonetes intermedius	Farfantepenaeus duorarum	Farfantepenaeus aztecus	Palaemonetes pugio	Acetes americanus
8	Palaemonetes vulgaris	Uca spp.	Palaemonetes intermedius	Palaemonetes intermedius	Callinectes sapidus	Rhithropanopeus harrisii
9	Dyspanopeus texana	Palaemonetes vulgaris	Dyspanopeus texana	Panopeus herbstii	Palaemonetes vulgaris	Farfantepenaeus duorarum
10	Tozeuma carolinense	Palaemonetes paludosus	Macrobrachium ohione	Clibanarius vittatus	Pagurus pollicaris	Callinectes similis
			Fishes			
1	Lagodon rhomboides	Gobiosoma bosc	Brevoortia patronus	Fundulus grandis	Anchoa mitchilli	Brevoortia patronus
2	Gobiosoma bosc	Lagodon rhomboides	Gobiosoma bosc	Adinia xenica	Gobiosoma bosc	Anchoa mitchilli
3	Gobiosoma robustum	Gobionellus boleosoma	Anchoa mitchilli	Cyprinodon variegatus	Gobiesox strumosus	Gobiosoma bosc
4	Gobionellus boleosoma	Brevoortia patronus	Cyprinodon variegatus	Mugil cephalus	Menidia beryllina	Leiostomus xanthurus
5	Brevoortia patronus	Menidia beryllina	Lucania parva	Poecilia latipinna	Pomatomus saltatrix	Menidia beryllina
6	Anchoa mitchilli	Lucania parva	Fundulus grandis	Fundulus pulvereus	Lepomis cyanellus	Symphurus plagiusa
7	Syngnathus scovelli	Fundulus grandis	Gambusia affinis	Brevoortia patronus	Lagodon rhomboides	Gobionellus boleosoma
8	Fundulus grandis	Anchoa mitchilli	Menidia beryllina	Mugil curema	Opsanus beta	Lagodon rhomboides
9	Lucania parva	Cynoscion nebulosus	Bairdiella chrysoura	Membras martinica	Chasmodes bosquianus	Micropogonias undulatus
10	Symphurus plagiusa	Cyprinodon variegatus	Fundulus pulvereus	Elops saurus	Mugil cephalus	Elops saurus

on oyster reefs were available only in summer and winter in the polyhaline salinity regime of Galveston Bay. Densities presented here may be underestimated due to inadequate sampling; Valentine et al. (1994) reported that stone crabs found near edges of sea grass beds burrowed as deep as 1.25 m into the substrate.

Blue crabs also inhabit estuaries as juveniles and adults. Although specimens as large as 128 mm CW were collected, most blue crabs were small juveniles (mean CW = 16.3 mm, SE = 0.30, based on 1,432 Galveston Bay samples). These juveniles were present in every estuarine area sampled (Table 10); they were most abundant in fall but were found throughout the year. Mean densities of blue crabs were lowest in the euhaline salinity regime (mainly SAV habitat of South Texas). The highest mean densities were found in polyhaline and mesohaline SAV and SAME. Mixed-vegetation marsh edge also appeared to support relatively high densities of this species, while inner marsh, SNB, and oyster reefs had relatively low mean densities.

TABLE 7.—Density (per m²) of brown shrimp *Farfantepenaeus aztecus* in different intrahabitat areas characterized by habitat type and salinity regime. The mean densities and standard errors (SE) were calculated using means in the database as the observations. The count represents the number of means in each calculation. Only data from spring, summer, and fall are included.

Habitat type	Statistic	Salinity regime				
		Euhaline	Polyhaline	Mesohaline	Oligohaline	Total
Submerged aquatic	Mean	5.68	11.03	5.71	0.08	7.20
vegetation	SE	0.96	1.94	2.93	0.08	1.02
	Count	20	21	5	6	52
Spartina alterniflora	Mean	8.56	10.44	4.02	3.43	8.31
marsh edge	SE	0.00	0.94	0.79	1.43	0.74
	Count	1	62	24	6	93
Mixed vegetation	Mean		3.94	3.42	1.45	2.60
marsh edge	SE		2.25	1.10	0.35	0.57
	Count	0	5	17	18	40
Inner marsh	Mean		2.00	0.21		0.49
	SE		1.40	0.09		0.26
	Count	0	2	11	0	13
Oyster reef	Mean		0.00			0.00
	SE		0.00			0.00
	Count	0	1	0	0	1
Shallow nonvegetated	Mean		2.50	1.34	0.83	1.99
bottom	SE		0.28	0.27	0.33	0.20
	Count	0	62	23	14	99
All habitats	Mean	5.82	6.91	2.70	1.33	4.88
	SE	0.92	0.58	0.42	0.29	0.35
	Count	21	153	80	44	298

Juvenile red drum (mean TL = 51.3 mm, SE = 7.67, based on 133 Galveston Bay samples) were abundant in the fall and also present in winter samples. This species was mainly found in polyhaline and euhaline salinity regimes (Table 11). By far, the highest mean density of red drum was found in polyhaline SAV. In contrast, no red drum were found in mesohaline or oligohaline SAV. Moderate densities were recorded in polyhaline SAME and SNB. Red drum were absent on oyster reefs and rare in inner marsh or MVME.

Gray snapper were rare in the estuarine areas examined; only four juveniles were recorded from the Galveston Bay and Terrebonne and Timbalier Bay systems. The overall mean density from Table 5 was around 16 fish per ha, but if you assumed that whenever gray snapper were not reported in a study the densities were zero (i.e., all fish specimens collected in the various studies were correctly identified and reported), this density would be around 2 fish per ha. Gray snapper were only recorded from polyhaline SAV and mesohaline SAME.

Bluefish were also rare; only five juveniles were collected from Galveston Bay, all on SNB. The overall mean density for this species in Table 5 was

around 50 fish per ha, but again, if you recorded a density of zero whenever this species was not reported in a study, the mean density would be considerably lower (around 4 fish per ha). Zimmerman et al. (1989) reported a density of 0.42 bluefish per m² on oyster reefs, but this value was in error; I reviewed the original data analyzed in the study and found no record of this species in the samples.

Juvenile spotted seatrout were found in all estuaries sampled and were commonly collected in summer and fall. The mean TL for this species was 48.7 mm (SE = 1.75), based on 265 Galveston Bay samples; the largest specimen collected in these samples was 145 mm TL. Spotted seatrout were concentrated in the high-salinity regions (Table 12). The highest mean density occurred in SAME followed by SAV. There was also a high mean density in MVME when it occurred in the polyhaline salinity regime. Juvenile spotted seatrout were not found on oyster reefs and were rare in inner marsh and in all oligohaline areas.

Most southern flounder were found in the spring and summer, but the species was present in estuarine habitats throughout the year. The mean TL of southern flounder was 127.2 mm (SE = 9.06), based

TABLE 8.—Density (per m^2) of white shrimp *Litopenaeus setiferus* in different intrahabitat areas characterized by habitat type and salinity regime. The mean densities and standard errors (SE) were calculated using means in the database as the observations.The count represents the number of means in each calculation. Only data from summer and fall are included.

Habitat type	Statistic	Salinity regime				Total
		Euhaline	Polyhaline	Mesohaline	Oligohaline	
Submerged aquatic	Mean	0.30	1.51	0.36	0.12	0.80
vegetation	SE	0.07	0.37	0.33	0.12	0.19
	Count	15	17	4	4	40
Spartina alterniflora	Mean		10.31	8.66	1.22	9.41
marsh edge	SE		1.77	4.02	0.61	1.60
	Count	0	39	14	3	56
Mixed vegetation	Mean		5.00	2.04	0.34	1.60
marsh edge	SE		3.82	0.94	0.16	0.61
	Count	0	3	11	12	26
Inner marsh	Mean		9.90	1.33		2.40
	SE		0.00	0.77		1.26
	Count	0	1	7	0	8
Oyster reef	Mean		0.00			0.00
	SE		0.00			0.00
	Count	0	1	0	0	1
Shallow nonvegetated	Mean		2.23	2.05	0.13	1.91
bottom	SE		0.54	0.52	0.07	0.38
	Count	0	43	15	9	67
All habitats	Mean	0.30	5.27	3.63	0.34	3.78
	SE	0.07	0.81	1.19	0.11	0.54
	Count	15	104	51	28	198

on 90 Galveston Bay samples, and the largest specimen was 395 mm TL. Southern flounder were collected in samples from 7 of the 10 estuaries in the database. The highest mean density of this species was in SAME followed by MVME, SNB, and SAV (Table 13). No southern flounder were recorded from inner marsh or oyster reef.

Sand seatrout (mean TL = 39.9 mm, SE = 3.08, based on 34 Galveston Bay samples) were found only in Galveston and Lavaca Bays, in polyhaline and mesohaline salinity regimes, and during spring, summer, and fall. The highest mean density was in SAV, and the mean density was also relatively high on SNB (Table 5).

Discussion

The essential fish habitat requirements of the Magnuson-Stevens Act represent a recognition of the importance of habitats to fishery resources, provide an opportunity to enhance protection for fish habitats, and promote awareness of the role habitat characteristics play in fishery ecology. However,

accurately delineating the habitat of a fishery species (or a particular life stage) requires a detailed and comprehensive assessment of where these animals live. In addition, the linkages between habitats and fishery production are complex, and the identification of intrahabitat areas as EFH is likely to be complicated.

In developing guidelines for identifying EFH, the National Marine Fisheries Service considered different levels of information available on interactions between habitats and fishery species (62 FR 66531) (NMFS 1997). The most basic information is presence and absence or frequency-of-occurrence data on the distribution of a fishery species. These data can be used to define the geographic range of a species; they also can be used to delineate the habitat of a species (where it lives) if sampling effort is adequate. However, a more informative examination of habitat-use patterns requires the measurement of relative densities in different intrahabitat areas. In addition, the only way to make legitimate comparisons among different biotopes and across different studies using different gear types is to measure actual densities of fishery species. In this pa-

TABLE 9.—Density (per m²) of pink shrimp *Farfantepenaeus duorarum* in different intrahabitat areas characterized by habitat type and salinity regime. The mean densities and standard errors (SE) were calculated using means in the database as the observations. The count represents the number of means in each calculation. Only data from summer and fall are included.

Habitat type	Statistic	Salinity regime			Total
		Polyhaline	Mesohaline	Oligohaline	
Submerged aquatic vegetation	Mean	3.55	0.22	0.10	2.12
	SE	1.76	0.22	0.10	1.08
	Count	11	4	4	19
Spartina alterniflora marsh edge	Mean	1.78	2.02	0.54	1.73
	SE	0.40	1.24	0.37	0.38
	Count	31	8	3	42
Mixed vegetation marsh edge	Mean	2.37	1.06	0.16	0.74
	SE	2.37	1.00	0.11	0.43
	Count	3	6	12	21
Inner marsh	Mean	0.00			0.00
	SE	0.00			0.00
	Count	1	0	0	1
Oyster reef	Mean	0.00			0.00
	SE	0.00			0.00
	Count	1	0	0	1
Shallow nonvegetated bottom	Mean	0.24	0.17	0.01	0.19
	SE	0.07	0.08	0.01	0.04
	Count	33	11	9	53
All habitats	Mean	1.36	0.87	0.15	1.01
	SE	0.32	0.41	0.07	0.21
	Count	80	29	28	137

per, I examined density patterns in shallow-water estuarine systems of Texas and Louisiana using available data collected with quantitative enclosure sampling devices. Enclosure samplers, which include throw traps, drop samplers, lift nets, and flume weirs, have high and relatively stable catch efficiencies and provide comparable density estimates for small nekton in different estuarine biotopes (Kneib 1997; Rozas and Minello 1997).

Historically, otter trawls commonly have been used for monitoring populations of fishery species in estuaries because of their relative ease of use, large areas swept, and clean samples. The data collected with trawls, however, are generally inappropriate for comparing densities among estuarine biotopes and conducting a detailed examination of habitat-use patterns. Trawls and other towed nets have low and variable catch efficiency. This efficiency varies in relation to the species and size of target animals (Kjelson and Johnson 1978; Lyons 1986; Hartman and Herke 1987; Parsley et al. 1989; Allen et al. 1992; Millar 1992) and the method of rigging, mesh size, noise of boat, towing speed and direction, tow duration, and method of net

retrieval (Kashkin and Parin 1983; Thayer et al. 1983; Carothers and Chittenden 1985; Creutzberg et al. 1987; DeAlteris et al. 1989; Millar 1992; Engas 1994; Workman et al. 1995).

Catch efficiency of towed nets varies with many habitat characteristics including:

- presence of vegetation (Miller et al. 1980; Howard and Lowe 1984; Gray and Bell 1986; Leber and Greening 1986; Orth and van Montfrans 1987);
- light (Glass and Wardle 1989; Engas 1994; Michalsen et al. 1996);
- turbidity (Nielsen 1983);
- temperature (Allen et al. 1992);
- water depth (Rogers 1985; Hartman and Herke 1987; Bishop and Khan 1991; Loneragan et al. 1995); and
- substrate type (Krieger 1993).

For species that burrow in the substrate such as penaeid shrimps and some crabs, catch efficiency of towed nets will vary with all of the environmental factors that affect burrowing. Burrowing behavior of penaeids has been shown to be affected by:

TABLE 10.—Density (per m²) of blue crab *Callinectes sapidus* in different intrahabitat areas characterized by habitat type and salinity regime. The mean densities and standard errors (SE) were calculated using means in the database as the observations. The count represents the number of means in each calculation. Data from all seasons are included.

| Habitat type | Statistic | Salinity regime | | | | Total |
		Euhaline	Polyhaline	Mesohaline	Oligohaline	
Submerged aquatic	Mean	0.76	13.04	5.58	1.60	5.05
vegetation	SE	0.17	2.89	3.67	0.92	1.16
	Count	35	21	5	6	67
Spartina alterniflora	Mean	1.63	6.08	7.20	4.79	6.24
marsh edge	SE	0.00	0.51	2.58	2.81	0.75
	Count	1	68	25	6	100
Mixed vegetation	Mean		3.23	1.94	3.27	2.70
marsh edge	SE		2.10	0.91	1.72	0.89
	Count	0	5	17	18	40
Inner marsh	Mean		1.15	0.42		0.53
	SE		0.45	0.10		0.12
	Count	0	2	12	0	14
Oyster reef	Mean		0.23			0.23
	SE		0.08			0.08
	Count	0	2	0	0	2
Shallow nonvegetated	Mean		0.96	0.90	0.61	0.90
bottom	SE		0.09	0.36	0.22	0.10
	Count	0	72	23	14	109
All habitats	Mean	0.79	4.56	3.25	2.40	3.54
	SE	0.17	0.51	0.89	0.82	0.36
	Count	36	170	82	44	332

- shrimp size (Dall 1958; Hughes 1968; Kurata 1981; Kenyon et al. 1995; Primavera and Lebata 1995; Liu and Loneragan 1997);
- light (Fuss and Ogren 1966; Wickham and Minkler 1975; Bishop and Herrnkind 1976);
- moon phase (Fuss and Ogren 1966; Bishop and Herrnkind 1976);
- food availability (Dall 1958);
- dissolved oxygen (Egusa and Yamamoto 1961);
- presence of predators (Fuss and Ogren 1966);
- pressure and water depth (Hughes 1966; Wickham 1967; Vance 1992);
- salinity (Lakshmi et al. 1976);
- temperature (Fuss and Ogren 1966; Aldrich et al. 1968; Hill 1985);
- sea grass type (Kenyon et al. 1995);
- substrate type (Williams 1958; Moller and Jones 1975; Aziz and Greenwood 1982);
- weather (Fuss and Ogren 1966);
- molting (Wassenberg and Hill 1984);
- endogenous rhythms (Wickham 1967; Hughes 1968, 1969; Bishop and Herrnkind 1976); and
- ammonia concentrations (Allan and Maguire 1995).

Unless one compensates for changing gear efficiency with habitat characteristics, one can never be sure whether differences in catch are due to density patterns of a target species or to gear selectivity.

The database developed for analysis in this study combines information from 22 research projects on animal densities in estuaries of Texas and Louisiana. This type of meta-analysis can provide valuable insights into patterns of species distribution, but by necessity the analysis is general in nature. To some degree, the results are dependent upon the distribution of samples in relation to intrahabitat areas. Although a large number (5,149) of enclosure samples were included in the database, patterns of animal densities and habitat use can be influenced by the distribution of samples among estuaries, salinity regimes, seasons, and habitat types. I tried to take these sampling patterns into consideration when reporting and interpreting the data.

Perhaps the most striking pattern apparent in the data was the high density of decapod crustaceans in relation to fishes. The highest overall mean density for all species was for daggerblade grass shrimp

TABLE 11.—Density (per m^2) of red drum *Sciaenops ocellatus* in different intrahabitat areas characterized by habitat type and salinity regime. The mean densities and standard errors (SE) were calculated using means in the database as the observations. The count represents the number of means in each calculation. Only data from fall and winter are included.

| Habitat type | Statistic | Salinity regime | | | | Total |
		Euhaline	Polyhaline	Mesohaline	Oligohaline	
Submerged aquatic	Mean	0.096	0.457	0.000	0.000	0.213
vegetation	SE	0.062	0.281	0.000	0.000	0.118
	Count	8	10	4	3	25
Spartina alterniflora	Mean		0.057	0.010	0.032	0.043
marsh edge	SE		0.018	0.007	0.032	0.013
	Count	0	25	10	3	38
Mixed vegetation	Mean		0.000	0.000	0.012	0.006
marsh edge	SE		0.000	0.000	0.012	0.006
	Count	0	2	5	8	15
Inner marsh	Mean			< 0.001		< 0.001
	SE			< 0.001		< 0.001
	Count	0	0	3	0	3
Oyster reef	Mean		0.00			0.00
	SE		0.000			0.000
	Count	0	1	0	0	1
Shallow nonvegetated	Mean		0.067	0.030	0.000	0.049
bottom	SE		0.020	0.024	0.000	0.014
	Count	0	28	8	7	43
All habitats	Mean	0.096	0.120	0.011	0.009	0.073
	SE	0.062	0.046	0.007	0.006	0.025
	Count	8	66	30	21	125

Palaemonetes pugio at 23.6 organisms per m^2; the mean density for this species in *Spartina alterniflora* marsh edge was 58.8 organisms per m^2. For fishery species (not all under federal management plans), overall mean densities per m^2 were 4.61 for brown shrimp, 3.54 for blue crab, 3.14 for gulf menhaden, 2.37 for white shrimp, 0.67 for pink shrimp, 0.15 for spot, 0.10 for spotted seatrout, 0.04 for red drum, 0.02 for gulf stone crab, and 0.02 for southern flounder. Bluefish and gray snapper (<0.01 per m^2) were reported in relatively few studies, and their actual overall densities would be considerably lower than those reported in this analysis if the fish were recorded as having zero densities (as is likely) in the other studies examined.

On the basis of mean densities in the six habitat types examined, *Spartina alterniflora* marsh edge was used most by brown shrimp, white shrimp, blue crab, spotted seatrout, and southern flounder. Pink shrimp, red drum, and sand seatrout were most abundant in submerged aquatic vegetation. Stone crab had highest mean densities on oyster reef and gulf menhaden on shallow nonvegetated bottom. Each of the six habitat types examined in my analysis

ranked first or second in use by at least one fishery species (Tables 4 and 5). The data indicate, therefore, that all estuarine areas examined are likely to be essential for some fishery species.

Few other studies in Gulf of Mexico estuaries provide nekton density comparisons for two or more of the habitat types examined in my analysis. Baltz et al. (1993) showed that marsh edge was used extensively by estuarine fishes in the Barataria Bay system of Louisiana; the 15 most abundant species sampled in their study (including red drum, gulf menhaden, spot, and spotted seatrout) were concentrated at the marsh–water ecotone. In Alabama, Williams et al. (1990) reported that blue crab densities were significantly higher in sea grass than on nonvegetated bottom. Sheridan (1992) compared nekton densities among sea grass, nonvegetated bottom, and mangrove prop roots in Rookery Bay, Florida. Sheridan et al. (in press) compared sea grass and nonvegetated bottom in Florida Bay; densities of pink shrimp and blue crab were highest in sea grass. In Florida, Valentine et al. (1994) reported stone crab densities to be highest at the edge of sea grass beds (0.8–6.0 crabs per m^2).

TABLE 12.—Density (per m^2) of spotted seatrout *Cynoscion nebulosus* in different intrahabitat areas characterized by habitat type and salinity regime. The mean densities and standard errors (SE) were calculated using means in the database as the observations. The count represents the number of means in each calculation. Only data from summer and fall are included.

Habitat type	Statistic	Salinity regime				
		Euhaline	Polyhaline	Mesohaline	Oligohaline	Total
Submerged aquatic	Mean	0.113	0.240	0.144	0.000	0.160
vegetation	SE	0.180	0.050	0.083	0.000	0.033
	Count	9	14	4	4	31
Spartina alterniflora	Mean		0.415	0.181	0.000	0.333
marsh edge	SE		0.045	0.059	0.000	0.038
	Count	0	36	13	3	52
Mixed vegetation	Mean		0.288	0.040	0.000	0.051
marsh edge	SE		0.167	0.020	0.000	0.026
	Count	0	3	10	12	25
Inner marsh	Mean		0.100	0.003		0.017
	SE		0.000	0.003		0.014
	Count	0	1	6	0	7
Oyster Reef	Mean		0.00			0.00
	SE		0.000			0.000
	Count	0	1	0	0	1
Shallow nonvegetated	Mean		0.059	0.023	0.024	0.046
bottom	SE		0.009	0.015	0.014	0.007
	Count	0	40	13	9	62
All habitats	Mean	0.113	0.227	0.079	0.008	0.149
	SE	0.180	0.025	0.021	0.005	0.016
	Count	9	95	46	28	178

Density patterns provide information on the intrahabitat areas used most extensively by a fishery species, but determining whether a habitat is essential for a species is more difficult. If intrahabitat areas are ranked on the basis of nekton density, there is no strong basis for deciding where to draw the line between essential and nonessential areas. However, intrahabitat areas with the highest densities are most likely to be essential for that species. An argument can be made that the entire habitat of a species is essential. This contention is supported if intrahabitat areas are essential not only for sustaining production of a fishery on the species but also for supporting the ecological contribution of the species to marine ecosystems. However, identifying every place where a species lives as EFH is not likely to enhance our ability to protect specific intrahabitat areas that are most essential in maintaining fishery productivity. Therefore, to help provide additional focus to conservation efforts, the interim final rule to implement the EFH policy also recognizes that some EFH may be identified as habitat areas of particular concern (HAPC) (NMFS 1997). These HAPC would be particularly important to the long-term productivity of a fishery species, or they would be particularly vulnerable to degradation.

In shallow estuarine areas of Texas and Louisiana, brown shrimp were concentrated in SAV and SAME (Table 7), and these intrahabitat areas are likely to be an HAPC for this species. White shrimp densities were high in most marsh habitats and nearby SNB (Table 8); thus, the entire marsh biotope appeared to be an HAPC for this species. For red drum, SAV in high-salinity areas of the bays might be HAPC, but the data available for determining habitat-use patterns for this species are still inconclusive (Table 11). For other managed fishery species that use estuarine nurseries in the Gulf of Mexico such as pink shrimp, bluefish, stone crab, and gray snapper, the data available for my analysis of habitat-use patterns are probably insufficient to make decisions on HAPC. In part, the inadequacy of available data are due to low densities caused by the geographic range of these species being centered in other areas. Data analyses from other Gulf estuaries may improve the database in this regard. For example,

TABLE 13.—Density (per m^2) of southern flounder *Paralichthys lethostigma* in different intrahabitat areas characterized by habitat type and salinity regime. The mean densities and standard errors (SE) were calculated using means in the database as the observations. The count represents the number of means in each calculation. Data from all seasons are included.

Habitat type	Statistic	Salinity regime				Total
		Euhaline	Polyhaline	Mesohaline	Oligohaline	
Submerged aquatic	Mean	0.015	0.018	0.000	0.000	0.013
vegetation	SE	0.014	0.010	0.000	0.000	0.007
	Count	18	16	5	6	45
Spartina alterniflora	Mean		0.028	0.055	0.000	0.033
marsh edge	SE		0.005	0.027	0.000	0.007
	Count	0	59	20	6	85
Mixed vegetation	Mean		0.048	0.023	0.017	0.023
marsh edge	SE		0.048	0.018	0.010	0.010
	Count	0	4	11	18	33
Inner marsh	Mean		0.000	0.000		0.000
	SE		0.000	0.000		0.000
	Count	0	1	5	0	6
Oyster reef	Mean		0.000			0.000
	SE		0.000			0.000
	Count	0	2	0	0	2
Shallow nonvegetated	Mean		0.027	0.023	0.005	0.023
bottom	SE		0.005	0.007	0.004	0.004
	Count	0	59	19	14	92
All habitats	Mean	0.015	0.027	0.030	0.009	0.024
	SE	0.014	0.003	0.010	0.005	0.003
	Count	18	141	60	44	263

gag *Mycteroperca microlepis* were not reported in any of the studies included in my analysis, but Koenig and Coleman (1998) measured densities between 0.042 and 0.055 fish per m^2 in sea grass beds of St. George Sound, Florida.

For many reasons, the delineation of habitat and the identification of essential intrahabitat areas should not be based solely on the density data in this analysis. All estuarine areas available to fishery species in Texas and Louisiana have not been adequately sampled. For example, few quantitative density estimates are available for deep (>1 m water depth) areas of these bays, although Hellier (1958), Jones et al. (1963), and Jones (1965) used large enclosure samplers to estimate fish biomass in Corpus Christi Bay. Tidal freshwater regions of these estuaries also have been infrequently sampled, although Castellanos (1997) documented extensive use of these habitats by blue crabs *Callinectes sapidus* in the Atchafalaya River Delta of Louisiana. The data included in my analysis on use of oyster reefs (Zimmerman et al. 1989) were limited in scope and probably do not adequately reflect the value of this biotope to managed fishery species. On the South At-

lantic coast of the United States, brown shrimp, white shrimp, pink shrimp, blue crab, red drum, gray snapper, bluefish, and gag have all have been found on oyster reefs (Wenner et al. 1996; Coen et al. 1999, this volume). In Gulf of Mexico estuaries outside Texas and Louisiana, other biotopes may be important for fishery species. For example, mangroves (Thayer et al. 1987; Sheridan 1992; Mullin 1995; Thayer and Sheridan, in press); calcium carbonate rock (Beck 1995); macroalgae beds (Herrnkind and Butler 1994); and sponge communities (Herrnkind et al. 1995) may be highly utilized in Florida estuaries.

Densities of fishery species are often centered in community habitats or biotopes, but there can be substantial variability within biotopes. In the salt marsh, for example, both the distance to the marsh–water interface and the extent of tidal inundation affect nekton density patterns (Rozas and Reed 1993; Minello et al. 1994; Peterson and Turner 1994; Minello and Webb 1997). McIvor and Rozas (1996) summarized patterns of salt-marsh use by nekton and discussed factors affecting this use. In sea grass beds, wave energy has been shown to affect use by pink shrimp (Murphey and Fonseca 1995), and the amount of edge affects use by red drum (Holt et al. 1983). Rooker (1997) and Sheridan et al. (in press) showed that nekton had different densities in *Halodule wrightii* sea grass beds compared with *Thalassia testudinum*, but Fonseca et al. (1996) found few differences in nekton densities among three species of sea grasses in Tampa Bay. Regional differences in habitat use also exist, and salt marshes of the southeastern United States appear to support much lower nekton densities than marshes on the Gulf coast (Rozas 1993; Wenner and Beatty 1993; Kneib 1997). Heck and Coen (1995) also reported regional differences in predation intensity in sea grass habitats. These patterns need to be examined with a directed sampling program.

Tidal flooding patterns also complicate the measurement of density and the identification of EFH in estuaries. The marsh surface is intertidal and only available for a portion of each tidal cycle. Densities measured in my analysis were almost all conducted at high tide when all habitat types were available for exploitation. However, fishery species using intertidal marsh at high tide must retreat into adjacent subtidal areas at low tide. In the northern Gulf of Mexico, astronomical tides are small, and meteorological events often control tidal flooding. Many salt marshes in this re-

gion are subsiding, and the marsh surface is flooded for extensive periods throughout the year (Rozas and Reed 1993). Over a 1-year period in Galveston Bay (1990–1991), the marsh edge was flooded 78.1% of the time, and inner marsh was flooded 66.3% of the time (Minello and Webb 1997). A seasonal pattern in tidal flooding is also apparent with the highest flooding durations during the spring and fall (Figure 2).

Although density patterns provide insights into the value of intrahabitat areas for fishery species, the determination of EFH probably should not be based on these distribution data alone. Information on functional relationships between habitats and fishery species is required to more accurately assess habitat value, and data on survival, growth, and reproductive success in different intrahabitat areas should be used to assess EFH. A limited amount of these data are available for federally managed fishery species that use estuaries of the northern Gulf of Mexico. Stone crabs have an affinity for structured habitats, and Beck (1995, 1997) showed that structure and shelter increased growth, survival, and fecundity for this species. Both brown shrimp and white shrimp have high densities in vegetated areas, but only brown shrimp exhibited increased growth within salt marsh vegetation compared with shallow nonvegetated bottom; white shrimp growth was

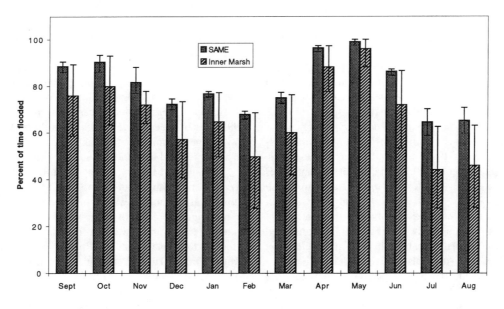

FIGURE 2.—Seasonal pattern of tidal inundation at *Spartina alterniflora* marsh edge (SAME) and inner marsh habitat types in lower Galveston Bay, Texas. Bar heights represent the mean percentage of time during each month that the habitat types were flooded in 1990–1991. Vertical lines through bars show the range for the five marshes examined. Adapted from Minello and Webb (1997).

similar between these intrahabitat areas (Minello and Zimmerman 1991). Vegetative structure also appears to reduce fish predation on juvenile brown shrimp (Minello and Zimmerman 1983; Minello et al. 1989), and survival time for tethered brown shrimp was higher in SAV and SAME compared with nonvegetated sand bottom (Minello 1993). Growth of red drum appears similar between sea grass and sand bottom (Nadeau 1991; Rooker et al. 1997), while survival of juvenile red drum was higher in SAV compared with nonvegetated bottom (Rooker et al. 1998). In estuaries of southern Florida, the structure of algae, sea grasses, and sponges has been shown to increase survival of juvenile Caribbean spiny lobsters *Panulirus argus* (Herrnkind and Butler 1986; Childress and Herrnkind 1994; Butler et al. 1995; Herrnkind et al. 1997). Similar comparative studies are needed for other habitats and other managed fishery species. Ideally, these kinds of data will be synthesized to determine relationships between productivity and the different intrahabitat areas used by fishery species.

Acknowledgments

I would like to thank Pete Sheridan, Lawrence Rozas, Ken Heck, and Roger Zimmerman for providing access to published and unpublished data sets. John Boyd helped with construction of the database, and Phil Caldwell made Figure 1. Lawrence Rozas, Donald Baltz, and two anonymous reviewers provided valuable suggestions that substantially improved the manuscript. Funding was provided by the National Oceanic and Atmospheric Administration Damage Assessment Center and the Southeast Fisheries Science Center of the National Marine Fisheries Service. This research was conducted through the Fishery Ecology Branch of the National Marine Fisheries Service Southeast Fisheries Science Center Galveston Laboratory; the assistance of everyone in the Branch was essential for the successful completion of the project.

References

Aldrich, D. V., C. E. Wood, and K. N. Baxter. 1968. An ecological interpretation of low temperature responses in *Penaeus aztecus* and *P. setiferus* postlarvae. Bulletin of Marine Science 18:61–71.

Allan, G. L., and G. B. Maguire. 1995. Effect of sediment on growth and acute ammonia toxicity for the school prawn, *Metapenaeus macleayi* (Haswell). Aquaculture 131:59–71.

Allen, D., S. Service, and M. Ogburn-Matthews. 1992. Factors influencing the collection efficiency of estuarine fishes. Transactions of the American Fisheries Society 121:234–244.

Aziz, K. A., and J. G. Greenwood. 1982. Response of juvenile *Metapenaeus bennettae* Racek & Dall, 1965 (Decapoda, Penaeidae) to sediments of differing particle size. Crustaceana 43:121–126.

Baltz, D. M. 1990. Autecology. Pages 585–607 in C. B. Schreck and P. B. Moyle, editors. Methods for fish biology. American Fisheries Society, Bethesda, Maryland.

Baltz, D. M., C. Rakocinski, and J. W. Fleeger. 1993. Microhabitat use by marsh-edge fishes in a Louisiana estuary. Environmental Biology of Fishes 36:109–126.

Beck, M. W. 1995. Size-specific shelter limitation in stone crabs: a test of the demographic bottleneck hypothesis. Ecology 76:968–980.

Beck, M. W. 1997. A test of the generality of the effects of shelter bottlenecks in four stone crab populations. Ecology 78:2487–2503.

Bishop, J. M., and W. F. Herrnkind. 1976. Burying and molting of pink shrimp, *Penaeus duorarum* (Crustacea: Penaeidae), under selected photoperiods of white light and U.V. light. Biological Bulletin 150:163–182.

Bishop, J. M., and M. H. Khan. 1991. Depth as a factor in abundance and size of juvenile penaeid shrimps in the absence of estuaries and marshes. Marine Biology 109:103–114.

Butler, M. J., and eight coauthors. 1995. Cascading disturbances in Florida bay, USA: cyanobacteria blooms, sponge mortality, and implications for juvenile spiny lobsters *Panulirus argus*. Marine Ecology Progress Series 129:119–125.

Carothers, P. E., and M. E. Chittenden. 1985. Relationships between trawl catch and tow duration for penaeid shrimp. Transactions of the American Fisheries Society 114:851–856.

Castellanos, D. L. 1997. Nekton use of submerged aquatic vegetation, marsh, and shallow unvegetated bottom in a Louisiana tidal freshwater ecosystem. Master's thesis. University of Southwestern Louisiana, Lafayette.

Childress, M. J., and W. F. Herrnkind. 1994. The behavior of juvenile Caribbean spiny lobster in Florida Bay: seasonality, ontogeny and sociality. Bulletin of Marine Science 54:819–827.

Coen, L. D., M. W. Luckenbach, and D. L. Breitburg. 1999. The role of oyster reefs as essential fish habitat: a review of current knowledge and some new perspectives. Pages 438–454 in L. R. Benaka, editor. Fish habitat: essential fish habitat, and rehabilitation. American Fisheries Society, Symposium 22, Bethesda, Maryland.

Creutzberg, F., G. C. Duineveld, and G. J. van Noort. 1987. The effect of different numbers of tickler chains on beam-trawl catches. Journal du Conseil. Conseil International pour l'Exploration de la Mer 43:159–168.

Czapla, T. E. 1991. Diets and prey selection of pinfish and southern flounder in a *Halodule wrightii* seagrass meadow. Doctoral dissertation. Texas A&M University, College Station.

Dall, W. 1958. Observations on the biology of the greentail prawn, *Metapenaeus mastersii* (Haswell) (Crustacea Decapoda: Penaeidae). Australian Journal of Marine and Freshwater Research 9:111–134.

Day, R. W., and G. P. Quinn. 1989. Comparisons of treatments after an analysis of variance in ecology. Ecological Monographs 59:433–463.

DeAlteris, J. T., C. W. Recksiek, A. Fahfouhi, and L. Xu. 1989. Comparison of the performance of two bottom-sampling trawls. Transactions of the American Fisheries Society 118:119–130.

Deegan, L. A., and B. A. Thompson. 1985. The ecology of fish communities in the Mississippi River deltaic plain. Pages 35–56 *in* A. Yanez-Arancibia, editor. Fish community ecology in estuaries and coastal lagoons: towards an ecosystem integration. UNAM Press, Mexico City.

Egusa, S., and T. Yamamoto. 1961. Studies on the respiration of the "Kuruma" prawn *Penaeus japonicus* Bate I. burrowing behavior, with special reference to environmental oxygen concentration. Bulletin of the Japanese Society of Scientific Fisheries 27:22–26.

Engas, A. 1994. The effects of trawl performance and fish behaviour on the catching efficiency of demersal sampling trawls. Pages 45–68 *in* A. Ferno and S. Olsen, editors. Marine fish behavior in capture and abundance estimation. Fishing News Books, Farnham, UK.

Fonseca, M. S., D. L. Meyer, and M. O. Hall. 1996. Development of planted seagrass beds in Tampa Bay, Florida, USA. 2. faunal components. Marine Ecology Progress Series 132:141–156.

Fuss, C. M., and L. H. Ogren. 1966. Factors affecting activity and burrowing habits of the pink shrimp, *Penaeus duorarum* Burkenroad. Biological Bulletin 130:170–191.

Glass, C. W., and C. S. Wardle. 1989. Comparison of the reactions of fish to a trawl gear at high and low light intensities. Fisheries Research 7:249–266.

Gray, C. A., and J. D. Bell. 1986. Consequences of two common techniques for sampling vagile macrofauna associated with the seagrass *Zostera capricorni*. Marine Ecology Progress Series 28:43–48.

Gunter, G. 1941. Death of fishes due to cold on the Texas coast, January, 1940. Ecology 22:203–208.

Gunter, G. 1961. Habitat of juvenile shrimp (family: Penaeidae). Ecology 42:589–600.

Hartman, R. D., and W. H. Herke. 1987. Relative selectivity of five coastal marsh sampling gears. Contributions in Marine Science 30:17–26.

Heck, K. L., and L. D. Coen. 1995. Predation and the abundance of juvenile blue crabs: a comparison of selected East and Gulf Coast (USA) studies. Bulletin of Marine Science 57:877–883.

Hellier, T. R., Jr. 1958. The drop-net quadrat, a new population sampling device. Publications of the Institute of Marine Science, University of Texas 5:165–168.

Herrnkind, W. F., and M. J. Butler. 1986. Factors regulating postlarval settlement and juvenile microhabitat use by spiny lobsters *Panulirus argus*. Marine Ecology Progress Series. 34(1-2):23–30.

Herrnkind, W. F., and M. J. Butler. 1994. Settlement of spiny lobster, *Panulirus argus* (Latreille, 1804) in Florida–pattern without predictability. Crustaceana 67:46–64.

Herrnkind, W. F., M. J. Butler, and J. H. Hunt. 1997. Can artificial habitats that mimic natural structures enhance recruitment of Caribbean spiny lobster? Fisheries 22(4):24–27.

Hildebrand, H. H., and G. Gunter. 1953. Correlation of rainfall with the Texas catch of white shrimp, *Penaeus setiferus* (Linnaeus). Transactions of the American Fisheries Society 82:151–155.

Hill, B. 1985. Effect of temperature on duration of emergence, speed of movement, and catchability of the prawn *Penaeus esculentus*. Pages 77–83 *in* P. C. Rothlisberg, B. J. Hill, and D. J. Staples, editors. Second Australian National Prawn Seminar NPS2, Cleveland, Australia.

Holt, S. A., C. L. Kitting, and C. R. Arnold. 1983. Distribution of young red drums among different sea-grass meadows. Transactions of the American Fisheries Society 112:267–271.

Howard, R. K., and K. W. Lowe. 1984. Predation by birds as a factor influencing the demography of an intertidal shrimp. Journal of Experimental Marine Biology and Ecology 74:35–52.

Hughes, D. A. 1966. Investigations of the "nursery areas" and habitat preferences of juvenile penaeid prawns in Mozambique. Journal of Applied Ecology 3:349–354.

Hughes, D. A. 1968. Factors controlling emergence of pink shrimp (*Penaeus duorarum*) from the substrate. Biological Bulletin 134:48–59.

Hughes, D. A. 1969. Evidence for the endogenous control of swimming in pink shrimp, *Penaeus duorarum*. Biological Bulletin 136:398–404.

Jones, R. S. 1965. Fish stocks from a helicopter-borne purse net sampling of Corpus Christi Bay, Texas 1962-1963. Publications of the Institute of Marine Science, University of Texas 10:68–75.

Jones, R. S., W. Ogletree, J. H. Thompson, Jr., and W. Flenniken. 1963. Helicopter borne purse net for population sampling of shallow marine bays. Publications of the Institute of Marine Science, University of Texas 9:1–6.

Kashkin, N. I., and N. V. Parin. 1983. Quantitative assessment of micronektonic fishes by nonclosing gear (a review). Biological Oceanography 2:263–287.

Keefe, M. L., and K. W. Able. 1994. Contributions of abiotic and biotic factors to settlement in summer flounder, *Paralichthys dentatus*. Copeia 2:458–465.

Kenyon, R. A., N. R. Loneragan, and J. M. Hughes. 1995. Habitat type and light affect sheltering behaviour of juvenile tiger prawns (*Penaeus esculentus* Haswell) and success rates of their fish predators. Journal of Experimental Marine Biology and Ecology 192:87–105.

Kjelson, M. A., and G. N. Johnson. 1978. Catch efficiency of a 6.1 m trawl for estuarine fish populations. Proceedings of the Southeast Association of Game and Fish Commissioners 27:653–662.

Kneib, R. T. 1997. The role of tidal marshes in the ecology of estuarine nekton. Oceanography and Marine Biology: An Annual Review 35:163–220.

Koenig, C. C., and F. C. Coleman. 1998. Absolute abundance and survival of juvenile gags in seagrass beds of the northeastern Gulf of Mexico. Transactions of the American Fisheries Society 127:44–55.

Krieger, K. J. 1993. Distribution and abundance of rockfish determined from a submersible and by bottom trawling. U.S. National Marine Fishery Service Fishery Bulletin 91:87–96.

Kurata, H. 1981. Shrimp fry releasing techniques in Japan, with special reference to the artificial tideland. Kuwait Bulletin of Marine Science 2:117–147.

Lakshmi, G. J., A. Venkataramiah, and G. Gunter. 1976. Effects of salinity and photoperiod on the burying behavior of brown shrimp Penaeus aztecus Ives. Aquaculture 8:327–336.

Leber, K. M., and H. S. Greening. 1986. Community studies in seagrass meadows: a comparison of two methods for sampling macroinvertebrates and fishes. U.S. National Marine Fishery Service Fishery Bulletin 84(2):443–450.

Liu, H., and N. R. Loneragan. 1997. Size and time of day affect the response of postlarvae and early juvenile grooved tiger prawns Penaeus semisulcatus De Haan (Decapoda:Penaeidae) to natural and artificial seagrass in the laboratory. Journal of Experimental Marine Biology and Ecology 211:263–277.

Loneragan, N. R., Y. G. Wang, R. A. Kenyon, D. J. Staples, D. J. Vance, and D. S. Heales. 1995. Estimating the efficiency of a small beam trawl for sampling tiger prawns Penaeus esculentus and P. semisulcatus in seagrass by removal experiments. Marine Ecology Progress Series 118:139–148.

Lyons, J. 1986. Capture efficiency of a beach seine for seven freshwater fishes in a north-temperate lake. North American Journal of Fisheries Management 6:288–289.

McIvor, C., and L. P. Rozas. 1996. Direct nekton use of intertidal saltmarsh habitat and linkage with adjacent habitats: a review from the southeastern United States. Pages 311–334 in K. F. Nordstrom and C. T. Roman, editors. Estuarine shores: evolution, environments and human alterations. Wiley, New York City.

Michalsen, K., O. R. Godo, and A. Ferno. 1996. Diel variation in the catchability of gadoids and its influence on the reliability of abundance indices. ICES Journal of Marine Science 53:389–395.

Millar, R. B. 1992. Estimating the size-selectivity of fishing gear by conditioning on the total catch. Journal of the American Statistical Association 87:962–968.

Miller, R. E., D. W. Campbell, and P. J. Lunsford. 1980. Comparison of sampling devices for the juvenile blue crab, Callinectes sapidus. U.S. National Marine Fishery Service Fishery Bulletin 78:196–198.

Milliken, G. A., and D. E. Johnson. 1984. Analysis of messy data. volume 1. designed experiments. Lifetime Learning Publications, Belmont, California.

Minello, T. J. 1993. Chronographic tethering: a technique for measuring prey survival time and testing predation pressure in aquatic habitats. Marine Ecology Progress Series 101:99–104.

Minello, T. J., and six coauthors. 1991. Habitat availability and utilization by benthos and nekton in Hall's Lake and West Galveston Bay. National Oceanic and Atmospheric Administration Technical Memorandum, NMFS-SEFC-275.

Minello, T. J., and J. W. Webb, Jr. 1997. Use of natural and created Spartina alterniflora salt marshes by fishery species and other aquatic fauna in Galveston Bay, Texas, USA. Marine Ecology Progress Series 151:165–179.

Minello, T. J., and R. J. Zimmerman. 1983. Fish predation on juvenile brown shrimp, Penaeus aztecus Ives: the effect of simulated Spartina structure on predation rates. Journal of Experimental Marine Biology and Ecology 72:211–231.

Minello, T. J., and R. J. Zimmerman. 1991. The role of estuarine habitats in regulating growth and survival of juvenile penaeid shrimp. Pages 1–16 in P. DeLoach, W. J. Dougherty, and M. A. Davidson, editors. Frontiers in shrimp research. Elsevier, Amsterdam.

Minello, T. J., and R. J. Zimmerman. 1992. Utilization of natural and transplanted Texas salt marshes by fish and decapod crustaceans. Marine Ecology Progress Series 90:273–285.

Minello, T. J., R. J. Zimmerman, and E. X. Martinez. 1989. Mortality of young brown shrimp Penaeus aztecus in estuarine nurseries. Transactions of the American Fisheries Society 118:693–708.

Minello, T. J., R. J. Zimmerman, and R. Medina. 1994. The importance of edge for natant macrofauna in a created salt marsh. Wetlands 14:184–198.

Moles, A., and B. L. Norcross. 1995. Sediment preference in juvenile Pacific flatfishes. Netherlands Journal of Sea Research 34:177–182.

Moller, T. H., and D. A. Jones. 1975. Locomotory rhythms and burrowing habits of Penaeus semisulcatus (de Hann) and P. monodon (Fabricus) (Crustacea: Penaeidae). Journal of Experimental Marine Biology and Ecology 18:61–77.

Mullin, S. J. 1995. Estuarine fish populations among red mangrove prop roots of small overwash islands. Wetlands 15:324–329.

Murphey, P. L., and M. S. Fonseca. 1995. Role of high and low energy seagrass beds as nursery areas for Penaeus duorarum in North Carolina. Marine Ecology Progress Series 121:91–98.

Nadeau, D. A. 1991. Relative growth rates of predatory fishes in vegetated and unvegetated habitats: field experiments with juvenile red drum, Sciaenops ocellatus. Master's thesis. University of South Alabama, Mobile.

Nielsen, L. 1983. Variation in the catchability of yellow perch in an otter trawl. Transactions of the American Fisheries Society 112:53–59.

NMFS (National Marine Fisheries Service). 1997. Magnuson-Stevens Act provisions: essential fish habitat: interim final rule and request for comments. Federal Register [Docket 961030300–7238–04; I.D. 120996A]: 66531–66559.

Odum, E. P. 1971. Fundamentals of ecology, 3rd edition. Saunders, Philadelphia.

Orlando, S. P., Jr., L. P. Rozas, G. H. Ward, and C. J. Klein. 1991. Analysis of salinity structure and stability for Texas estuaries. National Oceanic and Atmospheric Administration, National Ocean Service, Strategic Assessment Branch, Rockville, Maryland.

Orlando, S. P., Jr., L. P. Rozas, G. H. Ward, and C. J. Klein. 1993. Salinity characteristics of Gulf of Mexico estuaries. National Oceanic and Atmospheric Administration, Office of Ocean Resources Conservation and Assessment, Silver Spring, Maryland.

Orth, R. J., and J. van Montfrans. 1987. Utilization of a seagrass meadow and tidal marsh creek by blue crabs *Callinectes sapidus*. I. seasonal and annual variations in abundance with emphasis on postsettlement juveniles. Marine Ecology Progress Series 41:283–294.

Parsley, M. J., D. E. Palmer, and R. W. Burkhardt. 1989. Variation in capture efficiency of a beach seine for small fishes. North American Journal of Fisheries Management 9:239–244.

Perez Farfante, I., and B. Kensley. 1997. Penaeoid and sergestoid shrimps and prawns of the world: keys and diagnoses for the families and genera. Memoires du Museum National d'Histoire Naturelle, Tome 175, Paris.

Peters, D. S., and F. A. Cross. 1992. What is coastal fish habitat? Pages 17–22 *in* R. H. Stroud, editor. Stemming the tide of coastal fish habitat loss. National Coalition for Marine Conservation, Savannah, Georgia.

Peterson, G. W., and R. E. Turner. 1994. The value of salt marsh edge vs. interior as a habitat for fish and decapod crustaceans in a Louisiana tidal marsh. Estuaries 17:235–262.

Primavera, J. H., and J. Lebata. 1995. Diel activity patterns in *Metapenaeus* and *Penaeus* juveniles. Hydrobiologia 295:295–302.

Ricklefs, R. E. 1993. The economy of nature: a textbook in basic ecology, 3rd edition. Freeman, New York City.

Rogers, B. D. 1985. A small push-otter trawl for use in shallow marshes. North American Journal of Fisheries Management 5:411–413.

Rooker, J. 1997. Early life history of red drum (*Sciaenops ocellatus*) in subtropical seagrass meadows: patterns of condition, growth, and mortality. Doctoral dissertation. University of Texas, Marine Science Institute, Port Aransas.

Rooker, J. R., G. J. Holt, and S. A. Holt. 1997. Condition of larval and juvenile red drum (*Sciaenops ocellatus*) from estuarine nursery habitats. Marine Biology 127:387–394.

Rooker, J. R., G. J. Holt, and S. A. Holt. 1998. Vulnerability of newly settled red drum (*Sciaenops ocellatus*) to predatory fish: is early-life survival enhanced by seagrass meadows? Marine Biology 131:145–151.

Rozas, L. P. 1993. Nekton use of salt marshes of the Southeast region of the United States. Pages 528–537 *in* O. Magoon, W. S. Wilson, H. Converse, and L. T. Tobin, editors. Coastal Zone '93, volume 2. Proceedings of the 8th symposium on coastal and ocean management. American Society Of Civil Engineers, New York City.

Rozas, L. P., and T. J. Minello. 1997. Estimating densities of small fishes and decapod crustaceans in shallow estuarine habitats: a review of sampling design with focus on gear selection. Estuaries 20:199–213.

Rozas, L. P., and T. J. Minello. In press. Nekton use of salt marsh, seagrass, and nonvegetated habitats in a South Texas (USA) estuary. Bulletin of Marine Science.

Rozas, L. P., and D. J. Reed. 1993. Nekton use of marsh-surface habitats in Louisiana (USA) deltaic salt marshes undergoing submergence. Marine Ecology Progress Series 96:147–157.

Ruiz, G. M., A. H. Hines, and M. H. Posey. 1993. Shallow water as a refuge habitat for fish and crustaceans in nonvegetated estuaries—an example from Chesapeake Bay. Marine Ecology Progress Series 99:1–16.

Rulifson, R. A. 1981. Substrate preferences of juvenile penaeid shrimps in estuarine habitats. Contributions in Marine Science 24:35–52.

Sheridan, P., G. McMahan, G. Conley, A. Williams, and G. Thayer. In press. Nekton use of macrophyte patches following mortality of turtlegrass, *Thalassia testudinum*, in shallow waters of Florida Bay (Florida, USA). Bulletin of Marine Science 60.

Sheridan, P. F. 1992. Comparative habitat utilization by estuarine macrofauna within the mangrove ecosystem of Rookery Bay, Florida. Bulletin of Marine Science 50:21–39.

St. Amant, L. S., K. C. Corkum, and J. G. Broom. 1962. Studies on growth dynamics of the brown shrimp, *Penaeus aztecus*, in Louisiana waters. Proceedings of the Gulf and Caribbean Fishery Institute 18:1–16.

Thayer, G. W., D. R. Colby, and W. F. Hettler. 1987. Utilization of the red mangrove prop root habitat by fishes in south Florida. Marine Ecology Progress Series 35:25–38.

Thayer, G. W., D. R. Colby, M. A. Kjelson, and M. P. Weinstein. 1983. Estimates of larval-fish abundance: diurnal variation and influences of sampling gear and towing speed. Transactions of the American Fisheries Society 112:272–279.

Thayer, G. W., and P. F. Sheridan. In press. Fish, and aquatic invertebrate use of the mangrove prop root habitat in Florida: a review. *In* A. Yanez-Arancibia, and A. L. Lara-Dominguez, editors. Ecosistemas de Manglar en America Tropical: estructura, funcion, y manejo. Programa EPOMEX, Univ. Nac. Auton. Campeche, Campeche, Mexico.

Thomas, J. L., R. J. Zimmerman, and T. J. Minello. 1990. Abundance patterns of juvenile blue crabs (*Callinectes sapidus*) in nursery habitats of two Texas bays. Bulletin of Marine Science 46:115–125.

Turner, R. E. 1977. Intertidal vegetation and commercial yields of penaeid shrimp. Transactions of the American Fisheries Society 106:411–416.

Valentine, J. F., K. L. Heck, P. Harper, and M. Beck. 1994. Effects of bioturbation in controlling turtlegrass (*Thalassia testudinum* Banks *ex* Konig) abundance:

evidence from field enclosures and observations in the northern Gulf of Mexico. Journal of Experimental Marine Biology and Ecology 178:181–192.

Vance, D. J. 1992. Activity patterns of juvenile penaeid prawns in response to artificial tidal and day-night cycles: a comparison of three species. Marine Ecology Progress Series 87:215–226.

Wassenberg, T. J., and B. J. Hill. 1984. Moulting behavior of the tiger prawn *Penaeus esculentus* (Haswell). Australian Journal of Marine and Freshwater Research 35:561–571.

Wenner, E. L., and H. R. Beatty. 1993. Utilization of shallow estuarine habitats in South Carolina, USA, by postlarval and juvenile stages of *Penaeus* spp. (Decapoda, Penaeidae). Journal of Crustacean Biology 13:280–295.

Wenner, E., H. R. Beatty, and L. Coen. 1996. A method for quantitatively sampling nekton on intertidal oyster reefs. Journal of Shellfish Research 15:769–775.

Whitaker, R. H., and S. A. Levin. 1975. Introduction. Page 448 *in* R. H. Whitaker and S. A. Levin, editors. Niche; theory and application. Benchmark papers in ecology No. 3. Dowden, Hutchinson, and Ross, Stroudsburg, Pennsylvania.

Whitaker, R. H., S. A. Levin, and R. B. Root. 1973. Niche, habitat, and ecotope. American Naturalist 107:321–338.

Wickham, D. A. 1967. Observations on the activity patterns in juveniles of the pink shrimp, *Penaeus duorarum*. Bulletin of Marine Science 17:769–786.

Wickham, D. A., and F. C. Minkler. 1975. Laboratory observations on daily patterns of burrowing and locomotor activity of pink shrimp, *Penaeus duorarum*, brown shrimp, *Penaeus aztecus*, and white shrimp, *Penaeus setiferus*. Contributions in Marine Science 19:21–35.

Williams, A. B. 1958. Substrates as a factor in shrimp distribution. Limnology and Oceanography 3:283–290.

Williams, A. H., L. D. Coen, and M. S. Stoelting. 1990. Seasonal abundance, distribution, and habitat selection of juvenile *Callinectes sapidus* (Rathbun) in the northern Gulf of Mexico. Journal of Experimental Marine Biology and Ecology 137:165–183.

Workman, I. K., C. W. Taylor, and J. W. Watson. 1995. Improving pelagic fish retention in sampling trawls with a fish funnel. Scientia Marina 59:581–585.

Zein-Eldin, Z. 1963. Effect of salinity on growth of postlarval penaeid shrimp. Biological Bulletin 125:188–196.

Zimmerman, R. J., and T. J. Minello. 1984. Densities of *Penaeus aztecus*, *P. setiferus* and other natant macrofauna in a Texas salt marsh. Estuaries 7:421–433.

Zimmerman, R. J., T. J. Minello, T. J. Baumer, and M. C. Castiglione. 1989. Oyster reef as habitat for estuarine macrofauna. National Oceanic and Atmospheric Administration Technical Memorandum, NMFS-SEFC-249.

Zimmerman, R. J., T. J. Minello, M. C. Castiglione, and D. L. Smith. 1990a. The use of *Juncus* and *Spartina* marshes by fisheries species in Lavaca Bay, Texas, with reference to effects of floods. National Oceanic and Atmospheric Administration Technical Memorandum, NMFS-SEFC-251.

Zimmerman, R. J., T. J. Minello, M. C. Castiglione, and D. L. Smith. 1990b. Utilization of marsh and associated habitats along a salinity gradient in Galveston Bay. National Oceanic and Atmospheric Administration Technical Memorandum, NMFS-SEFC-250.

Zimmerman, R. J., T. J. Minello, and G. Zamora. 1984. Selection of vegetated habitat by brown shrimp, *Penaeus aztecus*, in a Galveston Bay salt marsh. U.S. National Marine Fishery Service Fishery Bulletin 82:325–336.

American Fisheries Society Symposium 22:76–92, 1999

Life History, Habitat Parameters, and Essential Habitat of Mid-Atlantic Summer Flounder

DAVID B. PACKER

National Oceanic and Atmospheric Administration
National Marine Fisheries Service, Northeast Fisheries Science Center
James J. Howard Marine Sciences Laboratory, Highlands, New Jersey, 07732, USA

TOM HOFF

Mid-Atlantic Fishery Management Council
Room 2115, Frear Federal Building, 300 South New Street
Dover, Delaware 19904-6790, USA

Abstract.—To satisfy the essential fish habitat (EFH) mandate of the reauthorized Magnuson-Stevens Fishery Conservation and Management Act, the Mid-Atlantic Fishery Management Council (MAFMC) and the National Marine Fisheries Service (NMFS) are developing objective, generic criteria to describe and identify the essential habitats for their managed species. Summer flounder or fluke *Paralichthys dentatus* is an important commercial and recreational species that occurs from shallow estuaries to the outer continental shelf from Nova Scotia to Florida. It is most abundant within the Middle Atlantic Bight from New England to Cape Hatteras, and this region is the focus of this paper. Summer flounder make seasonal inshore–offshore migrations; adults and juveniles normally inhabit shallow coastal and estuarine waters during the warmer months of the year and mostly move offshore with declining water temperature and day length during autumn. Adults spawn during the fall and winter migrations. The best habitat information available on summer flounder is for the estuarine-dependent transforming larvae and juveniles. They use several different estuarine habitats as nursery areas, including salt-marsh creeks, sea grass beds, mudflats, and open bay areas. In these habitats, water temperature affects the seasonal occurrence of summer flounder, drives the inshore–offshore migration, and, particularly during winter and spring, affects first-year growth and survival and thus subsequent year-class strength. The distribution of transforming larvae and juveniles within the estuaries is significantly influenced by salinity gradients and substrate. Transforming larvae and juveniles show a preference for sandy substrates in the laboratory but also have been captured on mud or mixed substrates. Juveniles are attracted to eelgrass and macroalgae habitats because of the presence of prey but remain in nearby sand to avoid predators as well as conceal themselves from the prey. The MAFMC used the life history and habitat parameter information developed by the NMFS Northeast Fisheries Science Center (NEFSC) to precisely describe the EFH of summer flounder by life stage. Because summer flounder are overexploited, the MAFMC wanted to be conservative in its EFH identification. Therefore, 90% of the areas where each life history stage has been collected from offshore surveys were identified as EFH. The MAFMC proposed that 100% of the estuaries where larvae and juveniles were identified as being present be identified as EFH because these life stages are estuarine dependent. Nursery habitats within the estuaries are essential because they provide the best conditions for growth and survival of the transforming larvae and juveniles. Submerged aquatic vegetation beds are especially vulnerable and were identified as habitat areas of particular concern. As more habitat-related density data become available from various local, state, and federal fishery-independent surveys, updated maps of distribution and abundance will be produced.

The geographical range of the summer flounder or fluke *Paralichthys dentatus* encompasses the shallow estuarine waters and outer continental shelf from Nova Scotia to Florida (Ginsburg 1952; Bigelow and Schroeder 1953; Anderson and Gehringer 1965; Leim and Scott 1966; Gutherz 1967; Gilbert 1986; Grimes et al. 1989). The center of its abundance lies within the Middle Atlantic Bight from Cape Cod, Massachusetts to Cape Hatteras, North Carolina (Figure 1) (Hildebrand and Schroeder 1928), and this region is the focus of this paper. North

of Cape Cod and south of Cape Fear, North Carolina, summer flounder numbers begin to diminish rapidly (Grosslein and Azarovitz 1982).

Summer flounder exhibit strong seasonal inshore–offshore movements (Figures 1 and 2). Adults normally inhabit shallow coastal and estuarine waters during the warmer months of the year and remain offshore on the outer continental shelf at depths down to 150 m during the colder months (Bigelow and Schroeder 1953; Grosslein and Azarovitz 1982). Tagging studies conducted by Poole (1962) and Lux

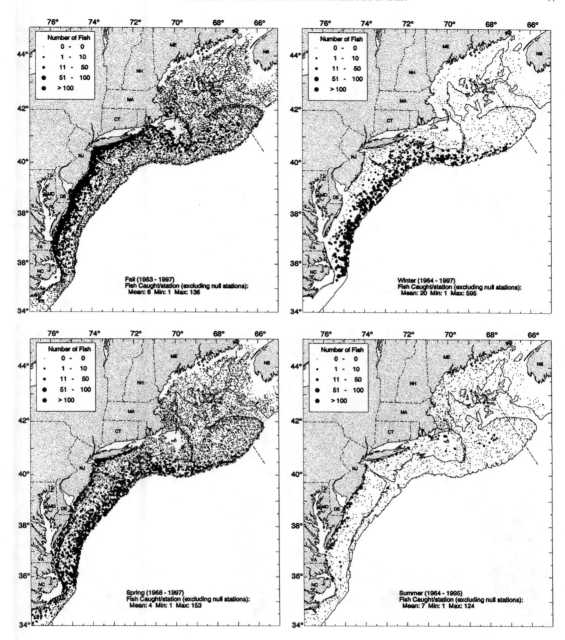

FIGURE 1.—Distribution of adult summer flounder (>28.1 cm tail length) from Nova Scotia to Cape Hatteras by season. From National Marine Fisheries Service Northeast Fisheries Science Center groundfish surveys for autumn (1963–1997), winter (1964–1997), spring (1968–1997), and summer (1964–1995). Sampling was conducted by stratified random design using 0.5-hr tows and a #36 Yankee trawl with a 12.7-mm mesh liner in the cod end. Stations where no adults were caught are shown as small dots. The 60- and 200-m contour lines are also shown.

and Nichy (1981) on flounder released off Long Island and southern New England revealed that the fish usually begin seaward migrations in September or October. Their wintering grounds are primarily between Norfolk and Veatch Canyons east of Virginia and Rhode Island, respectively, although they are known to migrate as far northeastward as Georges Bank. Fish that move as far north as the wintering

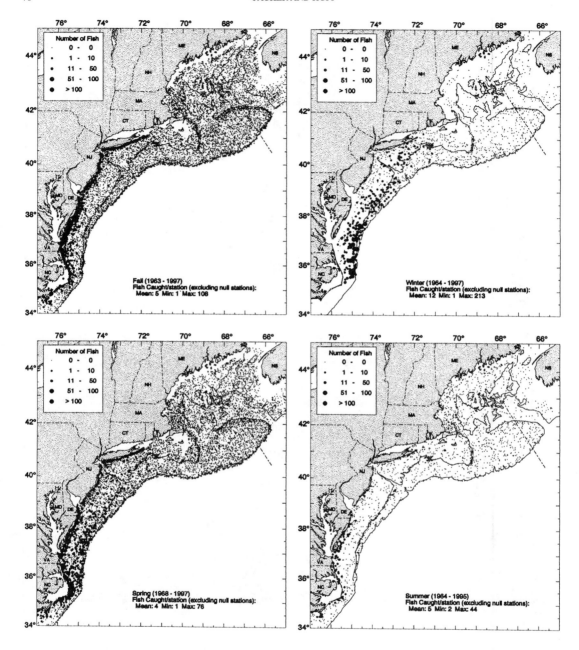

FIGURE 2.—Distribution of juvenile summer flounder (<28.0 cm tail length) from Nova Scotia to Cape Hatteras by season. From National Marine Fisheries Service Northeast Fisheries Science Center groundfish surveys for autumn (1963–1997), winter (1964–1997), spring (1968–1997), and summer (1964–1995). Sampling was conducted by stratified random design using 0.5-hr tows and a #36 Yankee trawl with a 12.7-mm mesh liner in the cod end. Stations where no juveniles were caught are shown as small dots. The 60- and 200-m contour lines are also shown.

grounds north of Hudson Canyon may become permanent residents of the northern segment of the Middle Atlantic Bight (Lux and Nichy 1981). New York and New Jersey flounder may move farther south in the winter months and generally may not move as far north in the summer as those from New England (Poole 1962). Summer flounder tagged in nearshore waters and sounds north of Cape Hatteras,

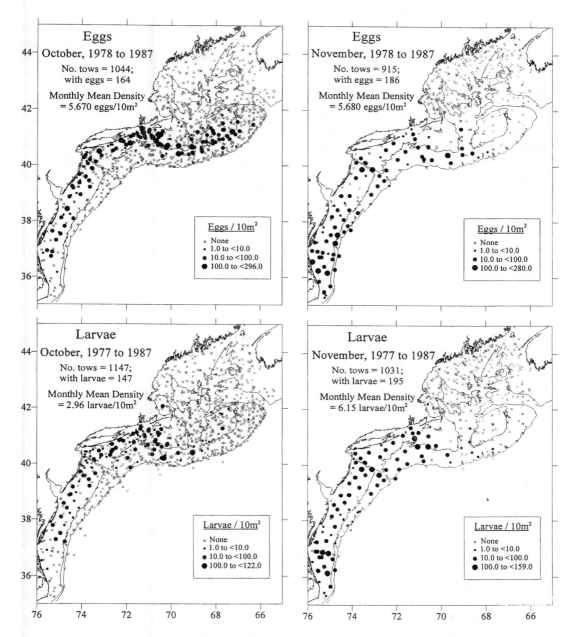

FIGURE 3.—Distribution and mean abundances of summer flounder eggs (top) and larvae (bottom) from Nova Scotia to Cape Hatteras for October and November, for the periods 1978–1987 for eggs and 1977–1987 for larvae. From National Marine Fisheries Service Marine Resources Monitoring, Assessment, and Prediction offshore surveys and Berrien and Sibunka (in press). Plankton sampling was conducted using 61-cm bongo frames fitted with 0.51-mm mesh. Stations where no eggs or larvae were collected are also shown, as are the 60- and 200-meter contour lines.

North Carolina generally remained in the tagging area or moved north, while those tagged south of the Cape remained in the tagging area or moved southward (Monaghan 1996). The southern population may undertake less-extensive offshore migra-

tions (Fogarty et al. 1983). Tagging studies indicate that fish that spend their summer in a particular bay tend largely to return to the same bay in the subsequent year or to move to the north and east (Westman and Neville 1946; Hamer and Lux 1962; Poole 1962;

Murawski 1970; Lux and Nichy 1981; Monaghan 1992; Desfosse 1995). Once inshore during the summer months, there appears to be very little movement of inshore fish to offshore waters (Westman and Neville 1946; Poole 1962; Desfosse 1995).

Summer flounder have a protracted spawning season of variable duration with early maturation (age 1 or 2), high fecundity, and serial spawning (multiplicity of egg batches that are continuously matured and shed) (Morse 1981; Grimes et al. 1989). Spawning occurs over the open ocean areas of the shelf (Figure 3) during the fall and winter while the fish are moving offshore onto their wintering grounds. The offshore migration is presumably keyed to declining water temperature and decreasing photoperiod during the autumn and begins near the peak of the summer flounders' gonadal development cycle, with the oldest and largest fish migrating first each year (Smith 1973).

The seasonal migratory and spawning patterns vary with latitude (Smith 1973); gonadal development, spawning, and offshore movements occur earlier in the northern part of the summer flounder's range (Powell 1974; Smith and Daiber 1977; Rogers and Van Den Avyle 1983). Spawning begins in September in the inshore waters of southern New England and the Mid-Atlantic. As the season progresses, spawning moves onto Georges Bank as well as southward and eastward into deeper waters across the entire breadth of the shelf (Berrien and Sibunka, in press). Spawning continues through December in the northern sections of the Middle Atlantic Bight and through February and March in the southern sections (Smith 1973; Morse 1981; Almeida et al. 1992). Spawning peaks in October north of Chesapeake Bay and in November south of the bay (Smith 1973; Able et al. 1990).

The pelagic and buoyant eggs are most abundant between Cape Cod–Long Island and Cape Hatteras (Figure 3); the heaviest concentrations have been reported within 45 km of shore off New Jersey and New York during 1965–1966 (Smith 1973) and from New York to Massachusetts during 1980–1986 (Able et al. 1990). Summer flounder eggs have been collected mostly at depths of 30–70 m in the fall, as deep as 110 m in the winter, and from 10 to 30 m in the spring. Smith (1973) reported concentrations of eggs off Long Island, Delaware and Virginia, and North Carolina. However, Fogarty et al. (1983) concluded that the distribution of eggs (and larvae) was continuous throughout the Middle Atlantic Bight, and apparent concentrations identified by Smith (1973) may have

been due to sampling variability. Able et al. (1990) discovered that the highest frequency of occurrence and greatest abundances of eggs in the northwest Atlantic occurs in October and November and possibly December (Figure 3). Festa (1974) also noted an October–November spawning period off New Jersey. In southern areas, eggs have been collected as late as January to May (Smith 1973; Able et al. 1990).

Planktonic larvae (2–13 mm) are often most abundant 19–83 km from shore at depths of around 10–70 m. They are found in the northern part of the Middle Atlantic Bight from September to February and in the southern part from November to May, with peak abundances occurring in November (Smith 1973; Able et al. 1990; Figure 3). The smallest larvae (<6 mm) are most abundant in the Middle Atlantic Bight during October to December, while the largest larvae (≥11 mm) are abundant during November to May with peaks in November to December and March to May (Able et al. 1990). Off eastern Long Island and Georges Bank, the earliest spawning and subsequent larval development occurs as early as September (Able and Kaiser 1994). By October, the larvae are primarily found on the inner continental shelf between Chesapeake Bay and Georges Bank. During November and December they are evenly distributed over both the inner and outer portions of the shelf. By January and February the remaining larvae are primarily found on the middle and outer portions of the shelf, and by April the remaining larvae are concentrated off North Carolina (Able and Kaiser 1994).

From October to May, larvae and postlarvae migrate inshore, entering coastal and estuarine nursery areas to complete transformation (Merriman and Sclar 1952; Olney 1983; Olney and Boehlert 1988; Able et al. 1990; Szedlmayer et al. 1992). Larval-to-juvenile metamorphosis, which involves the migration of the right eye across the top of head, occurs over the approximate range of 8–18 mm standard length (SL) (Burke et al. 1991; Keefe and Able 1993; Able and Kaiser 1994). The transforming larvae then leave the water column and settle to the bottom where they begin to bury in the sediment and complete development to the juvenile stage. However, they may not exhibit complete burial behavior until mid-late metamorphosis when eye migration is complete, often at sizes as large as 27 mm SL (Keefe and Able 1993, 1994).

Able et al. (1990) and Keefe and Able (1993) discovered that some transforming larvae (10–16 mm) entered New Jersey estuaries primarily during October to December, with continued ingress through April. Allen et al. (1978) collected larvae (12–15 mm) in February and April in Hereford Inlet near Cape May. In North Carolina, the highest densities of larvae were found in Oregon Inlet in April, while farther south in Ocracoke Inlet, the highest densities occurred in February (Hettler and Barker 1993). In the Cape Fear River Estuary, North Carolina, it has been reported that postlarvae first entered the marshes in March and April and were 9–16 mm SL during peak recruitment (Weinstein 1979; Weinstein et al. 1980). Schwartz et al. (1979a, 1979b) also noted that age-0 flounder appeared in the Cape Fear River between March and May, depending on the year. Powell and Robbins (1998) reported larval summer flounder in Onslow Bay (near Cape Lookout) in November, February, and May. Burke et al. (1998) sampled for transforming larvae and juveniles in Onslow Bay, Beaufort Inlet, and the Newport River estuary in February to March 1995. Although flounders were captured both in Onslow Bay and in the surf zone during the immigration period, densities were low and all were transforming larvae. After the immigration period, flounders were absent. Within the Newport River estuary, flounders were locally very abundant as compared to within Onslow Bay, and initial settlement was concentrated in the intertidal zone. During February most flounders were transforming larvae, and in March some were completely settled juveniles.

The juveniles are distributed inshore and in many estuaries throughout the range of the species during spring, summer, and fall (Deubler 1958; Pearcy and Richards 1962; Poole 1966; Powell and Schwartz 1977; Fogarty 1981; Rountree and Able 1992a, 1992b, 1997; Able and Kaiser 1994). During the colder months in the north there is some movement along with the adults to deeper waters offshore (Figure 2). Many juveniles will remain inshore through the winter months, while some juveniles in southern waters may generally overwinter in bays and sounds (Smith and Daiber 1977; Wilk et al. 1977; Able and Kaiser 1994). In estuaries north of Chesapeake Bay, some juveniles remain in their estuarine habitat for about 10–12 months before migrating offshore during their second fall and winter; in North Carolina sounds, juveniles often remain for 18–20 months (Powell and Schwartz 1977).

Juveniles make use of several different estuarine habitats. Estuarine marsh creeks are important as nursery habitat, as has been shown in New Jersey (Rountree and Able 1992b, 1997; Szedlmayer et al. 1992; Szedlmayer and Able 1993); Delaware

(Malloy and Targett 1991); Virginia (Wyanski 1990); and North Carolina (Burke et al. 1991). Other portions of the estuary that are used as nursery habitat include sea grass beds, mudflats, and open bay areas (Lascara 1981; Wyanski 1990; Szedlmayer et al. 1992).

Patterns of estuarine use by juveniles can vary with latitude. In New Jersey, juveniles often make extensive use of creek mouths and marsh creeks from Sandy Hook to Delaware Bay (Allen et al. 1978; Rountree and Able 1992a, 1992b, 1997; Szedlmayer et al. 1992; Szedlmayer and Able 1993). In Great Bay, young-of-the-year flounder stay for most of the summer and leave as early as August, with out-migration continuing until November to December (Able et al. 1990; Rountree and Able 1992a; Szedlmayer et al. 1992; Szedlmayer and Able 1992).

In Virginia, Wyanski (1990) reported recruitment from November to April on both sides of Virginia's Eastern Shore and from February to April on the western side of Chesapeake Bay. Peak recruitment occurred in November to December on the Eastern Shore compared to March to April on the western side of the bay. Wyanski (1990) and Norcross and Wyanski (1988) also found that young-of-the-year flounder occur in a variety of habitats, including shallow, mud-bottom marsh creeks; shallow sand substrates (including sea grass beds); deep sand substrates; and deep fine-sand substrates.

Tagged summer flounder have been recaptured from inshore areas to the northeast of their release sites in subsequent summers, leading to the hypothesis that their major nursery areas are the inshore waters of Virginia and North Carolina and that as they grow older and larger, summer flounder return inshore to areas farther north and east of these nursery grounds (Poole 1966; Murawski 1970; Lux and Nichy 1981). However, tagging studies by Desfosse (1995) indicated that it is not the older and larger fish but rather the smaller fish (length at tagging) that return to inshore areas north of Virginia. Summer flounder that were recaptured north of their release sites in subsequent years were smaller (length at tagging) than those recaptured at their release sites, or to the south, in later years. Desfosse (1995) suggested that although Virginia waters do indeed form part of the nursery grounds for fish that move north in subsequent years, the waters are primarily a nursery area for fish that will return to these same waters as they grow older and larger.

The estuarine waters of North Carolina, particularly those west and northwest of Cape Hatteras (Monaghan 1996) and in the high-salinity bays and tidal creeks of Core Sound (Noble and Monroe 1991), provide substantial habitat and serve as significant nursery areas for juvenile Middle Atlantic Bight summer flounder. Powell and Schwartz (1977) found that juveniles were most abundant in the relatively high salinities of the eastern and central parts of Pamlico Sound, all of Croatan Sound, and near inlets. Young-of-the-year flounder disappeared from the catch during late summer, suggesting that the fish were leaving the estuaries at that time (Powell and Schwartz 1977). Upon leaving the estuaries, the juveniles enter the north–south, inshore–offshore migration of Middle Atlantic Bight summer flounder (Monaghan 1996). Summer flounder >30 cm are rarely found in the estuaries of North Carolina, although larger fish are found near inlets and along coastal beaches.

Habitat Parameters

The highest-quality and greatest amount of habitat information available on summer flounder is for the estuarine-dependent transforming larvae and juveniles. By "highest-quality" we mean Level-3 information as defined in the essential fish habitat (EFH) Technical Manual (NMFS/OHC 1998) and the interim final rule to implement the EFH policy (NMFS 1997). This is important because the health and recruitment of larvae and juveniles ultimately affects the future growth and survival of the population. Therefore, in this paper we have chosen to concentrate on studies (experimental or otherwise) that focus on the habitat preferences of these critical life stages and are from published, peer-reviewed literature sources, rather than on information that merely attempts to correlate environmental variables with fish densities, such as information that often appears in general fisheries surveys. We heed the advice of Hettler et al. (1997), who suggested caution when interpreting correlations of environmental variables with fish abundances. For example, they reported an increase in summer flounder larval abundance with increasing temperatures in Beaufort Inlet, North Carolina. This increase could be caused by winter spawning and the arrival of larvae at the inlet after a two-to-three month cross-shelf transport time, resulting in a higher larval abundance corresponding with rising temperatures. The statistical analyses of

Hettler et al. suggested that unknown factors are probably more important in causing peaks in the abundances of immigrating larvae (see also Hettler and Hare 1998).

Distribution and habitat requirements information as well as fisheries survey data for all the life stages of summer flounder throughout its range can be found in Packer and Griesbach (in press). The Mid-Atlantic Fishery Management Council (MAFMC) used the Packer and Griesbach document in its identification of summer flounder EFH.

Temperature

Transforming larvae (~11–20-mm tail length [TL]) in Mid-Atlantic estuaries have been collected over a wide range of temperatures, for example, from -2.0–$14.0°C$ in Great Bay and Little Egg Harbor in New Jersey (Szedlmayer et al. 1992; Able and Kaiser 1994); from 2.1 to 17.6°C in the lower Chesapeake and Eastern Shore, Virginia (Wyanski 1990); and from 2 to 22°C in North Carolina (Williams and Deubler 1968a). The prevailing temperature conditions influence the duration of metamorphosis of pelagic larvae, with increasing temperatures resulting in a shorter metamorphic period. For example, Keefe and Able (1993) found that wild-caught flounder held in heated water (average 14.5°C) displayed advanced metamorphosis over controls kept at ambient winter temperatures (average 6.6°C). The total time required to complete metamorphosis in the heated water averaged 46.5 d; ambient winter temperature treatments resulted in delayed metamorphosis such that partial metamorphosis required as much as 92.9 d. Burke (1991) found that settling behavior of fish raised at 18–20°C occurred 28 d after hatching, although some took as long as 70 d.

Keefe and Able (1993) also found that mortality during metamorphosis in the laboratory was significantly greater in summer flounder maintained at 4°C relative to those maintained at ambient New Jersey estuarine temperatures of 10°C. Keefe and Able found no apparent effect of starvation on either mortality or time to completion of metamorphosis at cool water temperatures (<10°C). Szedlmayer et al. (1992) examined the temperature-induced mortality of young-of-the-year, early postmetamorphic (11–15-mm TL) flounder collected in New Jersey estuaries during November to May. Survival of metamorphosing larvae in the laboratory decreased drastically relative to controls when temperatures dropped below 2°C.

Malloy and Targett (1991) conducted temperature-tolerance experiments on juveniles from Delaware. Mortality was 42% after 16 d at 2–3°C, while all the juveniles survived above 3°C. Mean specific growth rates were not significantly different between 2 and 10°C, and these rates were not significantly different from zero growth. Additional mortality resulted from low growth rates caused by sub-optimal temperatures (<10°C). Malloy and Targett (1994a) also demonstrated that mortality of juveniles depends more on the rate of temperature decline than on the final exposure temperature; that is, increased rate of temperature decline led to decreased survival. Malloy and Targett's study showed that juveniles from Delaware had greater tolerances for low temperatures (1–4°C) than juveniles from North Carolina.

Malloy and Targett (1994a) showed that under maximum feeding conditions, juveniles from both Delaware and North Carolina do not exhibit positive growth rates at temperatures <7–9°C. Similarly, Peters and Angelovic (1971) in their laboratory studies of North Carolina juveniles reported predicted growth rates of close to zero at 10°C. Growth rates of Delaware and North Carolina juveniles at temperatures above 10°C were similar, and feeding rates increased with temperature (Peters and Angelovic 1971; Malloy and Targett 1991). Peters and Angelovic (1971) reported an increase in feeding and growth efficiency rates with increasing temperatures to an optimum; beyond that optimum increasing temperatures were detrimental. The optimal temperature in their experiments was 21°C. Malloy and Targett (1994a, 1994b) concluded that North Carolina juveniles had higher maximum growth rates and gross growth efficiencies than Delaware juveniles at temperatures between 6 and 18°C. Newly settled juveniles likely remain at settlement sizes for up to six months until temperatures are conducive for positive growth (Able et al. 1990; Malloy and Targett 1991, 1994b).

Malloy and Targett (1994a) also reported that juveniles from North Carolina and Delaware can survive at least 14 d without food at the 10–16°C temperatures typically found after settlement. However, growth rates were dependent on feeding rate at all temperatures examined by Malloy and Targett. In another study, Malloy and Targett (1994b) showed that juveniles from both Delaware and a North Carolina sandy marsh were severely growth limited in May and June when temperatures were 13–20°C.

Malloy and Targett (1994a, 1994b) concluded that prey availability is very important to the growth and condition of early juveniles during the months immediately following settlement, and changes in prey abundance may explain the patterns in growth limitation.

Mortality resulting from acute exposure to low temperatures in Middle Atlantic Bight estuaries probably occurs during a two-to-four-week period each winter. Szedlmayer et al. (1992) hypothesized that year-class strength may be affected by winter temperature in New Jersey estuaries, as has been suggested for juveniles over the entire Middle Atlantic Bight by Malloy and Targett (1991). Recruitment success may be lower in years with late-winter cold periods (i.e., March versus December) due to increased numbers of fish inshore at that time of the year being exposed to lethal low temperatures (Malloy and Targett 1991). Thus, the timing of ingress is critical. However, because Malloy and Targett (1991) found that there was 100% survival at temperatures above 3°C, juveniles are probably able to survive most winter water temperatures encountered throughout Middle Atlantic Bight estuaries.

Salinity

Transforming larvae and juveniles are most often captured in the higher-salinity portions of estuaries. In New Jersey, larval summer flounder have been captured at salinities from 20 to 36 ppt (Festa 1974; Able and Kaiser 1994). In North Carolina, although Williams and Deubler (1968b) found postlarvae in waters ranging from 0.02 to 35.00 ppt, optimal conditions appear to be at 18.00 ppt.

Malloy and Targett (1991) found that salinities of 10–30 ppt had no significant effect on feeding, growth, or survival of juvenile summer flounder in Delaware. However, there was a slight interaction of temperature and salinity on growth rate, suggesting that fish have higher growth rates at high salinities and at high temperatures. This agrees with other laboratory studies that show that larval and juvenile growth rates and growth efficiencies are greatest at salinities >10 ppt (Deubler and White 1962; Peters and Angelovic 1971; Watanabe et al. 1998), although Malloy and Targett (1991) suggested that there appears to be no significant physiological advantage or greater capacity for growth in waters of higher salinities, except at high temperatures. In other laboratory experiments, however, juveniles grew best at higher salinities and more moderate temperatures, typical of habitats close to the mouths of estuaries (Peters 1971). This could explain why Powell and Schwartz (1977) captured juveniles mostly in the central portions and around inlets of North Carolina estuaries at intermediate-to-high salinities of 12–35 ppt. Burke (1991) and Burke et al. (1991) also found newly settled flounder concentrated on tidal flats in the middle reaches of a North Carolina estuary. In the spring, older juveniles moved to high-salinity salt-marsh habitats. Young-of-the-year flounders in spring were also significantly correlated with salinity in eelgrass *Zostera marina* beds in the shallow-water (1.2 m), high-salinity (around 22–23 ppt) area near Hog Island in Pamlico Sound (Ross and Epperly 1985). However, Burke (1991) and Burke et al. (1991) made it clear that the summer flounder's distribution is due to substrate preference and is not affected by salinity. Malloy and Targett (1991) also suggested that reported distributions of juveniles at salinities >12 ppt are probably the result of substrate and prey availability.

Substrate and Specific Estuarine Habitat

Several studies in North Carolina indicate that substrate type may be the most important factor affecting the distribution of juvenile summer flounder. Juveniles appear to prefer sandy to sandy-mixed substrates (Turner and Johnson 1973; Powell and Schwartz 1977; Burke 1991; Burke et al. 1991). However, although Keefe and Able (1994) found that metamorphic and juvenile flounder collected from southern New Jersey estuaries showed a preference for sandy substrates in the laboratory, studies by Szedlmayer et al. (1992) and Rountree and Able (1992a, 1997) showed that in southern New Jersey, juvenile flounder also occur abundantly in marsh creeks with soft mud bottoms and shell hash. In Virginia, Wyanski (1990) and Norcross and Wyanski (1988) found newly recruited juveniles in shallow, mud-bottom marsh creek habitat until the juveniles were 60–80-mm TL in late spring, at which time they were on shallow sand substrates (including sea grass beds), deep sand substrates, and deep fine-sand substrates.

Substrate preferences may be correlated to the presence of predators and prey. For example, Timmons (1995) reported a preference for sand by juveniles from Delaware. The flounder were captured near large aggregations of the macroalgae

Agardhiella tenera only when large numbers of their principal prey, the marsh grass shrimp *Palaemonetes vulgaris*, were present. Timmons (1995) suggested that summer flounder are attracted to the algae because of the presence of the shrimp but remain near the sand to avoid predation (an "edge effect"). Indeed, in the laboratory, the juveniles did not show a preference for the macroalgae, and in caging experiments, blue crabs *Callinectes sapidus* were least able to prey on the flounder in cages with sand bottoms only but had an advantage in capturing the flounder in cages containing macroalgae. Similar results have been reported in laboratory experiments by Lascara (1981) on larger juveniles and adults from lower Chesapeake Bay. Flounder appeared to utilize submerged aquatic vegetation (eelgrass) as a "blind," that is, they lie in wait along the vegetative perimeter, effectively capturing prey (in this case, juvenile spot *Leiostomus xanthurus*) that moved from within the grass. In the absence of the eelgrass, the spot visually detected and avoided the flounder; the flounder therefore consumed fewer spot on average in the nonvegetated treatment than in the vegetated treatments. Thus, Lascara (1981) concluded that the ambush tactics of summer flounder are especially effective when the flounder are in patchy habitats where they remain in the bare substrate (sand) between eelgrass patches. Lascara (1981) also noted that if flounder remained within densely vegetated areas, they would probably be conspicuous to prey because as the flounder moved through the vegetation in his laboratory experiments, the grass blades were matted down and essentially "traced out" the flounder's body shape. The flounder might also be conspicuous to potential predators as well, again suggesting the edge-effect hypothesis of Timmons (1995). Thus, flounder remain near the sand to both avoid predation and conceal themselves from prey. Keefe and Able (1994) also concluded that the presence and types of both prey and predators may affect substrate preference as well as burying behavior in metamorphic and juvenile summer flounder. However, Burke (1991) reported that metamorphosing larvae raised in the laboratory preferred sand whether benthic prey species were present or excluded from test substrates.

Malloy and Targett (1994b) suggested that juvenile growth is related to substrate or habitat in the Newport River estuary, North Carolina because of the presence of specific prey. The growth limitation of juveniles (18–80-mm TL) in one sandy-marsh habitat could be explained by the low abundance of mysids from May into summer, while the increasing abundance of other prey (polychaetes and amphipods) during that same month at a muddier site may account for favorable growth seen there. Other diet studies in this estuary (Burke 1991, 1995; Burke et al. 1991) suggest that polychaetes are actually the preferred prey for juveniles of this size (see the "Food Habits" section below).

Although juveniles make extensive use of marsh creeks, other portions of the estuary are used as well. For example, eelgrass beds are important habitat, as has been shown in Virginia and Chesapeake Bay (Orth and Heck 1980; Lascara 1981; Weinstein and Brooks 1983; Heck and Thoman 1984) and North Carolina (Thayer and Adams 1975; Adams 1976a, 1976b; Ross and Epperly 1985). Hettler (1989) also reported juveniles in North Carolina salt-marsh cordgrass habitat during flood tides.

Timmons (1995) suggested that in the inland bays of Delaware, macroalgal systems appear to act as ecological surrogates to sea grass beds and sea grass–macroalgal systems as described by various authors. As with sea grass systems that attract juveniles when the submerged aquatic vegetation (SAV) increases from June to September, so does the macroalgae attract summer flounder because, as stated previously, macroalgae also attract the flounder's prey. This may also be true for southern New Jersey estuaries. Szedlmayer and Able (1996) reported that both juvenile and adult summer flounder were associated with a station considered to be a sea lettuce *Ulva lactuca* macroalgae habitat.

Food Habits

Food-habits studies on postlarvae and juveniles reveal that although the postlarvae and juveniles are opportunistic feeders, and differences in diet often are related to the availability of prey, there also are ontogenetic changes in diet. Small flounder <100 mm focus on crustaceans and polychaetes while fish become more important in the diets of larger juveniles. For example, in southern New Jersey, calanoid copepods were the primary prey of metamorphic (8.1–14.6-mm SL) flounder, indicating pelagic feeding (Grover 1998). Evidence of benthic feeding was observed only in late-stage metamorphic flounder, where the prey included polychaete tentacles, harpacticoid copepods, and a mysid. Burke (1991, 1995), in his North Carolina surveys of the Newport

and North Rivers, discovered that postlarvae (11–22-mm SL) also preyed on infauna, especially the appendages of benthic animals (e.g., polychaete tentacles, clam siphons); other prey items included harpactacoid copepods and polychaetes. For early juveniles (20–60-mm SL), polychaetes, primarily spionids *(Streblospio benedicti)*, were the most important part of the diet. Burke (1991, 1995) suggested that the distribution of these dominant polychaetes may influence the distribution of summer flounder in this area and could explain the movement of juveniles into marsh habitat (Burke et al. 1991; note the Malloy and Targett [1994b] study mentioned in the preceding section). Other prey items for this size-class included invertebrate parts (clam siphons), mysids and other shrimp, copepods, amphipods, blue crabs, and fish. Larger juveniles (100–200-mm TL) were reported to feed mainly on mysids (mostly *Neomysis americana*) and fishes throughout the year in Pamlico Sound, North Carolina (Powell and Schwartz 1979). Mysids were found in greater quantities in the smaller flounder, but as the flounder's size increased, the diet consisted of shrimps and fishes in similar quantities.

Rountree and Able (1992b) found that young-of-the-year summer flounder in southern New Jersey marsh creeks preyed on creek fauna in order of abundance (Rountree and Able 1992a); Atlantic silversides *Menidia menidia*, mummichogs *Fundulus heteroclitus*, marsh grass shrimp *Palaemonetes vulgaris*, and sevenspine bay shrimp *Crangon septemspinosa* contributed most importantly to their diets. Seasonal shifts in diet reflected seasonal changes in creek faunal composition. Rountree and Able (1992a) noted that the maximum abundance of young-of-the-year summer flounder in August coincided with the peak in Atlantic silverside abundances. Timmons (1995) reported that juvenile summer flounder from Rehobeth Bay, Delaware fed mostly on grass shrimp while flounder from Indian River Bay fed mostly on mysids. Postlarvae in Chesapeake Bay have been found with guts full of the mysid *Neomysis americana* (Olney 1983). In Magothy Bay, Virginia, small summer flounder also fed mainly on *Neomysis americana*, but in addition consumed larger proportions of amphipods, small fishes, gastropod molluscs, and plant material than the larger fish (Kimmel 1973). Wyanski (1990) found that mysids were also the dominant prey of 100–200-mm TL summer flounder in the lower Chesapeake Bay and Eastern Shore of Virginia. Lascara

(1981) reported that large juveniles and adults from lower Chesapeake Bay fed on juvenile spot *Leiostomus xanthurus*, northern pipefish *Syngnathus fuscus*, *Neomysis americana*, and shrimps *P. vulgaris* and *C. septemspinosa*.

Dissolved Oxygen

Dissolved oxygen, especially during periods of hypoxia (<3 ppm) or anoxia (0 ppm), also undoubtedly influences the distribution of transforming larvae and juveniles, as well as their growth and survival, but information on this parameter is lacking. Szedlmayer and Able (1993) suggested that tidal movements of juveniles in southern New Jersey estuaries may be in response to a preferred range of environmental parameters, including dissolved oxygen. Although the juveniles were collected in a wide range of habitats during their first year, they were found within a narrow range of dissolved oxygen (mean 6.4 ppm), and small changes in this parameter may force the fish to move. Festa (1977) reported that the high variability in catch rates of summer flounder off New Jersey in the summer of 1976 appeared to be directly related to the movement of an anoxic water mass present that year. Large numbers of summer flounder were forced into inlets and bays where they were more concentrated and vulnerable to the sport fishery (Freeman and Turner 1977). Postlarvae of the closely related southern flounder *Paralichthys lethostigma* responded negatively to water with dissolved oxygen concentrations <5.3 mg/l (Deubler and Posner 1963), and growth rates of young-of-the-year winter flounder *Pleuronectes americanus* [1] were significantly reduced for fish exposed to low (2.3 ppm) and diurnally fluctuating (2.5–6.5 ppm; average 5.1 ppm) levels of dissolved oxygen (Bejda et al. 1992). More research is needed on this parameter, especially in areas on the east coast where low levels of dissolved oxygen frequently occur.

Essential Habitat

Federal fishery management plans (FMPs) are required to identify and describe essential fish habitat using text that provides the best information on the biological requirements for each life history stage of the species. The general distribution and geographic limits of EFH for each life history stage must also be included in the form of maps.

In its description of summer flounder EFH, the Mid-Atlantic Fishery Management Council considered the life history, distribution, and habitat requirements as well as the status of the stocks. Because the summer flounder stock is at an average level of historical (1968–1996) abundance and is currently overexploited, the criteria the MAFMC used to describe its essential habitat differed from the criteria used for fully exploited or underexploited species.

The life history and habitat-requirement information presented above and in Packer and Griesbach (in press) were used by the MAFMC to precisely describe the EFH of summer flounder by life stage. The data available for creating EFH maps included habitat-related density data for all life history stages that occur on the continental shelf and presence–absence data for the life history stages that occur in estuaries.

To create the continental-shelf maps, habitat-related density data (catch-per-unit-effort [CPUE] data) from the NMFS Northeast Fisheries Science Center (NEFSC) bottom-trawl surveys (1963–1996; i.e., data used to create Figures 1 and 2) and from the Marine Resources Monitoring, Assessment, and Prediction (MARMAP) ichthyoplankton surveys (1977–1987; i.e., data used to create Figure 3) were binned into squares, each square being 10 min of longitude by 10 min of latitude. Squares with <4 tows were dropped from further analyses. The CPUE data within the squares were log transformed (ln [CPUE + 1]), and the mean was calculated for each 10-min square. Based on this mean, the squares with at least one positive catch were ranked in descending order, and the number of squares was cumulatively summed, with the assumption that areas (squares) of the highest value in regard to EFH contained the highest densities of fish. The 10-min squares contained in the top 50%, 75%, 90%, and 100% of this summation were then mapped separately onto the continental-shelf grid of squares to give percent of area occupied by summer flounder for each of the cutoff points (e.g., Figure 4 for the adults). Because summer flounder are overexploited and the MAFMC wanted to be conservative in its EFH identification, the MAFMC proposed the 90% option for each life stage on the shelf. (As fishing mortality is reduced and the summer flounder resource is rebuilt [projected for 2001], this 90% number may be reduced.)

Presence–absence data in the form of qualitative relative abundance data from the National Ocean Service's Estuarine Living Marine Resources (ELMR) program were available for the estuaries

---

[1] Cooper and Chapleau (1998) have revised the scientific name of winter flounder to *Pseudopleuronectes americanus*.

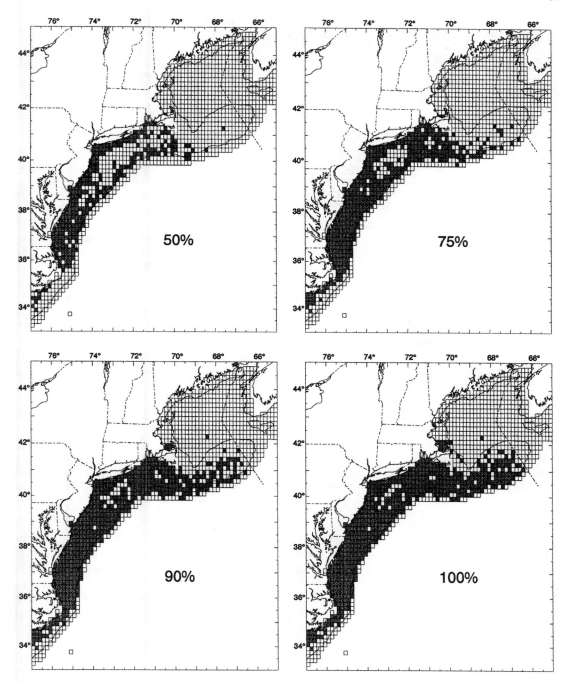

FIGURE 4.—An example of an essential fish habitat map for summer flounder adults on the continental shelf. Essential fish habitat was identified by the Mid-Atlantic Fishery Management Council as the area (using mean natural log) that encompassed the top 90% of the areas where summer flounder adults were collected by the Northeast Fisheries Science Center spring and fall surveys from 1963 to 1996.

used by summer flounder throughout its range (e.g., Figure 5). The MAFMC identified 100% of the estuaries where larvae and juveniles were present (i.e., rare, common, abundant, or highly abundant based on the ELMR classifications) as EFH because these life stages are estuarine dependent. Again, nursery

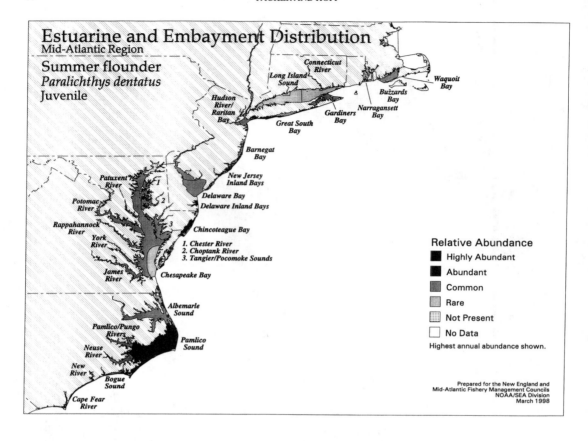

FIGURE 5.—Distribution and relative abundances of summer flounder juveniles in Mid-Atlantic estuaries from Waquoit Bay, Massachusetts to Cape Fear River, North Carolina. Data are combined over 12 months and 3 salinity zones, showing the highest level of annual abundance. Data are from the National Oceanic and Atmospheric Administration, National Ocean Service Estuarine Living Marine Resources program. For a complete description of the how the data were obtained and analyzed and an explanation of the relative abundance rankings, see Stone et al. (1994).

habitats within the estuaries (marsh creeks, SAV beds, open bay areas, etc.) are essential because they provide the best conditions for growth and survival of the transforming larvae and juveniles. However, because the adults are not estuarine dependent, the MAFMC identified as EFH those estuaries where the adults are considered common, abundant, or highly abundant, but not rare (based on the ELMR classifications). Submerged aquatic vegetation beds and aggregations are important habitat (Thayer and Adams 1975; Adams 1976a, 1976b; Orth and Heck 1980; Lascara 1981; Weinstein and Brooks 1983; Heck and Thoman 1984; Ross and Epperly 1985) and were identified as habitat areas of particular concern (HAPC). These HAPCs are important to the long-term productivity of the species and are rare or particularly sensitive or vulnerable to human-induced environmental degradation and development activities.

As more habitat-related density data become available from various local, state, and federal fishery-independent surveys, updated maps of distribution and abundance will be produced. The mapping of presence–absence and habitat-related density data satisfies the basic mapping requirements of the EFH mandate and also serves as the foundation for a geographic information system that will facilitate continued refinements to the MAFMC's EFH descriptions. In conclusion, the MAFMC identified EFH for each life stage of summer flounder in the Mid-Atlantic (1) based on the specific life history, distribution, and habitat parameter information presented above and in Packer and Griesbach (in press); (2) as those areas of nearshore and offshore waters that encompass 90% of the area where summer flounder were collected in the MARMAP ichthyoplankton and NEFSC trawl surveys; and (3) as the estuaries where all life stages were highly abundant, abundant, and common, plus those estuaries where larvae and juveniles were rare.

Acknowledgments

The authors thank Sara Griesbach, coauthor of the original EFH document. The authors also thank Christine Zetlin and Pete Berrien for creating the maps and Luca Cargnelli and Jeff Cross for reviews. Special thanks to Valerie Whalon, who provided much information and clarification on the Council's recommendations, and Jeff Cross, who interpreted the methods used for the 10-min squares.

References

Able, K. W., and S. C. Kaiser. 1994. Synthesis of summer flounder habitat parameters. NOAA (National Oceanic and Atmospheric Administration) Coastal Ocean Program, Decision Analysis Series. 1. NOAA Coastal Ocean Office, Silver Spring, Maryland.

Able, K. W., R. E. Matheson, W. W. Morse, M. P. Fahay, and G. Shepherd. 1990. Patterns of summer flounder *Paralichthys dentatus* early life history in the Mid-Atlantic Bight and New Jersey estuaries. Fishery Bulletin 88:1–12.

Adams, S. M. 1976a. The ecology of eelgrass, *Zostera marina* (L.), fish communities. I. Structural analysis. Journal of Experimental Marine Biology and Ecology 22:269–291.

Adams, S. M. 1976b. The ecology of eelgrass, *Zostera marina* (L.), fish communities. II. Functional analysis. Journal of Experimental Marine Biology and Ecology 22:293–311.

Allen, D. M., J. P. Clymer, III, and S. S. Herman. 1978. Fishes of the Hereford Inlet estuary, southern New Jersey. Lehigh University, Department of Biology and Center for Marine and Environmental Studies and The Wetlands Institute, Bethlehem, Pennsylvania.

Almeida, F. P., R. E. Castaneda, R. Jesien, R. E. Greenfield, and J. M. Burnett. 1992. Proceedings of the Northeast Fisheries Center/Atlantic States Marine Fisheries Commission summer flounder, *Paralichthys dentatus*, aging workshop, 11-13 June 1990, Northeast Fisheries Center, Woods Hole, Massachusetts. National Oceanic and Atmospheric Administration Technical Memorandum NMFS-F/NEC-89.

Anderson, W. W., and J. W. Gehringer. 1965. Biological-statistical census of the species entering fisheries in the Cape Canaveral Area. U.S. Fish and Wildlife Service, Special Scientific Report—Fisheries 514.

Bejda, A. J., B. A. Phelan, and A. L. Studholme. 1992. The effect of dissolved oxygen on the growth of young-of-the-year winter flounder, *Pseudopleuronectes americanus*. Environmental Biology of Fishes 34:321–327.

Berrien, P., and J. Sibunka. In press. Distribution patterns of fish eggs in the United States northeast continental shelf ecosystem, 1977-1987. NOAA Technical Report NMFS.

Bigelow, H. B., and W. C. Schroeder. 1953. Fishes of the Gulf of Maine. U.S. Fish and Wildlife Service, Fishery Bulletin 53.

Burke, J. S. 1991. Influence of abiotic factors and feeding on habitat selection of summer and southern flounder during colonization of nursery grounds. Doctoral dissertation. North Carolina State University, Raleigh.

Burke, J. S. 1995. Role of feeding and prey distribution of summer and southern flounder in selection of estuarine nursery habitats. Journal of Fish Biology 47:355–366.

Burke, J. S., and eight coauthors. 1998. The influence of environmental factors on early life history patterns of flounder. Journal of Sea Research 40:19–32.

Burke, J. S., J. M. Miller, and D. E. Hoss. 1991. Immigration and settlement pattern of *Paralichthys dentatus* and *P. lethostigma* in an estuarine nursery ground, North Carolina, U.S.A. Netherlands Journal of Sea Research 27:393–405.

Cooper, A. J., and F. Chapleau. 1998. Monophyly and intrarelationships of the family Pleuronectidae (Pleuronectiformes), with a revised classification. U.S. National Marine Fisheries Service Fishery Bulletin 96:686–726.

Desfosse, J. C. 1995. Movements and ecology of summer flounder, *Paralichthys dentatus*, tagged in the southern Mid-Atlantic Bight. Doctoral dissertation. College of William and Mary, Williamsburg, Virginia.

Deubler, E. E., Jr. 1958. A comparative study of postlarvae of three flounders (*Paralichthys*) in North Carolina. Copeia 1958:112–116.

Deubler, E. E., Jr., and G. S. Posner. 1963. Response of postlarval flounders, *Paralichthys lethostigma*, to water of low oxygen concentrations. Copeia 1963(2):312–317.

Deubler, E. E., Jr., and J. C. White. 1962. The influence of salinity on growth of post-larvae of the summer flounder *Paralichthys dentatus*. Copeia 1962(2):468–469.

Festa, P. J. 1974. A study of the distribution of young and larval summer flounder in New Jersey estuarine waters. New Jersey Department of Environmental Protection, Miscellaneous Report 11M, Trenton.

Festa, P. J. 1977. Observations on the summer flounder (*Paralichthys dentatus*) sport fishery in Great Bay, N.J. during summer of 1976 in reference to anoxic water conditions. Appendix VII. Pages 463–471 *in* Oxygen depletion and associated environmental disturbances in the Middle Atlantic Bight in 1976. National Marine Fisheries Service, Northeast Fisheries Center, Sandy Hook Laboratory Technical Series Report 3, Highlands, New Jersey.

Fogarty, M. J. 1981. Review and assessment of the summer flounder (*Paralichthys dentatus*) fishery in the northwest Atlantic. National Oceanic and Atmospheric Administration/National Marine Fisheries Service Woods Hole Laboratory Reference Document 81-25, Woods Hole, Massachusetts.

Fogarty, M. J., and seven coauthors. 1983. Stock discrimination of summer flounder (*Paralichthys dentatus*)
in the Middle and South Atlantic Bight: results of a
workshop. National Oceanic and Atmospheric Administration Technical Memorandum NMFS-F/NEC-
18.
Freeman, B. L., and S. C. Turner. 1977. The effects of
anoxic water on the flounder (*Paralichthys dentatus*),
a bottom dwelling fish. Appendix VI. Pages 451–462
in Oxygen depletion and associated environmental
disturbances in the Middle Atlantic Bight in 1976.
National Marine Fisheries Service, Northeast Fisheries Center, Sandy Hook Laboratory Technical Series Report 3, Highlands, New Jersey.
Gilbert, C. R. 1986. Species profiles: life histories and
environmental requirements of coastal fishes and invertebrates (south Florida)—southern, gulf, and summer flounders. Biological Report 82 (11.54), U.S. Fish
and Wildlife Service, Washington, D.C.
Ginsburg, I. 1952. Flounders of the genus *Paralichthys*
and related genera in American waters. U.S. Fish and
Wildlife Service, Fishery Bulletin 52:267–351.
Grimes, B. H., M. T. Huish, J. H. Kerby, and D. Moran.
1989. Species profiles: life histories and environmental requirements of coastal fishes and invertebrates
(Mid-Atlantic)—summer and winter flounder. Biological Report 82 (11.112), U.S. Fish and Wildlife
Service, Washington, D.C.
Grosslein, M. D., and T. R. Azarovitz. 1982. Fish distri-
bution. MESA (Marine Ecosystems Analysis) New
York Bight Atlas Monograph 15, New York Sea Grant
Institute, Albany.
Grover, J. J. 1998. Feeding habits of pelagic summer floun-
der, (*Paralichthys dentatus*), larvae in oceanic and
estuarine habitats. Fishery Bulletin 96:248–257.
Gutherz, E. J. 1967. Field guide to the flatfishes of the
family Bothidae in the western North Atlantic. U.S.
Fish and Wildlife Service Circular 263, Washington,
D.C.
Hamer, P. E., and F. E. Lux. 1962. Marking experiments
on fluke (*Paralichthys dentatus*) in 1961. Minutes 21st
annual meeting, appendix MA6, Atlantic States Marine Fisheries Commission, Tallahassee, Florida.
Heck, K. L., and T. A. Thoman. 1984. The nursery role of
seagrass meadows in the upper and lower reaches of
the Chesapeake Bay. Estuaries 7:70–92.
Hettler, W. F., Jr. 1989. Nekton use of regularly-flooded
saltmarsh cordgrass habitat in North Carolina, USA.
Marine Ecology Progress Series 56:111–118.
Hettler, W. F., Jr., and D. L. Barker. 1993. Distribution and
abundance of larval fishes at two North Carolina inlets.
Estuarine, Coastal and Shelf Science 37:161–179.
Hettler, W. F., Jr., and J. A. Hare. 1998. Abundance and
size of larval fishes outside the entrance to Beaufort
Inlet, North Carolina. Estuaries 21:476–499.
Hettler, W. F., Jr., D. S. Peters, D. R. Colby, and E. H. Laban.
1997. Daily variability in abundance of larval fishes in-
side Beaufort Inlet. Fishery Bulletin 95:477–493.

Hildebrand, S. F., and W. C. Schroeder. 1928. Fishes of
the Chesapeake Bay. Bulletin of the U.S. Bureau of
Fisheries 43(1).
Keefe, M., and K. W. Able. 1993. Patterns of metamor-
phosis in summer flounder, *Paralichthys dentatus*.
Journal of Fish Biology 42:713–728.
Keefe, M., and K. W. Able. 1994. Contributions of abiotic
and biotic factors to settlement in summer flounder,
Paralichthys dentatus. Copeia 1994(2):458–465.
Kimmel, J. J. 1973. Food and feeding of fishes from
Magothy Bay, Virginia. Master's thesis. Old Domin-
ion University, Norfolk, Virginia.
Lascara, J. 1981. Fish predator-prey interactions in areas
of eelgrass (*Zostera marina*). Master's thesis. Col-
lege of William and Mary, Williamsburg, Virginia.
Leim, A. H., and W. B. Scott. 1966. Fishes of the Atlantic
coast of Canada. Fisheries Research Board of Canada
Bulletin 155.
Lux, F. E., and F. E. Nichy. 1981. Movements of tagged summer flounder, *Paralichthys dentatus*, off southern New
England. NOAA Technical Report NMFS SSRF-752.
Malloy, K. D., and T. E. Targett. 1991. Feeding, growth and survival of juvenile summer flounder *Paralichthys dentatus*:
experimental analysis of the effects of temperature and salinity. Marine Ecology Progress Series 72:213–223.
Malloy, K. D., and T. E. Targett. 1994a. Effects of ration
limitation and low temperature on growth, biochemical condition, and survival of juvenile summer flounder from two Atlantic coast nurseries. Transactions
of the American Fisheries Society 123:182–193.
Malloy, K. D., and T. E. Targett. 1994b. The use of
RNA:DNA ratios to predict growth limitation of juvenile summer flounder (*Paralichthys dentatus*) from
Delaware and North Carolina estuaries. Marine Biology 118:367–375.
Merriman, D., and R. C. Sclar. 1952. The pelagic fish eggs
and larvae of Block Island Sound. Bulletin of the
Bingham Oceanographic Collection 13:165–219.
Monaghan, J. P., Jr. 1992. Migration and population dynamics of summer flounder (*Paralichthys dentatus*)
in North Carolina. Study 3A. Completion Report
Project F-29. North Carolina Department of Environment, Health, and Natural Resources, Division of
Marine Fisheries, Raleigh, North Carolina.
Monaghan, J. P., Jr. 1996. Life history aspects of selected
marine recreational fishes in North Carolina. Study 2,
migration of paralichthid flounders tagged in North
Carolina. Completion Report Grant F-43. North Carolina Department of Environment, Health, and Natural
Resources, Division of Marine Fisheries, Raleigh.
Morse, W. W. 1981. Reproduction of the summer flounder, *Paralichthys dentatus* (L.). Journal of Fish Biol-
ogy 19:189–203.
Murawski, W. S. 1970. Results of tagging experiments of
summer flounder, *Paralichthys dentatus*, conducted
in New Jersey waters from 1960-1967. New Jersey
Division of Fish, Game and Shellfish, Miscellaneous
Report No. 5M, Lebanon, New Jersey.

NMFS (National Marine Fisheries Service). 1997. Magnuson-Stevens Act provisions: Essential Fish Habitat: interim final rule and request for comments. Federal Register [Docket No. 961030300–7238–04; I.D. 120996A]: 66531–66559.

NMFS/OHC (National Marine Fisheries Service, Office of Habitat Conservation). 1998. Technical guidance to NMFS for implementing the essential fish habitat requirements for the Magnuson-Stevens Act. Draft, January 9, 1998. Silver Spring, Maryland.

Noble, E. B., and R. J. Monroe. 1991. Classification of Pamlico Sound nursery areas: recommendations for critical habitat criteria. Project No. 89–09. North Carolina Department of Environment, Health, and Natural Resources, Division of Marine Fisheries, Raleigh, North Carolina.

Norcross, B. L., and D. M. Wyanski. 1988. Chesapeake Bay Stock Assessment Committee III, project 40. (Mimeo.)

Olney, J. E. 1983. Eggs and early larvae of the bay anchovy *Anchoa mitchilli* and the weakfish *Cynoscion regalis*, in lower Chesapeake Bay with notes on associated ichthyoplankton. Estuaries 6:20–35.

Olney, J. E., and G. W. Boehlert. 1988. Nearshore ichthyoplankton associated with seagrass beds in the lower Chesapeake Bay. Marine Ecology Progress Series 45:33–43.

Orth, R. J., and K. L. Heck, Jr. 1980. Structural components of eelgrass (*Zostera marina*) meadows in the lower Chesapeake Bay—fishes. Estuaries 3:278–288.

Packer, D. B., and S. Griesbach. In press. Essential fish habitat source document: summer flounder, *Paralichthys dentatus*, life history and habitat characteristics. National Oceanic and Atmospheric Administration Technical Memorandum.

Pearcy, W. G., and S. W. Richards. 1962. Distribution and ecology of fishes in the Mystic River, Connecticut. Ecology 43:248–259.

Peters, D. S. 1971. Growth and energy utilization of juvenile flounder, *Paralichthys dentatus* and *Paralichthys lethostigma*, as affected by temperature, salinity, and food availability. Doctoral dissertation. North Carolina State University, Raleigh.

Peters, D. S., and J. W. Angelovic. 1971. Effect of temperature, salinity, and food availability on growth and energy utilization of juvenile summer flounder, *Paralichthys dentatus*. Pages 545–554 *in* D. J. Nelson, editor. Proceedings of the 3rd national symposium on radioecology. U.S. Atomic Energy Commission conference, 710501-PI. National Technical Information Service, Springfield, Virginia.

Poole, J. C. 1962. The fluke population of Great South Bay in relation to the sport fishery. New York Fish and Game Journal 9:93–117.

Poole, J. C. 1966. A review of research concerning summer flounder and needs for further study. New York Fish and Game Journal 13:226–231.

Powell, A. B. 1974. Biology of the summer flounder, *Paralichthys dentatus*, in Pamlico Sound and adjacent waters, with comments on *P. lethostigma* and *P. albigutta*. Master's thesis. University of North Carolina, Chapel Hill.

Powell, A. B., and R. E. Robbins. 1998. Ichthyoplankton adjacent to live-bottom habitats in Onslow Bay, North Carolina. NOAA Technical Report NMFS 133.

Powell, A. B., and F. J. Schwartz. 1977. Distribution of Paralichthid flounders (Bothidae: *Paralichthys*) in North Carolina estuaries. Chesapeake Science 18:334–339.

Powell, A. B., and F. J. Schwartz. 1979. Food of *Paralichthys dentatus* and *P. lethostigma* (Pisces: Bothidae) in North Carolina estuaries. Estuaries 2:276–279.

Rogers, S. G., and M. J. Van Den Avyle. 1983. Species profiles: life histories and environmental requirements of coastal fishes and invertebrates (South Atlantic)—summer flounder. U.S. Fish and Wildlife Service FWS/OBS-82/11.15, Washington, D.C.

Ross, S. W., and S. P. Epperly. 1985. Utilization of shallow estuarine nursery areas by fishes in Pamlico Sound and adjacent tributaries. Pages 207–232 *in* A. Yáñez-Arancibia, editor. Fish community ecology in estuaries and coastal lagoons: towards an ecosystem integration. UNAM Press, Mexico.

Rountree, R. A., and K. W. Able. 1992a. Fauna of polyhaline marsh creeks in southern New Jersey: composition, abundance and biomass. Estuaries 15:171–186.

Rountree, R. A., and K. W. Able. 1992b. Foraging habits, growth, and temporal patterns of salt-marsh creek habitat use by young-of-year summer flounder in New Jersey. Transactions of the American Fisheries Society 121:765–776.

Rountree, R. A., and K. W. Able. 1997. Nocturnal fish use of New Jersey marsh creek and adjacent bay shoal habitats. Estuarine, Coastal and Shelf Science 44:703–711.

Schwartz, F. J., and seven coauthors. 1979a. An ecological study of fishes and invertebrate macrofauna utilizing the Cape Fear River estuary, Carolina Beach Inlet, and adjacent Atlantic Ocean, a summary report 1973-1977. Volume 14. Institute of Marine Science, University of North Carolina, Morehead City.

Schwartz, F. J., and eight coauthors. 1979b. An ecological study of fishes and invertebrate macrofauna utilizing the Cape Fear River estuary, Carolina Beach Inlet, and adjacent Atlantic Ocean, annual report for 1978. Volume15. Institute of Marine Science, University of North Carolina, Morehead City.

Smith, R. W., and F. C. Daiber. 1977. Biology of the summer flounder, *Paralichthys dentatus*, in Delaware Bay. Fishery Bulletin 75:823–830.

Smith, W. G. 1973. The distribution of summer flounder, *Paralichthys dentatus*, eggs and larvae on the continental shelf between Cape Cod and Cape Lookout, 1965-66. Fishery Bulletin 71:527–548.

Stone, S. L., and seven coauthors. 1994. Distribution and abundance of fishes and invertebrates in Mid-Atlantic estuaries. Estuarine Living Marine Resources report 12. National Oceanic and Atmospheric Administration/National Ocean Service, Strategic Environmental Assessments Division, Silver Spring, Maryland.

Szedlmayer, S. T., and K. W. Able. 1992. Validation studies of daily increment formation for larval and juvenile summer flounder, *Paralichthys dentatus*. Canadian Journal of Fisheries and Aquatic Sciences 49:1856–1862.

Szedlmayer, S. T., and K. W. Able. 1993. Ultrasonic telemetry of age-0 summer flounder, *Paralichthys dentatus*, movements in a southern New Jersey estuary. Copeia 1993(3):728–736.

Szedlmayer, S. T., and K. W. Able. 1996. Patterns of seasonal availability and habitat use by fishes and decapod crustaceans in a southern New Jersey estuary. Estuaries 19:697–709.

Szedlmayer, S. T., K. W. Able, and R. A. Rountree. 1992. Growth and temperature-induced mortality of young-of-the-year summer flounder (*Paralichthys dentatus*) in southern New Jersey. Copeia 1992:120–128.

Thayer, G. W., and S. M. Adams. 1975. Structural and functional aspects of a recently established *Zostera marina* community. Pages 518–540 *in* L. E. Cronin, editor. Estuarine research, volume 1. Academic Press, New York.

Timmons, M. 1995. Relationships between macroalgae and juvenile fishes in the inland bays of Delaware. Doctoral dissertation. University of Delaware, Newark.

Turner, W. R., and G. N. Johnson. 1973. Distribution and relative abundance of fishes in Newport River, North Carolina. NOAA Technical Report NMFS SSRF-666.

Watanabe, W. O., M. W. Feeley, S. C. Ellis, and E. P. Ellis. 1998. Light intensity and salinity effects on eggs and yolk sac larvae of the summer flounder. Progressive Fish-Culturist 60:9–19.

Weinstein, M. P. 1979. Shallow marsh habitats as primary nurseries for fishes and shellfishes, Cape Fear River, North Carolina. Fishery Bulletin 77:339–357.

Weinstein, M. P., and H. A. Brooks. 1983. Comparative ecology of nekton residing in a tidal creek and adjacent seagrass meadow: community composition and structure. Marine Ecology Progress Series 12:15–27.

Weinstein, M. P., S. L. Weiss, and M. F. Walters. 1980. Multiple determinants of community structure in shallow marsh habitats, Cape Fear River Estuary, North Carolina, USA. Marine Biology 58:227–243.

Westman, J. R., and W. C. Neville. 1946. Some studies on the life history and economics of fluke (*Paralichthys dentatus*) of Long Island waters. An investigation sponsored jointly by the State of New York Conservation Department, U.S. Department of the Interior, and Town of Islip, New York.

Wilk, S. J., W. W. Morse, D. E. Ralph, and T. R. Azarovitz. 1977. Fishes and associated environmental data collected in New York Bight, June 1974-June 1975. NOAA Technical Report NMFS SSRF-716.

Williams, A. B., and E. E. Deubler, Jr. 1968a. A ten year study of macroplankton in North Carolina estuaries: assessment of environmental factors and sampling success among bothid flounders and penaeid shrimps. Chesapeake Science 9:27–41.

Williams, A. B., and E. E. Deubler, Jr. 1968b. Studies on macroplanktonic crustaceans and ichthyoplankton of the Pamlico Sound complex. North Carolina Department of Conservation and Development, Special Scientific Report 13, Morehead City, North Carolina.

Wyanski, D. M. 1990. Patterns of habitat utilization in age-0 summer flounder (*Paralichthys dentatus*). Master's thesis. College of William and Mary, Williamsburg, Virginia.

American Fisheries Society Symposium 22:93–107, 1999

Identification of Essential Fish Habitat for Salmon in the Pacific Northwest: Initial Efforts, Information Needs, and Future Direction

Philip Roni and Laurie A. Weitkamp

National Marine Fisheries Service, Northwest Fisheries Science Center
2725 Montlake Boulevard E., Seattle, Washington 98112, USA

Joe Scordino

National Marine Fisheries Service, Northwest Regional Office
7600 Sand Point Way NE, Seattle, Washington 98115, USA

Abstract.—Freshwater and marine essential fish habitat (EFH) for chinook *Oncorhynchus tshawytscha*, coho *O. kisutch*, pink *O. gorbuscha*, and sockeye *O. nerka* salmon within Washington, Oregon, California, and Idaho was described and identified using the available literature and databases on salmon distribution and life history. The diversity of freshwater habitats utilized by individual species of salmon coupled with the limitations of existing distribution maps precluded identification of specific stream reaches, wetlands, and other water bodies as EFH for Pacific salmon. A more holistic watershed approach consistent with the ecosystem method recommended by the revised Magnuson-Stevens Fishery Conservation and Management Act was necessary. Therefore, Pacific salmon freshwater EFH was delineated and described as all existing water bodies currently and historically utilized by Pacific salmon within selected watersheds defined by U.S. Geological Survey hydrologic units. Areas above some long-standing artificial barriers to juvenile and adult salmon migration were excluded from designation as Pacific salmon EFH. Delineation of marine EFH was also problematic because of the paucity of scientific studies on offshore Pacific salmon habitat use and distribution. However, available scientific data augmented by information from commercial fisheries indicate that juvenile salmon are found in high concentrations in the nearshore areas of the continental shelf off the Washington, Oregon, and California coasts from late spring through fall. Therefore, Pacific salmon marine EFH was identified as all waters within 60 km of the Washington, Oregon, and California coasts north of Point Conception, California. This initial effort to identify Pacific salmon EFH emphasized the need for accurate, fine-scale geographic information systems data on freshwater and marine salmon distribution and habitat quality and the need for compilation of uniform data sets. Future efforts should focus on developing accurate seasonal salmon distribution data at a 1:24,000 scale to aid in more precise and accurate delineation of Pacific salmon EFH. Furthermore, detailed information on winter distribution of Pacific salmon would be useful in delineating marine EFH.

Pacific salmon are one of the most commercially, economically, and culturally important species complexes along the west coast of North America. The Pacific Fisheries Management Council (PFMC) manages ocean fisheries for four species of salmon including chinook *Oncorhynchus tshawytscha* and coho *O. kisutch* salmon stocks from Washington, Idaho, Oregon, and California, and pink *O. gorbuscha* and sockeye *O. nerka* salmon stocks from Puget Sound. The 1996 amendments to the Magnuson-Stevens Fishery Conservation and Management Act (Magnuson-Stevens Act) (Public Law 104-267) included new requirements for essential fish habitat (EFH) descriptions in federal fishery management plans. In response, the National Marine Fisheries Service (NMFS) Northwest Fisheries Science Center and Northwest Regional Office developed recommended descriptions of EFH for the Pacific Coast Salmon Plan.

Pacific salmon *Oncorhynchus* spp. display diverse life history traits and habitat utilization both within and among species, which presented a unique challenge for EFH identification, delineation, and description. Pacific salmon spawn in streams from near tidewater to more than 3,200 km inland (Major et al. 1978), and their ocean migrations may be even more extensive, ranging from estuarine and coastal waters to the eastern Pacific and Bering Sea (Hartt and Dell 1986). Identification of EFH required identification of important areas for the species not only in estuarine and marine waters, but also freshwater habitats throughout much of Washington, Idaho, Oregon, and California. To identify EFH, we took a multistage approach that included describing life histories and habitat requirements for each species, reviewing and assimilating existing geographic information systems (GIS) and other information on marine and freshwater distribution, mapping overall species distribution, describing essential habitats for individual species, and recommending a description of EFH for all Pacific salmon species combined.

We developed Pacific salmon EFH descriptions and recommendations through a process that involved input from the PFMC, its advisory bodies, and the fishing industry at the PFMC's public meetings in September 1997, November 1997, and March 1998. In addition, a technical team consisting of state, tribal, university, federal, and industry scientists was convened to provide technical input and advice on the development of EFH recommendations for the Pacific Coast Salmon Plan. The following section summarizes the process and efforts to describe EFH for Pacific salmon within the waters under jurisdiction of the PFMC, which include waters north of the U.S.–Mexico border to the U.S. (Washington)–Canada border within the 200-mi exclusive economic zone. The EFH descriptions produced from this process were submitted as recommendations to the PFMC and are expected to be adopted by the Council in late 1998.

Overview of Pacific Salmon Life History

All four species of Pacific salmon managed by the PFMC are anadromous and semelparous; however, they display tremendous variation in life history both within and among species. Detailed descriptions of life histories and habitat requirements of Pacific salmon were prepared for the purposes of defining EFH. A brief overview of life history for each of the four species managed by the PFMC is provided here as background. More comprehensive reviews of individual Pacific salmon life histories and habitat requirements can be found in Groot and Margolis (1991), Weitkamp et al. (1995), Hard et al. (1996), Gustafson et al. (1997), and Myers et al. (1998). It should also be noted that the PFMC does not manage fisheries for chum salmon *O. keta*, steelhead *O. mykiss*, cutthroat trout *O. clarki*, or pink or sockeye salmon stocks originating from outside Puget Sound or the Fraser River basin.

Chinook Salmon

Chinook salmon are the largest Pacific salmon and were historically found in North America from the Ventura River, California (~34°N latitude) to

Kotzebue Sound in Alaska (~66°N) (Major et al. 1978). At present, the southernmost populations occur in the Sacramento and San Joaquin rivers and other tributaries to San Francisco Bay, although chinook salmon are occasionally observed in rivers south of San Francisco Bay, such as the San Luis Obispo and Carmel rivers (Myers et al. 1998). In marine environments, chinook salmon from the Pacific Northwest range widely throughout the North Pacific Ocean and the Bering Sea, and occasionally as far south as the U.S.–Mexico border (Figure 1). In coastal waters (less than approximately 300 km offshore), juvenile chinook salmon are found in highest concentrations in areas of pronounced coastal upwelling (Hartt and Dell 1986; Pearcy 1992). High-seas tag recovery data indicate that the oceanic distribution of Pacific Northwest chinook salmon includes the Pacific Ocean and Gulf of Alaska north of approximately 44EN and east of 180EW, including some areas of the Bering Sea (Hartt and Dell 1986; Myers et al. 1996). However, juvenile and maturing chinook salmon are generally found within 55 km of the Washington, Oregon, and California coasts from May to September, with the vast majority of fish found less than 28 km offshore (Pearcy and Fisher 1990; Fisher and Pearcy 1995).

Chinook salmon typically spawn in medium-to-large streams. The spawning environments for this species range from just above tidewater to over 3,200 km from the ocean, from coastal rainforest streams to arid mountain tributaries at elevations over 1,500 m (Major et al. 1978). Chinook salmon spawning may occur between July and March, depending primarily upon the geographic location and the specific race or population. In general, northern populations tend to spawn from July to October and southern populations from November to February. The Sacramento River supports a unique winter-run chinook population that spawns from March through July with peak spawning occurring in June (Myers et al. 1998).

Chinook salmon show tremendous variation in life history and may mature at 7 different ages (2–8 years), representing 16 different combinations of freshwater and marine residence (Healey 1986). This variation in life history has been partially explained by separating chinook salmon into two distinct races: stream- and ocean-type fish (Gilbert 1912; Healey 1983). Stream-type fish reside in freshwater for 1–2 years, migrate rapidly to oceanic habitats, and, as adults, often enter freshwater in spring and summer, spawning far upriver in late summer or early fall. In contrast, ocean-type

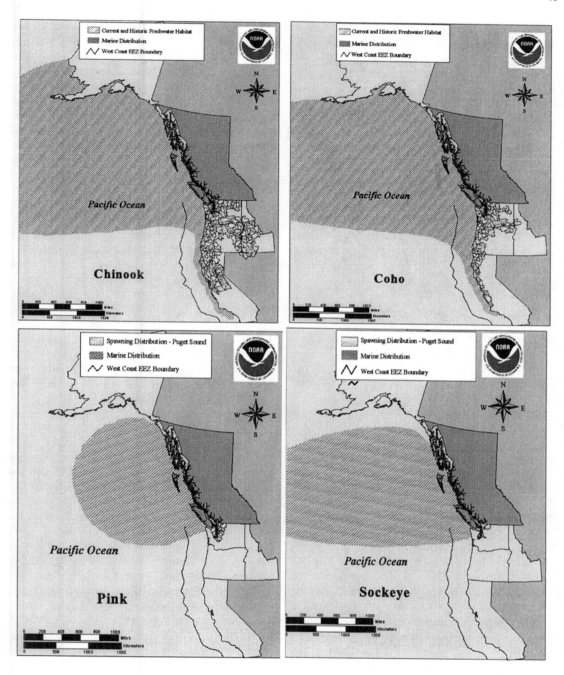

FIGURE 1.—Approximate freshwater and marine distribution of chinook, coho, and Puget Sound pink and sockeye salmon.

fish have short freshwater residencies (from a few days to several months), make extensive use of estuaries, and display considerable geographic variation in run timing. While rearing in freshwater, juvenile chinook inhabit primarily pools and stream margins, particularly undercut banks, behind and among woody debris accumulations and other areas with adequate cover and reduced water velocities (Bjornn and Reiser 1991).

In the estuarine environment, chinook salmon are found in a variety of habitats depending upon their size and life history type. Chinook salmon fry prefer protected estuarine habitats with low salinity, moving from the edges of marshes during high tide to protected tidal channels and creeks during low tide, although they venture into less-protected areas at night (Healey 1980, 1982; Kjelson et al. 1982; Levings 1982). As chinook salmon fry grow, they are found in higher-salinity waters and utilize less-protected estuarine habitats before finally dispersing into strictly marine habitats. In contrast to fry, larger chinook fingerlings and smolts (ocean- or stream-type) immediately take up residence in deeper-water estuarine habitats upon emigrating from freshwater (Everest and Chapman 1972; Healey 1991).

Coho Salmon

North American coho salmon populations are widely distributed along the Pacific coast and spawn in small streams and tributaries to most major river basins from the San Lorenzo River in Monterey Bay, California, to Point Hope, Alaska, and through the Aleutian Islands (Figure 1) (Godfrey 1965; Sandercock 1991). The species is most abundant in coastal areas from central Oregon to southeast Alaska and is widely distributed throughout the North Pacific (Manzer et al. 1965; French et al. 1975; Godfrey et al. 1975). In oceanic waters, coho salmon from Washington, Oregon, and California have been recovered in the North Pacific Ocean and Gulf of Alaska north of 44EN to 57EN, extending westward and southward along the Aleutian chain to the Emperor Sea Mounts area near 43EN and 175EE (Hartt and Dell 1986; Myers et al. 1996). Although juvenile and maturing coho are found in the open north Pacific, the highest concentrations appear to be found in more productive waters of the continental shelf. Most juvenile and maturing coho are within 55 km of the Washington and Oregon coasts from late spring through fall, although little information exists on their distribution during winter months (Pearcy and Fisher 1988; Pearcy 1992). Anecdotal information from commercial fisherman, ocean temperatures and upwelling patterns, and the narrow continental shelf all suggest a similar distribution of juvenile coho salmon off the California coast.

Coho salmon typically spawn in small to medium-sized streams (Burner 1951; Bjornn and Reiser 1991). Juveniles usually rear for at least 1 year in freshwater and spend about 18 months at sea before reaching maturity. Most coho salmon spawn between November and January, with some populations spawning as late as March (Godfrey et al. 1965; Sandercock 1991; Weitkamp et al. 1995). Typical coho salmon freshwater spawning and rearing habitat includes streams less than fourth order with low-gradient alluvial channels and abundant pools formed by large woody debris (Foerster and Ricker 1953; Chapman 1965). Juvenile coho salmon inhabit primarily pools and other slow-water habitats. Backwater pools, ponds, wetlands, and large slack-water areas provide some of the best rearing areas (Bustard and Narver 1975; Nickelson et al. 1992). Coho salmon smolt production is often limited by the availability of summer and winter freshwater rearing habitats (Williams et al. 1975; Reeves et al. 1989; Nickelson et al. 1992). Inadequate winter rearing habitats, such as backwater pools, beaver ponds, wetlands, and other off-channel rearing areas, are considered the primary factor limiting coho salmon production in many coastal streams (Cederholm and Scarlett 1981; Swales et al. 1988; Nickelson et al. 1992).

The amount of time juvenile coho salmon rear in estuaries appears to be highly variable, with more northern populations generally dwelling longer in estuaries than more southern populations (Simenstad et al. 1982; Tschaplinski 1982). For example, Oregon coast, Columbia River, and Puget Sound coho salmon are thought to remain in estuarine areas for several days to several weeks, while many British Columbia and Alaska populations remain in estuaries for several months (Myers and Horton 1982; Simenstad et al. 1982; Tschaplinski 1982; Levings et al. 1995). In estuaries, coho salmon smolts occur in intertidal and pelagic habitats, with deep, marine-influenced habitats often preferred (Dawley et al. 1986; MacDonald et al. 1987). As in stream environments, large woody debris is also an important element of juvenile coho salmon habitat in estuaries (McMahon and Holtby 1992).

Pink Salmon

Pink salmon are unique among Pacific salmon in that they exhibit a nearly invariant two-year life span within their natural range (Gilbert 1912; Heard

1991). The natural range of pink salmon includes the Pacific rim of Asia and North America north of approximately 40EN latitude. In North America, pink salmon regularly spawn as far south as Puget Sound and the Olympic Peninsula, although the largest populations in Washington state occur in northern Puget Sound (Williams et al. 1975; WDF et al. 1993; Hard et al. 1996). On rare occasions pink salmon are observed in rivers along the Washington, Oregon, and California coasts, but it is believed that spawning populations of pink salmon no longer regularly occur outside Puget Sound (Moyle et al. 1995; Hard et al. 1996). The marine distribution of Puget Sound pink salmon appears to be more limited than that of Canadian and Alaskan stocks (Figure 1). Tagging studies indicate that juvenile and maturing Puget Sound pink salmon are initially concentrated in nearshore areas of Vancouver Island and the Hecate Strait, and then extend as far north as approximately 58EN (Yukatat Bay, Alaska) and seaward to approximately 140EW (Hartt 1980; Hartt and Dell 1986; Myers et al. 1996). The southernmost marine distribution of Puget Sound pink salmon is not clear, but in general the largest concentrations of pink salmon of British Columbia and Washington origin are found north of 48EN (Hartt and Dell 1986; Myers et al. 1996).

Pink salmon spend approximately 18 months in the marine environment before returning to their natal streams to spawn. Because of their fixed two-year life cycle, pink salmon spawning in a particular river system in odd- and even-numbered years are reproductively isolated from each other and exist as genetically distinct lines (Gharrett et al. 1988; Hard et al. 1996). In Washington state and southern British Columbia, odd-numbered-year pink salmon are the most abundant (Aro and Shepard 1967; WDF et al. 1993). However, small even-numbered-year populations exist in the Snohomish River in Puget Sound and in several Vancouver Island rivers (Aro and Shepard 1967; Ricker and Manzer 1974; WDF et al. 1993). Puget Sound pink salmon typically enter freshwater between mid-July and late September and spawn shortly thereafter. Pink salmon spawn closer to tidewater than most other Pacific salmon species and typically spawn within 50 km of a river mouth (Heard 1991). However, some populations may migrate up to 500 km upstream to spawn, and a substantial fraction of other populations may spawn in intertidal stream reaches (Aro and Shepard 1967; WDF et al. 1993). Pink salmon typically spawn in medium-sized to large streams and often have spawning populations exceeding hundreds of thousands of adult fish (Takagi et al. 1981; Heard 1991; WDF et al. 1993).

Upon emergence, pink salmon fry spend little time in freshwater and migrate almost immediately to the estuarine and marine environment. The use of estuarine areas by pink salmon varies widely, ranging from passing directly through the estuary en route to nearshore areas to residing in estuaries for 1–2 months before moving to the ocean (Hoar 1956; McDonald 1960; Vernon 1966; Heard 1991). In general, most pink salmon populations use the former pattern and depend more on nearshore environments for their initial marine residence and rapid growth.

Sockeye Salmon

Sockeye salmon exhibit tremendous variation in freshwater and marine life history and characteristically make more use of lake-rearing habitat in juvenile stages than other species of Pacific salmon (Burgner 1991). The natural freshwater range of sockeye salmon includes the Pacific rim of Asia and North America north of approximately 40EN latitude (Aro and Shepard 1967; Foerster 1968; Forrester 1987). The southernmost populations in North America occur in the Columbia River Basin, although sockeye salmon have occasionally been observed in coastal streams in Oregon and California (Gustafson et al. 1997). In Puget Sound, sockeye salmon populations occur in the Lake Washington and Baker River watersheds.

In the marine environment, juvenile sockeye salmon typically remain relatively close to the coast during their first summer at sea (Hartt 1980; Hartt and Dell 1986). Once young sockeye salmon move offshore into the Gulf of Alaska, their seasonal locations and movements are not well understood. However, high-seas tagging studies indicate that Puget Sound and Columbia River sockeye populations are generally found in the North Pacific between 48EN and 58EN latitude and east of 175EE (Figure 1) (Myers et al. 1996).

Adult Puget Sound sockeye salmon generally enter freshwater from mid-June to August and spawn from September to December in small to large streams or submerged lakeshore beaches (Foerster 1968; Burgner 1991; Gustafson et al. 1997). After emerging from the gravel, juvenile sockeye typically rear in large lakes for 1–3 years before migrating to the marine environment (Burgner 1991; Bugaev 1992). The vast majority of sockeye from Baker Lake and Lake Washington spend 1 year in freshwater and emigrate to the estuarine and marine environment as smolts from late April to early June (Gustafson et al. 1997). In the estuarine environment they are generally found in faster-flowing mid-channel regions and are rarely observed in off-channel areas such as marshes and sloughs (Healey 1980; Levings et al. 1995). Sockeye salmon spend a few weeks to a few months in the estuarine and nearshore environments before moving into offshore waters (Burgner 1991).

Review of Data on Salmon Distribution

Prior to describing and delineating EFH for Pacific salmon, we reviewed existing databases and literature on salmon distribution and habitat in both marine and freshwater environments. This information was supplemented with data collected by NMFS during ongoing Endangered Species Act status reviews for Pacific salmon. The short time frame for preparing initial EFH descriptions and recommendations precluded the collection of new data. The following two subsections summarize the results of our review of existing databases and literature for the purposes of describing and identifying EFH.

Data on Freshwater Distribution

The geographic extent of Pacific salmon freshwater and estuarine distribution was determined using available information and databases on distribution. These databases fell into three general categories:

1. coarse-scale (e.g., 1:100,000- or 1:250,000-scale) regional GIS databases on Pacific salmon distribution (e.g., StreamNet, Washington Rivers Information System, Oregon Rivers Information System, etc.)
2. finer-scale GIS databases of limited scope (e.g., county, tribal data sets, etc.), and
3. habitat-survey and habitat-quality databases (e.g., U.S. Forest Service stream survey data, state and tribal stream survey data, etc.).

Databases in categories 2 and 3 were not useful in determining chinook and coho salmon freshwater distribution because they were comprised of many small, disparate, incompatible databases with incomplete geographic coverage. However, because pink and sockeye salmon were found in only a small number of watersheds within the Puget Sound basin, more detailed information existed on their freshwater distribution than for other species.

Coarse-scale databases (1:100,000- or 1:250,000-scale) outlined the overall distribution of Pacific salmon but were of limited utility for determining specific stream reaches used by various life stages. The stream hydrography layer in these coarse-scale databases excluded numerous small but important tributaries that can only be identified and depicted by 1:24,000-scale or larger maps or by field surveys. For example, Figure 2 demonstrates the large differences in stream network mapped at 1:24,000 and 1:100,000 scale. Lunetta et al. (1997) indicated that coarse-scale maps may underestimate total river miles by as much as 500% and potential accessible salmon habitat by 50%. The information on salmon distribution in these large GIS databases was based largely on professional judgment rather than extensive stream surveys (Doyle 1997). Further, databases on distribution were developed during recent periods of low salmon abundance and may not accurately reflect the distribution of and habitats utilized by the species historically. The creation, alteration, and modification of stream channels and habitats is a dynamic process, allowing the habitat available to and utilized by Pacific salmon to change frequently in response to floods, landslides, woody debris inputs, sediment delivery, and other natural events (Sullivan et al. 1987; Naiman et al. 1992; Reeves et al. 1995; Bisson et al. 1997). It is unrealistic to expect salmon distribution within a stream, watershed, province, or region to remain static over time. Therefore, coarse-scale regional GIS databases are useful for determining watersheds currently inhabited by Pacific salmon but not for identifying specific stream reaches and habitats currently or historically utilized by species or life stages.

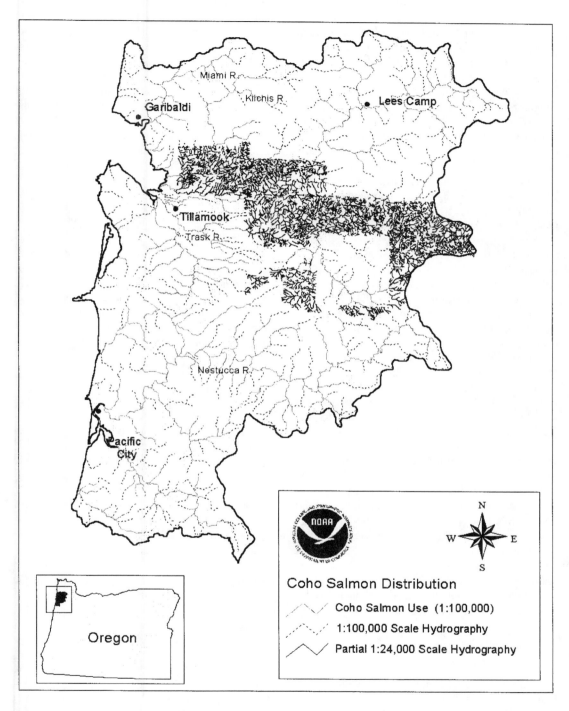

FIGURE 2.—Distribution of coho salmon within the Tillamook hydrologic unit (U.S. Geological Survey No. 17100203) based on 1:100,000-scale stream network (hydrography) and comparison of 1:100,000- and 1:24,000-scale hydrography. Partial 1:24,000-scale hydrography is shown where available.

Fisher 1988; Pearcy 1992; Myers et al. 1996, etc.); personal communications from commercial salmon fishermen; and data sets on coded-wire tag recoveries in commercial and recreational fisheries. Coded-wire tag recoveries from commercial and sport fisheries were of limited use due to the restricted geographic scope of the fisheries; frequent changes in seasons, regulations, and effort; and the imprecise location of most tag recoveries. The best sources of data were studies conducted on the coastal distribution of juvenile salmonids off the Oregon and Washington coasts (Pearcy and Fisher 1988; Pearcy 1992) and high-seas tagging data presented in Hartt and Dell (1986) and Myers et al. (1996). However, these studies occurred in different regions and years and under potentially different oceanic conditions, and the studies produced dissimilar results on overall ocean distribution. Nevertheless, patterns of recoveries of hatchery coho salmon indicated marked geographic differences in ocean distribution among regions, although most maturing coho were recovered in coastal waters near their stream of origin (Weitkamp et al. 1995). Further, personal communications with commercial fishermen through the Pacific Fisheries Management Council and Salmon EFH Technical Team were consistent with Pearcy and Fisher (1988), Pearcy (1992), and Weitkamp et al. (1995) and confirmed that the vast majority of maturing chinook and coho salmon are found within 60 km of the Washington, Oregon, and California coasts from May through September. Little information existed on ocean distribution of Pacific salmon during winter months, and winter distribution was assumed to be similar to summer and fall distribution. However, it is possible that salmon are distributed further offshore during winter months. Much less information was available for Puget Sound sockeye and pink salmon, but the available information suggests the majority of these fish are found in Canadian and international waters outside of the jurisdiction of the PFMC Pacific Coast Salmon Plan.

Description and Identification of Essential Fish Habitat

Initially, Pacific salmon EFH was identified for individual species; however, the EFH provisions of the Magnuson-Stevens Act indicate that the NMFS and Councils should identify EFH for the fishery rather than individual species. Because of the overlap in freshwater and marine distribution, EFH rec-

ommendations for individual salmon species were combined into one description for Pacific salmon. Furthermore, the Magnuson-Stevens Act indicates that EFH should be equivalent to or greater than aquatic areas identified as critical habitat for salmon populations listed under the Endangered Species Act (ESA). With this end in mind, and considering the need to streamline EFH and ESA consultations, EFH description, identification, and recommendations followed a format similar to that for critical habitat as designated for Pacific salmon listed under the ESA.

Recommended Description of Freshwater Essential Fish Habitat

Based on the available life history information, freshwater EFH for Pacific salmon consists of four major components: (1) spawning and incubation, (2) juvenile rearing, (3) juvenile migration corridors, and (4) adult migration corridors and adult holding habitat. Important features of essential habitat for spawning, rearing, and migration include adequate

1. substrate composition;
2. water quality (e.g., dissolved oxygen, nutrients, temperature, etc.);
3. water quantity, depth, and velocity;
4. channel gradient and stability;
5. food availability;
6. cover and habitat complexity (e.g., large woody debris, pools, channel complexity, aquatic vegetation, etc.);
7. space (habitat area);
8. access and passage; and
9. floodplain and habitat connectivity.

Pacific salmon EFH for the Pacific Coast Salmon Plan includes all streams, lakes, ponds, wetlands, and other water bodies currently and historically utilized by Pacific salmon within Washington, Oregon, Idaho, and California. The geographic extent of freshwater EFH is specifically described as all waters currently or historically accessible to salmon within the U.S. Geological Survey (USGS) hydrologic units identified by NMFS (Figure 3). Salmon EFH excludes areas upstream of long-standing naturally impassable barriers (i.e., natural waterfalls in existence for several hundred years) and some long-standing artificial barriers to be determined by NMFS (e.g., Grand Coulee Dam on the Columbia River, Hells Canyon Dam on the

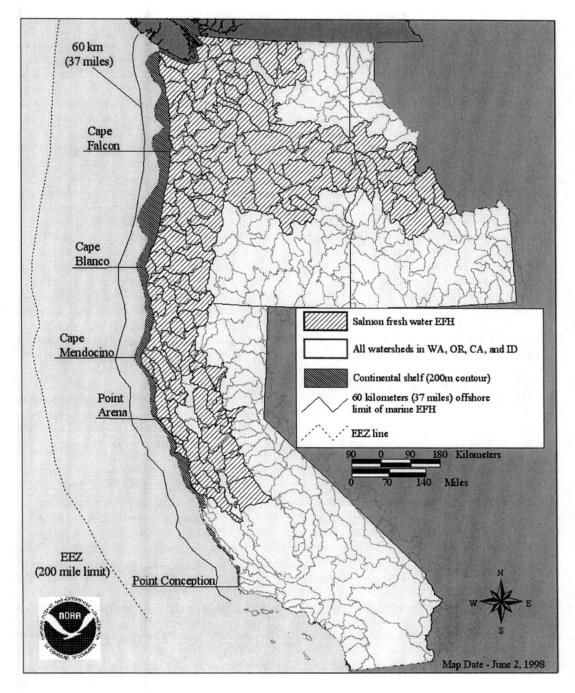

FIGURE 3.—Pacific salmon freshwater and marine essential fish habitat (EFH). Freshwater EFH includes only aquatic habitat currently and historically accessed by Pacific salmon within the shaded hydrologic units (watersheds).

Snake River, Friant Dam on the San Joaquin River, etc.). It should also be emphasized that EFH includes only aquatic areas and not land within the defined

USGS hydrologic units. Essential fish habitat for Alaskan waters was described by the NMFS and North Pacific Fisheries Management Council and therefore is not described in this chapter. In addition, EFH was not defined for international or Canadian waters.

The diversity of habitats utilized by Pacific salmon coupled with the inadequacy of existing species distribution maps precluded the identification of specific stream reaches, wetlands, and water bodies as Pacific salmon EFH. Defining specific river reaches was also complicated because of the current low abundance of the species and of our imperfect understanding of the species' freshwater distribution, both current and historic. Adopting a more inclusive, watershed-based description of EFH is appropriate because it

1. recognizes the species' use of diverse habitats and underscores the need to account for all of the habitat types supporting the species' freshwater and estuarine life stages, from small headwater streams to migration corridors and estuarine rearing areas;
2. takes into account the natural variability in habitat quality and use (e.g., some streams may have fish present only in years with plentiful rainfall) that makes precise mapping difficult;
3. reinforces the important linkage between aquatic areas and adjacent upslope areas; and
4. is consistent with the ecosystem approach recommended by the EFH regulations (NMFS 1997b).

Furthermore, this watershed-based approach is consistent with other Pacific salmon habitat protection and recovery efforts such as the Endangered Species Act (NMFS 1997a), the Northwest Forest Plan, the Oregon Coastal Salmon Restoration Initiative (the Oregon Plan), and numerous other recovery and restoration initiatives for threatened and endangered salmonids. Therefore, the geographic extent of Pacific salmon essential habitat was identified using hydrologic units (watersheds) defined in the U.S. Geological Survey 1:500,000-scale hydrologic-unit maps for Washington, Idaho, Oregon, and California (USGS 1975, 1976, 1978, 1989; Seaber et al. 1987). Although Pacific salmon EFH was primarily determined by using data on salmon distribution, detailed information on life history, habitat use, and habitat quality will be an important component of the consultation process.

Recommended Description of Marine Essential Fish Habitat

Important elements of Pacific salmon marine EFH are (1) estuarine rearing, (2) early ocean rearing, and (3) juvenile and adult migration and feed-

ing. Important features of this estuarine and marine habitat are (1) adequate water quality, (2) adequate temperature, (3) adequate prey species and forage base (food), and (4) adequate depth, cover, and marine vegetation in estuarine and nearshore habitats. Pacific salmon marine distribution is extensive; varies seasonally, interannually, and interdecadally; and can only be defined generally (Figure 1). Although limited information exists on Pacific salmon habitat use in marine waters, it is clear that habitats utilized during early-ocean entry are critical to salmon survival (Pearcy 1992). Further, as previously mentioned, available research (Pearcy and Fisher 1990; Pearcy 1992; Fisher and Pearcy 1995); catch data; and interviews with commercial fishermen all indicate that juvenile and maturing coho salmon are found in highest concentrations from late spring through fall along the continental shelf within 60 km of the Washington, Oregon, and California coastlines. Therefore, the geographic extent of marine EFH for Pacific salmon includes all waters from mean high water to 60 km (37 mi) offshore north of Point Conception, California (Figure 3). Point Conception (34E30´N) was used to identify the southern limit of marine EFH because it is considered the faunal break for marine fishes, with salmon and other temperate fishes found predominantly to the north and subtropical fishes predominantly to the south (Allen and Smith 1988).

Habitat Areas of Particular Concern

The EFH guidelines also recommend that the NMFS identify habitats within designated EFH that are particularly important or vulnerable (NMFS 1997b). Although existing GIS databases preclude identification of specific stream reaches as EFH, information exists on the type of stream reaches preferred by Pacific salmon for holding, spawning, incubation, and rearing. It is generally accepted that Pacific salmon spawn and rear in stream reaches and channels with a gradient (slope) less than 4–5% (Lunetta et al. 1997). Montgomery and Buffington (1997) proposed a geomorphically based channel classification system and identified five alluvial channel types based on slope, substrate, roughness elements, confinement, and pool spacing including

1. cascade (8.0–30.0% slope),
2. step-pool (4.0–8.0% slope),
3. plane-bed (1.0–4.0% slope),

4. pool-riffle (0.1–2.0% slope), and
5. dune-ripple/regime (<0.1% slope).

This channel-classification scheme allows for adjustment of channel type due to morphological influences of large woody debris and other roughness elements and has been used to define habitat use for juvenile and adult Pacific salmon (Inoue et al. 1997; Lunetta et al. 1997). For example, spawning adult coho and chinook salmon densities are generally low in plane-bed channels, highest in pool-riffle and forced-pool-riffle channels, and virtually absent in steeper channels (D. R. Montgomery, University of Washington, unpublished data). Pool-riffle and forced-pool-riffle channels also appear to represent areas of high-quality rearing habitat for juvenile salmonids (Inoue et al. 1997; Lunetta et al. 1997). Other channel types of less than 4% slope represent important or potentially important spawning and rearing areas for salmon but may lack some key roughness elements (e.g., large woody debris, boulders, etc.) and adequate pool frequency to support high juvenile and adult salmon densities (Montgomery and Buffington 1997; Montgomery, unpublished data). Stream reaches of greater than 4% slope are generally not utilized by Pacific salmon for spawning because of the reaches' high bed load transport rate, deep scour, and coarse substrate (Montgomery, unpublished data). Initially, stream reaches with slopes less than 4% can be identified using GIS technology or topographic maps and available stream survey data (Lunetta et al. 1997). However, channel types identified with GIS technology can differ from those actually present in the field (Lunetta et al. 1997; Montgomery and Buffington 1997). Therefore, it is important that 1:24,000- or larger-scale maps be used to determine potential channel type and a fine-scale (30 m or less) digital elevation model be used to calculate slopes. Further, slope and channel type should be confirmed by site visits in a representative number of reaches or with existing habitat surveys. Although the technology exists to develop this information, data at this scale and resolution were available only for selected watersheds and therefore could not be used for initial EFH delineation and description.

The delineation of channel types based on slope allows identification of potentially important and vulnerable habitats in the absence of accurate salmon distribution or habitat data. This process will also identify degraded stream reaches, such as those lacking key roughness elements, and stream reaches with a high potential for restoration as high-quality salmon habitat. Initially, we recommend that the protection and restoration of Pacific salmon freshwater habitat focus on low-gradient (<4%) stream reaches such as pool-riffle, plane-bed, and forced-pool-riffle channel types. This list of channel types should be modified as more data are collected on habitat use in other channel types and in other regions. Furthermore, any upstream or adjacent activity that could influence the quality of these stream reaches and important habitats should be evaluated. Overwintering habitats, which may include lakes, wetlands, and other off-channel rearing habitats, are extremely important juvenile salmonid habitats and are also habitat areas of particular concern. Large lakes (e.g., Lake Washington, Baker Lake) are particularly important rearing habitats for juvenile sockeye and to a lesser extent juvenile coho salmon. Off-channel habitats can also be identified with remote-sensing techniques such as aerial and infrared photography rather than costly field surveys (Belknap 1994). Moreover, it is critical that connectivity is maintained among habitats and throughout a basin to provide for the diverse habitat requirements of various life stages and species. Finally, the factors limiting salmon production vary among watersheds, basins, and geographic provinces. A basin or watershed analysis should be conducted to help determine the factors limiting salmon production and to help prioritize restoration and protection of EFH within a watershed (Bisson et al. 1997)

It was more difficult to define habitat areas of particular concern in the marine environment due to the lack of information on marine habitat use and distribution. However, estuaries are particularly important rearing areas for most juvenile salmonids and are especially vulnerable to anthropogenic activities. Finally, submarine canyons and other regions of pronounced upwelling are also thought to be particularly important during El Niño events (N. Bingham, Pacific Coast Federation of Fishermen's Associations, personal communication) and may need additional consideration for protection.

Information Needs and Future Direction

Although far more research has been conducted on Pacific salmon life history and habitat requirements than most other marine fishes, significant research gaps exist on distribution, marine life history, and habitat requirements. The lack of specific and comprehensive information on distribution prevented detailed delineation and fine-scale mappings of EFH. The process of identifying Pacific salmon EFH emphasized the need for accurate, fine-scale GIS data on freshwater and marine distribution and habitat conditions and the need for compilation of uniform and compatible datasets. Future efforts should focus on developing accurate seasonal salmon distribution data at a 1:24,000 or finer scale (particularly in freshwater) to aid in more accurate and precise delineation of EFH and in the EFH consultation process. It should be noted, however, that more detailed and precise freshwater distribution data will not eliminate the need for a watershed-based approach for recovery and protection of Pacific salmon EFH.

Defining salmon EFH using USGS fourth-field hydrologic units resulted in entire watersheds being defined as EFH even when large portions of the watershed were not historically used by Pacific salmon. For example, a large impassible waterfall historically and currently precludes salmon from approximately 50% of Snoqualmie hydrologic unit (USGS No. 17110010). The waters above this natural barrier are not considered EFH, although activities that may impact the quality and quantity of downstream EFH could be subject to EFH provisions. Classification by subwatersheds, defined by the USGS as fifth-field hydrologic units, would allow more restrictive and precise delineation of EFH. These subwatershed boundaries and codes are in development for some areas but were not available for initial EFH delineation. Detailed, fine-scale information on seasonal salmon distribution would allow accurate delineation of freshwater EFH using fifth- or even sixth-field hydrologic units. Further, such information would help provide the basis for more accurate descriptions of habitat areas of particular concern. Additional physical variables such as water quality, riparian vegetation, land use, and other physical features could be incorporated into this watershed framework to determine the most productive watersheds, to determine watersheds in need of restoration, and to develop priorities for restoration. Ultimately, a detailed analysis of salmon production and watershed condition throughout the Pacific Northwest is needed to determine the characteristics of productive watersheds and stream reaches for Pacific salmon.

Few studies exist on Pacific salmon oceanic and coastal distributions, and EFH descriptions for Pacific salmon relied heavily upon a few key studies on juvenile salmon (e.g., Pearcy 1992; Hartt and Dell 1986; etc.) and anecdotal information from commercial fishermen. Fine (large)-scale seasonal information on salmon marine distribution is needed to more accurately depict the distribution of juvenile, maturing, and adult Pacific salmon, which is thought to be dynamic, changing with ocean conditions. Moreover, early ocean residence is believed to be a critical period for salmon survival (Pearcy 1992), and little information exists on habitat utilization, feeding, and survival during this period. Similarly, there is a paucity of data on estuarine habitat utilization, survival, and marine distribution during winter months.

In contrast to the marine environment, considerable information exists on the freshwater life history requirements of Pacific salmon. However, little habitat- and season-specific survival information exists for most life stages. Furthermore, models are needed to predict juvenile and adult production in relation to habitat quality, ocean conditions, and the effects of anthropogenic activities such as forest practices, agriculture, grazing, and urbanization. Finally, the development of models and research on habitat impacts and salmon production will prove critical for effective consultation and refinement of Pacific salmon EFH descriptions.

Acknowledgments

We thank Kathleen Neely of the National Marine Fisheries Service and Eric Doyle of the American Fisheries Society for assistance in developing GIS maps, and members of the Salmon EFH Technical Team for their comments and suggestions during development of EFH recommendations. We also thank three anonymous reviewers for their helpful comments.

References

Allen, M. J., and G. B. Smith. 1988. Atlas and zoogeography of common fishes in the Bering Sea and northeast Pacific. NOAA (National Oceanic and Atmospheric Administration) Technical Report NMFS (National Marine Fisheries Service) 66.

Aro, K. V., and M. P. Shepard. 1967. Salmon of the North Pacific Ocean–part IV. Spawning populations of North Pacific salmon, Pacific salmon in Canada. International North Pacific Fisheries Commission Bulletin 23:225–327.

Belknap, W. D. 1994. Wall-based channels in western Washington: location, detection, mapping and winter use by juvenile salmonid fishes. Master's thesis. University of Washington, Seattle.

Bisson, P. A., G. H. Reeves, R. E. Bilby, and R. J. Naiman. 1997. Watershed management and Pacific salmon: desired future condition. Pages 447–474 *in* D. J. Stouder, P. A. Bisson, and R. J. Naiman, editors. Pacific salmon and their ecosystems: status and future options. Chapman and Hall, New York.

Bjornn, T. C., and D. W. Reiser. 1991. Habitat requirements of salmonids in streams. Pages 519–557 *in* W. R. Meehan, editor. Influences of forest and rangeland management on salmonid fishes and their habitats. American Fisheries Society, Special Publication 19, Bethesda, Maryland.

Bugaev, V. F. 1992. Age structure of sockeye salmon, *Oncorhynchus nerka*, and methods for its study. Journal of Ichthyology 32(8):1–19.

Burgner, R. L. 1991. Life history of sockeye salmon *Oncorhynchus nerka*. Pages 3–117 *in* Groot and Margolis (1991).

Burner, C. J. 1951. Characteristics of spawning nests of Columbia River salmon. U.S. Fish and Wildlife Service Fishery Bulletin 52:95–110.

Bustard, D. R., and D. W. Narver. 1975. Aspects of the winter ecology of juvenile coho salmon (*Oncorhynchus kisutch*) and steelhead trout (*Salmon gairdneri*). Journal of the Fisheries Research Board of Canada 32:667–680.

Cederholm, C. J., and W. J. Scarlett. 1981. Seasonal immigrations of juvenile salmonids into four small tributaries of the Clearwater River, Washington, 1977-81. Pages 98–110 *in* E. L. Brannon and E. O. Salo, editors. Proceedings of the salmon and trout migratory behavior symposium. University of Washington, School of Fisheries, Seattle.

Chapman, D. W. 1965. Net production of juvenile coho salmon in three Oregon streams. Transactions of the American Fisheries Society 94:40–52.

Dawley, E. M., and eight coauthors. 1986. Migrational characteristics, biological observations, and relative survival of juvenile salmonids entering the Columbia River estuary, 1966-1983. Final report to Bonneville Power Administration, Contract DE-A179-84BP39652, Portland, Oregon.

Doyle, E. G. 1997. The habitat restoration cost estimation model (HCREM): a cooperative tool for watershed management. Master's thesis. University of Washington, Seattle.

Everest, F. H., and D. W. Chapman. 1972. Habitat selection and spatial interaction by juvenile chinook salmon and steelhead trout in two Idaho streams. Journal of the Fisheries Research Board of Canada 29:91–100.

Fisher, J. P., and W. G. Pearcy. 1995. Distribution, migration, and growth of juvenile chinook salmon, *Oncorhynchus tshawytscha*, off Oregon and Washington. U.S. National Marine Fisheries Service Fishery Bulletin 93:274–289.

Foerster, R. E. 1968. The sockeye salmon, *Oncorhynchus nerka*. Fisheries Research Board of Canada Bulletin 162.

Foerster, R. E., and W. E. Ricker. 1953. The coho salmon of Cultus Lake and Sweltzer Creek. Journal of the Fisheries Research Board of Canada 10:293–319.

Forrester, C. R. 1987. Distribution and abundance of sockeye salmon (*Oncorhynchus nerka*). Canadian Special Publication of Fisheries and Aquatic Sciences 96:2–10.

French, R. R., R. G. Bakkala, and D. F. Sutherland. 1975. Ocean distribution of stocks of Pacific salmon, *Oncorhynchus* spp., and steelhead trout, *Salmo gairdnerii*, as shown by tagging experiments. NOAA (National Oceanic and Atmospheric Administration) Technical Report NMFS (National Marine Fisheries Service SSRF-689.

Gharrett, A. J., C. Smoot, and A. J. McGregor. 1988. Genetic relationships of even-year northwestern Alaskan pink salmon. Transactions of the American Fisheries Society 117:536–545.

Gilbert, C. H. 1912. Age at maturity of the Pacific coast salmon of the genus *Oncorhynchus*. U.S. Bureau of Fisheries Bulletin 32:3–22.

Godfrey, H. 1965. Coho salmon. International North Pacific Fisheries Commission Bulletin 16.

Godfrey, H., K. A. Henry, and S. Machidori. 1975. Distribution and abundance of coho salmon in offshore waters of the North Pacific Ocean. International North Pacific Fisheries Commission Bulletin 31.

Groot, C., and L. Margolis. 1991. Pacific salmon life histories. University of British Columbia Press, Vancouver.

Gustafson, R. G., and five coauthors. 1997. Status review of sockeye salmon from Washington and Oregon. NOAA (National Oceanic and Atmospheric Administration) Technical Memorandum NMFS (National Marine Fisheries Service)-NWFSC-33.

Hard, J. J., R. G. Kope, W. S. Grant, F. W. Waknitz, L. T. Parker, and R. S. Waples. 1996. Status review of pink salmon from Washington, Oregon, and California. U.S. Department of Commerce, National Oceanic and Atmospheric Administration Technical Memorandum NMFS-NWFSC-25.

Hartt, A. C. 1980. Juvenile salmonids in the oceanic ecosystem—the critical first summer. Pages 25–57 *in* W. J. McNeil and D. C. Himsworth, editors. Salmonid ecosystems of the North Pacific. Oregon State University Press and Oregon State University Sea Grant College Program, Corvallis.

Hartt, A. C., and M. B. Dell. 1986. Early oceanic migrations and growth of juvenile Pacific salmon and steelhead trout. International North Pacific Fisheries Commission Bulletin 46.

Healey, M. C. 1980. The ecology of juvenile salmon in Georgia Strait, British Columbia. Pages 203–229 *in* W. J. McNeil and D. C. Himsworth, editors. Salmonid ecosystems of the North Pacific. Oregon State University Press and Oregon State University Sea Grant College Program, Corvallis.

Healey, M. C. 1982. Juvenile Pacific salmon in estuaries: the life support system. Pages 215–341 *in* Kennedy (1982).

Healey, M. C. 1983. Coastwide distribution and ocean migration patterns of stream-type and ocean-type chinook salmon. Canadian Field-Naturalist 97:427–433.

Healey, M. C. 1986. Optimum size and age at maturity in Pacific salmon and effects of size-selective fisheries. Pages 39–52 *in* D. J. Meerburg, editor. Salmonid age at maturity. Canadian Special Publication of Fisheries and Aquatic Sciences 89.

Healey, M. C. 1991. The life history of chinook salmon (*Oncorhynchus tshawytscha*). Pages 311–393 *in* Groot and Margolis (1991).

Heard, W. R. 1991. Life history of pink salmon, *Oncorhynchus gorbuscha*. Pages 119–230 *in* Groot and Margolis (1991).

Hoar, W. S. 1956. The behavior of migrating pink and chum salmon fry. Journal of the Fisheries Research Board of Canada 13:309–325.

Inoue, M., S. Nakano, and F. Nakamura. 1997. Juvenile masu salmon (*Oncorhynchus masou*) abundance and stream habitat relationships in northern Japan. Canadian Journal of Fisheries and Aquatic Sciences 54:1331–1341.

Kennedy, V. S. 1982. Estuarine comparisons. Academic Press, New York.

Kjelson, M. A., P. F. Raquel, and F. W. Fisher. 1982. Life history of fall-run juvenile chinook salmon, *Oncorhynchus tshawytscha*, in the Sacramento-San Joaquin estuary, California. Pages 393–411 *in* Kennedy (1982).

Levings, C. D. 1982. Short term use of a low tide refuge in a sandflat by juvenile chinook, *Oncorhynchus tshawytscha*, in the Fraser River estuary. Canadian Technical Report of Fisheries and Aquatic Sciences 1111.

Levings, C. D., D. E. Boyle, and T. R. Whitehouse. 1995. Distribution and feeding of juvenile Pacific salmon in freshwater tidal creeks of the lower Fraser River, British Columbia. Fisheries Management and Ecology 2:299–308.

Lunetta, R. S., B. L. Cosentino, D. R. Montgomery, E. M. Beamer, and T. J. Beechie. 1997. GIS-based evaluation of salmon habitat in the Pacific Northwest. Photogrammetric Engineering and Remote Sensing 63:1219–1229.

MacDonald, J. S., I. K. Birtwell, and G. M. Kruzynski. 1987. Food and habitat utilization by juvenile salmonids in the Campbell River estuary. Canadian Journal of Fisheries and Aquatic Sciences 44:1233–1246.

Major, R. L., J. Ito, S. Ito, and H. Godfrey. 1978. Distribution and origin of chinook salmon in offshore waters of the North Pacific Ocean. International North Pacific Fisheries Commission Bulletin 38.

Manzer, J. I., T. Ishida, A. E. Peterson, and M. G. Hanavan. 1965. Salmon of the North Pacific Ocean. Part V: offshore distribution of salmon. International North Pacific Fisheries Commission Bulletin 15.

McDonald, J. 1960. The behavior of Pacific salmon fry during their downstream migration to freshwater and saltwater nursery areas. Journal of the Fisheries Research Board of Canada 17:655–676.

McMahon, T. E., and L. B. Holtby. 1992. Behavior, habitat use, and movements of coho salmon (*Oncorhynchus kisutch*) smolts during seaward migration. Canadian Journal of Fisheries and Aquatic Sciences 49:1478–1485.

Montgomery, D. R., and J. M. Buffington. 1997. Channel-reach morphology in mountain drainage basins. Geological Society of America Bulletin 109:596–611.

Moyle, P. B., R. M. Yoshiyama, J. E. Williams, and E. D. Wikramanayake. 1995. Fish species of special concern in California, 2nd edition. California Department of Fish Game, Sacramento.

Myers, J. M., and ten coauthors. 1998. Status review of chinook salmon from Washington, Oregon, Idaho, and California. NOAA (National Oceanic and Atmospheric Administration) Technical Memorandum NMFS (National Marine Fisheries Service)-NWFSC 35.

Myers, K. W., K. Y. Aydin, R. V. Walker, S. Fowler, and M. L. Dahlberg. 1996. Known ocean ranges of stocks of Pacific salmon and steelhead as shown by tagging experiments, 1956-1995. University of Washington, Fisheries Research Institute (NPAFC Document 192) FRI-UW-961, Seattle.

Myers, K. W., and H. F. Horton. 1982. Temporal use of an Oregon estuary by hatchery and wild juvenile salmon. Pages 377–392 *in* Kennedy (1982).

Naiman, R. J., and eight coauthors. 1992. Fundamental elements of ecologically healthy watersheds in the Pacific Northwest coastal ecoregion. Pages 127–188 *in* R. J. Naiman, editor. Watershed management. Springer-Verlag, New York.

Nickelson, T. E., J. D. Rodgers, S. L. Johnson, and M. F. Solazzi. 1992. Seasonal changes in habitat use by juvenile coho salmon (*Oncorhynchus kisutch*) in Oregon coastal streams. Canadian Journal of Fisheries and Aquatic Sciences 49:783–789.

NMFS (National Marine Fisheries Service). 1997a. Designated critical habitat; central California coast and southern Oregon/northern California coast coho salmon. Federal Register [Docket 971029257-7257-01; I.D 101097A] 62(227):627641–62751.

NMFS (National Marine Fisheries Service). 1997b. Magnuson-Stevens Act provisions: essential fish habitat: interim final rule and request for comments. Federal Register [Docket 961030300–7238–04; ID 120996A]: 66531–66559.

Pearcy, W. G. 1992. Ocean ecology of North Pacific salmonids. University of Washington Press, Seattle.

Pearcy, W. G., and J. P. Fisher. 1988. Migrations of coho salmon, *Oncorhynchus kisutch*, during their first summer in the ocean. U.S. National Marine Fisheries Service Fishery Bulletin 86(2):173–186.

Pearcy, W. G., and J. P. Fisher. 1990. Distribution and abundance of juvenile salmonids off Oregon and Washington, 1981-1985. NOAA (National Oceanic and Atmospheric Administration) Technical Report 87.

Reeves, G. H., L. E. Benda, K. M. Burnett, P. A. Bisson, and J. R. Sedell. 1995. A disturbance-based approach to maintaining and restoring freshwater habitats of evolutionarily significant units of anadromous salmonids in the Pacific Northwest. Pages 334–349 in J. L. Nielsen, editor. American Fisheries Society, Symposium 17, Bethesda, Maryland.

Reeves, G. H., F. H. Everest, and T. E. Nickelson. 1989. Identification of physical habitats limiting the production of coho salmon in western Oregon and Washington. U.S. Forest Service General Technical Report PNW-GTR-245.

Ricker, W. E., and J. I. Manzer. 1974. Recent information on salmon stocks in British Columbia. International North Pacific Fisheries Commission Bulletin 29:1–24.

Sandercock, F. K. 1991. Life history of coho salmon (Oncorhynchus kisutch). Pages 396–445 in Groot and Margolis (1991).

Seaber, P. R., F. P. Kapinos, and G. L. Knapp. 1987. Hydrologic unit maps. U.S. Geological Survey Water Supply Paper 2294.

Simenstad, C. A., K. L. Fresh, and E. O. Salo. 1982. The role of Puget Sound and Washington coastal estuaries in the life history of Pacific salmon: an unappreciated function. Pages 343–363 in Kennedy (1982).

Sullivan, K., T. E. Lisle, C. A. Dolloff, G. E. Grant, and L. M. Reid. 1987. Stream channels, the link between forests and fishes. Pages 39–97 in E. O. Salo and T. W. Cundy, editors. Streamside management: forestry and fisheries interactions. Contribution 57, Institute of Forest Resources, University of Washington, Seattle.

Swales, S., F. Caron, J. R. Irvine, and C. D. Levings. 1988. Overwintering habitats of coho salmon (Oncorhynchus kisutch) and other juvenile salmonids in the Keogh River system, British Columbia. Canadian Journal of Zoology 66:254–261.

Takagi, K., K. V. Aro, A. C. Hartt, and M. B. Dell. 1981. Distribution and origin of pink salmon (Oncorhynchus gorbuscha) in offshore waters of the North Pacific Ocean. International North Pacific Fisheries Commission Bulletin 40.

Tschaplinski, P. J. 1982. Aspects of the population biology of estuary-reared and stream-reared juvenile coho salmon in Carnation Creek: a summary of current research. Pages 289–305 in G. Hartman, editor. Proceedings of the Carnation Creek workshop, a 10 year review. Department of Fisheries and Oceans, Pacific Biological Station, Nanaimo, British Columbia.

USGS (United States Geological Survey). 1975. Hydrologic unit map, 1974, state of Idaho. U.S. Geological Survey, Denver.

USGS (United States Geological Survey). 1976. Hydrologic unit map, 1974, state of Washington. U.S. Geological Survey, Denver.

USGS (United States Geological Survey). 1978. Hydrologic unit map, 1974, state of California. U.S. Geological Survey, Denver.

USGS (United States Geological Survey). 1989. Hydrologic unit map, 1974, state of Oregon. U.S. Geological Survey, Denver.

Vernon, E. H. 1966. Enumeration of migrant pink salmon fry in the Fraser River estuary. International Pacific Salmon Fisheries Commission Bulletin 19.

WDF (Washington Department of Fisheries), Washington Department of Wildlife, and Western Washington Treaty Indian Tribes. 1993. 1992 Washington state salmon and steelhead stock inventory (SASSI). Washington Department Fish and Wildlife, Olympia.

Weitkamp, L. A., and six coauthors. 1995. Status review of coho salmon from Washington, Oregon, and California. NOAA (National Oceanic and Atmospheric Administration) Technical Memorandum NMFS (National Marine Fisheries Service)-NWFSC-24.

Williams, R. W., R. M. Laramie, and J. Ames. 1975. A catalog of Washington streams and salmon utilization. Volume 1, Puget Sound region. Washington Department of Fisheries, Olympia.

American Fisheries Society Symposium 22:108–133, 1999
© Copyright by the American Fisheries Society 1999

Suitability Modeling to Delineate Habitat Essential to Sustainable Fisheries

PETER J. RUBEC, JENNIFER C. W. BEXLEY, AND HENRY NORRIS
Florida Marine Research Institute, Florida Department of Environmental Protection
100 8th Avenue SE, St. Petersburg, Florida 33701, USA

MICHAEL S. COYNE AND MARK E. MONACO
Strategic Environmental Assessments Division, U.S. Department of Commerce, NOAA/NOS
1305 East-West Highway, 9th Floor, Silver Spring, Maryland 20910, USA

STEVEN G. SMITH AND JERALD S. AULT
Rosenstiel School of Marine and Atmospheric Science, University of Miami
4600 Rickenbacker Causeway, Miami, Florida 33149, USA

Abstract.—A need exists to scientifically determine optimal fish habitats to support decision making for management of essential fish habitat. Scientists have been collaborating to conduct habitat suitability index (HSI) modeling to spatially delineate fish habitats for estuarine fish and invertebrate species in Tampa Bay and Charlotte Harbor, Florida. Results from HSI modeling of juvenile spotted seatrout *Cynoscion nebulosus* in Charlotte Harbor are presented. Data obtained from 1989–1997 by fisheries-independent monitoring in the two estuaries were used along with environmental data from other sources. Standardized catch-per-unit-effort (catch rates) were calculated across gear types using fisheries-monitoring data from Charlotte Harbor and Tampa Bay. Suitability index functions were determined using three methods: (1) frequency of occurrence, (2) mean catch rates within ranges, and (3) smooth-mean catch rates determined by polynomial regression. Mean catch rates were estimated within biologically relevant ranges and, where sufficient data were available, for finer intervals across environmental gradients. Suitability index functions across environmental gradients were then derived by scaling catch rates. Gridded habitat layers for temperature, salinity, depth, and bottom type in Charlotte Harbor were also created using a geographic information system. Habitat suitability index modeling was conducted using the U.S. Fish and Wildlife Service geometric mean method linked to the ArcView Spatial Analyst module. The model integrated suitability indices associated with the habitat layers for Charlotte Harbor to create a map of the predicted distribution for juvenile spotted seatrout during the fall season. Suitability indices developed for Tampa Bay were used with Charlotte Harbor habitat layers to test transfer of the indices to another estuary. Predicted HSI maps depicted low to optimum habitat suitability zones in Charlotte Harbor. Model performance was evaluated by statistically comparing the relative ranking of mean catch rates with mean suitability indices for corresponding zones. Suitability indices obtained using polynomial regression methods yielded more-reliable HSI maps for juvenile spotted seatrout than those derived using mean catch rates within biologically relevant ranges. The observed map, derived using smooth-mean suitability indices transferred from Tampa Bay, was not significantly different (Chi-square goodness-of-fit test) from the expected map derived using smooth-mean indices from Charlotte Harbor. Our modeling efforts using transferred indices indicate that it is possible to predict the geographic distributions of fish species by life stage in estuaries lacking fisheries monitoring.

The "essential fish habitat" provisions of the Magnuson-Stevens Fishery Conservation and Management Act mandate that spatial relationships between fishery species and habitats need to be included in fishery management plans (NOAA 1996). Conservation of living marine resources requires effective management of both fishing effort and the mosaic of habitats used by different life stages of marine fish and invertebrate species that sustain fisheries production. This view broadens management considerations to a whole ecosystem perspective.

Some early attempts to define linkages between fish and "habitat" stem from the U.S. Fish and Wildlife Service (FWS) habitat evaluation program that mostly studied freshwater and riparian environments (FWS 1980a, 1980b, 1981; Terrell and Carpenter 1997). Habitat suitability index (HSI) models were developed to support rapid decision making using qualitative methods based on expert opinion. Many of the early HSI models developed for various species were not verified or validated with actual field data. In cases where data were collected by fisheries monitoring, rigorous sampling designs that provide comprehensive spatial or temporal coverages were rarely employed. These problems have limited the development of quantitative HSI models capable of supporting prudent fishery management strategies to build sustainable fisheries.

The Florida Department of Environmental Protection (FDEP) is developing a program to define and delineate fish habitat in Florida estuaries (Rubec and McMichael 1996; Monaco and Christensen 1997; Rubec et al. 1997, 1998). Estuaries are important nursery grounds for many fish and macroinvertebrate species that support Florida's multibillion-dollar recreational and commercial fisheries (Comp and Seaman 1988). The present work is part of the Florida Estuarine Living Marine Resources (FL-ELMR) program, which is a joint effort between the FDEP's Florida Marine Research Institute, the National Oceanic and Atmospheric Administration (NOAA), and the University of Miami. In the program's initial phase, we have been evaluating HSI models for several species in key Florida estuaries (Rubec et al. 1998). Florida currently conducts fisheries-independent monitoring to collect fish abundance, water quality, and benthic habitat type data in 5 of 18 major estuaries (McMichael 1991). Suitability indices based on the same response variable can be used to assess whether HSI models are indicative of reality (Terrell and Nickum 1984). It is desirable to know whether indices developed for one estuary can be transferred to another without significant loss of precision and biological interpretability.

In this paper we report on our recent efforts in developing an HSI model for a single-species life history stage in one estuary. We also report on the transfer of the methodology to support predicting the distribution and relative abundance of that life stage in a similar nearby estuary. We evaluate HSI model performance as compared to empirical data.

Methods

Habitat Suitability Index model

The central premise of the HSI approach derives from ecological theory relating habitat carrying capacity to density-dependent population regulation. The theory states that the "value" of an area in terms of population productivity for a given species can be determined by relating animal abundance in space to the quality and availability of given habitats (FWS 1980a, 1980b, 1981; Terrell et al. 1982; Terrell 1984; Bovee 1986; Bovee and Zuboy 1988). The HSI model we used is a simple deterministic expression that calculates a dimensionless index of habitat quality for a given species. The modeling procedure has two main steps. First, a function relating suitability index S_i to an environmental or habitat variable X_i

$$S_i = f(X_i) \qquad (1)$$

is derived for each ith factor. As described below, we employed several different methods for deriving equation (1) using species-abundance habitat data. The second step computes a composite score termed the habitat suitability index (HSI) as the geometric mean of S_i scores for n environmental factors (Li et al. 1984)

$$HSI = \left(\prod_{i=1}^{n} S_i \right)^{\frac{1}{n}} \qquad (2)$$

In general, the theory makes the simplest possible assumption that a linear relationship exists between the habitat carrying capacity and HSI (FWS 1981). In the present study, we have used a measure of density—the mean catch per unit effort (CPUE)—as the response variable. The CPUE was used as a surrogate for carrying capacity. Hence, we wished to determine whether an increasing relationship existed between mean CPUE and mean HSI values. The geometric-mean HSI method assumes that each environmental variable is equally important, that S_i functions across environmental gradients are independent, that environmental associations of a species life stage are constant during the time period modeled, and that species distributions are independent across seasons (Layer and Maughan 1985; Brown et al. 1997).

Species Abundance and Habitat Databases

Spotted seatrout relative abundance.—We focused our analyses on the habitat affinities of early juvenile spotted seatrout *Cynoscion nebulosus* with a size range from 10 to 119 mm standard length, which corresponds to the first six months of life (McMichael and Peters 1989). Data from the period 1989 to mid-1997 were obtained from FMRI's fisheries-independent monitoring program that employed numerous gears with differing size selectivities and capture efficiencies (see Gunderson

1993 for a discussion of gear properties). The size selectivity of juvenile seatrout indicated they were fully vulnerable to six gears outfitted with 3.1-mm mesh:

- three types of 21.3-m haul seines (onshore-beach, boat, and offshore-circular);
- a 61-m block net;
- a 6.1-m otter trawl; and
- a 1 m² drop net.

Capture data for other sampling gears with larger meshes were excluded from this analysis. A total of 3,716 and 6,286 stations in Charlotte Harbor and Tampa Bay, respectively, were sampled with these gears. Relative density (fish captured per unit area sampled) or CPUE data at each station were computed as the average of replicate samples. Station CPUE values were then standardized based on gear-specific capture efficiency relative to a 21.3-m offshore-circular seine gear using a modification of Robson's (1966) "fishing power" estimation method. Complete details of the procedure are described in Ault and Smith (1998).

Habitat variables and GIS layers.—Measurements of habitat variables—salinity, temperature, depth, and bottom type—at each sampling station were also obtained from the Charlotte Harbor and Tampa Bay fishery-independent monitoring databases. These databases were used exclusively in the development of suitability index S_i functions (equation 1) because they contained co-occurrent information on habitat and spotted seatrout relative abundance. Bottom type was comprised of two variables: sediment category and presence–absence of submerged aquatic vegetation (SAV). Sediment categories were defined as sand, mud, or other, where "other" included gravel, pebble, and boulder. Habitat data for Charlotte Harbor were supplemented with information from other sources in creating habitat maps of high spatial resolution. Temperature and salinity data were obtained from the Southwest Florida Water Management District and the FDEP Shellfish Environmental Assessment Section. Bathymetry data originated from 1:40,000 NOAA nautical charts. Charlotte Harbor SAV data were obtained as a vector-based GIS coverage from the FWS National Wetlands Inventory.

The ArcView Spatial Analyst extension was used to create raster-based habitat data layers called grids (ESRI 1996). Environmental data sets underwent a series of formatting and quality-assurance operations. Inconsistencies among data sets—such as units of measure, null-value codes, precision, field names, and unique record identifiers—were rectified. The environmental variables temperature and salinity were subsequently averaged over surface and bottom depths. Samples collected at the same location were averaged first by month and then by season. Seasons were defined as winter (December to February), spring (March to May), summer (June to August), and fall (September to November).

Depending on the data type, either integer or floating point grids were created. Discrete or "categorical" data with distinct boundaries between zones were converted from polygons to integer grids. However, sediment sample points required an intermediate step to form Thiessen polygons (Tomlin 1990). By delineating boundary lines midway between neighboring sample points, the polygons inherited the same sediment categories (e.g., sand, mud, or other) as their centroid. The intermediate polygon data were then converted to an integer grid. The SAV and sediment grids were combined to create the final bottom-type grid layer.

Continuous data that varied along a gradient, such as temperature, salinity, and bathymetry, were represented by floating point grids through spatial interpolation. Point samples measured at discrete, irregularly spaced locations were converted into continuous, regularly spaced grids using inverse distance weighting (ESRI 1996). The interpolation results differed depending on the number of neighboring points and the weighting power chosen. Bathymetry points were relatively dense and numerous. The bathymetry grid used 6 significant neighbors and a weighting power of 2. With fewer data points, the temperature and salinity grid layers were created using 4 significant neighbors and a weighting power of 4. Shoreline barriers prevented interpolation between neighboring points across land. Overlay analysis operations were simplified by maintaining uniformity among output grids, for example, by specifying a common coordinate system and projection resolution (100-by-100-m cell size), and spatial extent (x, y, minimum and maximum) and by assigning a no-data value to grid cells outside the study area.

Suitability Index Functions

Investigators at NOAA have recently explored the use of several quantitative approaches to deriving S_i functions (equation 1) from species-abundance habitat data (Coyne and Christensen 1997). Three of the methods used in the development of HSI models for the FL-ELMR program are described here. The methods are introduced in order of lowest to highest data requirement.

Cumulative frequency method.—The cumulative frequency method utilizes species presence–absence data. Figure 1 and Table 1 illustrate the method for deriving seatrout S_i as a function of temperature. The cumulative frequency of sampling stations that captured juvenile seatrout is computed along the gradient of observed temperatures (Figure 1a; figures appear at the end of the chapter). Straight lines are drawn along discrete parts of the cumulative frequency curve to identify "biologically relevant ranges" within which the organism exhibits a relatively uniform affinity (Figure 1b). The intersection of these straight lines identifies break points along the environmental gradient for biologically relevant ranges. The slope of each straight line is determined using linear regression, and a relative S_i value is calculated by dividing each slope by the maximum slope for the data set (Table 1). For this study, final S_i values were then converted to a scale from 0 to 10, as were all S_i functions developed in this study. It should be noted that any scale for the suitability index can be applied as long as it is uniform among S_i functions.

Range-Mean method.—The range-mean method for deriving S_i functions utilizes relative abundance data and follows from the cumulative frequency method. Sampling station CPUE observations are averaged across biologically relevant ranges of an environmental variable as identified by the cumulative frequency method. An illustration for spotted seatrout S_i as a function of temperature is presented in Table 2. In this study, suitability index values were determined by dividing the mean CPUE by the maximum mean CPUE observed and then scaling from 0 to 10.

Smooth-Mean method.—The smooth-mean method for constructing S_i functions is a further refinement of the range-mean method. Figure 2 and Table 3 illustrate this approach for deriving seatrout S_i as a function of temperature. Mean CPUEs for juvenile spotted seatrout were estimated at 1°C temperature intervals (Table 3). A polynomial regression curve was then fit to the mean CPUE values (Figure 2) using JMP software (SAS 1995). Predicted CPUE values along the curve were then used to calculate relative S_i values at each °C by dividing each CPUE by the maximum observed CPUE across the temperature gradient (Table 3). Final S_i values were

TABLE 1.—Slope and relative suitability index (using the cumulative frequency method) of each line (see Figure 1) for which a uniform frequency response is observed along the temperature gradient. Relative suitability indices are calculated by dividing each slope by the maximum slope observed. Final S_i values are scaled from 0 to 10.

Temperature	Slope (m)	m/m$_{max}$	S$_i$
13–17	0.00367	0.032	0
17–22	0.02209	0.191	2
22–25	0.05437	0.470	5
25–30	0.11577	1.000	10
30–33	0.05207	0.450	4
>33	0.00306	0.026	0

obtained by scaling from 0 to 10. The smooth-mean method thus requires relative abundance observations at fine-scale intervals along a gradient of an environmental covariate. In some cases, it was necessary to develop higher-order polynomials and truncate the extremes of the curve where no data were available (Kinzie and Ford 1988; Slauson 1988).

Habitat Suitability Maps

Map construction.—Using equation 2, composite spotted seatrout HSI scores for Charlotte Harbor during the fall season were estimated from S_i functions for salinity, temperature, depth, and bottom type. Computations were carried out using ArcView Spatial Analyst for each 100-by-100-m grid cell. The procedure is illustrated in Figure 3. For mapping purposes, grid cell HSI values were grouped into four classes: low (0.0–1.9), moderate (2.0–3.9), high (4.0–5.9), and optimum (6.0–10.0). Two observed maps were created using Charlotte Harbor habitat layers and Charlotte Harbor S_i functions, derived by the two mean CPUE methods

TABLE 2.—Mean catch per unit effort (CPUE) and derived relative suitability indices (S_i) for juvenile spotted seatrout in Charlotte Harbor within biologically relevant ranges as determined using cumulative frequency analysis and the range-mean method.

Temperature	N	Mean CPUE ($\bar{x}$)	$\bar{x}/\bar{x}_{max}$	S$_i$
13–17	81	0.00178	0.125	1
17–22	468	0.00284	0.199	2
22–25	467	0.00835	0.586	6
25–30	987	0.01220	0.855	9
30–33	202	0.01426	1.000	10
>33	16	0.00415	0.291	3

TABLE 3.—Mean catch per unit effort (CPUE), fitted CPUE, and suitability indices (S$_i$) along the temperature gradient for juvenile spotted seatrout in Charlotte Harbor, Florida.

Temperature	N	Mean CPUE	Fitted CPUE ($\overline{x}$)	$\overline{x}/\overline{x}_{max}$	S$_i$
11	1	0.00000	0.00061	0.04986	0
12	4	0.00000	0.00012	0.01004	0
13	7	0.00062	-0.00009	-0.00753	0
14	3	0.00000	-0.00006	-0.00502	0
15	6	0.00000	0.00019	0.01539	0
16	22	0.00215	0.00063	0.05152	1
17	36	0.00243	0.00125	0.10121	1
18	61	0.00247	0.00200	0.16226	2
19	84	0.00172	0.00286	0.23251	2
20	98	0.00264	0.00382	0.30977	3
21	86	0.00299	0.00483	0.39188	4
22	139	0.00372	0.00587	0.47664	5
23	146	0.00983	0.00692	0.56188	6
24	152	0.00837	0.00795	0.64544	6
25	169	0.00706	0.00893	0.72512	7
26	206	0.00823	0.00984	0.79875	8
27	218	0.00906	0.01064	0.86416	9
28	219	0.01181	0.01132	0.91917	9
29	183	0.02214	0.01184	0.96160	10
30	161	0.01074	0.01219	0.98927	10
31	108	0.02661	0.01232	1.00000	10
32	68	0.01168	0.01221	0.99162	10
33	27	0.01209	0.01185	0.96196	10
34	10	0.00158	0.01119	0.90882	9
35	4	0.00298	0.01022	0.83005	8
36	2	0.01935	0.00891	0.72345	7

previously described. Two expected maps were also created using Charlotte Harbor habitat layers and S$_i$ functions transferred from Tampa Bay.

Model performance evaluation.—The number of grid cells within each suitability zone of the predicted HSI distribution maps was determined using functions in ArcView Spatial Analyst. The process was repeated for the HSI maps associated with range-mean S$_i$ functions and with smooth-mean S$_i$ functions). Chi-square goodness-of-fit tests were conducted to determine whether grid-cell frequencies were significantly different between predicted HSI maps for juvenile spotted seatrout in Charlotte Harbor (Simpson et al. 1960). The CPUE data at point localities from the fisheries-independent monitoring program were overlaid on the predicted HSI maps, and the points were associated with the suitability zones. The process was repeated with the HSI maps produced from range-mean S$_i$ values and from smooth-mean S$_i$ values. The CPUE data sets were then used to determine mean CPUEs within suit-

ability zones for (1) the expected and observed range-mean HSI maps and (2) the expected and observed smooth-mean HSI maps. The zonal mean CPUEs were then graphed versus the zonal mean HSI values for each of the four HSI maps.

Grid-cell frequencies were compared between observed (derived from Charlotte Harbor S$_i$ values) and expected (derived from Tampa Bay S$_i$ values) data. Graphical comparisons were conducted by subtracting suitability-zone rankings (1–4) for grid cells in the expected map from cell rankings associated with the observed map. A third map was produced representing the differences between grid cell rankings.

Results

Comparison of Suitability Index Methods

Spotted seatrout suitability index functions (equation 1) dependent on temperature were derived by the cumulative frequency, range-mean, and smooth-mean methods and are diagrammed in Figure 4. All three methods yielded similar S_i values for temperatures below 25°C. The cumulative frequency method indicated peak S_i values ($S_i = 10$) from 25 to 30°C. With the range-mean and smooth-mean methods, the S_i functions peaked between 31 and 33°C, whereas the cumulative frequency method predicted much lower suitability scores ($S_i = 4$). We also observed similar disparities between cumulative frequency S_i functions and the S_i functions derived by the two mean CPUE methods for other environmental variables. Subsequent analyses were thus directed toward comparing the range-mean and smooth-mean methods for constructing S_i functions. Cumulative frequencies were only used to define biologically relevant intervals of a given environmental variable (e.g., Figure 1b) for applying the range-mean method.

Charlotte Harbor suitability data.—Charlotte Harbor range-mean S_i functions for salinity, temperature, depth, and bottom type are shown in Figure 5 (open bars). Biologically relevant intervals of environmental parameters are denoted by class numbers. Smooth-mean S_i functions for the continuous environmental variables salinity, temperature, and depth are graphed in Figure 6 (solid lines). Corresponding polynomial regression equations are presented in Table 4. The range-mean and smooth-mean methods produced generally similar S_i patterns for continuous habitat variables. High suitability indices for seatrout in Charlotte Harbor occurred at mid-range salinities (15–25‰), high temperatures (>26°C), and shallow depths (<1.5 m). Only the range-mean method was used for the categorical variable bottom type (Figure 5). With bottom type, the highest suitability indices occurred in areas that contained SAV.

The HSI model (equation 2) was applied to Charlotte Harbor for the fall season using two different sets of S_i functions. The range-mean HSI model incorporated the four range-mean S_i functions of Figure 5, whereas the smooth-mean HSI model incorporated the three smooth-mean S_i curves of Figure 6 along with the range-mean S_i function for bottom type (Figure 5). Predicted areas (i.e., number of map grid cells) of four broad HSI zones were somewhat different for the two models (Table 5 and Figure 7, solid bars). The smooth-mean model (Figure 7) estimated a smaller moderate HSI zone and larger high and optimal HSI zones compared to the range-mean model (Figure 7). For each HSI zone, Table 5 presents HSI scores averaged over grid cells and CPUE values averaged over sampling stations for the two HSI models. Plots of HSI zone mean CPUE against mean HSI score are shown in Figure 8. Mean CPUE increased with increasing HSI score in Figure 8 (bottom) as expected, indicating adequate performance of the smooth-mean HSI model. This was not the case for the range-mean HSI model, where relative abundance data and model-predicted habitat suitability for seatrout did not correspond (Figure 8 [top]).

Tampa Bay suitability data.—Seatrout suitability index functions for salinity, temperature, depth, and bottom type derived from Tampa Bay data are depicted in Figures 5 and 6. As was the case for Charlotte Harbor data, range-mean (Figure 5, solid bars) and smooth-mean (Figure 6, dashed lines) S_i functions were in general agreement. However, HSI models based on the two S_i methods differed with respect to the areal extent of HSI zones predicted for Charlotte Harbor (Table 5 and Figure 7, shaded bars). The range-mean HSI model (Figure 7 [top])

TABLE 4.—Polynomial regression suitability index (S_i) equations for Charlotte Harbor and Tampa Bay derived from mean CPUEs across gradients of temperature, salinity, and depth. (CH = Charlotte Harbor, TB = Tampa Bay, T=temperature, G = salinity, D = depth. The coefficient of determination (r^2) is based on the fitted mean CPUEs.)

Location	Regression equation	Coefficient
	Temperature ($i = 1$)	
CH	$S_1 = 0.0317758 - 0.00557T + 0.000298T^2 - 0.00000447T^3$	$r^2 = 0.582$
TB	$S_1 = 0.3478437 - 0.048949T + 0.0021345T^2 - 0.000028T^3$	$r^2 = 0.602$
	Salinity ($i = 2$)	
CH	$S_2 = 0.0040184 - 0.000393G + 0.0001427G^2 + 0.00000654G^3 + 0.000000007869G^4$	$r^2 = 0.705$
TB	$S_2 = 0.0027424 + 0.0007294G + 0.000018G^2 - 0.0000009034G^3$	$r^2 = 0.600$
	Depth ($i = 3$)	
CH	$S_3 = 0.00223614 + 0.0212379D - 0.019623D^2 + 0.0061119D^3 - 0.000792D^4 + .0000363D^5$	$r^2 = 0.604$
TB	$S_3 = 0.0041553 + 0.036787D - 0.035219D^2 + 0.0124316D^3 - 0.002082D^4 + 0.000167D^5 - 0.000005D^6$	$r^2 = 0.659$

TABLE 5.—Zonal comparison of the relative frequency of the number of grid cells in Charlotte Harbor from habitat suitability index (HSI) modeling using either range-mean suitability index (S_i) functions or smooth-mean S_i functions. The rankings associated with mean S_i values and mean catch rates (CPUEs) are given in parentheses. (CH = S_is from within Charlotte Harbor, TB = S_is transferred from Tampa Bay.)

Grid name	Zone	Cell count (1,000s)	Mean S_i	Mean CPUE (No./m²)
CH range-mean	Low	21.232	1.1 (1)	0.0002584 (1)
	Moderate	19.197	3.0 (2)	0.0053771 (2)
	High	9.266	5.0 (3)	0.0142007 (4)
	Optimum	8.498	7.1 (4)	0.0092430 (3)
TB range-mean	Low	4.157	0.0 (1)	0.0038670 (2)
	Moderate	30.632	3.1 (2)	0.0019351 (1)
	High	16.623	4.9 (3)	0.0133140 (4)
	Optimum	6.681	6.6 (4)	0.0085345 (3)
CH smooth-mean	Low	18.856	0.0 (1)	0.0000275 (1)
	Moderate	7.087	3.0 (2)	0.0004515 (2)
	High	16.787	5.0 (3)	0.0085384 (3)
	Optimum	15.464	7.7 (4)	0.0106259 (4)
TB smooth-mean	Low	12.530	0.0 (1)	0.0000110 (1)
	Moderate	8.689	3.2 (2)	0.0002036 (2)
	High	20.266	5.0 (3)	0.0072092 (3)
	Optimum	16.708	7.6 (4)	0.0104078 (4)

estimated a larger moderate HSI zone and smaller low and optimum HSI zones compared to the smooth-mean model (Figure 7 [bottom]). Plots of mean CPUE against mean HSI score by HSI zone indicate that the smooth-mean HSI model (Figure 9 [bottom]) was superior in performance to the range-mean model (Figure 9 [top]).

Between-estuary comparisons.—We evaluated the efficacy of using S_i functions developed for one estuary as inputs for a HSI model for another estuary within the context of the range-mean and smooth-mean methods. Seatrout S_i functions based on the two methods are compared for Charlotte Harbor and Tampa Bay data in Figures 5 and 6. Index functions for bottom type were nearly identical between the two estuaries (Figure 5). Suitability index functions respectively for salinity, temperature, and depth were similar for Charlotte Harbor and Tampa Bay but were somewhat offset from one another (Figures 5 and 6). This effect is more visibly pronounced in the range-mean results (Figure 5) than in the smooth-mean results (Figure 6).

The range-mean HSI model, using Charlotte Harbor-derived S_i functions, estimated seatrout HSI zone areas (i.e., grid-cell frequencies) for Charlotte Harbor that differed significantly ($\chi^2 = 26.87$, 3 df, $p < 0.001$) from the zone areas estimated using S_i functions transferred from Tampa Bay (Table 5; Figure 7 [top]). In contrast, estimates of zone ar-

eas derived from the smooth-mean HSI model were not significantly different ($\chi^2 = 3.306$, 3 df, $p > 0.05$) when S_i functions from Charlotte Harbor and from Tampa Bay were used (Table 5; Figure 7 [bottom]).

Habitat Suitability Maps for Charlotte Harbor

Maps of habitat layers for salinity, temperature, depth, and bottom type for Charlotte Harbor during fall are shown in Figures 10a–10d. The predicted spotted seatrout HSI map based on Charlotte Harbor smooth-mean S_i functions is presented in Figure 11. "Optimal" and "high" regions of seatrout suitability (Figure 11) corresponded with shallow areas (Figure 10c) and bottom types containing SAV (Figure 10d). Fall patterns of salinity (Figure 10a) and temperature (Figure 10b) did not geographically correspond with the spatial distribution of seatrout predicted from the model.

The HSI map based on smooth-mean S_i curves transferred from Tampa Bay (Figure 12) was quite similar to the map based on Charlotte Harbor data (Figure 11), as evidenced by the difference map of Figure 13. Most of the differences between the maps were in the "low" and "moderate" zones. These zonal differences in the predicted maps for Charlotte Harbor using Charlotte Harbor S_i functions (Figure 11) and S_i functions from Tampa Bay (Figure 12) may be related to differences in the fitted curves for depth

(Figure 6). Juvenile spotted seatrout occurred at greater depths in Tampa Bay than were found in Charlotte Harbor.

Discussion

The HSI modeling approach has been adapted to address Florida's need to transfer information on species habitat affinities between estuaries (Rubec et al. 1998). The models were designed to be developed, applied, and modified relatively quickly with minimal resources. Therefore, our approach relied on a few selected parameters (e.g., salinity, temperature, depth, and bottom type) and simple arithmetic relationships. The geometric mean HSI modeling method has often been applied (Terrell and Carpenter 1997) and was used in the present study to determine simple arithmetic relationships between species abundance and habitats and to coalesce S_i functions to predict spatial distributions of juvenile spotted seatrout.

Several researchers have questioned the assumptions associated with the geometric mean method (Orth and Maughan 1982; Mathur et al. 1985). Mathur et al. (1985) noted that suitability functions are ratios based on shifting denominators. One habitat variable may have a response (i.e., mean CPUE) that is much higher than another variable, but both are given equal weight when they are scaled to the same maximum value (i.e., 1 or 10). We examined our data and determined that the highest mean CPUEs were very similar across gradients of bottom type, salinity, temperature, and depth. Hence, the assumption that the variables had equal weight may not have been violated.

One would expect a low correlation between fish standing stock and suitability if the factors had unequal weights (Mathur et al. 1985). The range-mean method failed to demonstrate agreement between rankings (Table 5) and did not exhibit an increasing relationship between mean CPUE and mean HSI values by suitability zones using S_i functions from Charlotte Harbor (Figure 8 [top]) and transferred from Tampa Bay (Figure 9 [top]). The smooth-mean method demonstrated agreement between rankings by suitability zones (Table 5) and increasing relationships between mean CPUE and mean HSI values using S_i functions from Charlotte Harbor (Figure 8 [bottom]) and transferred from Tampa Bay (Figure 9 [bottom]). Failure of the range-mean method may be because the mean CPUEs within biologically relevant ranges were not smoothed to determine the S_i functions across environmental gradients. Smoothing mean CPUE data and scaling fitted CPUEs from 0 to 10 contributed to the success of the smooth-mean method in verifying the HSI model.

One might also find low correlations between mean CPUE and mean HSI values if there were significant interactions between factors (Mathur et al. 1985; Vadas 1994). We plan to examine the influence of interaction between factors by developing regression-based HSI models, in parallel with the geometric mean approach, in future work.

Our HSI model results for Charlotte Harbor (Figure 11) suggest that shallow, vegetated areas provide the best habitat for juvenile spotted seatrout during fall (Figures 5, 10c–10d). Our results also indicate that deeper, unvegetated areas are less-suitable habitats for juvenile spotted seatrout. Temperature and salinity appear to have little influence on the fall spatial distribution of juvenile seatrout in Charlotte Harbor (Figures 6, 10a–10b, 11). The scientific literature indicates that juvenile spotted seatrout can tolerate wide ranges of salinity and temperature (Rutherford et al. 1989; Killam et al. 1992). The ranges observed in Charlotte Harbor are well within minimum and maximum tolerance levels. Hence, the predicted distribution maps of juvenile spotted seatrout agree with published literature describing the habitats commonly occupied by juvenile spotted seatrout (McMichael and Peters 1989; Killam et al. 1992; Christensen et al. 1997; Patillo et al. 1997).

We draw much the same conclusions with respect to juvenile seatrout habitat affinities when S_i functions derived from Tampa Bay data are used to create HSI maps in Charlotte Harbor (Figure 12). Suitability curves for bottom type (Figure 5) and depth (Figure 6) were very similar for Tampa Bay and Charlotte Harbor. Salinity and temperature S_i functions also displayed similar trends in the two estuaries (Figure 6). These results are encouraging from a pragmatic point of view, suggesting that it may be possible to extrapolate abundance–habitat associations from well-studied estuaries to similar, nearby estuaries for which little or no fisheries sampling data exist. A key objective for the next phase of our research program is to thoroughly examine what constitutes "similar" and "nearby" in transferring information from one estuary to another.

Several studies have attempted to transfer suitability functions between different aquatic ecosystems with limited success (Kinzie and Ford 1988;

Freeman et al. 1997). The similarity of the scaled S_i functions for bottom type (Figures 5) and salinity, temperature, and depth (Figure 6) contributed to our success in transferring Tampa Bay S_i functions to predict the juvenile spotted seatrout distribution in Charlotte Harbor (Figure 12). Scaling mean CPUE data appeared to be necessary to help infer the spatial distribution of juvenile spotted seatrout by life stage in Charlotte Harbor using Tampa Bay S_i functions. Hence, curve-fitting and scaling the data appeared to facilitate transfer of suitability index functions to help predict species distributions in a nearby estuary.

The method used to construct S_i functions appears to be very important in producing reliable habitat maps. We employed three different methods, namely cumulative frequency, range-mean, and smooth-mean, that respectively reflect increasing levels of data requirements. The smooth-mean method, with the most stringent data requirements, was the only approach that adequately predicted HSI zones (Figures 11 and 12) when compared to empirical CPUE data (Figure 14). This is an important result given that HSI models were specifically developed for use in minimal-data situations (FWS 1980a, 1980b, 1981; Schamberger et al. 1982; Schamberger and O'Neil 1986). In past applications, a panel of "experts" was employed to develop S_i functions (equation 1) by assigning suitability scores according to some scale (e.g., 0–10) along the range of each potentially relevant environmental variable (Terrell et al. 1982; Crance 1987; Brown et al. 1997; Christensen et al. 1997).

Habitat suitability index models are designed to rank the relative contribution of animals based on habitat quality. Thus HSIs are not designed to predict CPUE, and in certain instances the disagreements between HSI rankings and CPUE are valid. This was evidenced by Brown et al. (1997), who demonstrated a poor relationship between CPUE and HSI rankings in areas where softshell clams were harvested. In addition, in areas where environmental degradation has occurred, suitable structural and water quality habitats may be available but are not utilized due to contamination (M. E. Monaco, NOAA; R. S. Easton, Versar Inc.; J. L. Hyland, NOAA; W. Rickus, Versar Inc.; and S. W. Ross, North Carolina Estuarine Research Reserves, unpublished data). Further studies are needed to compare expert-opinion-based HSI methods with more quantitative approaches to evaluate the methods' benefits and limitations.

The geometric mean HSI models only utilized a fraction of the potential information content of the fishery-independent sampling database. A limitation of this approach for developing S_i functions and computing HSI scores is that it is exclusively focused on expected mean values. The variability or variance of the relationships was not considered. The HSI modeling approach (FWS 1980a, 1980b, 1981) offers no formal guidance for determining which environmental factors to include or exclude, that is, what variables constitute "habitat."

We suspect that HSI models that treat factors as being independent may be adequate to predict spatial distributions but probably cannot be used to predict actual abundance. Because Florida is interested in predicting mean CPUEs by suitability zones to support fisheries management, we plan to develop more-sophisticated HSI models that explore abundance–habitat relationships. A natural extension of equations 1 and 2 are multivariate regression models that relate CPUE response to a suite of habitat variables X_i according to the general form

$$CPUE = f(X_1, X_2, \ldots X_n) + \epsilon \quad (3)$$

where ϵ is an error term. Methodologies including general and generalized linear regression, nonlinear regression, and generalized additive models offer considerable flexibility in specifications of equation (3) model forms (e.g., linear, nonlinear) and error-term distributions (e.g., normal, gamma, negative binomial) in estimating model parameters (McCullagh and Nelder 1989; Seber and Wild 1989; Hastie and Tibshirani 1990).

As the next phase of our research program expands to include more species and estuaries, we plan to develop both simplistic HSI models and more-advanced regression-type HSI models in concert to gain a deeper understanding of abundance–habitat relationships and predictions of spatial distributions and abundance of estuarine species important for the sustainability of marine fish and invertebrate fisheries.

Acknowledgments

We thank G. McRae, G. Nelson of FMRI, and two anonymous reviewers for reading the manuscript and suggesting improvements. In addition, R. H. McMichael, Jr., and M. Mitchell, who are associated with FMRI's Fisheries-Independent Monitoring Program, provided input concerning spotted seatrout and the Charlotte Harbor ecosystem. The research was supported by a combined grant (NA 76RG-0120) through the National Sea Grant College Program.

References

Ault, J. S., and S. G. Smith. 1998. Gear inter-calibration for FLELMR catch-per-unit-effort data. University of Miami, Rosenstiel School of Marine and Atmospheric Science, Technical Report to Florida Marine Research Institute, FDEP Contract No. MR243.

Bovee, K. 1986. Development and evaluation of habitat suitability criteria for use in the instream flow incremental methodology. U.S. Department of the Interior, U.S. Fish and Wildlife Service, National Ecology Center, Division of Wildlife and Contaminant Branch, Instream Flow Information Paper No. 21, Biological Report 86(7), Washington, D.C.

Bovee, K., and J. R. Zuboy, editors. 1988. Proceedings of a workshop on the development and evaluation of habitat suitability criteria. U.S. Department of the Interior, U.S. Fish and Wildlife Service, Biological Report 88(11).

Brown, S. K., K. B. Buja, S. H. Jury, and A. Banner. 1997. Habitat suitability index models for Casco and Sheepscot Bays, Maine. National Oceanic and Atmospheric Administration, Strategic Environmental Assessments Division, Silver Spring, Maryland, and U.S. Fish and Wildlife Service, Falmouth, Maine.

Christensen, J. D., T. A. Battista, M. E. Monaco, and C. J. Klein. 1997. Habitat suitability index modeling and GIS technology to support habitat management: Pensacola Bay, Florida case study. Technical Report to the U.S. Environmental Protection Agency, Gulf of Mexico Program, National Oceanic and Atmospheric Administration, National Ocean Service, Strategic Environmental Assessments Division, Silver Spring, Maryland.

Comp, G. S., and W. Seaman, Jr. 1988. Estuaries. Pages 337–435 in W. Seaman, Jr., editor. Florida Aquatic Habitat and Fishery Resources. Florida Chapter of American Fisheries Society, Eustis, Florida.

Coyne, M. S., and J. D. Christensen. 1997. NOAA's Biogeography Program Technical Report. Habitat suitability index modeling–species habitat suitability index guidelines. U.S. Department of Commerce, National Oceanic and Atmospheric Administration Strategic Environmental Assessments Division, Technical Document 1-19, Silver Spring, Maryland.

Crance, J. H. 1987. Guidelines for using the Delphi technique to develop habitat suitability index curves. U.S. Department of the Interior, U.S. Fish and Wildlife Service, National Ecology Center, Division of Wildlife and Contaminant Research, Biological Report 82(10.134).

ESRI (Environmental Systems Research Institute). 1996. ArcView Spatial Analyst: advanced spatial analysis using raster and vector data. Environmental Systems Research Institute, Inc., Redlands, California.

Freeman, M. C., Z. H. Bowen, and J. H. Crance. 1997. Transferability of habitat suitability criteria for fishes in warmwater streams. North American Journal of Fisheries Management 17:20–31.

FWS (U.S. Fish and Wildlife Service). 1980a. Habitat as a basis of environmental assessment. U.S. Department of the Interior, U.S. Fish and Wildlife Service, Washington, D.C., ESM Report 101(4-80).

FWS (U.S. Fish and Wildlife Service). 1980b. Habitat evaluation procedures. U.S. Department of the Interior, U.S. Fish and Wildlife Service, Washington, D.C., ESM Report 102 (2-80).

FWS (U.S. Fish and Wildlife Service). 1981. Standards for the development of habitat suitability index models for use with habitat evaluation procedures. U.S. Department of the Interior, U.S. Fish and Wildlife Service, Division of Ecological Services, Washington D.C., ESM Report 103(1-81).

Gunderson, D. R. 1993. Surveys of fisheries resources. J.H. Wiley & Sons, New York

Hastie, T. J., and R. J. Tibshirani. 1990. Generalized additive models. Chapman and Hall, London.

Killam, K. A., R. J. Hochberg, and E. C. Rzemien. 1992. Spotted seatrout (Cynoscion nebulosus). Pages 3–40-3-57 in Synthesis of basic life histories of Tampa Bay species. Tampa Bay National Estuary Program Technical Publication 10-92, St. Petersburg, Florida.

Kinzie, R. A., III, and J. I. Ford. 1988. A test of transferability of habitat utilization curves. Pages 336–363 in K. Bovee and J. R. Zuboy, editors. Proceedings of a workshop on the development and evaluation of habitat suitability criteria, U.S. Department of the Interior, U.S. Fish and Wildlife Service, Biological Report 88(11).

Layer, W. G., and O. E. Maughan. 1985. Spotted bass habitat evaluation using an unweighted geometric mean to determine HSI values. Proceedings of the Oklahoma Academy of Sciences 65:11–17.

Li, H. W., C. B. Schreck, and K. J. Rodnick. 1984. Assessment of habitat quality models for cutthroat trout (Salmo clarki clarki) and coho salmon (Oncorhynchus kisutch) for Oregon's coastal streams. Pages 57–111 in J. W. Terrell, editor. Proceedings of a workshop on fish habitat suitability index models. U.S. Department of the Interior, U.S. Fish and Wildlife Service, Division of Biological Services, Washington D.C., Biological Report 85(6).

Mathur, D., W. H. Bason, E. J. Purdy, Jr., and C. A. Silver. 1985. A critique of the instream flow methodology. Canadian Journal of Fisheries and Aquatic Sciences 42:825–831.

McCullagh, P., and J. A. Nelder. 1989. Generalized linear models, 2nd edition. Chapman and Hall, London.

McMichael, R. H., Jr. 1991. Florida's marine fisheries-independent monitoring program. Pages 255–261 in S. F. Treat and P. A. Clark, editors. Proceedings of the Tampa Bay Area Scientific Information Symposium 2, Tampa Bay Regional Planning Council Publication, St. Petersburg, Florida.

McMichael, R. H., Jr., and K. M. Peters. 1989. Early life history of spotted seatrout, *Cynoscion nebulosus* (Pisces: Sciaenidae), in Tampa Bay, Florida. Estuaries 12(2):98–110.

Monaco, M. E., and J. D. Christensen. 1997. Biogeography program: coupling species distributions and habitat. Pages 133–138 in G. W. Boehlert and J. D. Schumacher, editors. Changing oceans and changing fisheries: environmental data for fisheries research and management. National Oceanic and Atmospheric Administration Strategic Environmental Assessments Division, Silver Spring, Maryland, NOAA Technical Memorandum NOAA-TM-NMFS-SWFSC-239.

NOAA (National Oceanic, and Atmospheric Administration). 1996. Magnuson-Stevens Fishery Conservation and Management Act amended through 11 October 1996. U.S. Department of Commerce, National Marine Fisheries Service, Washington D.C., NOAA Technical Memorandum NMFS-F/SPO-23.

Orth, D. J., and O. E. Maughan. 1982. Evaluation of the incremental methodology for recommending instream flows for fishes. Transactions of the American Fisheries Society 111(4):413–445.

Patillo, M. E., T. E. Czapla, D. M. Nelson, and M. E. Monaco. 1997. Spotted seatrout. Pages 259–268 in Distribution and abundance of fishes and invertebrates in Gulf of Mexico estuaries, volume II: species life history summaries. National Oceanic and Atmospheric Administration, National Ocean Service Strategic Environmental Assessments Division, Estuarine Living Marine Resources Report Number 11, Silver Spring, Maryland.

Robson, D. S. 1966. Estimation of the relative fishing power of individual ships. International Commission on Northwest Atlantic Fisheries Research Bulletin 3:5–14.

Rubec, P. J., M. S. Coyne, R. H. McMichael, Jr., and M. E. Monaco. 1998. Spatial methods being developed in Florida to determine essential fish habitat. Fisheries 23(7):21–25.

Rubec, P. J., and R. H. McMichael, Jr. 1996. Ecosystem management relating habitat to marine fisheries in Florida. Pages 113–145 in P. J. Rubec, and J. O'Hop, editors. GIS applications for fisheries and coastal resources management. Gulf States Marine Fisheries Commission, Ocean Springs, Mississippi.

Rubec, P. J., M. E. Monaco, and J. D. Christensen. 1997. The FLELMR spatial decision support system for coastal resources management. Pages 135–138 in GIS '97, Proceedings of the Eleventh Annual Symposium on Geographic Information Systems. GIS World, Fort Collins, Colorado.

Rutherford, E. S., T. W. Schmidt, and J. T. Tilimant. 1989. Early life history of spotted seatrout (*Cynoscion nebulosus*) and gray snapper (*Lutjanus griseus*) in Florida Bay, Everglades National Park, Florida. Bulletin of Marine Science 44(1):49–64.

SAS. 1995. JMP statistics and graphics guide: version 3. SAS Institute, Cary, North Carolina.

Schamberger, M., A. H. Farmer, and J. W. Terrell. 1982. Habitat suitability index models: introduction. U.S. Fish and Wildlife Service, Office of Biological Services, Document 88(10).

Schamberger, M. L., and L. J. O'Neil. 1986. Concepts and constraints of habitat-model testing. Pages 5–10 in J. Verner, M. L. Morrison, and C. J. Ralph, editors. Wildlife 2000: modeling habitat relationships of terrestrial vertebrates. University of Wisconsin Press, Madison.

Seber, G. A. F., and C. J. Wild. 1989. Nonlinear regression. Wiley, New York.

Simpson, G. S., A. Roe, and R. C. Lewontin. 1960. Quantitative zoology. Harcourt, Brace and Company, New York.

Slauson, W. L. 1988. Constructing suitability curves from data. Pages 225–258 in K. Bovee and J. R. Zuboy, editors. Proceedings of a workshop on the development and evaluation of habitat suitability criteria. U.S. Department of the Interior, U.S. Fish and Wildlife Service, Biological Report 88(11).

Terrell, J. W., editor. 1984. Proceedings of a workshop on fish habitat suitability index models. U.S. Department of the Interior, U.S. Fish and Wildlife Service, Division of Biological Services, Washington D.C., Biological Report 85(6).

Terrell, J. W., and J. Carpenter, editors. 1997. Selected habitat suitability index model evaluations. U.S. Department of the Interior, U.S. Geological Survey, Information and Technology Report USGS/BRD/ITR–1997-0005.

Terrell, J. W., T. E. McMahon, P. D. Inskip, R. F. Raleigh, and K. L. Williamson. 1982. Habitat suitability index models: appendix A, guidelines for riverine, and lacustrine applications of fish HSI models with the habitat evaluation procedures. U.S. Department of the Interior, U.S. Fish and Wildlife Service, Biological Services Program, and Division of Ecological Services, FWS/O.S.-82/10A.

Terrell, J. W., and J. G. Nickum. 1984. Workshop synthesis and recommendations. Pages 1–16 in J. W. Terrell, editor. Proceedings of a workshop on fish habitat suitability index models. U.S. Department of the Interior, U.S. Fish and Wildlife Service, Division of Biological Services, Washington D.C., Biological Report 85(6).

Tomlin, C. D. 1990. Geographic information systems and cartographic modeling. Prentice Hall, Englewood Cliffs, New Jersey.

Vadas, R. L., Jr. 1994. Habitat tools for assessing instream-flow needs for fishes in the upper Roanoke River, Virginia. Doctoral dissertation. Virginia Polytechnic Institute and State University, Blacksburg Virginia.

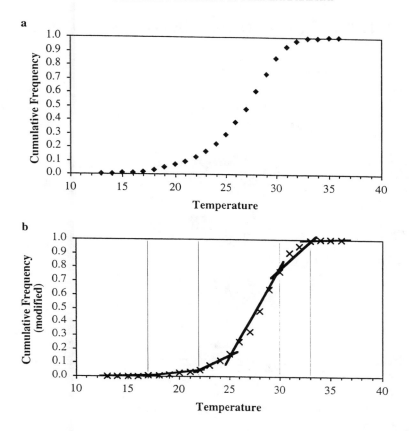

FIGURE 1.—(a) Cumulative frequency distribution of juvenile spotted seatrout in Charlotte Harbor and Tampa Bay along the temperature gradient based upon sample count. (b) Cumulative frequency distribution of juvenile spotted seatrout along a temperature gradient with straight lines intersecting to determine biologically relevant ranges along the curve.

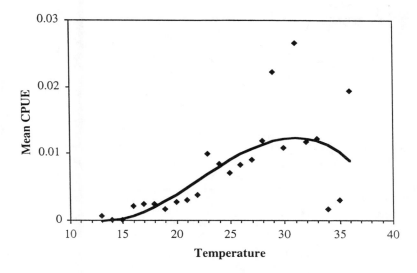

FIGURE 2.—Polynomial regression curve fit to mean catch rates (CPUEs) along the temperature gradient for juvenile spotted seatrout in Charlotte Harbor.

HABITAT SUITABILITY INDEX MODELING

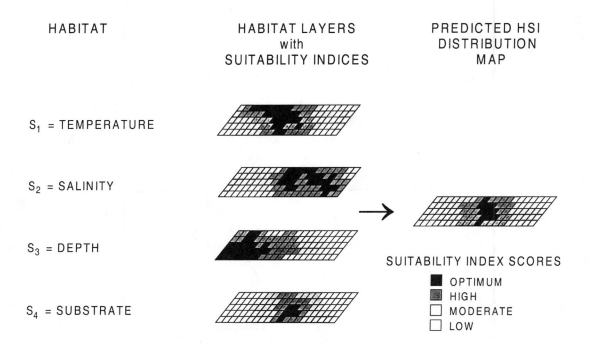

FIGURE 3.—Habitat suitability index (HSI) modeling process used to create predicted fish distribution maps with a geographic information system.

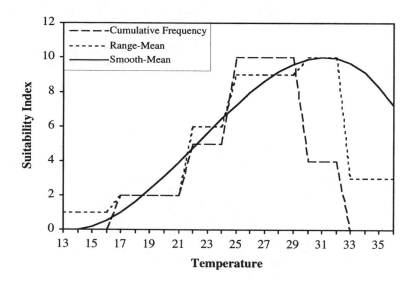

FIGURE 4.—Comparison of suitability index functions derived using the cumulative frequency, range-mean, and smooth-mean methods.

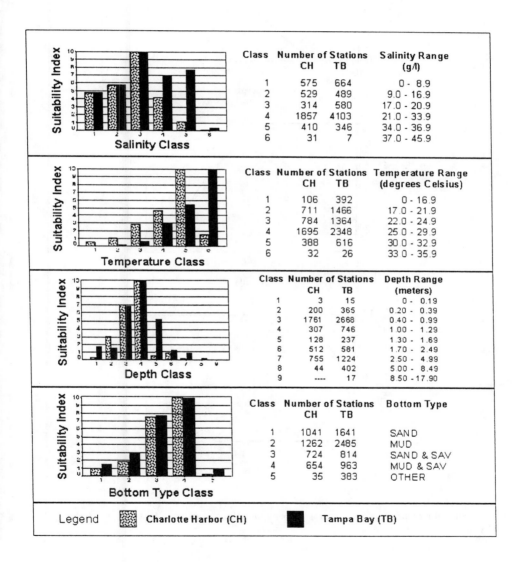

The following data tables appear within the figure:

Salinity

Class	Number of Stations CH	Number of Stations TB	Salinity Range (g/l)
1	575	664	0 - 8.9
2	529	489	9.0 - 16.9
3	314	580	17.0 - 20.9
4	1857	4103	21.0 - 33.9
5	410	346	34.0 - 36.9
6	31	7	37.0 - 45.9

Temperature

Class	Number of Stations CH	Number of Stations TB	Temperature Range (degrees Celsius)
1	106	392	0 - 16.9
2	711	1466	17.0 - 21.9
3	784	1364	22.0 - 24.9
4	1695	2348	25.0 - 29.9
5	388	616	30.0 - 32.9
6	32	26	33.0 - 35.9

Depth

Class	Number of Stations CH	Number of Stations TB	Depth Range (meters)
1	3	15	0 - 0.19
2	200	365	0.20 - 0.39
3	1761	2668	0.40 - 0.99
4	307	746	1.00 - 1.29
5	128	237	1.30 - 1.69
6	512	581	1.70 - 2.49
7	755	1224	2.50 - 4.99
8	44	402	5.00 - 8.49
9	----	17	8.50 - 17.90

Bottom Type

Class	Number of Stations CH	Number of Stations TB	Bottom Type
1	1041	1641	SAND
2	1262	2485	MUD
3	724	814	SAND & SAV
4	654	963	MUD & SAV
5	35	383	OTHER

Legend: Charlotte Harbor (CH) — Tampa Bay (TB)

FIGURE 5.—Suitability index (S_i) functions across biologically relevant gradients of salinity, temperature, depth, and bottom type for Charlotte Harbor and Tampa Bay obtained using the range-mean method.

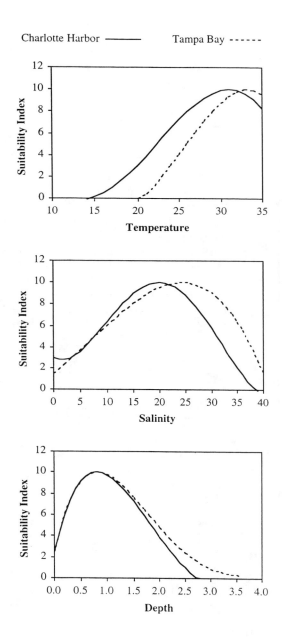

FIGURE 6.—Suitability index functions (S_i) for temperature, salinity, and depth for Charlotte Harbor and Tampa Bay obtained by the smooth-mean method.

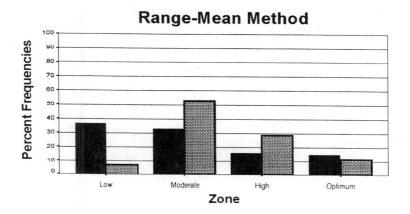

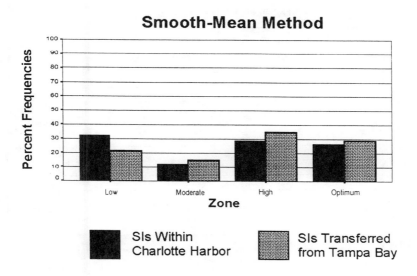

FIGURE 7.—Comparison of the relative frequency of grid cells by zone predicted from (top) the range-mean habitat suitability index (HSI) model and (bottom) the smooth-mean HSI model.

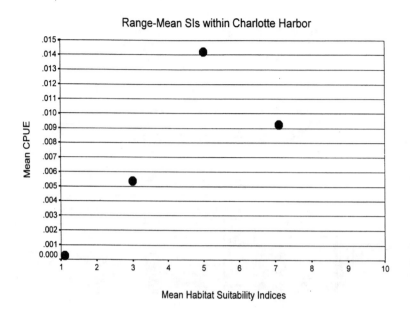

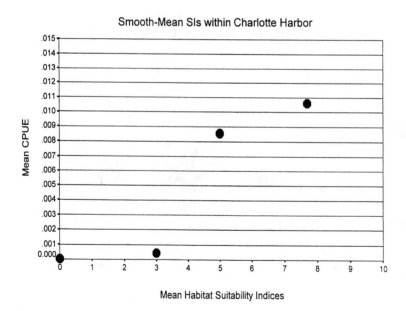

FIGURE 8.—Plots of mean catch rates (CPUEs) versus mean habitat suitability indices (HSIs) by suitability zones derived using suitability index (S_i) functions from Charlotte Harbor, determined using the range-mean method (top), and the smooth-mean method (bottom).

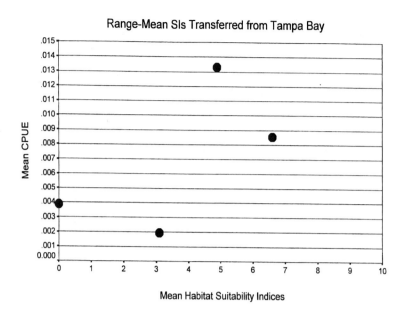

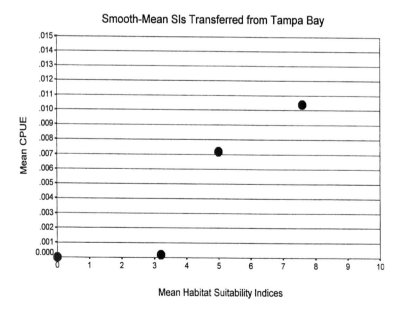

FIGURE 9.—Plots of mean catch rates (CPUEs) versus mean habitat suitability indices (HSIs) by suitability zones derived using suitability index (S_i) functions transferred from Tampa Bay, determined using the range-mean method (top), and the smooth-mean method (bottom).

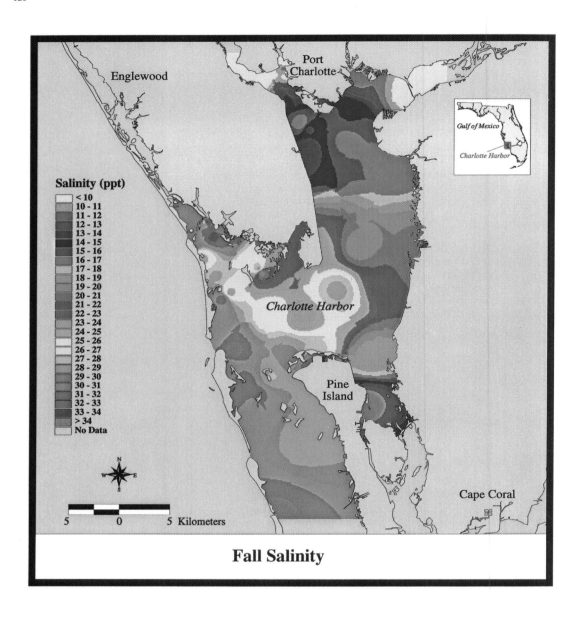

FIGURE 10A.—Salinity habitat map for the fall season in Charlotte Harbor, Florida.

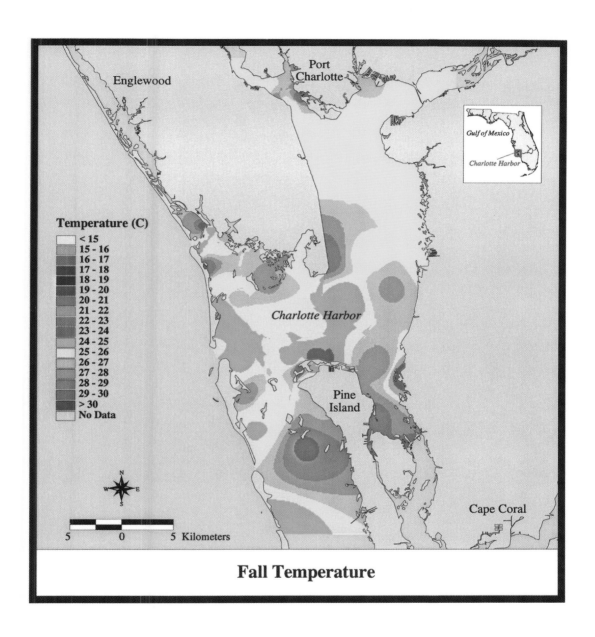

FIGURE 10B.—Temperature habitat map for the fall season in Charlotte Harbor, Florida.

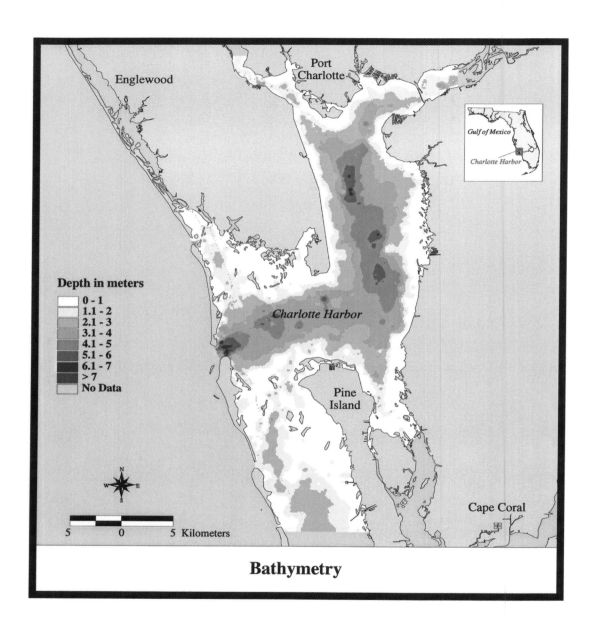

FIGURE 10C.—Bathymetry map for Charlotte Harbor, Florida.

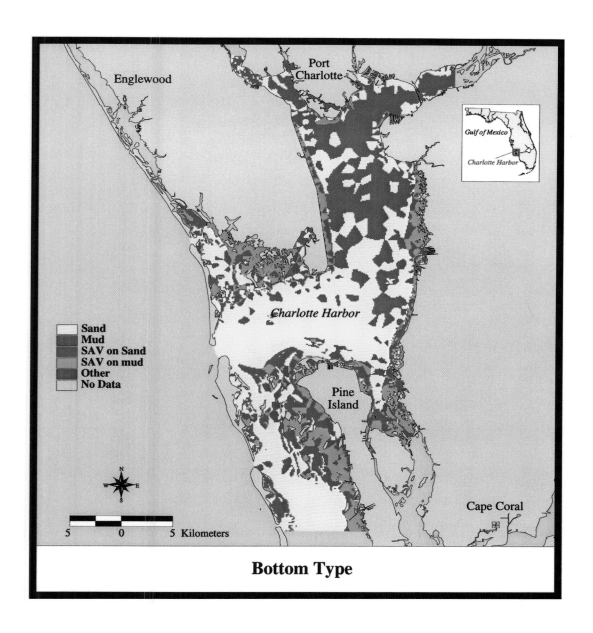

FIGURE 10D.—Bottom type map in Charlotte Harbor, Florida. (SAV = submerged aquatic vegetation.)

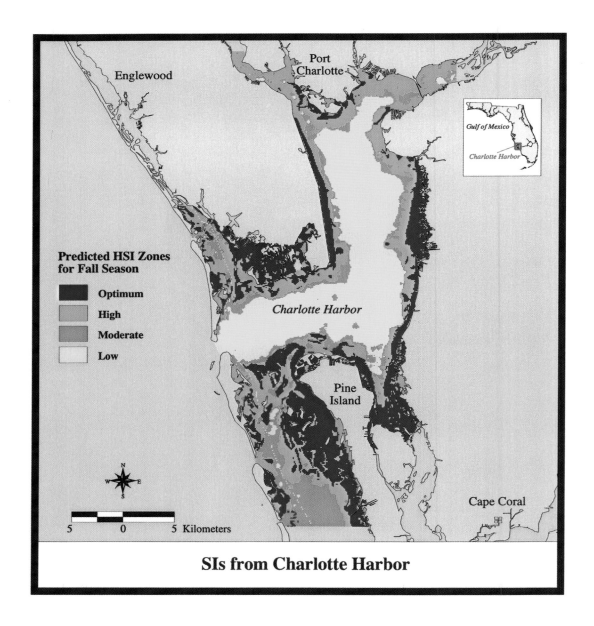

FIGURE 11.—Habitat suitability index (HSI) map of juvenile spotted seatrout in Charlotte Harbor, produced by the smooth-mean model using suitability indices (SIs) and habitat layers from Charlotte Harbor.

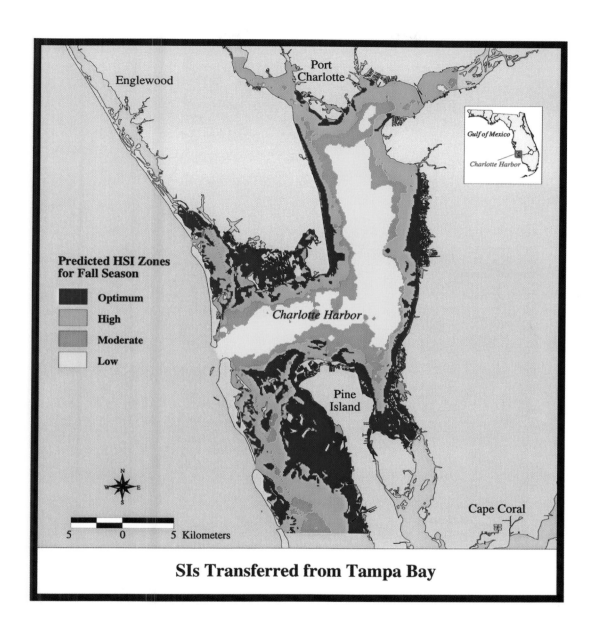

FIGURE 12.—Habitat suitability index (HSI) map of juvenile spotted seatrout in Charlotte Harbor, produced by the smooth-mean model using suitability indices (SIs) transferred from Tampa Bay and habitat layers from Charlotte Harbor.

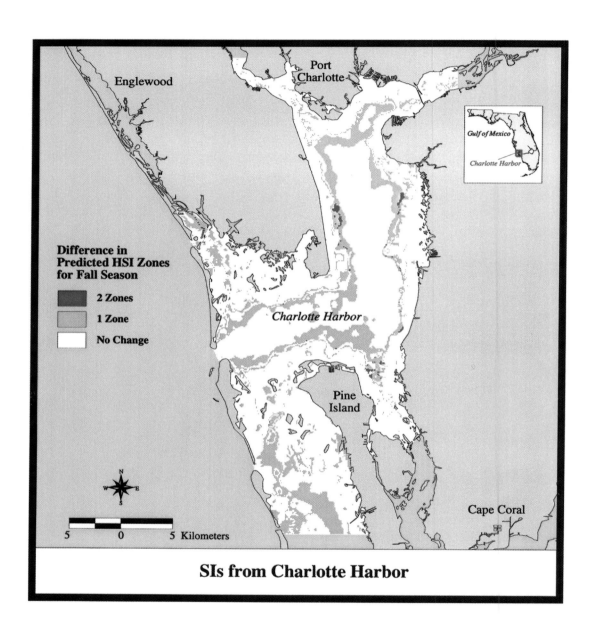

FIGURE 13.—Map of Charlotte Harbor depicting differences in grid rankings between the HSI maps in Figures 11 and 12.

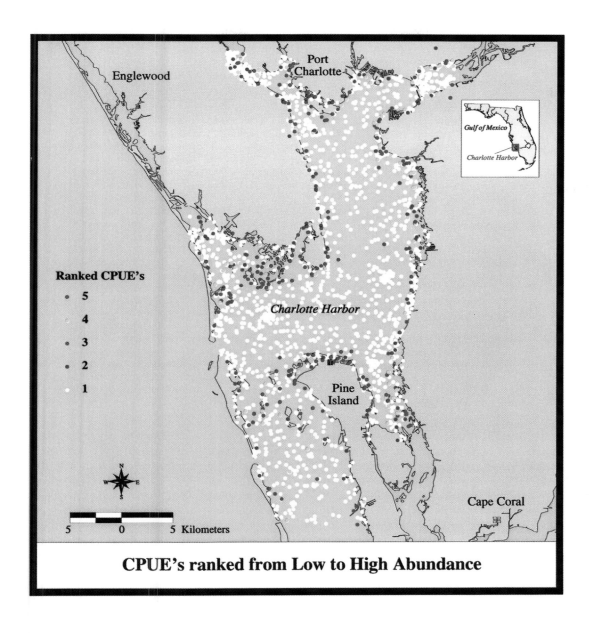

FIGURE 14.—Map depicting the abundance of juvenile spotted seatrout determined from catch rates (CPUE) by fisheries-independent monitoring in Charlotte Harbor. The CPUEs were ranked from low (1) to high (5), with low representing zero catches, and ranks 2 to 5 determined as quartiles of the highest CPUE.

American Fisheries Society Symposium 22:134–147, 1999
© Copyright by the American Fisheries Society 1999

Measures of Juvenile Fish Habitat Quality: Examples from a National Estuarine Research Reserve

KENNETH W. ABLE

Rutgers University Marine Field Station
132 Great Bay Boulevard, Tuckerton, New Jersey 08087-2004, USA

Abstract.—Defining and quantifying essential fish habitat is difficult, perhaps particularly so in estuaries, which are typically dynamic. Yet we need habitat data to make informed decisions about the management of estuarine habitats and associated fish populations. Our ongoing efforts to resolve issues of fish habitat quality have been centered in the relatively unaltered Jacques Cousteau National Estuarine Research Reserve (the Reserve) in the Mullica River–Great Bay estuary in southern New Jersey, where extensive studies of fishes and their habitats have been conducted during the last decade. Much of our effort to define essential fish habitat has focused on a variety of shallow-water habitats (eelgrass, macroalgae, marsh creeks, unvegetated substrates of different grain sizes) where it is easier to sample in a quantitative manner (e.g., using throw traps and beam trawls) and conduct experimental manipulations (e.g., caging, deploying of artificial habitats). Although our studies in the Reserve have been extensive, they still have been focused on a relatively small component (less than 3%) of the fish fauna of the Reserve, including several species of economic importance. These species include winter flounder *Pseudopleuronectes americanus*, summer flounder *Paralichthys dentatus*, tautog *Tautoga onitis*, and black sea bass *Centropristis striata*. This work has examined the period from larval ingress and settlement through the first year using a variety of complementary approaches. To date, these studies have included measures of habitat-specific distribution, abundance, residence time, and growth. Attempts to identify both habitat-specific measures of mortality and sources of mortality have proven especially difficult for the migratory fishes typical of Middle Atlantic Bight estuaries. In fact, this mobility, which occurs at seasonal, diel, tidal, and episodic (storms, upwelling, etc.) scales, makes it difficult to assess residence times and confounds attempts to measure habitat quality. The measures of habitat quality that we have used suggest that there are species-specific and habitat-specific responses; however, data sets for multiple years are seldom available to confirm these responses. Efforts to quantify essential fish habitat will be limited in their effectiveness until inter-annual variability can be assessed.

Habitat destruction and alteration are ongoing concerns that have recently been elevated to a national level (Langton et al. 1996; Thayer et al. 1996; Waste 1996) as recognized by the amendment of the Magnuson-Stevens Fishery Conservation and Management Act (Magnuson-Stevens Act) in 1996 to include fish habitat provisions (NOAA 1996). The Magnuson-Stevens Act defined essential fish habitat (EFH) as those waters and substrate necessary for spawning, breeding, feeding, or growth to maturity. This definition of habitat quality is difficult to interpret because the linkages between fish and their habitats are complex and often dynamic. As a result, the identification of EFH is problematic (Langton et al. 1996). In an attempt to simplify the designation of EFH, the National Marine Fisheries Service has identified four levels of information that may be used (Minello 1999, this volume). Level 1 is based on presence–absence data whose usefulness is limited because the data only describe the geographical distribution of a species relative to habitat. Most data at Level 1, when combined in a multiple-species approach, either do not differentiate among habitats or identify all habitats as essential. Thus, these data do not allow us to prioritize habitats relative to their quality (Minello 1999). Prioritization is important if we are to manage our estuarine resources or enhance ecological studies in estuarine habitats. We must provide a more rigorous definition of EFH by improving our understanding of more-complex levels. Level 2 examines the habitat-specific densities of fish. This approach assumes that the greater the abundance in a habitat, the higher the quality of (or the more essential) the habitat. It is important to recognize that densities can be influenced by gear biases as well as the dynamic nature of estuaries. Such dynamism includes seasonal and annual variation in abundance of marine transient species due to variation in larval supply to the estuary, tidal stage, and diel variation in availability. Level-3 information is based on habitat-related measures of growth, reproduction, or survival. Level 4 relies on fish production by habitat. Data for the latter two levels are much more difficult to collect and often are lacking.

In an attempt to increase the resolution of habitat quality and EFH, our emphasis has been on the first year of life because several events during that period are likely to be critical to survival and thus influence recruitment to the adult population (Rothschild 1986; Sale 1990; Able and Fahay 1998). These events have fostered studies on larval supply (Able and Fahay 1998; Witting et al., in press); settlement (Cushing 1996); and postsettlement (Sissenwine 1984; Smith 1985; Houde 1987; Elliot 1989; Doherty 1991; Beverton and Iles 1992; Myers and Cadigan 1993; Sogard 1997).

Here we emphasize habitat-specific studies that might further elucidate the processes that influence EFH. Almost all of these studies have taken place in the Jacques Cousteau National Estuarine Research Reserve at Mullica River–Great Bay in southern New Jersey (the Reserve). For these studies, we summarize some of our progress on assessing the habitat-

specific structure of fish assemblages, that is, distribution and abundance, and our efforts to derive the more difficult measures of habitat function, including reproduction, growth, and survival.

Study Site

The Reserve (Psuty et al. 1993; Able et al. 1996) is comprised of approximately 46,000 ha. The relatively pristine watershed of this estuarine system drains an area of about 400,000 ha of largely undeveloped pinelands in southern New Jersey (Figure 1), which has been designated as the Pinelands National Reserve (Good and Good 1984). The watershed drains into Great Bay, a drowned river valley, and the adjacent Little Egg Harbor, a barrier-beach estuary. The shorelines of these relatively shallow (1.7 m average depth at mean low water) polyhaline marsh systems total 283 km² and consist of exten-

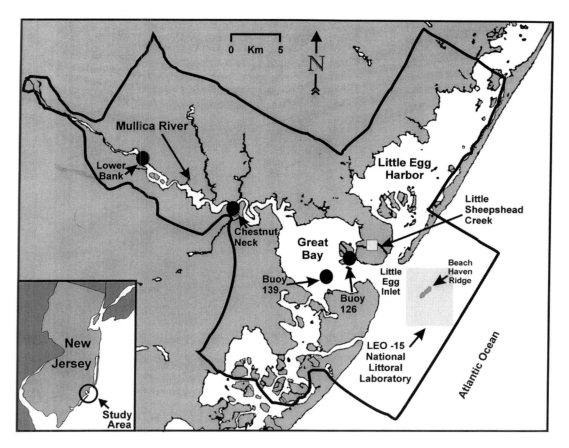

FIGURE 1.—Study area in southern New Jersey including details within the Jacques Cousteau National Estuarine Research Reserve at Mullica River–Great Bay boundary. Closed circles indicate data-logger locations. Open square indicates location of long-term ichthyoplankton sampling.

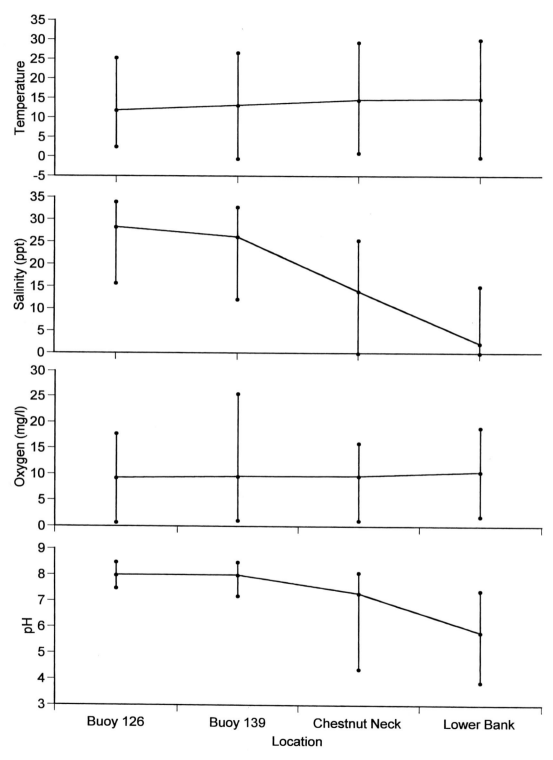

FIGURE 2.—Bottom water characteristics for permanent data-logger locations from May 1997 to April 1998. Vertical bars indicate range of values observed. See Figure 1 for locations of data loggers.

sive stands of salt marsh cordgrass *Spartina alterniflora*. This system shares qualities with many other estuaries in the Middle Atlantic Bight, including a broad seasonal temperature range (-2° to 28°C; Figure 2) and a moderate tidal range (<0.7 m to 1.1 m) (Chizmadia et al. 1984; Durand 1984; Able et al. 1992; Able and Fahay 1998). The Great Bay portion of the estuary is polyhaline; salinity drops somewhat in the Mullica River but is still mesohaline in the lower portion of the river. The freshwater–saltwater interface occurs near Lower Bank (Figure 2). The pH is low in the Mullica River due to tannic acids coming from the pine-and-oak-dominated watershed (Durand 1984). As a result, pH is low at Lower Bank and is slightly acidic in the river at Chestnut Neck, but in both locations pH can reach below a value of 5. This estuary differs from many others in the Middle Atlantic Bight in that it is relatively unaltered and unpolluted with low human population density, and as a result the estuary is possibly the cleanest estuary in the northeastern United States (Psuty et al. 1993; Able et al. 1996).

Included within the Reserve is a portion of the inner continental shelf that is centered around Beach Haven Ridge (Figure 1). The ridge is representative of shoreface submarine sand ridges along the east coast of the United States (McBride and Moslow 1991). Beach Haven Ridge extends northeastward from the ebb tidal delta of Little Egg Inlet, New Jersey and is about 1 km wide along its central and southern portions and broadens to 1.5 km at the northeastern end (Stahl et al. 1974; Twichell and Able 1993). It has a maximum relief of 8 m between the ridge crest and the trough of the shoreward side. Surficial sediments are complex and heterogeneous (Twichell and Able 1993). To provide real-time observations and forecasting in this portion of the Reserve, a unique Long-term Ecosystem Observatory has been developed (Figure 1; von Alt and Grassle 1992; von Alt et al. 1997).

Characteristics of the Reserve's Fish Fauna

The number of resident and transient species found in the Reserve includes 70 commonly recorded species and another 50 species that are infrequently collected. The contribution of the latter in the estuary may vary with life history stage (see Table 4.2 in Able and Fahay 1998). However, an extensive review of new studies and historical literature by Able and Fahay (1998) indicates that many life history and ecological characteristics of estuarine fishes in

the Reserve are unknown (see Tables 77.1 and 77.2 in Able and Fahay 1998). Based on our understanding to date, use of the estuary by transient and resident fauna is characterized by a rich variety of temporal and spatial patterns. Among the transients are species that are (1) facultative users of the estuary, (2) regular but seasonal residents, (3) anadromous species, (4) species that only use the estuary very early in postsettlement and then leave, (5) species that delay use of the estuary until they are older, and (6) species that spawn a long distance from the estuary. Another group of transients is those that move into the estuary but probably do not survive the winter and thus are expatriates and never recruit to the adult population. Other transient species do not seem to fit any of these categories. Among the resident species are those that (1) spawn in the summer, (2) spawn in the winter, or (3) migrate within the estuary to spawn.

We are attempting to improve our understanding of fish use of Reserve habitats by incorporating long-term monitoring to determine larval supply for those species spawning outside the estuary and to assess the impacts of annual variation in their abundance on interpretation of fish habitat-use patterns. This monitoring has allowed us to document the increased availability and abundance of the recovering stocks of Atlantic herring *Clupea harengus*, the unusually large but episodic year classes of tautog *Tautoga onitis*, and the relatively stable abundance patterns of the glass eels of American eel *Anguilla rostrata* (Figure 3).

Presence–Absence (EFH Level 1)

The presence or absence of a fish species is a crude measure of habitat quality at best. Designation at this level may be most useful at the end of a species' range or as the result of extreme alterations of habitats or pollution. It is also possible that habitat use varies with population size; as abundance increases, suboptimal habitats may be occupied, as suggested with MacCall's (1990) basin model. It is unlikely that infrequent degradation of a single natural habitat would result in the disappearance of a species in most estuaries because these typically tolerant species are not limited to a single habitat (see Able and Fahay 1998). A possible exception within the Reserve is for anadromous fishes such as river herrings (*Alosa* spp.), which could become locally extinct when access to freshwater spawning areas is

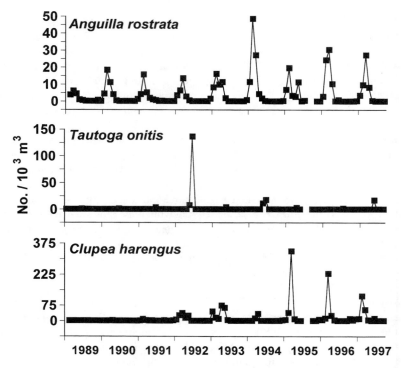

Figure 3.—Annual variation in abundance of American eel *Anguilla rostrata*, tautog *Tautoga onitis*, and Atlantic herring *Clupea harengus* larvae ingressing into the estuary based on plankton sampling from a bridge over Little Sheepshead Creek. See Figure 1 for location.

blocked by dams or when freshwater flow is diverted. There are also selected species that could have reduced population sizes within the Reserve if some habitats were completely eliminated. For example, a number of species such as inland silverside *Menidia beryllina*, rainwater killifish *Lucania parva*, and sheepshead minnow *Cyprinodon variegatus* use the marsh surface and marsh pools for spawning and as nursery areas (Able and Fahay 1998). The elimination of salt-marsh pools would likely cause a serious decline in their numbers, but the species probably would not be eliminated. The same suite of species may have been heavily impacted by elimination of marsh pools through construction of mosquito ditches in the Reserve during the 1930s. This elimination of marsh pool habitat has probably occurred throughout the northeastern United States, where ditching was so prevalent (Headlee 1936). Other species such as fourspine stickleback *Apeltes quadracus*, lined seahorse *Hippocampus erectus*, and northern pipefish *Syngnathus fuscus* are consistently and abundantly found in eelgrass *Zostera marina* beds, yet these species are such

generalists that they could likely persist, as they do in Delaware Bay, where there is no eelgrass (Able and Fahay 1998).

In some instances, the presence of a certain species could be a misleading indication of functional habitat use. For example, in the Reserve relatively large numbers of strays from tropical and subtropical waters—including lutjanids (snappers), serranids (groupers), and chaetodontids (butterflyfish)—are present as young-of-the-year in late summer and fall (Able and Fahay 1998). The fate of these strays is unknown, but they probably do not survive in estuarine habitats at winter water temperatures. This appears to be the case for spotfin butterflyfish *Chaetodon ocellatus*, which has a restricted distribution in the estuary after settlement in late summer and early fall (McBride and Able, in press). When water temperatures reach about 12°C, they become disoriented and die. Thus, although spotfin butterflyfish may be present in selected habitats in this estuary, they probably do not survive to recruit to the adult population, and records of their presence do not indicate essential fish habitat.

Distribution and Abundance (EFH Level 2)

Measures of distribution and abundance can be determined either qualitatively or quantitatively. There are convincing arguments that these measures should be based on quantitative density estimates (Rozas and Minello 1997). However, density estimates are often limited to shallow water (intertidal to approximately 2-m depths) for logistical reasons, and the same techniques are often difficult if not impossible to apply to deeper habitats. In addition, where gear efficiency estimates are available, the estimates are often quite variable in this estuary (Smith 1995; K. W. Able, Rutgers University, unpublished data) and elsewhere (Kneib 1997; Rozas and Minello 1997; Minello 1999). Alternatively, relative comparisons of qualitative fish abundance are often useful. For example, in our examination of fish use of salt marsh cordgrass *Spartina alterniflora*-versus common reed *Phragmites australis*-dominated habitats, it is clear that catch per unit effort of early life history stages is consistently greater in the *Spartina* habitats based on qualitative estimates of abundance (catch per unit effort) from pit trap collections (Figure 4). This result is counter to recent estimates of the distribution and abundance of fishes in other marshes (Fell et al. 1998). In other qualitative observations, such as night-lighting, we have identified stages (leptocephali of conger eel *Conger oceanicus*, the "half beak" stage of Atlantic needlefish *Strongylura marina*, and the "queremana" stage

of white mullet *Mugil curema*) and species (pollock *Pollachius virens*, mackerel scad *Decapterus macarellus*) that are infrequently collected by other gears (Able et al. 1997; Able and Fahay 1998).

In our attempts to define and quantify patterns of habitat use in the Reserve, we have attempted to measure the distribution and abundance of juvenile fishes with a variety of sampling gears (Figure 5). During the period from 1988 to 1997, our sampling effort included >16,000 samples across a variety of habitats. Much of this effort has been summarized in individual publications (see Able and Fahay 1998).

Our efforts have necessarily relied on a variety of gears because there are often habitat-specific sampling limitations. Thus, in shallow habitats (macroalgae, eelgrass, unvegetated substrates, marsh creeks, vegetated marsh surface) we have used a variety of quantitative gears such as throw traps (Sogard and Able 1991); enclosures (Able et al. 1989); flumes (K. W. Able and S. M. Hagan, Rutgers University, unpublished data); and beam trawls (D. A. Witting and K. W. Able, Rutgers University, unpublished data). In addition, qualitative samplers including wire mesh traps (Able and Hales 1997), pit traps (Talbot and Able 1984), night lights (Able et al. 1997), and seines (Able et al. 1996) have proven useful in habitat comparisons. In deeper (>1 m) habitats, beam trawls have been the most effective quantitative benthic samplers, but even in these instances the values for distance traveled over the bottom have

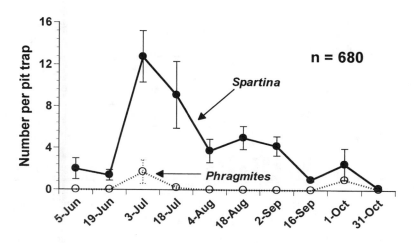

FIGURE 4.—Temporal pattern of fish abundance collected from pit traps on marsh surfaces dominated by salt marsh cordgrass *Spartina alterniflora* versus common reed *Phragmites australis* during 1997. Data points (±SE) are composite averages. The differences observed are not due to higher elevation of the *Phragmites* marsh surface (a typical condition) because the actual elevation was lower, and thus the hydroperiod somewhat longer, than that for the *Spartina* sites.

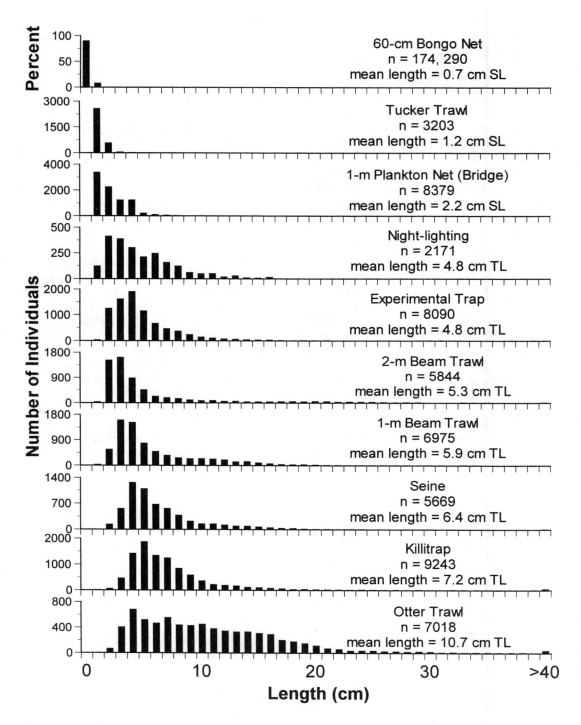

FIGURE 5.—Variation in fish length distribution (all species) from different gears deployed in the Jacques Cousteau National Estuarine Research Reserve at Mullica River–Great Bay to identify habitat associations, and aspects of life history. (y-axis indicates percent in the top panel, and number of individuals in the remaining panels; n = number of individuals; SL = standard length; TL = total length). Adapted from Able and Fahay (1998).

varied with substrate type (Able, personal observation). Large pop nets (5-m diameter) have proven useful for sampling pelagic fishes in a quantitative fashion (Hagan and Able 1997), whereas plankton nets have provided important insights into larval supply (Witting et al., in press). Large block nets deployed in subtidal creeks have been useful in determining seasonal and diel patterns of fish use as well (Rountree and Able 1992, 1993). In other efforts to determine patterns of fish habitat use within the Reserve, we have deployed and quantitatively sampled habitat mimics, for example, artificial eelgrass (Sogard 1989). For the deepest inner continental shelf waters of the Reserve, we have relied on historical studies with otter trawls (Able and Hagan 1995) and larger beam trawls (2 m) (Able et al. 1990, 1995). With each gear, it is important to keep in mind the inherent biases, not the least of which may be the result of gear size selection (Figure 5).'

One major drawback of sampling to assess juvenile fish distribution and abundance is the implication that distribution is static. This implication is often reinforced by emphasis on daytime sampling at fairly infrequent intervals (e.g., weekly, monthly) at fixed sites. Differences in diel distribution and abundance have been observed frequently in this estuary for benthic and pelagic species (Rountree and Able 1993; Sogard and Able 1994; Hagan and Able, unpublished data). More intensive sampling would help to elucidate habitat use on diel, tidal, and episodic (e.g., storms, upwelling) scales. The more-frequent use of mark-and-recapture studies may help to alleviate this problem. In the Reserve we have used anchor tags (Rountree and Able 1992), bee tags (Able and Hales 1997), acrylic and elastomer marks (Smith and Able 1994), and ultrasonic tags (Szedlmayer and Able 1993) to elucidate finer temporal and spatial-scale patterns of habitat use. These studies indicate that there are species-specific residence times and home ranges that vary across habitats and seasons (e.g., Szedlmayer and Able 1993; Able and Hales 1997) and thus make extrapolation from infrequent sampling to the whole estuarine fish assemblage risky. Habitat-use patterns are also difficult to interpret because postsettlement habitat use may be extremely variable. Within the Reserve, there appear to be a number of species that do not "settle and stay" (Sogard 1989). For example, winter flounder disperse from

settlement habitats after they grow large enough to avoid some of their common crustacean predators (Witting 1995). The importance of accurate, quantitative estimates of distribution and abundance is underscored by the fact that our estimates of some Level-3 measures of EFH such as growth and mortality are directly dependent on these simple but often difficult to achieve measures of distribution and abundance.

Annual variability in the occurrence and abundance of some species, particularly marine transients, can be extreme, and this variation has to be considered when assessing EFH. If we had attempted to define EFH for Atlantic herring in the Reserve in 1989 or 1990, we probably would have concluded that there were no such habitats within the Reserve (Figure 3). Subsequently, corresponding with the recovery of the stocks (Smith and Morse 1990), Atlantic herring abundance is quite high, and they are a dominant component of the estuarine water column (Hagan and Able 1997). The same annual variability, as indicated for the larval abundance of tautog (Figure 3), could easily confound determination of EFH. These examples clearly point out the need to have access to the results of long-term sampling to assess EFH at Level 1 or 2.

On a broader spatial scale, it is important to recognize that many "estuarine" species may also occur in and use inner continental shelf habitats as EFH. Our sampling efforts at the LEO-15 National Littoral Laboratory (Figure 1) within the Reserve have made that apparent. For example, the black sea bass was originally considered to be "estuarine dependent," but recent data have clearly shown that both the estuary and the inner shelf serve as nurseries for this species, at least in some years (Able et al. 1995). This pattern of use of both estuarine and inner continental shelf habitats may also occur for other species, including seaboard goby *Gobiosoma ginsburgi* (Duval and Able 1998), striped cusk-eel *Ophidion marginatum* (Fahay 1992), and cunner *Tautogolabrus adspersus* (Able and Fahay 1998). Also, a variety of young-of-the-year of other species such as seasonal migrants between the estuary and the continental shelf may be facultative users of estuarine habitats (Able and Fahay 1998). Thus, in many instances, the determination of EFH requires comparable sampling in the estuary and the adjacent ocean. Our knowledge of and experience with small young-of-the-year fishes in the ocean often limit our understanding in this regard.

Reproduction, Growth, and Survival (EFH Level 3)

Reproduction

Reproduction by fishes in the Reserve, and in many other estuaries along the east coast of the United States, is often limited to small species, either residents such as the killifishes (*Fundulus* spp., *Cyprinodon variegatus*) or seasonal residents such as Atlantic silverside *Menidia menidia* and bay anchovy *Anchoa mitchilli* (Able and Fahay 1998). Specific habitats essential for reproduction may not be limiting for many pelagic species such as bay anchovy. However, habitat may be limiting for anadromous species because of human impacts on water quality and benthic habitats in the tidal freshwaters where anadromous species spawn. When considering the Mullica River portion of the Reserve, the potential impacts of naturally low pH (Figure 2) are unclear. For example, there is little evidence of striped bass *Morone saxatilis* spawning in the Mullica River even though large adults are often caught there. Many of the other species reproducing in the estuary have benthic eggs, and many species have long chorionic filaments (i.e., atheriniforms) that presumably deposit their eggs in vegetation such as *Spartina alterniflora* (i.e., *Menidia menidia* [Middaugh and Takita 1983] and mummichog *Fundulus heteroclitus* [Taylor et al. 1977; Taylor and DiMichele 1983; Able 1984]). These vegetative habitat types may never be limiting in most relatively unaltered estuaries like the Reserve. Species that reproduce in marsh pools, for example, possibly *M. beryllina* (Coorey et al. 1985), *Cyprinodon variegatus,* and *Lucania parva* (Smith 1995), may be negatively impacted by ditching for mosquito control. This procedure, which occurred in parts of the Reserve during the 1930s, drastically reduces or eliminates marsh pools, and adverse conditions created by ditching persist today.

Growth

Growth of fishes may be a good index of habitat quality because fast growth implies that (1) sufficient food is available, (2) individuals may achieve a size refuge from predators quickly, and (3) individuals may be larger at the end of the growing season, thus enhancing the chances of overwinter survival (Sogard 1997). There are several caveats, however, that might influence growth as a measure of habitat quality. As always, the mobility of fishes

is an issue to be considered, and, as a result, food resources may come from multiple habitats. Fast growth may appear optimal, but the presence of large predators in the same habitat may require a trade-off between habitats (see Sogard 1992 for discussion relative to the Reserve). In addition, it may be difficult to reach a size refuge if there are suites of predators of different sizes to prevent this.

The accurate determination of growth rates can be difficult. Within the Reserve we have used modal increases in length frequencies over relatively large time spans (i.e., months; Able and Fahay 1998), yet these are relatively crude estimates. Even if we accept this qualification, it is clear that growth is much faster in the summer than in the winter and that most of the growth occurs in three to four months (Able and Fahay 1998); thus, future studies should emphasize this period. More-accurate measures of fish growth in the Reserve have been based on recapture of anchor-tagged individuals of summer flounder (Rountree and Able 1992). These studies and others (Szedlmayer and Able 1993) have indicated that the functional habitat for these estimates is the entire subtidal (and occasionally intertidal) portion of a 1.2-km-long marsh creek because of extensive tidal and diel movements. These growth estimates were similar to estimates obtained from modal length-frequency progressions (Szedlmayer et al. 1992) and tag-and-recapture experiments (Rountree and Able 1992).

In other attempts to measure habitat-specific growth within the Reserve, we have confined young-of-the-year winter flounder, tautog, naked goby *Gobiosoma bosc,* and summer flounder in cages and compared growth rates in different habitats (Sogard 1992; Able and Kaiser 1994 as adapted from Keefe and Able 1992). These studies indicated that the growth response was species specific, with tautog growing faster in vegetated (eelgrass and macroalgae) habitats and winter and summer flounder growing in a similar fashion across habitats. All three species showed some site- (not habitat-) specific differences in growth under this experimental regime. Temperature and food availability may also have influenced growth.

Determination of differences in growth between habitats may be confounded by differences between estuaries as well. Comparisons of winter flounder and tautog growth in cages in the heavily impacted Hudson River estuary indicate that growth is much lower there than in the cleaner waters of the Reserve (Sogard 1992; Duffy-Anderson and Able, in press). Other studies, in progress, compare growth rates from caging experiments in specific habitats (eelgrass, macroalgae, marsh creeks, and unvegetated substrates) within the Reserve to the same habitats in other estuaries within the northeastern United States. Despite the advantages of this habitat-specific caging approach, it is important to remember many of the difficulties associated with these types of field manipulations (Peterson and Black 1994). In this instance, fish are confined to a small area, which may present all kinds of difficulties if the fish typically move over much larger areas to obtain food or avoid poor water quality. Other artifacts may also occur, such as the effects of the cage itself on the concentration or removal of nektonic food sources.

The determination of growth rates is now possible as a result of the increased ability to back-calculate growth rates based on daily increments in otoliths. Although we may calculate growth rates of fishes captured in different habitats, because of fish mobility, we frequently are unable to associate specific growth rates with specific habitats. Before using this approach to estimate growth, the daily increments must be validated. Within the Reserve, we have been unable to validate the method for larval summer flounder. We were successful, however, for tautog held in the laboratory (Sogard et al. 1992), field-caged juvenile summer flounder (Szedlmayer and Able 1992), and free-ranging black sea bass (Hales and Able 1995).

Survival

The ability to identify habitat-specific mortality rates would provide important insights into habitat quality and the ultimate question of recruitment success. Unfortunately, this type of information is difficult to quantify. Even published estimates of "mortality" should often be referred to as "loss" because the estimates are often confounded by immigration and emigration. This becomes especially important when attempting to test theories that incorporate mortality estimates (Houde 1997). Within the Reserve, we have been able to derive separate estimates for natural mortality and egress from a settlement area for winter flounder (Witting 1995). In this instance, presumed egress represented a much larger portion of the daily loss than did mortality due to predation by decapod crustaceans. Separate laboratory studies identified the size at which winter flounder reached a refuge from a dominant shrimp predator sevenspine bay shrimp *Crangon septemspinosa*, and this size corresponded roughly with the size of egress from the settlement area.

Other studies of natural mortality within the Reserve have focused on the occurrence and size-selective effects of overwinter mortality where the responses observed for juveniles were species specific. As an example, mortality due to cold temperature shock at ambient winter temperatures was 100% for a subtropical form (spotfin butterflyfish; McBride and Able, in press); negligible for a cold temperate species (cunner); and size selective for others (tautog; L. S. Hales and K. W. Able, Rutgers University, unpublished data). In another example, the mortality of metamorphosing larvae of summer flounder varied with the harshness (minimum temperature, duration of low temperatures) of the winter (Szedlmayer et al. 1992; Keefe and Able 1993, 1994).

Alternative methods for identifying the sources and rates of mortality are largely unavailable. Extensive analysis of food habits might demonstrate predator–prey relationships, but these relationships are extremely difficult to quantify. Before attempting field tethering experiments to determine habitat-specific rates of predation with fishes, we conducted laboratory trials that identified potential artifacts associated with tethering that could easily compromise the use of this technique in the field (Curran and Able 1998). Our difficulties in attempting to assess mortality rates in this estuary probably reflect difficulties for other estuaries as well.

Fish Production (EFH Level 4)

Methods to determine fish production in different habitats as a measure of EFH are largely lacking in this Reserve and most other estuaries. Determination of fish production is difficult because of many of the problems indicated above. For example, less than 3% of the fish fauna in the Reserve has been studied sufficiently to determine EFH at Level 2 or 3. In addition, it is likely to be some time before production measures for specific habitats can be upgraded to the landscape level, which is what is probably necessary to understand production for mobile estuarine fishes.

Future Considerations

To achieve an adequate level of understanding of fish habitat quality, it is probably necessary to attain a much-improved understanding of growth and survival (EFH Level 3) for the dominant fishes in any estuary. This in turn requires a much-improved understanding of the dynamics of habitat-specific distribution and abundance (EFH Level 2), particularly for young-of-the-year fishes. However, we do not even understand the most basic aspects of the natural history of many species, as indicated in a recent compendium (Able and Fahay 1998).

Specific suggestions to resolve this lack of understanding of estuarine fish habitat quality include the following. First, we need more extensive, long-term (multiple-year) observations of habitat use. These observations should encompass years of strong and poor year classes for dominant economically and ecologically important species. With this information we may begin to understand the role of larval supply and its impact on habitat use patterns and have sufficient data to have some confidence in the data. Second, we need a more thorough understanding of the distribution and stability of subtidal habitats. We have the techniques to develop a broad understanding of terrestrial and semiterrestrial habitats within estuarine watersheds, but subtidal habitats are not well mapped, and this is a critical first stage to make some progress on EFH Level-2 understanding of fish distribution by habitat. Third, an improved understanding of the habitat-specific behavior of fishes will be difficult to obtain but necessary to determine habitat quality. Information on the natural behavior of fishes, as well as other aspects of their natural history (see Futuyma 1998), is often lacking, and a dearth of information often leads to inadequate and unrealistic field and laboratory experiments. This lack of information could be addressed with the application of in situ imagery designed to overcome the high turbidity typical of many estuaries. Fourth, more-integrative techniques—such as the use of stable isotopes, remote sensing of estuaries at short and long time intervals, and an improved understanding of watershed, estuary, and ocean interactions need to be applied to questions of habitat quality. Fifth, all of the above types of observations need to be extended to estuaries with different degrees of human impact to assess the estuaries' status and guide their restoration.

Acknowledgments

Numerous funding sources, particularly the National Oceanic and Atmospheric Administration's National Undersea Research Program and National Estuarine Research Reserve programs, as well as the Institute of Marine and Coastal Sciences (IMCS) at Rutgers University, have contributed funding for the research in this Reserve, but consistent Sea Grant funding has provided the "glue" to bring the projects together and turn them into something that resembles a coherent program. This paper is IMCS Contribution Number 98-30.

References

Able, K. W. 1984. Variation in spawning site selection of the mummichog, *Fundulus heteroclitus*. Copeia 1984(2):522–525.

Able, K. W., and M. P. Fahay. 1998. The first year in the life of estuarine fishes in the Middle Atlantic Bight. Rutgers University Press, New Brunswick, New Jersey.

Able, K. W., M. P. Fahay, and G. R. Shepherd. 1995. Early life history of black sea bass *Centropristis striata* in the Mid-Atlantic Bight and a New Jersey estuary. Fishery Bulletin U.S. 93:429–445.

Able, K. W., and S. M. Hagan. 1995. Fishes in the vicinity of Beach Haven Ridge: annual and seasonal patterns of abundance during the early 1970s. Rutgers University, Institute of Marine and Coastal Sciences, Technical Report 95–24, New Brunswick, New Jersey.

Able, K. W., and L. S. Hales, Jr. 1997. Movements of juvenile black sea bass, *Centropristis striata* (Linnaeus), in a southern New Jersey estuary. Journal of Experimental Marine Biology and Ecology 213:153–167.

Able, K. W., R. Hoden, D. A. Witting, and J. B. Durand. 1992. Physical parameters of the Great Bay-Mullica River Estuary (with a list of research publications). Rutgers University, Institute of Marine and Coastal Sciences, Technical Report 92-06, New Brunswick, New Jersey.

Able, K. W., and S. C. Kaiser. 1994. Synthesis of summer flounder habitat parameters. National Oceanic and Atmospheric Administration Coastal Ocean Program, Decision Analysis Series No. 1. NOAA Coastal Ocean Office, Silver Spring, Maryland.

Able, K. W., A. Kustka, D. Witting, K. Smith, R. Rountree, and R. McBride. 1997. Fishes of Great Bay, New Jersey: larvae and juveniles collected by nightlighting. Rutgers University, Institute of Marine and Coastal Sciences, Technical Report 97–05, New Brunswick, New Jersey.

Able, K. W., R. Lathrop, and M. P. De Luca. 1996. Background for research and monitoring in the Mullica River-Great Bay Estuary. Institute of Marine and Coastal Sciences, Rutgers, The State University of New Jersey, New Brunswick.

Able, K. W., R. E. Matheson, W. W. Morse, M. P. Fahay, and G. R. Shepherd. 1990. Patterns of summer flounder *Paralichthys dentatus* early life history in the Mid-Atlantic Bight and New Jersey estuaries. Fishery Bulletin U.S. 88(1):1–12.

Able, K. W., K. A. Wilson, and K. L. Heck, Jr. 1989. Fishes of vegetated habitats in New Jersey estuaries: composition, distribution and abundance based on quantitative sampling. Rutgers University, Center for Coastal and Environmental Studies, Technical Report 1041, New Brunswick, New Jersey.

Beverton, R. J. H., and T. C. Iles. 1992. Mortality rates of 0-group plaice (*Pleuronectes platessa* L.), dab (*Limanda limanda* L.) and turbot (*Scophthalmus maximus* L.) in European waters III. density-dependence of mortality rates of 0-group plaice and some demographic implications. Netherlands Journal of Sea Research 29(1-3):61–79.

Chizmadia, P. A., M. J. Kennish, and V. L. Ohori. 1984. Physical description of Barnegat Bay. Pages 1–28 *in* M. J. Kennish and R. A. Lutz, editors. Lecture notes on coastal and estuarine studies, ecology of Barnegat Bay, New Jersey. Springer-Verlag, New York.

Coorey, D. N., K. W. Able, and J. K. Shisler. 1985. Life history and food habits of the inland silversides, *Menidia beryllina*, in a New Jersey salt marsh. Bulletin of the New Jersey Academy of Science 30(1):29–38.

Curran, M. C., and K. W. Able. 1998. The value of tethering fishes (winter flounder and tautog) as a tool for assessing predation rates. Marine Ecology Progress Series 163:45–51.

Cushing, D. H. 1996. Towards a science of recruitment in fish populations. Ecology Institute, Oldendorf/Luhe, Germany.

Doherty, P. J. 1991. Spatial and temporal patterns in recruitment. Pages 271–287 *in* P. F. Sale, editor. The ecology of fishes on coral reefs. Academic Press, San Diego.

Duffy-Anderson, J. T., and K. W. Able. In press. Effects of municipal piers on the growth of juvenile fish in the Hudson River estuary: a study across the pier edge. Marine Biology.

Durand, J. B. 1984. Nitrogen distribution in New Jersey coastal bays. Pages 29–51 *in* M. J. Kennish and R. A. Lutz, editors. Lecture notes on coastal and estuarine studies, ecology of Barnegat Bay, New Jersey. Springer-Verlag, New York.

Duval, E. J., and K. W. Able. 1998. Aspects of the life history of the seaboard goby, *Gobiosoma ginsburgi*, in estuarine and continental shelf waters. Bulletin of the New Jersey Academy of Sciences 43(1):5–10.

Elliot, J. M. 1989. The critical-period concept for juvenile survival and its relevance for population regulation in young sea trout, *Salmo trutta*. Journal of Fish Biology 35A:91–98.

Fahay, M. P. 1992. Development and distribution of cusk eel eggs and larvae in the Middle Atlantic Bight with a description of *Ophidion robinsi* n. sp. (Teleostei: Ophidiidae). Copeia 1992(3):799–819.

Fell, P. E., and eight coauthors. 1998. Does invasion of oligohaline tidal marshes by reed grass, *Phragmites australis* (Cav.) Tin. ex Steud., affect the availability of prey resources for the mummichog, *Fundulus heteroclitus* L.? Journal of Experimental Marine Biology and Ecology 222:59–77.

Futuyma, D. J. 1998. Wherefore and whither the naturalist? The American Naturalist 151(1):1–6.

Good, R. E., and N. F. Good. 1984. The Pinelands National Reserve: an ecosystem approach to management. Bioscience 34(3):169–173.

Hagan, S. M., and K. W. Able. 1997. Initial results for the pop net as a tool for collecting pelagic estuarine fishes. Pages 431–434 *in* Forage fish in marine ecosystems, proceedings of the international symposium on the role of forage fishes in marine ecosystems. Alaska Sea Grant College Program, Fairbanks.

Hales, L. S., Jr., and K. W. Able. 1995. Effects of oxygen concentration on somatic and otolith growth rates of juvenile black sea bass, *Centropristis striata*. Pages 135–153 *in* D. H. Secor et al. editors. Recent developments in fish otolith research. University of South Carolina, Columbia.

Headlee, J. J. 1936. Mosquito control facts taught by the passing years. Proceedings of the New Jersey Mosquito Control Association 23:204–209.

Houde, E. D. 1987. Fish early life dynamics and recruitment variability. Pages 17–29 *in* R. D. Hoyt, editor. 10th annual larval fish conference. American Fisheries Society, Symposium 2, Bethesda, Maryland.

Houde, E. D. 1997. Patterns and consequences of selective processes in teleost early life histories. Pages 173–196 *in* R. C. Chambers and E. A. Trippel, editors. Early life history and recruitment in fish populations. Chapman and Hall, London.

Keefe, M., and K. W. Able. 1992. Habitat quality in New Jersey estuaries: habitat-specific growth rates of juvenile summer flounder in vegetated habitats. Final Report, New Jersey Department of Environmental Protection and Energy, New Brunswick.

Keefe, M., and K. W. Able. 1993. Patterns of metamorphosis in summer flounder, *Paralichthys dentatus*. Journal of Fish Biology 42:713–728.

Keefe, M., and K. W. Able. 1994. Contributions of abiotic and biotic factors to settlement in summer flounder, (*Paralichthys dentatus*). Copeia 1994(2):458–465.

Kneib, R. T. 1997. The role of tidal marshes in the ecology of estuarine nekton. Oceanography and Marine Biology: An Annual Review 35:163–220.

Langton, R. W., R. S. Steneck, V. Gotceitas, F. Juanes, and P. Lawton. 1996. The interface between fisheries research and habitat management. North American Journal of Fisheries Management 16:1–7.

MacCall, A. D. 1990. Dynamic geography of marine fish populations. Washington Sea Grant Program, University of Washington Press, Seattle.

McBride, R. A., and Moslow, T. F. 1991. Origin, evolution and distribution of shoreface sand ridges, Atlantic inner shelf, USA. Marine Geology 97:57–85.

McBride, R. S., and K. W. Able. In press. Ecology, and fate of butterflyfish, *Chaetodon* spp., in a temperate, western north Atlantic. Bulletin of Marine Science.

Middaugh, D. P., and T. Takita. 1983. Tidal and diurnal spawning cues in the Atlantic silverside, *Menidia menidia*. Environmental Biology of Fishes 8:97–104.

Minello, T. J. 1999. Nekton densities in shallow estuarine habitats of Texas and Louisiana and the identification of essential fish habitat. Pages 43–75 *in* L. R. Benaka, editor. Fish habitat: essential fish habitat and rehabilitation. American Fisheries Society, Symposium 22, Bethesda, Maryland.

Myers, R. A., and N. G. Cadigan. 1993. Density-dependent juvenile mortality in marine demersal fish. Canadian Journal of Fisheries and Aquatic Sciences 51:78–90.

NOAA (National Oceanic, and Atmospheric Administration). 1996. Magnuson-Stevens Fishery Conservation and Management Act amended through 11 October 1996. National Marine Fisheries Service, National Oceanic and Atmospheric Administration Technical Memorandum NMFS-F/SPO-23, U.S. Department of Commerce, Washington, D.C.

Peterson, C. H., and R. Black. 1994. An experimentalist's challenge: when artifacts of intervention interact with treatments. Marine Ecology Progress Series 111:289–297.

Psuty, N. P., M. P. De Luca, R. Lathrop, K. W. Able, S. Whitney, and J. F. Grassle. 1993. The Mullica River–Great Bay National Estuarine Research Reserve: a unique opportunity for research, preservation and management. Pages 1557–1568 in O. T. Magoon, W. S. Wilson, H. Converse, and L. T. Tobin, editors. Coastal Zone '93, proceedings, 8th symposium on coastal and ocean management, volume 2. American Society of Civil Engineers, New York.

Rothschild, B. J. 1986. Dynamics of marine fish populations. Harvard University Press, Cambridge, Massachusetts.

Rountree, R. A., and K. W. Able. 1992. Fauna of polyhaline subtidal marsh creeks in southern New Jersey: composition, abundance and biomass. Estuaries 15(21):171–185.

Rountree, R. A., and K. W. Able. 1993. Diel variation in decapod crustacean and fish assemblages in New Jersey polyhaline marsh creeks. Estuarine Coastal and Shelf Science 37:181–201.

Rozas, L. P., and T. J. Minello. 1997. Estimating densities of small fishes and decapod crustaceans in shallow estuarine habitats: a review of sampling design with focus on gear selection. Estuaries 20:199–213.

Sale, P. F. 1990. Recruitment of marine species: is the bandwagon rolling in the right direction? Trends in Ecology and Evolution 5:25–27.

Sissenwine, M. P. 1984. Why do fish populations vary? Pages 59–94 in R. M. May, editor. Exploitation of marine communities. Dahlem Konferenzen. Springer-Verlag, New York.

Smith, C. L. 1985. The inland fishes of New York State. New York State Department of Environmental Conservation, Albany.

Smith, K. J. 1995. Processes regulating habitat use by salt marsh nekton in a southern New Jersey estuary. Doctoral dissertation. Rutgers University, New Brunswick, New Jersey.

Smith, K. J., and K. W. Able. 1994. Salt-marsh tide pools as winter refuges for the mummichog, Fundulus heteroclitus, in New Jersey. Estuaries 17(1B):226–234.

Smith, W. G., and W. W. Morse. 1990. Larval distribution patterns: evidence for the collapse/recolonization of Atlantic herring on Georges Bank. International Council for the Exploration of the Sea C.M. 1990/H:17:1–16.

Sogard, S. M. 1989. Colonization of artificial seagrass by fishes and decapod crustaceans: importance of proximity to natural eelgrass. Journal of Experimental Marine Biology and Ecology 133:15–37.

Sogard, S. M. 1992. Variability in growth rates of juvenile fishes in different estuarine habitats. Marine Ecology Progress Series 85:35–53.

Sogard, S. M. 1997. Size-selective mortality in the juvenile stage of teleost fishes: a review. Bulletin of Marine Science 60(3):1129–1157.

Sogard, S. M., and K. W. Able. 1991. A comparison of eelgrass, sea lettuce macroalgae, and marsh creeks as habitats for epibenthic fishes and decapods. Estuarine Coastal and Shelf Science 33:501–519.

Sogard, S. M., and K. W. Able. 1994. Diel variation in immigration of fishes and decapod crustaceans to artificial seagrass habitat. Estuaries 17(3):622–630.

Sogard, S. M., K. W. Able, and M. P. Fahay. 1992. Early life history of the tautog Tautoga onitis in the Mid-Atlantic Bight. Fishery Bulletin U.S. 90:529–539.

Stahl, L., J. Koczan, and D. Swift. 1974. Anatomy of a shoreface-connected sand ridge on the New Jersey shelf: implications for the genesis of the shelf surficial sand sheet. Geology 2:117–120.

Szedlmayer, S. T., and K. W. Able. 1992. Validation studies of daily increment formation for larval and juvenile summer flounder, Paralichthys dentatus. Canadian Journal of Fisheries and Aquatic Sciences 49(9):1856–1862.

Szedlmayer, S. T., and K. W. Able. 1993. Ultrasonic telemetry of age-0 summer flounder, Paralichthys dentatus, movements in a southern New Jersey estuary. Copeia 1993(3):728–736.

Szedlmayer, S. T., K. W. Able, and R. A. Rountree. 1992. Growth and temperature-induced mortality of young of the year summer flounder (Paralichthys dentatus) in southern New Jersey. Copeia 1992(1):120–128.

Talbot, C. W., and K. W. Able. 1984. Composition and distribution of larval fishes in New Jersey high marshes. Estuaries 7(4A):434–443.

Taylor, M. H., and L. DiMichele. 1983. Spawning site utilization in a Delaware population of Fundulus heteroclitus (Pisces: Cypriniodontidae). Copeia 1983:719–725.

Taylor, M. H., L. DiMichele, and G. J. Leach. 1977. Egg stranding in the life cycle of the mummichog, Fundulus heteroclitus. Copeia 1977:397–399.

Thayer, G. W., J. P. Thomas, and K. V. Koski. 1996. The Habitat Research Plan of the National Marine Fisheries Service. Fisheries 21(5):6–10.

Twichell, D. C., and K. W. Able. 1993. Bathymetry, sidescan sonar image, and surficial geological interpretation of the inner shelf off Little Egg Inlet, New Jersey. Miscellaneous Field Studies Map, MAP MF-2221, U.S. Geological Survey, Reston, Virginia.

von Alt, C. J., M. P. De Luca, S. M. Glenn, J. F. Grassle, and D. B. Haidvogel. 1997. LEO-15: monitoring and managing coastal resources. Sea Technology 8:10–16.

von Alt, C. J., and J. F. Grassle. 1992. LEO-15: an unmanned long term environmental observatory. Pages 849–854 *in* Proceedings of the Oceans '92 conference, volume 2. Institute of Electrical and Electronics Engineers, New York.

Waste, S. M. 1996. The NMFS Office of Habitat Conservation: protecting the habitats of living marine resources. Fisheries 21(2):24–29.

Witting, D. A. 1995. Settlement of winter flounder, *Pleuronectes americanus*, in a southern New Jersey estuary: spatial and temporal dynamics and the effects of decapod predation. Doctoral dissertation. Rutgers University, New Brunswick, New Jersey.

Witting, D. A., K. W. Able, and M. P. Fahay. In press. Larval fishes of a Middle Atlantic Bight estuary: assemblage structure, and temporal stability. Canadian Journal of Fisheries and Aquatic Sciences.

American Fisheries Society Symposium 22:149, 1999

Part Three:
Fishing Impacts on Fish Habitat

ANN BUCKLIN

Director, University of New Hampshire Sea Grant
142 Morse Hall, Durham, New Hampshire 03824, USA

As ocean researchers and commercial harvesters increasingly acknowledge the importance of habitat in building sustainable fisheries, questions about the effects of man's activities on marine biodiversity, fisheries productivity, and ecosystem health will become of even greater concern. In their examination of the impact of commercial harvesting on fish habitat, the speakers in this session demonstrated the value of diverse perspectives and approaches to questions of environmental policy.

Peter Auster and Richard Langton discussed the use of conceptual models, based on ecological disturbance theory, for needed predictive assessments of gear impacts on fish habitat. The models are particularly useful to understand impacts on fish population dynamics, species composition, and diversity for a variety of gear types used in a variety of habitats. An examination (by Judith Pederson and Madeline Hall-Arber) of fishermen's perspectives on fishing gear impacts on habitat represented an important—and usually ignored—aspect of this issue. This preliminary study makes clear the need for more extensive and carefully designed methods of seeking information on the attitudes, opinions, and knowledge base of commercial fishermen. Michel Kaiser et al. compared diverse benthic communities in shallow and deep water in the southern North Sea and eastern English Channel to infer the communities' vulnerability to disturbance and their topographic complexity—and to hypothesize about the importance of these habitat characteristics for various fish species. Joseph DeAlteris et al. provided a synthesis of comprehensive side-scan sonar survey data from Narragansett Bay, Rhode Island and provided a valuable comparison of anthropogenic impacts and natural disturbance.

The studies included in this section demonstrated the need for the integration of physical, biological, and social science perspectives in the examination of any issue in marine resource use. Integration of these perspectives is particularly important when the results of scientific inquiry have profound import for the environment, the health of marine ecosystems, the economic viability of coastal communities, and the preservation of a traditional way of life.

American Fisheries Society Symposium 22:150–187, 1999

The Effects of Fishing on Fish Habitat

PETER J. AUSTER

National Undersea Research Center for the North Atlantic and Great Lakes
University of Connecticut at Avery Point
1084 Shennecossett Road, Groton, Connecticut 06340, USA

RICHARD W. LANGTON

Maine Department of Marine Resources, Marine Resources Laboratory
Post Office Box 8, West Boothbay Harbor, Maine 04575, USA

Abstract.—The 1996 Magnuson–Stevens Fishery Conservation and Management Act mandates that regional fishery management councils must designate essential fish habitat (EFH) for each managed species, assess the effects of fishing on EFH, and develop conservation measures for EFH where needed. This synthesis of fishing effects on habitat was produced to aid the fishery management councils in assessing the impacts of fishing activities. A wide range of studies was reviewed that reported effects of fishing on habitat (i.e., structural habitat components, community structure, and ecosystem processes) for a diversity of habitats and fishing gear types. Commonalities of all studies included immediate effects on species composition and diversity and a reduction in habitat complexity. Studies of acute effects were found to be a good predictor of chronic effects. Recovery after fishing was more variable depending on habitat type, life history strategy of component species, and the natural disturbance regime. The ultimate goal of gear impact studies should not be to retrospectively analyze environmental impacts but ultimately to develop the ability to predict outcomes of particular management regimes. Synthesizing the results of these studies into predictive numerical models is not currently possible. However, conceptual models can coalesce the patterns found over the range of observations and can be used to predict effects of gear impacts within the framework of current ecological theory. Initially, it is useful to consider fishes' use of habitats along a gradient of habitat complexity and environmental variability. Such considerations can be facilitated by a model of gear impacts on a range of seafloor types based on changes in structural habitat values. Disturbance theory provides the framework for predicting effects of habitat change based on spatial patterns of disturbance. Alternative community state models and type 1–type 2 disturbance patterns may be used to predict the general outcome of habitat management. Primary data are lacking on the spatial extent of fishing-induced disturbance, the effects of specific gear types along a gradient of fishing effort, and the linkages between habitat characteristics and the population dynamics of fishes. Adaptive and precautionary management practices will therefore be required until empirical data become available for validating model predictions.

Habitat alteration by the fishing activities themselves is perhaps the least understood of the important environmental effects of fishing.—National Research Council (1994)

Stationary fishing gear (e.g., traps, gill nets, and longlines) and small-scale mobile gear (i.e., beam trawls and shellfish dredges) towed from sailing vessels were used in the 19th century to harvest living marine resources. The widespread use of mobile fishing gear beyond nearshore regions and the use of larger vessels for all gear types became possible only after the development of motorized propulsion and the steam capstan and winch. This widespread and critical change in fishing technology began in England with the launch of the steam trawler *Berta* in the late 1800s. Fishing effort and the range of technologies that support the industry have increased greatly during the last century. For a large number of harvested species, catch per unit effort has greatly

decreased, and the populations of those species have also declined (FAO 1997). Many species are targeted throughout their geographic range, and the wide array of harvesting systems (e.g., traps, gill nets, longlines, trawls, scallop dredges, hydraulic clam dredges) allow fishing to occur over the widest range of habitat types.

A lack of understanding of the ecological consequences of removals of fish, and the direct effects of fishing and fishing gear on community and ecosystem functions, have produced questions about the sustainability of current levels of fishing. The number of reviews on this topic that have been produced during the past decade is perhaps the best indicator of this concern (ICES 1988, 1992, 1996; Hutchings 1990;

Messieh et al. 1991; Jones 1992; Langton 1994; National Research Council 1994, 1995; Dayton et al. 1995; Roberts 1995; Jennings and Kaiser 1998). In the United States, the need for information leading to predictive capabilities and precautionary approaches to this topic will only increase as a result of the legal requirement to manage essential fish habitat (Langton et al. 1996; Auster et al. 1997a).

The 1996 reauthorization of the Magnuson–Stevens Fishery Conservation and Management Act (the Magnuson–Stevens Act) requires the regional fishery management councils and the National Marine Fisheries Service (NMFS) to identify and designate essential fish habitat (EFH) for each managed species, identify adverse impacts to EFH (including those caused by fishing activities), and develop actions to conserve and enhance EFH. The Magnuson–Stevens Act defines EFH as "those waters and substrate necessary to fish for spawning, breeding, feeding, or growth to maturity." For the purpose of interpreting the definition (and for defining the scope of this report), "waters" is interpreted by NMFS as "aquatic areas and their associated physical, chemical, and biological properties that are used by fish, and may include areas historically used by fish where appropriate," and "substrate" is defined to include sediment, hard bottom, structures, and associated biological communities. These definitions provide substantial flexibility in defining EFH based on our knowledge of the different species and allow EFH to be interpreted within a broad ecosystem perspective. "Disturbance" has been defined as "any discrete event in time that disrupts ecosystem, community, or population structure and changes resources, substrate availability, or the physical environment" (Pickett and White 1985). Disturbance can be caused by many natural processes including currents, predation, and iceberg scour (Hall 1994). Human-caused disturbance can result from activities such as harbor dredging and fishing with fixed and mobile gear. Disturbance can be gauged by both intensity (as a measure of the force of disturbance) and severity (as a measure of impact on the biotic community). Table 1 summarizes the relative effects of the range of agents that produce disturbances in marine communities. From an ecological perspective, fishing is the most widespread form of direct disturbance in marine systems below depths that are affected by storms (Watling and Norse 1998).

One of the most difficult aspects of estimating the extent of fishing impacts on habitat is the lack of high-resolution data on the distribution of fishing effort. Fishers are often resistant to reporting effort based on locations of individual tows or sets (for the obvious reason of divulging productive locations to competitors and regulators). Effort data in many fisheries are therefore apportioned to particular statistical areas for monitoring purposes. Using this type of data it has been possible to obtain averages of effort, and subsequent extrapolations of area impacted, for larger regions. For eight of the most heavily fished areas in the southern North Sea, for example, Rijnsdorp et al. (1996) estimated that between 1993 and 1996 a mean of 51% of the area was trawled one to five times per year, 33% was trawled less than once per year, and 4% was trawled 10–50 times per year. Trawling effort in the Middle Atlantic Bight off the northeast United States was summarized by Churchill (1989). Trawled area estimates were extrapolated from fishing effort data in 30′ latitude × 30′ longitude blocks. The range of effort was quite variable but the percent area impacted in some blocks off southern New England in 1985 was more than 200% with one block reaching 413%. Estimating the spatial impact of fixed gears is even more problematic. For example, during 1996 there were 2,690,856 lobster traps fished in the state of Maine (Maine Department of Marine Resources, unpublished data). These traps were hauled on average every 4.5 d, or 81.4 times per year. Assuming a 1-m² footprint for each trap, the area impacted was 219 km². If each trap was dragged across an area three times the footprint during set and recovery, the area impacted was 657 km². A lack of data on the extent of the area actually disturbed makes analysis of the impacts of fishing on habitat in those fisheries difficult.

The overall impact of fishing on the North American continental shelf is unknown despite research efforts in the United States spanning nearly 80 years. Alexander et al. (1914) reported that the effect of trawling on the bottom was negligible and stated that "otter trawls do not seriously disturb the bottom over which they are fished nor materially denude it of organisms which directly or indirectly serve as food for commercial fishes." Their conclusion was based on data from the catches, discounting the lack of data on organisms that passed through the trawl meshes. They also attributed shifts in species composition and abundance only to harvesting by the fishery with no connection to

TABLE 1.—Comparisons of intensity and severity of three types of sources of physical disturbance to the seafloor (based on Hall 1994; Watling and Norse 1998). Intensity is a measure of the force of physical disturbance, and severity is the impact on the benthic community.

Source	Intensity	Severity
Abiotic		
Waves	Low during long temporal periods but high during storm events (to 70–80 m depth)	Low over long temporal periods because taxa adapted to these events but high locally depending on storm behavior
Currents	Low because bed shear normally lower than critical velocities for large volume and rapid sediment movement	Low because benthic stages rarely lost due to currents
Iceberg scour	High locally because scouring results in significant sediment movement but low regionally	High locally due to high mortality of animals but low regionally
Biotic		
Bioturbation	Low because sediment movement rates are small	Low because infauna have time to repair tubes and burrows
Predation	Low on a regional scale but high locally due to patchy foraging	Low on a regional scale but high locally due to small spatial scales of high mortality
Human		
Dredging	Low on a regional scale but high locally due to large volumes of sediment removal	Low on a regional scale but high locally due to high mortality of animals
Land alteration (causing silt-laden runoff)	Low because sediment-laden runoff per se does not exert a strong physical force	Low on a regional scale but high locally where siltation over coarser sediments causes shifts in associated communities
Fishing	High due to regionwide fishing effort	High due to regionwide disturbance of most types of habitat

changes in habitat structure or the benthic community. This conclusion is not surprising given the state of ecological knowledge at the time (Auster 1988). Many more studies, using a wide range of gear types, have been conducted since that time at locations around the world.

Herein we summarize and interpret the current scientific literature on fishing impacts as they relate to fish habitat. We discuss these studies within three broad subject areas: effects on structural components of habitat, effects on benthic community structure, and effects on ecosystem-level processes. The interpretation is based on commonalities and differences between studies. Fishing gear types are discussed as general categories (e.g., trawls, dredges, fixed gear). The necessity for these generalizations is based on two overriding issues: (1) many studies do not specify the exact type and configuration of fishing gear used, and (2) each study reports on a limited range of habitat types. We recognize that individual units of fishing effort with different gears will produce a gradient of results (e.g., a scallop dredge or beam trawl will produce a greater force on the seafloor than a small whiting trawl, tickler chains will produce a different

effect than rock-hopper or "street-sweeper" gear on the groundline of a trawl, king crab *Paralithodes camtshaticus* pots are larger and heavier than pots used for American lobster *Homarus americanus*). However, our interpretation of the wide range of studies is based on the type and direction of impacts, not absolute levels of impacts. We do not address the issues of bycatch (Alverson et al. 1994), mortality of gear escapees (Chopin and Arimoto 1995), or ghost-fishing gear (Jennings and Kaiser 1998) as these issues do not directly relate to fish habitat and because recent reviews have been published that address these subjects.

Effects on Structural Components of Habitat

Interpretation of Results

The environmental characteristics that define species distributions can be found at a variety of spatial and temporal scales (e.g., Langton et al. 1995). At regional scales, the seasonal variations in

TABLE 2.—Studies of the impacts of mobile fishing gear on the structural components of fish habitat.

Habitat	Gear type	Location	Results	Reference(s)
Eelgrass	Scallop dredge	North Carolina	Comparison of reference quadrats with treatments of 15 and 30 dredgings in hard sand and soft mud substrates within eelgrass meadows. Eelgrass biomass was significantly greater in hard sand than soft mud sites. Increased dredging resulted in significant reductions in eelgrass biomass and number of shoots.	Fonseca et al. (1984)
Eelgrass and shoalgrass	Clam rake and "clam kicking"	North Carolina	Comparison of effect of two fishing methods. In raking and "light" clam-kicking treatments, biomass of seagrass was reduced approximately 25% below reference sites but recovered within 1 year. In "intense" clam-kicking treatments, biomass of seagrass declined approximately 65% below reference sites. Recovery did not begin until more than 2 years after impact, and biomass was still 35% below the level predicted from controls to show no effect.	Peterson et al. (1987)
Eelgrass and shoalgrass	Clam rakes (pea digger and bull rake)	North Carolina	Compared impacts of two clam rake types on removal of seagrass biomass. The bull rake removed 89% of shoots and 83% of roots and rhizomes in a completely raked 1 m² area. The pea digger removed 55% of shoots and 37% of roots and rhizomes.	Peterson et al. (1983)
Sea grass	Trawl	Western Mediterranean	Noted loss of *Posidonia* meadows due to trawling (45% of study area). Monitored recovery of the meadows after installing artificial reefs to stop trawling. After three years plant density has increased by a factor of six.	Guillen et al. (1994)
Sponge–coral hard-bottom	Roller-rigged trawl	Off Georgia coast	Assessed effect of single tow. Damage to all species of sponge and coral observed; 31.7% of sponges, 30.4% of stony corals, and 3.9% of octocorals. Only density of barrel sponges (*Cliona* spp.) significantly reduced. Percent of stony coral damage high because of low abundance. Damage to other sponges, octocorals, and hard corals varied but changes in density not significantly different. No significant differences between trawled and reference sites after 12 months.	Van Dolah et al. (1987)
Sponge–coral hard-bottom	Roller-frame shrimp trawl	Biscayne Bay, Florida	Damage to approximately 50% of sponges, 80% of stony corals, and 38% of soft corals.	Tilmant (1979) (cited in Van Dolah et al. 1987)
Various tropical emergent benthos	Trawl	Northwest shelf, Australia	Catch rates of all fish and large and small benthos show that in closed areas, fish and small benthos abundance increased over 5 years while large benthos (>25 cm) stayed the same or increased slightly. In trawled areas all groups of animals declined. Found that settlement rate and growth to 25 cm was on the order of 15 years for the benthos.	Sainsbury et al. (1997)

TABLE 2.—(Continued.)

Habitat	Gear type	Location	Results	Reference(s)
Gravel pavement	Scallop dredge	Georges Bank	Assessed cumulative impact of fishing. Undredged sites had significantly higher percent cover of the tube-dwelling polychaete *Filograna implexa* and other emergent epifauna than dredged sites. Undredged sites had higher numbers of organisms, biomass, species richness, and species diversity than dredged sites. Undredged sites were characterized by bushy epifauna (bryozoans, hydroids, worm tubes), while dredged sites were dominated by hard-shelled molluscs, crabs, and echinoderms.	Collie et al. (1996, 1997)
Gravel– boulder	Assumed roller-rigged trawl	Gulf of Maine	Comparison of site surveyed in 1987 and revisited in 1993. Initially, mud-draped boulders and high-density patches of diverse sponge fauna. In 1993, evidence of moved boulders, reduced densities of epifauna, and extreme trucation of high-density patches.	Auster et al. (1996)
Cobble– shell	Assumed trawl and scallop dredge	Gulf of Maine	Comparison of fished site and adjacent closed area. Statistically significant reduction in cover provided by emergent epifauna (e.g., hydroids, bryozoans, sponges, serpulid worms) and sea cucumbers.	Auster et al. (1996)
Gravel	Beam trawl	Irish Sea	An experimental area was towed 10 times. Density of epifauna (e.g., hydroids, soft corals, *Alcyonium digitatum*) was decreased approximately 50%.	Kaiser and Spencer (1996a)
Boulder– gravel	Roller-rigged trawl	Gulf of Alaska	Comparisons of single-tow trawled lane with adjacent reference lane. Significant reductions in density of structural components of habitat (two types of large sponges and anthozoans). No significant differences in densities of small sponge and mobile invertebrate fauna. However, 20.1% of boulders moved or dragged, and 25% of ophiuroids *(Amphiophiura ponderosa)* in trawled lanes were crushed or damaged compared to 2% in reference lanes.	Freese et al. (in press)
Gravel over sand	Scallop dredge	Gulf of St. Lawrence	Assessed effects of single tows. Suspended fine sediments and buried gravel below the sediment–water interface. Overturned boulders.	Caddy (1973)
Bryozoan beds (on sand and cobble)	Otter trawl and roller-rigged trawl	New Zealand	Qualitative comparison of closed and open areas. Two bryozoans produce "coral-like" forms and provide shelter for fishes and their prey. Comparisons of fished site with reference sites and prior observations from fishers show reduced density and size of bryozoan colonies.	Bradstock and Gordon (1983)
Mussel bed	Otter trawl	Strangford Lough, Northern Ireland	Comparison of characteristics of trawled and untrawled *Modiolus modiolus* beds as pre- and post-impacts of a trawl. Trawled areas, confirmed with sidescan sonar, showed mussel beds disconnected with reductions in attached epibenthos.	Magorrian (1995)

TABLE 2.—(Continued.)

Habitat	Gear type	Location	Results	Reference(s)
			The most impacted sites were characterized by few or no intact clumps, mostly shell debris, and sparse epifauna. Trawling resulted in a gradient of complexity with flattened regions at the extreme. Immigration of *Nephrops* into areas previously dominated by *Modiolus* may result in burial of new recruits due to burrowing activites, precluding a return to a functional mussel bed habitat.	
Sand–mud	Trawl and scallop dredge	Hauraki Gulf, New Zealand	Comparisons of 18 sites along a gradient of fishing effort (i.e., heavily fished sites through unfished reference sites). A gradient of increasing large epifaunal cover correlated with decreasing fishing effort.	Thrush et al. (in press)
Soft sediment	Scallop dredge	Port Phillip Bay, Australia	Compared reference and experimentally towed sites. Bedforms consisted of cone-shaped callianasid mounds and depressions prior to impact. Depressions often contained detached sea grasses and macroalgae. Only dredged plot changed after dredging. Eight days after dredging the area was flattened; mounds were removed and depressions filled. Most callianasids survived, and density did not change in three months following dredging. One month post impact, seafloor remained flat and dredge tracks distinguishable. Six months post impact mounds and depressions were present, but only at 11 months did the impacted plot return to control plot conditions.	Currie and Parry (1996)
Sand	Beam trawl	North Sea	Observations of effects of gear. As pertains to habitat, trawl removed high numbers of the hydroid *Tubularia*.	de Groot (1984)
Gravel–sand–mud	Trawl	Monterey Bay	Comparison of heavily trawled (HT) and lightly (LT) sites. The seafloor in the HT area had significantly higher densities of trawl tracks while the LT area had significantly greater densities of rocks >5 cm and mounds. The HT area had shell debris on the surface while the LT area had a cover of flocculent material. Emergent epifauna density was significantly higher for all taxa (anenomes, sea pens, sea whips) in the LT area.	Engel and Kvitek (1998)
Sand	Otter trawl	North Sea	Observations of direct effects of gear. Well-buried boulders removed and displaced from sediment. Trawl doors smoothed sand waves. Penetrated seabed 0–40 mm (sand and mud).	Bridger (1970, 1972)
Sand–shell	Assumed trawl and scallop dredge	Gulf of Maine	Comparison of fished site and adjacent closed area. Statically significant reduction of habitat complexity based on reduced cover provided by biogenic depressions and sea cucumbers. Observations at another site showed multiple scallop dredge paths resulting in smoothed bedforms. Scallop dredge paths removed cover provided by hydrozoans, which reduced local densities of associated shrimp species. Evidence of shell aggregates dispersed by scallop dredge.	Auster et al. (1996)

TABLE 2.—(Continued.)

Habitat	Gear type	Location	Results	Reference(s)
Sand–silt to mud	Otter trawl with chain sweep and roller gear	Long Island Sound	Diver observations showed doors produced continuous furrows. Chain gear in wing areas disrupted amphipod tube mats and bounced on bottom around mouth of net, leaving small scoured depressions. In areas with drifting macroalgae, the algae draped over net groundgear during tows and buffered effects on the seafloor. Roller gear also created scoured depressions. Spacers between discs lessened impacts.	Smith et al. (1985)

seawater temperature can explain annual variations in the distribution of fishes (e.g., Murawski 1993). Within regions, temporally stable associations of species have been found and tend to follow isotherms and isobaths (Gabriel and Tyler 1980; Colvocoresses and Musick 1984; Overholtz and Tyler 1985; Phoel 1986; Gabriel 1992). Species groups are sometimes seasonal and may split or show changes in composition that correlate with temperature patterns. Nested within regional scale patterns are small-scale variations in abundance and distribution of demersal fishes that can be partially attributed to variation in topographic structure. In contrast, habitat associations for coral reef fishes, kelp bed fishes, sea grass fishes, and rock reef fishes are relatively clear (e.g., Heck and Orth 1980; Ebeling and Hixon 1991; Sale 1991). The entire demersal stage of the life history of many species associated with these unique habitats have obligate habitat requirements or demonstrate recruitment bottlenecks. Without the specific structural components of habitat, the populations of fishes with these habitat requirements would not persist. However, a gradient of habitat dependence can be found in the range of demersal fish species globally. For example, early benthic phase Atlantic cod *Gadus morhua* require cobble or similar complex bottom for survival but have a refuge in size, and habitat associations are more facultative as size increases (Lough et al. 1989; Gotceitas and Brown 1993; Tupper and Boutilier 1995). Other species, however, have facultative habitat associations throughout their life (e.g., Auster et al. 1991, 1995, 1997b; Sogard and Able 1991; Able et al. 1995; Langton et al. 1995; Szedlmayer and Howe 1997). These associations may increase survivorship of individuals and may contribute to wide variations in recruitment, but they are not obligate for the survival of populations (e.g., Lindholm et al. 1998).

"Habitat" has been defined as "the structural component of the environment that attracts organisms and serves as a center of biological activity" (Peters and Cross 1992). Habitat in this case includes the range of sediment types (i.e., mud through boulders), bed forms (e.g., sand waves and ripples, flat mud) as well as the co-occurring biological structures (e.g., shell, burrows, sponges, sea grass, macroalgae, coral). A review of 22 studies (Table 2) all show measurable impacts of mobile gear on the structural components of habitat (e.g., sand waves, emergent epifauna, sponges, coral) when defining habitat at this spatial scale. Results of each of the studies show similar classes of impacts despite the wide geographic range of the studies (i.e., tropical to boreal). In summary, mobile fishing gear reduced habitat complexity by: (1) directly removing epifauna or damaging epifauna leading to mortality, (2) smoothing sedimentary bedforms and reducing bottom roughness, and (3) removing taxa that produce structure (i.e., taxa that produce burrows and pits). Studies that have addressed both acute and chronic impacts have shown the same types of effects (Figure 1).

Little has been written about the recovery of seafloor habitat from fishing gear effects. Recovery of storm-caused sedimentary features depends primarily on grain sizes of sediment and depth to which storm-generated surge and currents occur. Some features can be reformed after seasonal or annual storm events, while others will depend on larger meteorological events that occur on decadal time scales or longer. Recovery of biogenic features will depend on recruitment or immigration, depending on the spatial extent of impacts. Recovery will also depend on whether impacts are short term or chronic. For example, on coral–sponge hard bottom off the coast of Georgia, Van Dolah et al. (1987) found no long-term effects of trawling on the benthic community. After one year the sponges and octocorals that were experimentally trawled recovered with densities reaching or exceeding pretrawling levels at the study site. However, it is important to note that this study did not address chronic effects but rather a single tow of a roller-rigged trawl.

Few accounts of the impacts of fixed gears on habitat have been published. Eno et al. (1996) studied the effects of crustacean traps in British and Irish waters. One experiment assessed the effects of setting and hauling pots on emergent epifaunal species (sea pens) on soft bottom. Both impacts from dragging pots across the bottom and pots resting for extended periods on sea pens showed that the group was able to mostly recover from such disturbances. Limited qualitative observations of fish traps, longlines, and gill nets dragged across the seafloor during set and recovery showed results similar to mobile gear such that some types of epibenthos were dislodged, especially emergent species such as erect sponges and corals (SAFMC 1991; W. L. High, Alaska Fisheries Science Center, unpublished data). Although the area impacted per unit of effort is smaller for fixed gear than for mobile fishing gear, the types of damage to emergent benthos appear to be similar (but not necessarily equivalent per unit effort). Quantitative studies of fixed-gear effects, based on acute and chronic impacts, have not been conducted.

The issue of defining pelagic habitats and elucidating effects of fishing is difficult because these habitats are poorly described at the scales that allow for measurements of change based on gear use. Although pelagic habitat can be defined based on temperature, light intensity, turbidity, oxygen concentration, currents, frontal boundaries, and a host of other oceanographic parameters and patterns, there are few published data that attempt to measure change in any of these types of parameters or conditions concurrently with fishing activity and associations of fishes. Kroger and Guthrie (1972) showed that menhaden (*Brevortia patronus* and *B. tyrannus*) were subjected to greater predation pressure, at least from visual predators, in clear versus turbid water, suggesting that turbid habitats were a greater refuge from predation. This same type of pattern was found for menhaden in both naturally turbid waters and in the turbid plumes generated by oyster shell dredging activities (Harper and Hopkins 1976). However, no work has been published that addresses the effects of variation in time and space of the plumes or the effects of turbid water refugia

on feeding and growth. There are also examples of small-scale aggregations of fishes with biological structures in the water column and at the surface. Aggregations of fishes may have two effects on predation patterns by: (1) reducing the probability of predation on individuals within the aggregation, and (2) providing a focal point for the activities of predators (a cue that fishermen use to set gear). For example, small fishes aggregate under mats of *Sargassum* (e.g., Moser et al. 1998), and high-density vessel traffic may disaggregate mats. Also, fishes have been observed to co-occur with aggregations of gelatinous zooplankton and pelagic crustaceans (Auster et al. 1992; Brodeur, in press). Gelatinous zooplankton are greatly impacted as they pass through the mesh of either mobile or stationary gear (P. J. Auster, unpublished observations), which may reduce the size and number of zooplankton aggregations and disperse associated fishes. These changes could reduce the value of aggregating, resulting in increased mortality or reduced feeding efficiency.

Implications for Management

Commonalities in gear impact studies on habitat structure allow for the production of a conceptual model to visualize the patterns in gear impacts across a gradient of habitat types. Auster et al. (1998) developed a hierarchical, categorical approach for classifying habitats on the cold temperate and boreal continental shelf of the northwest Atlantic. This type of classification scheme has proven very useful in habitat management for freshwater fisheries. The range of habitat types was condensed into eight habitat categories increasing from simple to complex (Table 3). For example, currents form sand wave fields that provide shelter for fish from high current speeds. This shelter reduces the energy needed to maintain position on the bottom and permits ambush predation of drifting demersal zooplankton. Storm currents sort loose sediments and deposit shells and cobbles in the troughs of sand waves. These small crevices provide an ephemeral habitat for small fishes and crustaceans. Cobble bottoms provide interstices for shelter sites but also provide a hard surface for epibenthic organisms such as sponges and bryozoans to attach. These emergent epifauna provide additional cover value. Scattered boulders also provide shelter from currents, and boulder piles provide deep crevices for shelter required by some species such as redfish *Sebastes* spp.

FIGURE 1.—Photographs A–G compare impacts at sites with acute and chronic disturbance by fishing gear. Acute disturbance by a single pass of a scallop dredge at a coastal site in the Gulf of Maine (ca. 20 m depth). Photographs were taken within hours after the pass of the scallop dredge. Photographs A and B represent before-and-after images from a cobble–shell habitat. Note that the sponge colonies that stabilize the shell aggregates are removed in the impacted state. Photographs C and D represent before-and-after images from a sand–shell habitat. Note that the worm tube mats are severely disrupted in the impacted state (Auster, in press). Photographs E–G show chronic disturbance due to continued fishing on the northeast peak of Georges Bank. All photographs taken in July 1997. Photograph E shows an undisturbed area on the Canadian side of the bank which has been closed to fishing (84 m depth). Photograph F shows a site closed to fishing since December 1994. Photograph G shows a site still impacted by fishing gear. (Georges Bank images courtesy of Page Valentine, U.S. Geological Survey).

TABLE 3.—Hierarchical classification of fish habitat types (from Auster 1998; Auster et al. 1998) on the outer continental shelf of the cold temperate and boreal northwest Atlantic. (Categories are based on Auster et al. 1995; Langton et al. 1995; Auster et al. 1996; and unpublished observations).

Category	Habitat type	Description and rationale	Complexity score
1	Flat sand and mud	Areas such as depressions, ripples, or epifauna that provide no vertical structure.	1
2	Sand waves	Troughs that provide shelter from currents. Previous observations indicate that species such as silver hake *Merluccius bilinearis* keep on the down-current sides of sand waves and ambush drifting demersal zooplankton and shrimp.	2
3	Biogenic structures	Features such as burrows, depressions, cerianthid anenomes, and hydroid patches that are created and used by mobile fauna for shelter.	3
4	Shell aggregates	Areas that provide complex interstitial spaces for shelter. As an aside, shell aggregates also provide a complex high-contrast background that may confuse visual predators.	4
5	Pebble–cobble	Areas that provide small interstitial spaces and may be equivalent in shelter value to shell aggregate. However, shell is a more ephemeral habitat.	5
6	Pebble–cobble with sponge cover	Attached fauna such as sponges provide additional spatial complexity for a wider range of size classes of mobile organisms.	10
7	Partially buried or dispersed boulders	Although not providing small interstitial spaces or deep crevices, partially buried boulders do exhibit high vertical relief, and dispersed boulders on cobble pavement provide simple crevices. The shelter value of this type of habitat may be less or greater than previous types based on the size class and behavior of associated species.	12
8	Piled boulders	Areas that provide deep interstitial spaces of variable sizes.	15

Habitat value for each habitat type does not increase linearly. Each category was assigned a numerical score based on its level of physical complexity (note that this model does not include effects of fishing on biodiversity per se). Categories 1 through 5 increase linearly. Starting at category 6, the score of 10 is based on a score of 5 (i.e., the score for cobble) from the previous category plus a score of 5 for dense emergent epifauna that is assumed to double the cover value of small interstices alone. Category 7 is scored for cobble and emergent epifauna (i.e., 10) plus 2 more points for shallow boulder crevices and refuges from current. Finally, category 8 is scored as 15 because of the presence of shallow crevices and current refuges (previously scored as 12), plus deep crevices scored as 3. These scores are therefore the starting points representing unimpacted habitats.

A pictorial representation of the model, shown in Figure 2, indicates the response of the range of seafloor habitat types to increases in fishing effort (Auster, in press). The range of fishing effort increases from left to right along the x-axis with 0 indicating no gear impacts and 4 indicating the maximum effort required to produce the greatest possible change in habitat complexity. The numbers at present are dimensionless because better data are needed on the effects of various gear types at various levels of effort over specific habitats. The y-axis is a comparative index of habitat complexity. Each habitat type starts near the y-axis at the value of the habitat in an unimpacted condition. The habitat categories are representative of the common types of habitat found across the northeast U.S. continental shelf and are likely to be found on most other continental shelf areas of the world. The responses to different types of bottom-contact fishing gear are assumed to be similar.

This model shows a range of changes in habitat complexity based on gear impacts. It predicts reductions in the complexity provided by bedforms from direct smoothing by gear. Biogenic structures are reduced by a number of mechanisms such as direct gear impacts as well as removal of organisms

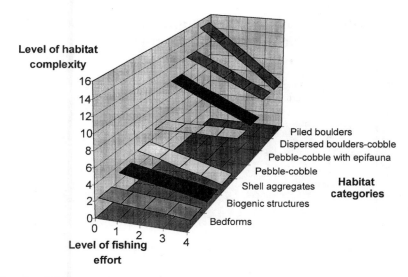

Figure 2.—Conceptual fishing gear impact model. The range of fishing effort increases from left to right along the x-axis with 0 as a pristine condition and 4 as a maximally impacted state. The y and z axes are based on information in Table 3. The y-axis is a comparative index of habitat complexity. The z axis shows the range of habitat categories from simple (bedforms) to complex (piled boulders).

that produce structures (e.g., crabs that produce burrows). There are some habitats where the model shows no significant reductions, such as gravel areas with very little epifaunal settlement. Although mobile gear would overturn pebbles and cobbles, the actual structural integrity of the habitat would not be reduced (although organisms on the undersides of cobbles are exposed to predation). However, the value of cobble pavements are greatly reduced when epifauna are removed, as biogenic structures provide additional cover. Gear can move boulders and still provide some measure of hydraulic complexity to the bottom by providing shelter from currents. On the other hand, piles of boulders can be dispersed by large trawls, and this reduces the cover value for crevice dwellers. The model should be widely applicable as the habitat types are widely distributed worldwide and the impacts are consistent with those described in the literature.

This conceptual model serves two purposes. First, it provides a holistic summary of the range of gear impacts across a range of habitat types. The end points in the model are based on empirical data and observations and should be useful for considering management actions for the conservation of fish habitat. The second purpose for developing the model is to provide a basis for future research. Although it is possible to ascribe the endpoints of habitat complexity at both unimpacted and fully impacted states, the slope of the line remains unknown, and the level of fishing effort

required to produce specific rates of change is also unknown for all gear types. Responses may be linear or nonlinear (e.g., logarithmic). Perhaps there are thresholds of disturbance beyond which some habitat types exhibit a response. Regardless, responses will most likely be habitat specific.

The impact model does not have an explicit time component. Here we add such a conceptual framework to the discussion. Cushing's match–mismatch hypothesis (Cushing 1975) has served as one of several hypotheses that explain annual variation in larval recruitment dynamics and has been the focus of large amounts of research effort for several decades. Here we propose a similar type of match–mismatch paradigm for linking variation in the survivorship of early benthic-phase fishes with the abundance of epibenthic organisms, particularly those with annual life histories, that may serve as habitat. Figure 3 shows the pattern in percent cover for an idealized benthic species that produces emergent structure (e.g., hydroid stalk, amphipod tube, mussel). This type of species has widespread settlement and occurs at high densities. At the time of settlement, large areas of the seafloor are occupied by this species. Over the course of time, predation and senescence reduce the cover provided by such taxa. The timing of settlement of early benthic-phase fish will greatly effect the cover value provided by the benthic taxa. In addition to natural processes, fishing gear impacts further reduce the cover value over time and can

Decline in Cover (Epifaunal Density) Over Time:
Natural Versus Impacted

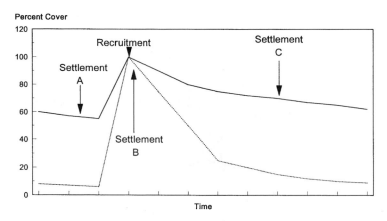

FIGURE 3.—Habitat match–mismatch paradigm that links variation in the survivorship of early benthic-phase fishes with abundance of epibenthic organisms. The illustration shows a temporal pattern in percent cover for an "idealized" benthic species with emergent structure (e.g., hydroid, amphipod tubes) under conditions of natural variation (solid line) and when impacted by fishing activities (dotted line). The habitat value of such areas is dependent on the timing of recruitment of fishes in relation to settlement and subsequent mortality of epibenthos from natural and human-caused sources. For example, at the time period marked A, settlement into unimpacted benthos provides greater cover for fishes than an area impacted by fishing. However, at the settlement period marked B, recruitment of epibenthos has recently occurred and the cover provided under either state is nearly identical. The settlement period marked C is similar to A and reflects the dichotomy of natural versus fishing-enhanced changes in a dynamic habitat.

narrow the window in which particular patches of epibenthos serve as effective cover for newly settled fishes. The time scale (x-axis) and patterns in the figure were developed to show an annual pattern representative of many taxa with such life history strategies, but this pattern can also be extended in time for longer-lived organisms. Like the conceptual impact model above, the timing and changes in slope of these lines are critical for understanding the dynamics of this interaction.

Ultimately, it will be necessary to develop models that include sensitivity indices for specific habitats, communities, and key taxa based on the effects of specific gear types, levels of effort, and life history patterns (of both fish and taxa that serve a habitat function). MacDonald et al. (1996) has developed such a sensitivity index to quantify the impact of fishing on particular epifaunal taxa in the North Sea region. The index is a function of recovery time after damage, fragility of the animal, and intensity of the impact.

Lack of information on the small-scale distribution and timing of fishing makes it difficult to ascribe the patterns of impacts observed in field studies to specific levels of fishing effort. Auster et al. (1996) estimated that between 1976 and 1991, Georges Bank was impacted by mobile gear (e.g., otter trawl,

roller-rigged trawl, scallop dredge) on average between 200 and 400% of its area on an annual basis, and the Gulf of Maine was impacted 100% annually. Fishing effort, however, was not homogeneous. Sea sampling data from NMFS observer coverage demonstrated that the distribution of tows was nonrandom (Figure 4). Although these data represent less than 5% of overall fishing effort, they illustrate that the distribution of fishing gear impacts is quite variable.

Recovery of habitat following trawling is difficult to predict as well. Timing, severity, and frequency of the impacts all interact to mediate processes that lead to recovery (Watling and Norse 1998). For example, sand waves may not be reformed until storm energy is sufficient to produce bedform transport of coarse sand grains (Valentine and Schmuck 1995), and storms may not be common until a particular time of year or may infrequently reach a particular depth, perhaps only on decadal time scales. Sponges are particularly sensitive to disturbance because they recruit aperiodically and are slow growing in deeper waters (Reiswig 1973; Witman and Sebens 1985; Witman et al. 1993). However, many species such as hydroids and ampelescid amphipods reproduce once or twice an-

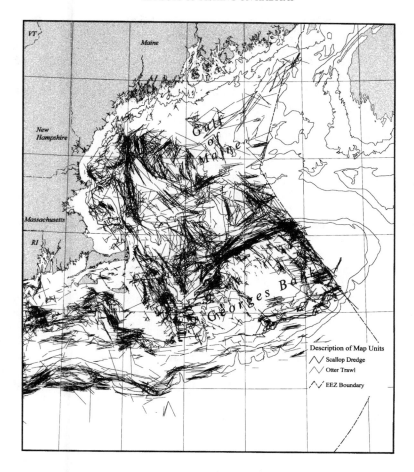

FIGURE 4.—Spatial distribution of trawl and scallop dredge tows from the National Marine Fisheries Service sea sampling database for 1989–1994 (April). This illustration represents a total of 14,908 tows. Note that the spatial distribution of effort is not homogeneous but aggregated in productive fishing areas.

nually, and their stalks and tubes provide cover for the early benthic phases of many fish species and their prey (e.g., Auster et al. 1996, 1997b). Where fishing effort is constrained within particular fishing grounds, and where data on fishing effort are available, studies that compare similar sites along a gradient of effort have produced the types of information on effort impact that will be required for effective habitat management (e.g., Collie et al. 1996, 1997; Thrush et al., in press).

The role these impacts on habitat have on harvested populations is unknown in most cases. However, a growing body of empirical observations and modeling demonstrates that effects can be seen in population responses at particular population levels. For example, Lindholm et al. (1998) have modeled the effects of habitat alteration on the survival of 0-year cohorts of Atlantic cod. The model results

indicate that a reduction in habitat complexity has measurable effects on population dynamics when the adult stock is at low levels (i.e., when spawning and larval survivorship does not produce sufficient recruits to saturate available habitats). At high adult population levels, when larval abundance may be high and settling juveniles would greatly exceed habitat availability, predation effects would not be mediated by habitat, and no effect in the response of the adult population to habitat change was found.

Empirical studies that most directly link changes due to gear impacts on habitat structure to population responses are being carried out in Australia. Sainsbury (1987, 1988, 1991) and Sainsbury et al. (1997) have shown a very tight coupling between a loss of emergent epifauna and fish productivity along the northwest continental shelf. In these studies there was a documented decline in the bycatch of invertebrate epifauna in trawl catches, from 500 kg hr^{-1} to only a few kg hr^{-1}, and replacement of the most commercially desirable fish associated with the epifaunal communities by less valuable species associated with more open habitat. By restricting fishing the decline in the fish population was reversed. This corresponded to an observed recovery in the epifaunal community, although the recovery for the larger epifaunal invertebrates showed a considerable lag time after trawling ceased. This work is based on a management framework developed to test hypotheses regarding the habitat dependence of harvested species. The hypotheses, described in Sainsbury (1988, 1991), assessed whether population responses were the result of:

1. independent single-species (intraspecific) responses to fishing and natural variation;
2. interspecific interactions such that as specific populations are reduced by fishing, nonharvested populations experienced a competitive release;
3. interspecific interactions such that as nonharvested species increase from some external process, their population inhibits the population growth rate of the harvested species; and
4. habitat mediation of the carrying capacity for each species, such that gear-induced habitat changes alter the carrying capacity of the area.

This is a primary example of adaptive management in which regulations were developed to test hypotheses and were the basis for modifying subsequent management measures. This type of management process exemplifies management of fisheries based primarily on an understanding of ecological relationships.

Effects on Community Structure

Interpretation of Results

Studies on the effects of fishing on benthic communities have often produced variable results regarding the impact on community structure. The reasons for these differences may include sampling strategies, use of different metrics, different methods of fishing, different functional groups of species that compose the community, and subtle differences in habitat type. Furthermore, studies have often been conducted in areas that have a history of fishing activity and therefore may not have truly undisturbed reference areas for comparison, despite the efforts of the investigator (see Hall

et al. 1993; M. J. Kaiser, University of Wales-Bangor, unpublished data). Changes in benthic community structure also have to be understood against a background of natural disturbance and variability (Thrush et al., in press). Bearing in mind these caveats, the literature on fishing gear impacts can be divided into short-term and long-term studies that reveal some common characteristics and patterns resulting from fishing on the seafloor.

An immediate reduction in the density of non-target species is often reported following impacts from mobile gear (Table 4). In assessing this effect it is common to compare numbers and densities for each species before and after fishing and with an undisturbed reference site. Kaiser and Spencer (1996a), for example, found a reduction in diversity and abundance of some taxa at one location in the Irish Sea where sediments were relatively stable. They reported a 58% decrease in mean abundance and 50% reduction in the mean number of species per sample. In contrast, at a location where the sediments were more mobile the impact of beam trawling was not as substantial. In other European studies, Bergman and Hup (1992) and Santbrink and Bergman (1994) have documented species- and size-specific differences in macrofaunal abundance and mortality, with densities decreasing for some species, and mortality increasing, after trawling. However, in other cases there were no observable effects. In a scallop-dredging study in New Zealand, two experimentally fished sites showed an immediate decrease in macrofaunal densities in comparison to corresponding reference sites (Thrush et al. 1995). In an 88-d study of scallop dredging in Australia, Currie and Parry (1994) found that the number of individuals at the dredged sites was always lower than at the reference sites despite an overall increase in animal numbers due to amphipod recruitment to both the experimental and reference areas.

Time series data sets that allow for a direct long-term comparison of sites before and after fishing are essentially nonexistent, primarily because the extent to which the world's oceans are currently fished was not foreseen, or because time series data collection focused on the fish themselves rather than the impact of fishing on the environment. Nevertheless, there are several benthic data sets that allow for an examination of observational or correlative comparisons before and after fishing (Table 5). Perhaps the longest time series comparisons of long-term impact of fishing on benthic community structure are

TABLE 4.—Studies of short-term impacts of fishing on benthic communities.

Taxa	Gear; sediment type	Location	Results	Reference
Infauna	Beam trawl; megaripples and flat substrate	Irish Sea	Assessed the immediate effects of beam trawling and found a reduction in diversity and abundance of some taxa in the more stable sediments of the northeast sector of the experimental site but could not find similar effects in the more mobile sediments. Out of the top 20 species, 19 had lower abundance levels at the fished site, and 9 showed a statistically significant decrease. Coefficient of variation for numbers and abundance was higher in the fished area of the northwest sector, supporting the hypothesis that heterogeneity increases with physical disturbance. Measured a 58% decrease in mean abundance and a 50% reduction in the mean number of species per sample in the sector resulting from removal of the most common species. Less dramatic change in the sector where sediments are more mobile.	Kaiser and Spencer (1996a)
Starfish	Beam trawl; coarse sand, gravel and shell, muddy sand, mud	Irish Sea	Evaluated damage to starfish at three sites in the Irish Sea that experienced different degrees of trawling intensity. Used International Council for the Exploration of the Sea data to select sites and used side scan to confirm trawling intensity. Found a significant correlation between starfish damage (arm regeneration) and trawling intensity.	Kaiser (1996)
Horse mussels	Otter trawl; horse mussel beds	Strangford Lough; N. Ireland	Used video and remotely operated vehicle, side-scan sonar, and benthic grabs to characterize the effect of otter trawling and scallop dredging on the benthic community. There was special concern over the impact on *Modiolus* beds in the Lough. Plotted the known fishing areas and graded impacts based on a subjective six-point scale. Found significant trawl impacts. Side-scan sonar supported video observations and showed areas of greatest impact. Found that in otter trawl areas, the otter boards did the most damage. Side scan suggested that sediment characteristics had changed in heavily trawled areas.	Industrial Science Division (1990)
Benthic fauna	Beam trawl; mobile mega-ripple structure and stable uniform sediment	Irish Sea	Sampled trawled areas 24 hours after trawling and 6 months later. On stable sediment found siginificant difference immediately after trawling, specifically, a reduction in polychaetes but increase in hermit crabs. After six months there was no detectable impact. On megaripple substrate no significant differences were observed immediately after trawling or six months later.	Kaiser et al. (in press)

TABLE 4.—(Continued.)

Taxa	Gear; sediment type	Location	Results	Reference
Bivalves, sea scallop, surf clams, ocean quahog	Scallop dredge, hydraulic clam dredge; various substrate types	Mid-Atlantic Bight, USA	Submersible study of bivalve harvest operations. Scallops harvested on soft sediment (sand or mud) had low dredge-induced mortality rates for uncaught animals (<5%). Culling mortality (discarded bycatch) was low, approximately 10%. Over 90% of the quahogs that were discarded reburrowed and survived whereas 50% of the surf clams died. Predators, crabs, starfish, fish, and skates moved in on the quahogs and clams with predator density 10 times control-area levels within eight hours post dredging. Noted numerous "minute" predators feeding in trawl tracks. Non-harvested animals, sand dollars, crustaceans, and worms significantly disrupted, but sand dollars suffered little apparent mortality.	Murawski and Serchuk (1989)
Ocean quahog	Hydraulic clam dredge; sand–silt	Long Island, NY, USA	Evaluated clam dredge efficiency over a transect and changes up to 24 hours later. After dredge filled it created a "windrow of clams." Dredge penetrated up to 30 cm and pushed sediment into track shoulders. After 24 hours track looked like a shallow depression. Clams can be cut or crushed by dredge with mortality ranging from 7 to 92%, which is dependent on size and location along dredge path. Smaller clams survived better and were capable of reburrowing in a few minutes. Predators, crabs, starfish, and snails moved in rapidly and departed within 24 hours.	Meyer et al. (1981)
Macro-benthos	Scallop dredge; coarse sand	Mercury Bay, New Zealand	Benthic community composed of small short-lived animals at two experimental and adjacent control sites. Sampling before and after dredging and three months later. Dredging caused an immediate decrease in density of common macrofauna. Three months later some populations had not recovered. Immediately after trawling, snails, hermit crabs, and starfish were feeding on damaged and exposed animals.	Thrush et al. (1995)
Scallops and associated fauna	Scallop dredge; "soft sediment"	Port Phillip Bay, Australia	Sampled twice before dredging and three times afterwards, up to 88 days later. The mean difference in species number increased from 3 to 18 after trawling. The total number of individuals increased over the sampling time on both experimental and control sites primarily as a result of amphipod recruitment, but the number of individuals at the dredged sites was always lower than the control. Dissimilarity increased significantly as a result of dredging because of a decrease in species numbers and abundance.	Currie and Parry (1994)

TABLE 4.—(Continued.)

Taxa	Gear; sediment type	Location	Results	Reference
Sea scallops and associated fauna	Otter trawl and scallop dredge; gravel and sand	Gulf of St. Lawrence, Canada	Observed physical change to seafloor from otter doors and scallop dredge and lethal and nonlethal damage to the scallops. Noted an increase in the most active predators within the trawl tracks compared to outside, specifically, winter flounder, sculpins, and rock crabs. No increase in starfish or other sedentary forms within an hour of dredging.	Caddy (1973)
Macrofauna	Beam trawl; hard–sandy substrate	North Sea, coast of Holland	Sampling before and after beam trawling (*hours, 16 hours, and 2 weeks) showed species-specific changes in macrofaunal abundance. Decreasing density ranged from 10 to 65% for species of echinoderms (starfish and sea urchins but not brittle stars), tube-dwelling polychaetes, and molluscs at the two-week sampling period. Density of some animals did not change. Other animals' densities increased, but these increases were not significant after two weeks.	Bergman and Hup (1992)
Benthic fauna	Beam trawl and shrimp trawl; hard sandy bottom, shell debris, and sandy substrate–mud	North Sea, German coast	Preliminary report using video and photographs comparing trawled and untrawled areas. Presence and density of brittle stars, hermit crabs, other "large" crustaceans, and flatfish was higher in the controls than the beam trawl site. Difference in sand ripple formation in trawled areas was also noted. Formations looked disturbed, not round and well developed. Found a positive correlation with damage to benthic animals and individual animal size. Found less impact with the shrimp trawl; diver observations confirmed low level of impact although the net was "festooned" with worms. Noted large megafauna, mainly crabs, in trawl tracks.	Rumohr et al. (1994)
Soft bottom macrofauna	Beam trawl; very fine sand	North Sea, Dutch sector	Compared animal densities before and after trawling and looked at fish stomach contents. Found that total mortality due to trawling varied among species and size class of fish, ranging from 4 to 139% of pretrawling values. (Values >100% indicate animals moving into the trawled area.) Mortality for echinoderms was low (3 to 19%) and undetectable for some molluscs (especially solid shells or small animals), while larger molluscs had a 12 to 85% mortality. Burrowing crustaceans had low mortality, but epifaunal crustaceans approximated 30% mortality and ranged as high as 74% mortality. Annelids were generally unaffected except for *Pectinaria*, a tube-building animal.	Santbrink and Bergman (1994)

TABLE 4.—(Continued.)

Taxa	Gear; sediment type	Location	Results	Reference
			Generally, mortality increased with number of times the area was trawled (once or twice). Dab *Limanda limanda* were found to be the major scavanger, immigrating into the area and eating damaged animals.	
Hemit crabs	Beam trawl	Irish Sea	Compared the catch and diet of two species of hermit crab on trawled and control sites. Found significant increases in abundance on the trawl lines two to four days after trawling for both species but also no change for one species on one of two dates. Found a general size shift toward larger animals after trawling. Stomach-contents weight was higher post-trawling for one species. Diets of the crabs were similar, but proportions differed.	Ramsay et al. (1996)
Sand macro-fauna and infauna	Scallop dredge	Irish Sea	Compared experimental treatments based on frequency of tows (i.e., 2, 4, 12, 25). Bottom topography changes did not change grain size distribution, organic carbon content, or chlorophyll content. Bivalve molluscs and peracarid crustaceans did not show signficant changes in abundance or biomass. Polychaetes and urchins showed significant declines. Large molluscs, crustaceans, and sand eels were also damaged. In general, there was selective elimination of fragile and sedentary components of the infauna as well as large epifaunal taxa.	Eleftheriou and Robertson (1992)

the studies of Reise (1982) and Riesen and Reise (1982) in the Wadden Sea. In reviewing change for 101 species in the benthic community over 100 years, Reise (1982) noted no long-term trends in abundance for 42 common species but found 11 of these species showed considerable variation. Sponges, coelenterates, and bivalves suffered the greatest losses while polychaetes showed the biggest gains. Subtidally there was a decrease in the most common species from 53 to 44 while intertidally the opposite was observed, an increase from 24 to 38. Riesen and Reise (1982) examined a 55-year data set and documented increases in mussel beds and the associated fauna. They noted a loss of oysters due to overexploitation and a loss of *Sabellaria* reefs because they were systematically targeted by trawlers, as well as the loss of sea grass from disease. In another European study, Pearson et al. (1985) compared changes in the Kattegatt (an arm of the North Sea) following a 73-year hiatus in sampling. In this case, community composition had changed to the extent that there was only a 30% similarity between stations over time, with the primary shift being a decrease in sea urchins and an increase in brittle stars. They observed a general decline in deposit feeders and an increase in suspension feeders and carnivores as well as a decline in animal size. Holme (1983) also made some comparisons from data collected over an 85-year time span in the English Channel and noted changes in the benthic community that he speculated might relate to the queen scallop fishery. The results of these long-term studies are consistent with the patterns found in short-term studies of habitat and community structure.

Data sets on the order of months to a few years are more typical of the longer-term studies on fishing impacts on benthic community structure. The impact of experimental trawling has been monitored

TABLE 5.— Studies of long-term impacts of fishing on benthic communities.

Habitat type; taxa	Time period	Location	Results	Reference
Sand; macro-benthos and meiofauna	2–7 months	Bay of Fundy	Experimental trawling in high-energy area. Otter trawl doors dug up to 5 cm deep, and marks were visible for 2 to 7 months. Initial significant effects on benthic diatoms and nematodes but no significant impact on macrofauna. No significant long-term effects.	Brylinsky et al. (1994)
Quartz sand; benthic infauna	5 months	South Carolina estuary	Compared benthic community in two areas, one open to trawling and one closed, before and after shrimp season. Found variation with time but no relationship between variations and trawling per se.	Van Dolah et al. (1991)
Sandy; ocean quahogs		Western Baltic	Observed otter board damage to bivalves, especially ocean quahogs, and found an inverse relation between shell thickness and damage and a positive correlation between shell length and damage.	Rumohr and Krost (1991)
Subtidal shallows and channel; macrobenthos	100 years	Wadden Sea	Reviewed changes in benthic community documented over 100 years. Considered 101 species. No long-term trends in changing abundance for 42 common species, with 11 showing considerable variation. Sponges, coelenterates, and bivalves suffered greatest losses while polychaetes showed the largest gains. Decrease subtidally for common species from 53 to 44 species and increase intertidally for common species from 24 to 38 species.	Reise (1982)
Intertidal sand; lug worms	4 years	Wadden Sea	Studied impact of lugworm harvesting versus control site. Machine dug 40-cm gullies. Immediate impact was a reduction in several benthic species and slow recovery for some of the larger long-lived species like soft-shelled clams. With one exception, a polychaete, the shorter-lived macrobenthic animals showed no decline. It took several years for the area to recover to prefishing conditions.	Beukema (1995)
Various habitat types; all species		North Sea	Review of fishing effects on the North Sea based primarily on International Council for the Exploration of the Sea North Sea Task Force reports. Starfish, sea urchins, and several polychaetes showed a 40 to 60% reduction in density after beam trawling, but some less-abundant animals showed no change, and one polychaete increased. At the scale of the North Sea, the effect of trawling on the benthos is unclear.	Gislason (1994)

TABLE 5.— (Continued.)

Habitat type; taxa	Time period	Location	Results	Reference
Sand; macrofauna	73 years	Kattegatt, coast of Sweden and Denmark	Compared benthic surveys from 1911 to1912 with surveys from 1984. Community composition changed with only approximately 30% similarity between years at most stations. Primary change was a decrease in sea urchins and increase in brittle stars. Animals were also smaller in 1984. Deposit feeders decreased while suspension feeders and carnivores increased.	Pearson et al. (1985)
Subtidal shallows and channels; macrofauna	55 years	Wadden Sea	Documented increase in mussel beds and associated species such as polychaetes and barnacles when comparing benthic survey data. Noted loss of oyster banks, *Sabellaria* reefs, and subtidal sea grass beds. Oysters were overexploited and replaced by mussels; *Zostera* were lost to disease. Concluded that major habitat shifts were the result of human influence.	Riesen and Reise (1982)
Various habitats; ocean quahogs		Southern North Sea	Arctica valves were collected from 146 stations in 1991, and the scars on the valve surface were dated using internal growth bands, as an indicator of the frequency of beam trawl damage between 1959 and 1991. Numbers of scars varied regionally and temporally and correlated with fishing.	Witbaard and Klein (1994)
Various habitats; macrofauna	85 years	Western English Channel	Discussed change and causes of change observed in benthic community based on historic records and collections. Discussed role of fishing gear in dislodging hydroid and bryozoan colonies and speculated that gear effects reduce settlement sites for queen scallops.	Holme (1983)
Gravel and sand; macrofauna	3 years	Central California	Compared heavily trawled area with lightly trawled (closed) area using Smith MacIntyre grab samples and video transect data collected over three years. Trawl tracks and shell debris were more numerous in heavily trawled area, as were amphinomid polychaetes and oligochaetes in most years. Rocks, mounds, and flocculent material were more numerous at the lightly trawled station. Commercial fish were more common in the lightly trawled area as were epifaunal invertebrates. No significant differences were found between stations in terms of biomass of most other invertebrates.	Engel and Kvitek (1998)
Fine sand; razor clams		Barrinha, Southern Portugal	Evaluated disturbance lines in the shell matrix of the razor clam and found an increase in number of disturbance lines with length and age of the clams. Sand grains were often incorporated into the shell, suggestive of a major disturbance such as trawling damage and subsequent recovery and repair of the shell.	Gaspar et al. (1994)

TABLE 5.— (Continued.)

Habitat type; taxa	Time period	Location	Results	Reference
Fine to medium sand; ocean quahogs		Southern New Jersey	Compared areas unfished, recently fished, and currently fished for ocean quahogs using hydraulic dredges. Sampled invertebrates with a Smith MacIntyre grab. Few significant differences in numbers of individuals or species were noted, and no pattern suggesting any relationship to dredging was found.	MacKenzie (1982)
Gravel, shell debris, and fine mud; horse mussel community	8 years	Strangford Lough, Northern Ireland	Review paper of effects of queen scallop fishery on the horse mussel community. Compared benthic survey from the 1975–1980 period with work in 1988. Scallop fishery began in 1980. *Modiolus* community remained unchanged essentially from 1857 to 1980. The scallop fishery has a large benthic faunal bycatch, including horse mussels. Changes in the horse mussel community were directly related to the initiation of the scallop fishery, and there was concern about the extended period it would take for this community to recover.	Brown (1989)
Shallow muddy sand; scallops	6 months	Maine	Sampled site before, immediately after, and up to six months after trawling. Loss of surficial sediments and lowered food quality of sediments, measured as microbial populations, enzyme hydrolyzable amino acids, and chlorophyll *a*, were observed. Variable recovery by benthic community. Correlation with returning fauna and food quality of sediment.	L. Watling, R. H. Findlay, L. M. Mayer, and D. F. Schick (unpublished data)
Sand and sea grass; hard shelled clams and bay scallops	4 years	North Carolina	Evaluated effects of clam raking and mechanical harvesting on hard clams, bay scallops, macroinvertebrates, and sea grass biomass. In sand, harvesting adults showed no clear pattern of effect. With light harvesting, sea grass biomass dropped 25% immediately but recovered in a year. In heavy harvesting, sea grass biomass fell 65%, recovery did not start for >2 years, and sea grass had not recovered up to 4 years later. Clam harvesting showed no effect on macroinvertebrates. Scallop densities correlated with sea grass biomass.	Peterson et al. (1987)
Gravel pavement; benthic megafauna	Not known	Northern Georges Bank, USA	Used side-scan sonar, video, and naturalist dredge sampling to characterize disturbed and undisturbed sites based on fishing activity records. Documented a gradient of community structure from deep undisturbed to shallow disturbed sites. Undisturbed sites had more individual organisms, greater biomass, greater species richness, and greater diversity and were characterized by an abundant bushy epifauna. Disturbed sites were dominated by hard-shelled molluscs, crabs, and echinoderms.	Collie et al. (1997)

TABLE 5.— (Continued.)

Habitat type; taxa	Time period	Location	Results	Reference
Sand; epifauna	3 years	Grand Banks, Canada	Experimentally trawled site 12 times each year within 31 to 34 hours for 3 years. Total invertebrate bycatch biomass in trawls declined over the three-year study. Epibenthic sled samples showed lower biomass, averaging 25%, in trawled areas versus reference sites. Scavanging crabs were observed in trawl tracks after first six hours, and trawl damage to brittle stars and sea urchins was noted. No significant effects of trawling were found for four dominant species of mollusc.	Prena et al. (1996)
Sand; shrimp and macrobenthos	7 months	New South Wales, Australia	Sampled macrofauna before trawling, after trawling, and after commercial shrimp season using Smith McIntyre grab at experimental and control sites. Underwater observations of trawl gear were also made. No detectable changes in macrobenthos were found or observed.	Gibbs et al. (1980)
Soft sediment; scallops and associated fauna	17 months	Port Phillip Bay, Australia	Sampled 3 months before trawling and 14 months after trawling. Most species showed a 20 to 30% decrease in abundance immediately after trawling. Dredging effects generally were not detectable following the next recruitment within 6 months, but some animals had not returned to the trawling site 14 months post trawling.	Currie and Parry (1996)
Bryozoans; fish and associated fauna		Tasman Bay, New Zealand	Review of ecology of the coral-like bryozoan community and changes in fishing gear and practices since the 1950s. Points out the interdependence of fish within this benthic community and that the area was closed to fishing in 1980 because gear had developed that could fish in and destroy the benthic community, thereby destroying the fishery.	Bradstock and Gordon (1983)
Various habitat types diverse tropical fauna	5+ years, ongoing	Northwest Shelf, Australia	Describes a habitat-dependent fishery and an adaptive management approach to sustaining the fishery. Catch rates of all fish and large and small benthos show that in closed areas, fish and small benthos abundance increased over 5 years while large benthos (>25 cm) stayed the same or increased slightly. In trawled areas all groups of animals declined. Found that settlement rate and growth to 25 cm was on the order of 15 years for the benthos.	Sainsbury et al. (1997)

TABLE 5.— (Continued.)

Habitat type; taxa	Time period	Location	Results	Reference
Mudflat; commercial clam cultivation and benthos	7 months	Southeast England	Sampled benthic community on a commercial clam culture site and control area at the end of a two-year growing period, immediately after sampling, and again seven months later. Infaunal abundance was greatest under the clam culture protective netting, but species composition was similar to controls. Harvesting with a suction dredge changed the sediment characteristics and reduced the numbers of individual animals and species. Seven months later the site had essentially returned to the unharvested condition.	Kaiser et al. (1996)
Sand; razor clam and benthos	40 days	Loch Gairloch, Scotland	Compared control and experimentally harvested areas using a hydraulic dredge at 1 day and 40 days after dredging. On day 1 a nonselective reduction in the total numbers of all infaunal species was apparent, but no differences were observed after 40 days.	Hall et al. (1990)
Sand and muddy areas; macrozoobenthos	3 years, ongoing	German Bights	Investigated macrozoobenthos communities around a sunken ship that had been "closed" to fishing for three years. Compared this site with a heavily fished area. Preliminary results showed an increase in polychaetes and the bivalve *Tellina* in the fished, sandy area. The data did not allow for a firm conclusion regarding the unfished area, but there was some (nonsignificant) increase in species numbers, and some delicate, sensitive species occurred within the protected zone.	Arntz et al. (1994)

over a series of months, for example, in the Bay of Fundy at a high-energy sandy site (Brylinsky et al. 1994; L. Watling, R. H. Findlay, L. M. Mayer, and D. F. Schick, unpublished data). Trawl door marks were visible for 2–7 months, but no sustained significant impact on the benthic community was noted. However, Watling, Findlay, Mayer, and Schick (unpublished data) measured community-level changes caused by scallop dredging at a lower-energy muddy sand location in the Gulf of Maine. They detected a loss in surficial sediments and lowered sedimentary food quality. The subsequent variable recovery of the benthic community over the following 6 months correlated with sedimentary food quality, which was measured as microbial populations, abundance of chlorophyll *a*, and enzyme-hydrolizable amino acid concentrations. Although some taxa recolonized the impacted areas quickly, the abundances of other taxa

(i.e., cumaceans, phoxocephalid and photid amphipods, nephtyid polychaetes) did not recover until food quality also recovered.

The most consistent pattern in fishing impact studies at shallow depths is the resilience of the benthic community to fishing. Two studies in intertidal depths that involved harvesting worms and clams using suction and mechanical harvesting gear demonstrated a substantial immediate effect on the macrofaunal community. However, from 7 months to 2 years later, the study sites had recovered to prefished conditions (Beukema 1995; Kaiser and Spencer 1996a). Peterson et al. (1987) and Hall et al. (1990) harvested at nearshore subtidal depths bay scallops in a North Carolina sea grass bed and razor clams in a Scottish sea loch (respectively) and found little long-term impact on the benthic community structure except at the most intense level of fishing.

After 40 d, the loch showed no effect of fishing, and in the lightly harvested sea grass bed, with <25% sea grass biomass removal, recovery occurred within a year. In the sea grass bed where harvesting was most extensive, with 65% of the sea grass biomass removed, recovery was delayed for 2 years, and after 4 years preharvesting biomass levels were still not obtained. In a South Carolina estuary, Van Dolah et al. (1991) found no long-term effects of trawling on the benthic community. The study site was assessed before and after the commercial shrimp season and demonstrated variation over time but no trawling effects per se. Other studies of pre and post impacts from mobile gear on shallow sandy to hard bottoms have generally shown similar results (Gibbs et al. 1980; MacKenzie 1982; Currie and Parry 1996) with either no or minimal long-term impact detectable.

Other benthic communities show clear effects that can be related to fishing. Collie et al. (1997) have, for example, characterized disturbed and undisturbed sites on Georges Bank, based on fishing records, and found more individuals, a greater biomass, and greater species richness and diversity in the undisturbed areas. Engel and Kvitek (1998) also found more fish and epifaunal invertebrates in a lightly trawled area compared to a more heavily trawled site over a 3-year period off Monterey, California. Perhaps the most convincing cases of fishing-related impacts on the benthic community are from studies in Northern Ireland, Australia, and New Zealand. Brown (1989) has reported the demise of the horse mussel community in Strangford Loch with the development of the queen scallop fishery. The horse mussel beds were essentially unchanged from 1857 until 1980 when the trawl fishery for scallops was initiated. Along the northwest Australian shelf Bradstock and Gordon (1983); Sainsbury (1987, 1988, 1991); and Sainsbury et al. (1997) describe a habitat-dependent fishery with fish biomass related to the coral-like byrozoan community. With the demise of this epifaunal community, there was a shift in fish species composition to less commercially desirable species. In experimentally closed areas there has been a recovery of fish and an increase in the small benthos but, based on settlement and growth of larger epifaunal animals, it may take 15 years for the system to recover. Finally, sampling of fishing grounds along a gradient of fishing effort in the Hauraki Gulf of New Zealand has shown that 15–20% of the variability in the macrofauna community could be attributed to fishing (Thrush et al., in press). As fishing effort decreased there were increases in the density of large epifauna, in long-lived surface dwellers (with a decrease in deposit feeders and small opportunistic species), and in the Shannon–Weiner diversity index. These results validated most predictions made from small-scale studies, suggesting that there is value in continuing such work. However, where data are available to determine patterns of fishing effort at the scale of fishing grounds, large-scale studies such as this are beneficial for validating predictions from limited experimental work and, most importantly, establishing the range of ecological effects along a gradient of disturbance produced by resource extraction and the variable intensity of impacts from particular harvesting methods. Ultimately, such data can be used to develop strategies for the sustainable harvest of target species while maintaining ecosystem integrity.

Implications for Management

Clearly the long-term effects of fishing on benthic community structure are not easily characterized. The pattern that does appear to be emerging from the available literature is that communities that are subject to variable environments and are dominated by short-lived species are fairly resilient. Depending on the intensity and frequency of fishing, the impact of such activity may well fall within the range of natural perturbations. In communities that are dominated by long-lived species in more stable environments, the impact of fishing can be substantial and longer term. Studies of Strangford Loch and the Australian shelf show that recovery from trawling will be on the order of decades. In many areas, these two patterns correlate with shallow and deep environments. However, water depth is not the single variable that can be used to characterize fishing impacts. Few studies describe fishing impacts on shallow mud-bottom communities or on deep areas at the edge of the continental shelf. Such sites would be expected to be relatively low-energy zones, similar to areas in Strangford Loch, and might not recover rapidly from fishing disturbances. Studies in these relatively stable environments are required to pattern fishing impacts over the entire environmental range, but, in anticipation of such results, it is suggested that one should expect a tighter coupling between fish production and benthic community structure in the more stable marine environments.

Effects on Ecosystem Processes

Interpretation of Results

A number of studies indicate that fishing has measurable effects on ecosystem processes, but it is important to compare these effects with natural process rates at appropriate scales. Both primary production and nutrient regeneration have been shown to be affected by fishing gear. These studies are small in scope, and it is difficult to apply small-scale studies at the level of entire ecosystems. Understanding that processes are affected confirms the need to understand the relative changes in vital rates caused by fishing and the spatial extent of the disturbances.

Disturbance by fishing gear in relatively shallow depths (i.e., 30–40 m) can reduce primary production by benthic microalgae. Recent studies in several shallow continental shelf habitats have shown that primary production by a distinct benthic microflora can be a significant portion of overall primary production (i.e., water column plus benthic primary production) (Cahoon et al. 1990, 1993; Cahoon and Cooke 1992). Benthic microalgal production supports a variety of consumers, including demersal zooplankton (animals that spend part of each day on or in the sediment and migrate regularly into the water) (Cahoon and Tronzo 1992). Demersal zooplankton include harpacticoid copepods, amphipods, mysids, cumaceans, and other animals that are eaten by planktivorous fishes and soft-bottom foragers (Thomas and Cahoon 1993).

The effects of fishing were elucidated at Stellwagen Bank in the northwest Atlantic during 1991 and 1994. Measurements showed that a productive benthic microflora existed on the crest of the Bank (Cahoon et al. 1993; Cahoon et al., unpublished data) but that demersal zooplankton was low in comparison to the other shelf habitats and lower than would be expected given the available food supply (Cahoon et al. 1995). Several explanations can be advanced for this anomalously low zooplankton abundance. These include competitive or predatory interactions with meiofauna or the holozooplankton, disturbance by macrobenthos, intense predation by planktivorous fishes, and physical disturbance by mobile fishing gear. Many demersal zooplankters appear to construct and inhabit small burrows or capsules made of accreted or agglutinated sand. These formations provide shelter for demersal zooplankters in a habitat otherwise devoid of structure.

Many small biogenic structures were observed on the sediment surface, and even gentle handling by divers destroyed them easily. Movement by divers and a remotely operated vehicle caused demersal zooplankters to exhibit escape responses. Events that disturb the bottom, particularly such relatively powerful events as storms and towing mobile fishing gear along the sediment surface, must destroy these delicate habitat features. Disturbance of demersal zooplankters may result in increased predation that reduces local populations of zooplankters. Juvenile fish that feed on these taxa may require greater times and longer distances away from benthic shelter sites to forage in the water column to capture prey, exposing themselves to greater predation risk (Walters and Juanes 1993).

Recovery rates of populations of benthic primary producers are not well known. Brylinsky et al. (1994) showed that trawling had significant effects on benthic diatoms, but recovery occurred at all stations after about 30 d. The experimental sites that were trawled were in the intertidal zone in the Bay of Fundy. Trawling occurred during high tides and sampling at low tide. It is important to note that light intensity (and spectral composition) in this experiment was much greater than at sites where trawling normally occurs, that is, where seawater constantly overlays the substrate.

Experimental measurements from scallop dredge and otter trawl impacts off coastal Maine showed that dragging can both resuspend and bury labile organic matter (Mayer et al. 1991). Burial shifts organic matter decomposition and availability from aerobic eucaryotic-microbial pathways to anerobic pathways. Short-term effects may include shifts from metazoan communities that support harvested species (e.g., meiofauna, polychaetes, flounders) toward anerobic microbial respiration. Studies by Watling, Findlay, Mayer, and Schick (unpublished data) empirically demonstrate these short-term trends. Longer-term effects of chronic dragging and burial are difficult to predict.

Riemann and Hoffmann (1991) measured the short-term effects of mussel dredging and bottom trawling off Denmark in a shallow coastal marine system. Dredging and trawling increased suspended particulates immediately to 1,361% and 960–1,000%, respectively, above background. Oxygen decreased and nutrients such as ammonia and silicate increased. Dyekjaer et al. (1995) calculated the annual effects of mussel dredging in the same region. The total annual release of suspended particles during dredging is relatively minor when compared with total wind-induced resuspension. Similarly, the release of nutrients is minor when compared with the nutrient loading from land runoff. However, local effects may be significant when near-bottom dissolved oxygen concentrations are low and reduced substances are resuspended, depending upon the depth of stratification, water flow rates, and the number of dredges operating simultaneously.

Direct movement of fishing gear over and through the sediment surface can change sediment grain size characteristics, change suspended load, and change the magnitude of sediment transport processes. Churchill (1989) showed that trawling could resuspend sediments on the same magnitude as storms and can be the primary factor regulating sediment transport over the outer continental shelf in areas where storm-related currents and bottom stresses are weak. Gear-induced resuspension of sediments can potentially have important impacts on nutrient cycling (Pilskaln et al. 1998). Open continental shelf environments typically receive approximately half of their nutrients for primary production from sediment resuspension and pore water exchange. The nutrients are produced from the microbial-based decay of organic matter and remineralization within sediments. Changes in rates of resuspension from periodic to steady pulses of nutrients (e.g., nitrate fluxes) caused by gear disturbance to the seafloor can shift phytoplankton populations from picoplankton towards diatoms, which may ultimately be beneficial for production of harvested species, although changes in nutrient ratios may stimulate harmful algal blooms.

Implications for Management

The disturbances caused by fishing to benthic primary production and organic matter dynamics are difficult to predict. Semiclosed systems such as bays, estuaries, and fjords are subject to such effects at relatively small spatial scales. Open coastal and outer continental shelf systems can also experience perturbations in these processes. However, the relative rates of other processes (e.g., natural processes) may minimize the effects of fishing disturbances depending upon the level of fishing effort.

Mayer et al. (1991) discuss the implications of organic matter burial patterns in sediments versus soils. Their results are similar to organic matter patterns found in terrestrial soils. Sediments are essen-

tially part of a burial system while soils are erosional. Although gear disturbance can enhance remineralization rates by transforming surficial fungal-dominated communities into subsurface communities with dominant bacterial decomposition processes, burial caused by gear disturbance might also enhance preservation if material is sequestered in anaerobic systems. Given the importance of carbon cycling in estuaries and on continental shelves to the global carbon budget, understanding the magnitude of effects caused by human disturbances on primary production and organic matter decomposition will require long-term studies like those conducted on land.

Discussion

Direct Alteration of Food Webs

In heavily fished areas of the world, it is undebatable that fishing has ecosystem-level effects (Gislason 1994; Fogarty and Murawski 1998) and that shifts in benthic community structure have occurred. The data to confirm that such shifts have taken place are limited at best (Riesen and Reise 1982), but the fact that it has been documented at all is highly significant. If benthic communities change, what are the ecological processes that might bring about such change?

One of these processes involves enhanced food supply resulting from trawl-damaged animals and the discarding of both nonharvested species and offal from fish gutted at sea. The availability of this food source might affect animal behavior and influence survival and reproductive success. There are numerous reports of predatory fishes and invertebrate scavengers foraging in trawl tracks after a trawl passes through an area (Medcof and Caddy 1971; Caddy 1973; Kaiser and Spencer 1994; Evans et al. 1996; Ramsay et al. 1997a, 1997b). The prey available to scavengers is a function of the ability of animals to survive the capture process, which can involve being discarded as unwanted bycatch or passed through or over by the gear (Meyer et al. 1981; Fonds 1994; Rumohr et al. 1994; Santbrink and Bergman 1994; Kaiser and Spencer 1995). Studies in both the Irish and North Seas on the reaction of scavengers to a trawling event, usually involving beam trawling, are the most comprehensive. In the Irish Sea studies focused on the movement of animals over time into experimentally trawled areas at locations that ranged in sediment type from mud to gravel. Results were found to be habitat dependent (Ramsay et al. 1997a, 1997b) and not always consistent (Kaiser and Ramsay 1997), although the general trends are that the rate of movement of scavengers into a trawled area reflects the mobility of the animals, their sensory abilities, and their behavior (Kaiser and Spencer 1996b). Fish were usually the first to arrive, and slower-moving invertebrates like whelks and starfish, which were also attracted to the area, required a longer time to respond to the availability of damaged or dead prey. That the scavengers are feeding has been documented both by direct diver observations and analysis of stomach contents (see Caddy 1973; Rumohr et al. 1994). Stomach-contents data demonstrate that fish not only feed on discarded or damaged animals and often eat more than their conspecifics at control sites, but they also consume animals that were not damaged but simply displaced by the trawling activity, or even those invertebrates that have themselves responded as scavengers (Kaiser and Spencer 1994; Santbrink and Bergman 1994). Hence the biomass available for consumption from discards and offal are not effecting the community equally but selectively providing additional food resources for those taxa that differentially react to the disturbance created by fishing.

Kaiser and Spencer (1994) make the comment, as others have before them, that it is common practice for fishermen to re-fish recently fished areas to take advantage of the aggregations of animals attracted to the disturbed benthic community. The long-term effect of opportunistic feeding following fishing disturbances is an area of speculation. In the North Sea, for example, the availability of "extra" food, either from discarded bycatch or as a more direct result of trawling-induced mortality, has been suggested as one reason why the population of dab *Limanda limanda* has increased. Kaiser and Ramsay (1997) argue that the combination of predator and competitor removal by fishing together with an increased food supply has resulted in the increase in the dab population. Obviously the negative effects on the prey organisms themselves are also important and may have an equal but opposite effect on their density. Faunal changes in the North Sea have been noted with major shifts in the composition of the benthic community that can be correlated with trawling. The general decline in populations of hard-bodied animals such as bivalves and heart urchins has been suggested to be the direct result of trawl damage with, one might speculate, this hard-bodied food becoming available to scavengers.

Another process that can indirectly alter food webs is the removal of keystone predators. Removal of herbivorous fishes and invertebrates produced a shift in coral reef communities from coral-invertebrate-dominated systems to filamentous and fleshy algae-dominated systems. (Roberts 1995 provides a synoptic review.) The removal of sea otters from kelp-bed communities in the western Pacific has also had cascading effects on urchin populations and the dynamics of kelp (Duggins 1980; Estes 1996). In the northwest Atlantic, Witman and Sebens (1992) showed that onshore–offshore differences in cod and wolffish *Anarhichas lupus* populations reduced predation pressure on cancrid crabs and other megafauna in deep coastal communities. They suggest that this regional difference in predation pressure is the result of intense harvesting of cod, a keystone predator, with cascading effects on populations of epibenthos (e.g., mussels, barnacles, urchins), which are prey of crabs.

American lobsters have also been considered a keystone predator because they control urchin populations, which in turn control the distribution of kelp (e.g., Mann and Breen 1972; Mann 1982). Communities shifted from kelp dominated to coralline algae dominated under the influence of intense urchin predation, with concomitant shifts in the mobile species that use such habitats. A hypothesis about this shift in communities focused on the role of lobster removals by fishing. Urchins, which are a primary prey of lobsters, had large population increases resulting in greater herbivory on kelp. However, Elner and Vadas (1990) brought the keystone predation hypothesis into question as urchins did not react to lobster predation by forming defensive aggregations and lobster diets were not dominated by urchins. Although understanding the ultimate control of such shifts remains elusive, recent harvesting of urchins has coincided with a return of kelp-dominated habitats. Other processes (e.g., annual variation in physical processes affecting survivorship of recruits, climate change, El Niño, recruitment variability of component species caused by predator-induced mortality) can also result in food web changes. Although it is important to understand all the underlying causes of food web shifts, precautionary management approaches should be considered given the strong inference of human-caused effects in studies focusing on identifying causes of food web shifts.

Predicting the Effects of Disturbance

This review of the literature indicates that fishing, using a wide range of gear, produces measurable impacts. However, most studies were conducted at small spatial scales, and it is difficult to apply such information at regional levels where predictive capabilities would allow fisheries management at an ecosystem scale (Jennings and Kaiser 1998). Studies can be divided into those focused on acute impacts (caused by a single or a small number of tows) and those focused on chronic effects. Although the former type of study is most common and amenable to experimental manipulation, the latter type is most directly applicable in the arena of habitat management. Unfortunately, few long-term monitoring programs allow for an analysis of all the appropriate metrics needed to ascertain the effects of fishing on EFH. Additionally, although there are clear effects on local and regional patterns of biodiversity—an obvious metric needed to monitor the effects of ecosystem-level management—we do not have a good understanding of how communities respond to large-scale disturbances. This level of knowledge is needed to separate responses due to natural variability from responses due to human-caused variability.

Our current understanding of ecological processes related to the chronic disturbances caused by fishing makes results difficult to predict. Disturbance has been widely shown to be a mechanism that shifts communities (Dayton 1971; Pickett and White 1985; Witman 1985; Suchanek 1986). Although a full discussion of this area of ecology is beyond the scope of this review, general models produced from such work are useful for understanding fishing as an agent of disturbance from an ecological perspective. Assumptions regarding the role of fishing in the dynamics of marine communities generally assert that the cessation or reduction of fishing will allow populations and communities to recover to a climax community state, as is the case in long-lived terrestrial plant communities. Succession of communities implies a predictable progression in species composition and abundance (Connell 1989; Bell et al. 1991). Such knowledge of successional patterns would allow managers to predict future marine community states and directly manage EFH. Although direct successional linkages have been found in some communities, others are less predictable.

Two types of patterns in shifts in community states due to disturbance are illustrated in Figure 5. The first model is the traditional successional model where communities change from type A to B to C

and so forth. There are empirical examples of this type of succession in soft substrate benthic communities (e.g., Rhoads et al. 1978). Succession is based on one community of organisms producing a set of local environmental conditions (e.g., enriching the sediments with organic material) that make the environment unsuitable for continued survival and recruitment but are favorable for another community of organisms. Disturbance can move succession back in single or multiple steps, depending on the types of conditions that prevail after the disturbance. The successional stages are predictable based on conditions that result from the organisms themselves or from conditions after a perturbation. The second model of community states is disturbance mediated and lottery based (based on Horn 1976). Empirical studies of such relationships generally examine hard substrate communities (e.g., Dayton 1971; Horn 1976; Sebens 1986; Witman 1987). Shifts in community type are produced by competition and disturbance (e.g., predation, grazing, storms, fishing gear), which can result in shifts toward community types that are often unpredictable because they are based on the pool of recruits available in the water column at the time that niche space is available.

The spatial extent of disturbed and undisturbed communities is a concern in designing and interpreting studies (Pickett and White 1985; Barry and Dayton 1991; Thrush et al. 1994). Single, widely

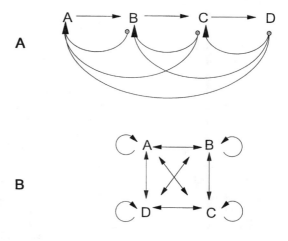

FIGURE 5.—Models of alternative community states. Arrows indicate direction of community shifts. Model A is the successional model, which has relatively predictable shifts in community type. Model B is a lottery-based model, which has more stochastic, nonlinear responses to disturbance.

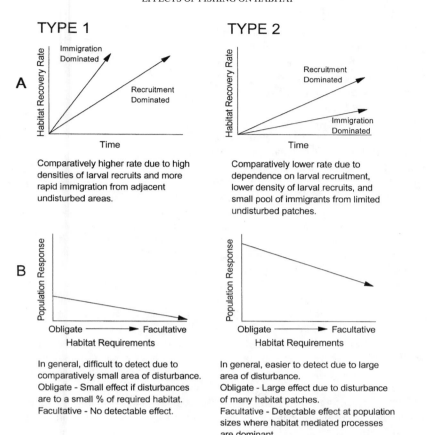

FIGURE 6.—Comparison of biogenic habitat structure and population responses to type-1 and type-2 habitat disturbances.

spaced disturbances may have little overall effect on habitat integrity and benthic communities, and these disturbed areas may show reduced recovery times as a result of immigration of mobile taxa (e.g., polychaetes, gastropods). In the ecological literature this is a type-1 disturbance, where a small patch is disturbed but surrounded by a large unimpacted area. In contrast, type-2 disturbances are those in which small patches of undisturbed communities are surrounded by large areas of disturbed communities. Immigration into such disturbed patches requires large-scale transport of propagules from outside source patches, or significant reproductive output (and high planktonic survival and larval retention) from the small undisturbed patches. Making predictions about the outcome of disturbances even where spatial extent is known is difficult because transport of colonizers (i.e., larvae, juveniles, and adults) depends on oceanographic conditions, larval period, movement rates of juveniles and adults, time of year, and dis-

tance from source. However, as an example of disturbance effects given specific sets of conditions, it is possible to illustrate general trends in the response of biogenic habitat structure to type-1 and type-2 disturbances and population responses based on characteristics of obligate and facultative habitat users (Figure 6). Type-1 disturbances generally have faster recovery rates because they are subject to immigration-dominated recovery in contrast to type-2 disturbances, which are dependent on larval recruitment for recovery. Population responses to such disturbances also are variable. Obligate habitat users have a much greater response to habitat disturbance such that type-1 disturbances would produce substantial small-scale effects but overall population responses would be small. Comparatively, it would be difficult to detect responses from populations of facultative habitat users because of the large areas of undisturbed habitat in type-1 disturbances. However, type-2 disturbances would produce large responses in obligate habitat users in that a large percentage of required habitat would be affected. Facultative habitat users would have a measurable response at population levels where habitat-mediated processes are important.

The dependence of fish communities on particular habitat features is well represented in the literature on coral reef, kelp forest, and sea grass fish communities (e.g., Heck and Orth 1980; Ebeling and Hixon 1991; Sale 1991). Studies at this particular scale are generally lacking for most harvested taxa on outer continental shelves. One problem in interpreting existing studies is the tendency to compartmentalize the processes that structure these communities and not apply our general knowledge of habitat-mediated processes to other fish assemblages using other habitats. In reality, fish assemblages occur in a continuum along two gradients: one of habitat complexity and the other of environmental variation (Figure 7). Only limited numbers of species and communities have hard (limited) linkages between parts of the food web where gear impacts on prey communities would have obvious and easily measurable effects. Large temperate and boreal marine ecosystems are characterized by soft (flexible) linkages with most species having flexible prey requirements. Measuring effects that can be linked to changes in prey availability and ultimately back to effects of fishing gear will be challenging in these situations. New molecular and stable-isotope techniques offer the possibility for better tracking of trophic transfer of carbon and labeling of the role of particular prey taxa in secondary and tertiary production. The same can be said for effects of structural habitat change. It is difficult to detect signal changes because variability in populations is the cumulative result of many factors. Small-scale field studies producing information on the patterns of survivorship and predator–prey interactions in particular habitats, laboratory tests to determine relative differences in habitat-mediated survivorship under constant predator–prey densities, and numerical modeling to link the small-scale approaches with population-level responses provide the bridge to link small-scale studies to large-scale patterns.

Further Considerations for Management

Fishing is one of the most widespread human impacts to the marine environment. The removal of fish for human consumption from the world's oceans has effects not only on the target species but also on associated communities. Although the size-specific

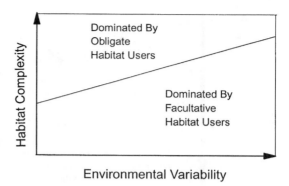

FIGURE 7.—Habitat complexity and environmental variability domain of fish assemblages as it relates to obligate and facultative habitat users. Fish assemblages occur in a continuum along the two gradients.

and species-specific removal of fish can change the system structure, the regions of the continental shelf that are normally fished appear to be fairly resilient. The difficulty for managers is defining the level of resilience—in the practical sense of time and area closures, mesh regulations, or overall effort limits—that will allow for the harvest of selected species without causing human-induced alterations of ecosystem structure to the point that recovery is unduly retarded or community and ecosystem support services are shifted to an alternate state (Steele 1996). Natural variability forms a backdrop against which managers must make such decisions, and, unfortunately, natural variability can be both substantial and unpredictable. The preceding discussion of the impact of fishing on marine communities does not address the role of natural variability directly, but it is apparent that in many of the systems studied there is an inherent resistance to biological change. In the very long term one can expect natural variability to generate regime shifts, but the challenge for natural resource managers is not to precipitate these shifts prematurely or in unintended directions.

Much of the research described herein is not at a scale that directly relates to effects on fish populations and therefore does not link directly to fishery management decisions. The research on fishing gear impacts does offer an indication of the types and direction of changes in benthic communities over large spatial scales as well as confirmation that benthic communities are dynamic and will ultimately compensate for perturbations. However, as observations show, shifts in communities are not necessarily beneficial to the harvested species. The scale of fishing is a confounding factor in management because systems are being fished to the point where recovery is delayed so long that the economic consequences are devastating. We are currently seeing this pattern in many U.S. fisheries (and many other fisheries worldwide for that matter). Because our knowledge of ecosystem dynamics is still rather rudimentary, managers bear the responsibility of adopting a precautionary approach when considering the environmental consequences of fishing rather than assuming that the extraction of fish has no ecological price and therefore no feedback loop to our nonecologically based economic system.

This review has revealed that primary information is lacking for us to strategically manage fishing impacts on EFH without invoking precautionary measures. The following list identifies three areas where primary data are lacking; improved primary data would allow better monitoring and improved experimentation leading to improved predictive capabilities:

1. *The spatial extent of fishing-induced disturbance.* Although many observer programs collect data at the scale of single tows or sets, fisheries reporting systems often lack this level of spatial resolution. The available data make it difficult to make observations along a gradient of fishing effort to assess the effects of fishing effort on habitat, community, and ecosystem-level processes.
2. *The effects of specific gear types, along a gradient of effort, on specific habitat types.* These data are the first-order needs to allow an assessment of how much effort produces a measurable level of change in structural habitat components and associated communities. Second-order data should assess the effects of fishing disturbance in a gradient of type-1 and type-2 disturbance treatments.
3. *The role of seafloor habitats in the population dynamics of fishes.* Although good time series data often exist for late-juvenile and adult populations and larval abundance, there is a general lack of empirical information (except perhaps for coral reef, kelp bed, and sea grass fishes) on linkages between habitat and survival that would allow modeling and experimentation to predict outcomes of various levels of disturbance.

These data and research results should allow managers to better strategically regulate where, when, and how much fishing will be sustainable in regards to EFH. Conservation engineering should play a large role in developing fishing gears that are economical to operate and minimize impacts to environmental support functions.

The ultimate goal of research on fishing impacts is not to retrospectively evaluate what fishing does to the environment but to predict cause and effect given a particular management protocol. This requires applying the conceptual models introduced in this discussion to actual management decisions and, at the same time, increasing our understanding of ecological mechanisms and processes at the level of the fish populations and associated communities. This demands in particular an appreciation of the importance of both the intensity and frequency of fishing impacts. If the objective is maintenance of habitat integrity, fishing should be conducted with an intensity that does not create isolated patches of communities whose progeny are required to recolonize impacted areas. Similarly, the habitat requirements of the harvested species must be taken into account to ensure that harvesting strategies do not disturb habitats more frequently than is required to balance economic as well as ecological sustainability.

Acknowledgments

This review and synthesis was funded, in part, by a contract from the American Fisheries Society with funds from the National Fish and Wildlife Foundation. In addition, Peter J. Auster was supported with funds from the National Undersea Research Program and Stellwagen Bank National Marine Sanctuary. Richard W. Langton was supported with funds from The Sport Fish Restoration Act and the state of Maine. The authors would like to thank the seven reviewers for comments that significantly improved the manuscript and Lee Benaka for organizing the symposium. The views expressed herein are those of the authors and do not necessarily reflect the views of the National Oceanic and Atmospheric Administration or any of its subagencies.

References

Able, K. W., M. P. Fahay, and G. R. Shepard. 1995. Early life history of black sea bass, *Centropristis striata*, in the mid-Atlantic Bight and a New Jersey estuary. Fishery Bulletin 93:429–445.

Alexander, A. B., H. F. Moore, and W. C. Kendall. 1914. Otter-trawl fishery. Report of the U.S. Fisheries Commission for 1914, Appendix VI, Washington, D.C.

Alverson, D. L., M. H. Freeberg, J. G. Pope, and S. A. Murawski. 1994. A global assessment of fisheries bycatch and discards. FAO (Food and Agriculture Organization of the United Nations) Fisheries Technical Paper 339.

Arntz, W., E. Rachor, and S. Kuhne. 1994. Mid- and long-term effects of bottom trawling on the benthic fauna of the German Bight. Pages 59–74. NIOZ Rapport 1994-11, Netherlands Institute of Fisheries Research, Texel.

Auster, P. J. 1988. A review of the present state of understanding of marine fish communities. Journal of Northwest Atlantic Fishery Science 8:67–75.

Auster, P. J. 1998. A conceptual model of the impacts of fishing gear on the integrity of fish habitats. Conservation Biology 12(6):1198–1203.

Auster, P. J., R. J. Malatesta, S. C. LaRosa, R. A. Cooper, and L. L. Stewart. 1991. Microhabitat utilization by the megafaunal assemblage at a low relief outer continental shelf site - Middle Atlantic Bight, USA. Journal of Northwest Atlantic Fishery Science 11:59–69.

Auster, P. J., C. A. Griswold, M. J. Youngbluth, and T. G. Bailey. 1992. Aggregations of myctophid fishes with other pelagic fauna. Environmental Biology of Fishes 35:133–139.

Auster, P. J., R. J. Malatesta, and S. C. LaRosa. 1995. Patterns of microhabitat utilization by mobile megafauna on the southern New England (USA) continental shelf and slope. Marine Ecology Progress Series 127:77–85.

Auster, P. J., and eight coauthors. 1996. The impacts of mobile fishing gear on seafloor habitats in the Gulf of Maine (northwest Atlantic): implications for conservation of fish populations. Reviews in Fisheries Science 4(2):185–202.

Auster, P. J., L. Watling, and A. Rieser. 1997a. Comment: The interface between fisheries research and habitat management. North American Journal of Fisheries Management 17:591–595.

Auster, P. J., R. J. Malatesta, and C. L. S. Donaldson. 1997b. Distributional responses to small-scale habitat variability by early juvenile silver hake, Merluccius bilinearis. Environmental Biology of Fishes 50:195–200.

Auster, P. J., C. Michalopoulos, P. C. Valentine, and R. J. Malatesta. 1998. Delineating and monitoring habitat management units in a temperate deep-water marine protected area. Pages 169–185 in N. W. Munro and J. H. M. Willison, editors. Linking protected areas with working landscapes, conserving biodiversity. Science and Management of Protected Areas Association, Wolfville, Nova Scotia.

Barry, J. P., and P. K. Dayton. 1991. Physical heterogeneity and the organization of marine communities. Pages 270–320 in J. Kolasa and T. A. Pickett, editors. Ecological heterogeneity. Springer-Verlag, New York.

Bell, S. S., E. D. McCoy, and H. R. Mushinsky. 1991. Habitat structure: the physical arrangement of objects in space. In S. Bell, E. D. McCoy, and H. R. Mushinsky, editors. Population and community biology series. Chapman and Hall, New York.

Bergman, M. J. N., and M. Hup. 1992. Direct effects of beamtrawling on macrofauna in a sandy sediment in the southern North Sea. ICES Journal of Marine Science 49:5–11.

Beukema, J. J. 1995. Long-term effects of mechanical harvesting of lugworms Arenicola marina on the zoobenthic community of a tidal flat in the Wadden Sea. Netherlands Journal of Sea Research 33:219–227.

Bradstock, M., and D. Gordon. 1983. Coral-like bryozoan growths in Tasman Bay, and their protection to conserve commercial fish stocks. New Zealand Journal of Marine and Freshwater Research 17:159–163.

Bridger, J. P. 1970. Some effects if the passage of a trawl over the seabed. ICES C.M. 1970/B:10 Gear and Behavior Committee.

Bridger, J. P. 1972. Some observations on the penetration into the sea bed of tickler chains on a beam trawl. ICES C.M. 1972/B:7.

Brodeur, R. D. In press. In situ observations of the association between juvenile fishes and scyphomedusae in the Bering Sea. Marine Ecology Progress Series.

Brown, R. A. 1989. Bottom trawling on Strangford Lough: problems and policies. Proceedings reprints, Distress signals, signals from the environment in policy and decision making, May 31–June 2, 1989. Rotterdam, Netherlands.

Brylinsky, M., J. Gibson, and D. C. Gordon, Jr. 1994. Impacts of flounder trawls on the intertidal habitat and community of the Minas Basin, Bay of Fundy. Canadian Journal of Fisheries and Aquatic Sciences 51:650–661.

Caddy, J. F. 1973. Underwater observations on tracks of dredges and trawls and some effects of dredging on a scallop ground. Journal of the Fisheries Research Board of Canada 30:173–180.

Cahoon, L. B., and J. E. Cooke. 1992. Benthic microalgal production in Onslow Bay, North Carolina. Marine Ecology Progress Series 84:185–196.

Cahoon, L. B., and C. R. Tronzo. 1992. Quantitative estimates of demersal zooplankton abundance in Onslow Bay, North Carolina. Marine Ecology Progress Series 87:197–200.

Cahoon, L. B., R. L. Redman, and C. R. Tronzo. 1990. Benthic microalgal biomass in sediments of Onslow Bay, North Carolina. Estuarine Coastal and Shelf Science 31:805–816.

Cahoon, L. B., G. R. Beretich, Jr., C. J. Thomas, and A. M. McDonald. 1993. Benthic microalgal production at Stellwagen Bank, Massachusetts Bay, USA. Marine Ecology Progress Series 102:179–185.

Cahoon, L. B., M. F. Feeley, and C. F. Jensen. 1995. Quantitative estimates of demersal zooplankton abundance at Stellwagen Bank, Massachusetts Bay. Proceedings of the American Academy of Underwater Sciences. Costa Mesa, California.

Chopin, F. S., and T. Arimoto. 1995. The condition of fish escaping from fishing gears–a review. Fisheries Research 21:315–327.

Churchill, J. H. 1989. The effect of commercial trawling on sediment resuspension and transport over the Middle Atlantic Bight continental shelf. Continental Shelf Research 9:841–864.

Collie, J. S., G. A. Escanero, L. Hunke, and P. C. Valentine. 1996. Scallop dredging on Georges Bank: photographic evaluation of effects on benthic fauna. ICES C.M. 1996/Mini:9.

Collie, J. S., G. A. Escanero, and P. C. Valentine. 1997. Effects of bottom fishing on the benthic megafauna of Georges bank. Marine Ecology Progress Series 155:159–172.

Colvocoresses, J. A., and J. A. Musick. 1984. Species associations and community composition of Middle Atlantic Bight continental shelf demersal fishes. Fishery Bulletin 82:295–313.

Connell, J. H. 1989. Change and persistence in some marine communities. Pages 339–352 in A. J. Gray, M. J. Crawley, and P. J. Edwards, editors. Colonization, succession and stability. The 26th symposium of the British Ecological Society. Blackwell Scientific Publications Scientific Publishers, Oxford.

Currie, D. R., and G. D. Parry. 1994. The impact of scallop dredging on a soft sediment community using multivariate techniques. Memoirs of the Queensland Museum 36:316–326.

Currie, D. R., and G. D. Parry. 1996. Effects of scallop dredging on a soft sediment community: a large-scale experimental study. Marine Ecology Progress Series 134:131–150.

Cushing, D. H. 1975. Marine ecology and fisheries. Cambridge University Press, Cambridge and New York.

Dayton, P. K. 1971. Competition, disturbance, and community organization: the provision and subsequent utilization of space in a rocky intertidal community. Ecological Monographs 41:351–389.

Dayton, P. K., S. F. Thrush, M. T. Agardy, and R. J. Hofman. 1995. Environmental effects of marine fishing. Aquatic Conservation: Marine and Freshwater Ecosystems 5:205–232.

de Groot, S. J. 1984. The impact of bottom trawling on benthic fauna of the North Sea. Ocean Management 9:177–190.

Duggins, D. O. 1980. Kelp beds and sea otters: an experimental approach. Ecology 61:447–453.

Dyekjaer, S. M., J. K. Jensen, and E. Hoffmann. 1995. Mussel dredging and effects on the marine environment. ICES C.M. 1995/E:13.

Ebeling, A. W., and M. A. Hixon. 1991. Tropical and temperate reef fishes: comparison of community structures. Pages 509–563 in P. F. Sale, editor. The ecology of fishes on coral reefs. Academic Press, New York.

Eleftheriou, A., and M. R. Robertson. 1992. The effects of experimental scallop dredging on the fauna and physical environment of a shallow sandy community. Netherlands Journal of Sea Research 30:289–299.

Elner, R. W., and R. L. Vadas. 1990. Inference in ecology: the sea urchin phenomenon in the Northwest Atlantic. American Naturalist 136:105–108.

Engel, J., and R. Kvitek. 1998. Impacts of otter trawling on a benthic community in Monterey Bay National Marine Sanctuary. Conservation Biology 12:1204–1214.

Eno, N. C., D. S. MacDonald, and S. C. Amos. 1996. A study on the effects of fish (crustacea/mollusc) traps on benthic habitats and species. Final report to the European Commission.

Estes, J. A. 1996. The influence of large, mobile predators in aquatic food webs: examples from sea otters and kelp forests. Pages 65–72 in S. P. R. Greenstreet and M. L. Tasker, editors. Aquatic predators and their prey. Blackwell Scientific Publications Scientific, Oxford.

Evans, P. L., M. J. Kaiser, and R. N. Hughes. 1996. Behavior and energetics of whelks, Buccinum undatum (L.), feeding on animals killed by beam trawling. Journal of Experimental Marine Biology and Ecology 197:51–62.

FAO (Food, and Agriculture Organization of the United Nations). 1997. Review of the state of world fishery resources: marine fisheries. FAO Fisheries Circular No. 920.

Fogarty, M. J., and S. A. Murawski. 1998. Large-scale disturbance and the structure of marine systems: fishery impacts on Georges Bank. Ecological Applications 8(1) Supplement:S6-S22.

Fonds, M. 1994. Mortality of fish and invertebrates in beam trawl catches and the survival chances of discards. Pages 131–146. NIOZ Rapport 1994-11, Netherlands Institute for Fisheries Research, Texel.

Fonseca, M. S., G. W. Tanyer, A. J. Chester, and C. Foltz. 1984. Impact of scallop harvesting on eelgrass (Zostera marina) meadows: implications for management. North American Journal of Fisheries Management 4:286–293.

Freese, L., P. Auster, J. Heifetz, and B. Wing. In press. Effects of trawling on sea floor habitat and associated invertebrate taxa in the Gulf of Alaska. Marine Ecology Progress Series.

Gabriel, W. L. 1992. Persistence of demersal fish assemblages between Cape Hatteras and Nova Scotia, northwest Atlantic. Journal of Northwest Atlantic Fisheries Science 14:29–46.

Gabriel, W. L., and A. V. Tyler. 1980. Preliminary analysis of Pacific coast demersal fish assemblages. Marine Fisheries Review 42(3-4):83–88.

Gaspar, M. B., C. A. Richardson, and C. C. Monteiro. 1994. The effects of dredging on shell formation in the razor clam Ensis siliqua from Barrinha, southern Portugal. Journal of the Marine Biological Association of the United Kingdom 74:927–938.

Gibbs, P. J., A. J. Collins, and L. C. Collett. 1980. Effect of otter prawn trawling on the macrobenthos of a sandy substratum in a New South Wales estuary. Australian Journal of Marine and Freshwater Research 31:509–516.

Gislason, H. 1994. Ecosystem effects of fishing activities in the North Sea. Marine Pollution Bulletin 29(6-12):520–527.

Gotceitas, V., and J. A. Brown. 1993. Substrate selection by juvenile Atlantic cod (Gadus morhua): effects of predation risk. Oecologia 93:31–37.

Guillén, J. E., A. A. Ramos, L. Martínez, and J. Sánchez Lizaso. 1994. Antitrawling reefs and the protection of *Posidonia oceanica* (L.) meadows in the western Mediterranean Sea: demands and aims. Bulletin of Marine Science 55(2–3):645–650.

Hall, S. J. 1994. Physical disturbance and marine benthic communities: life in unconsolidated sediments. Oceanography and Marine Biology: An Annual Review 32:179–239.

Hall, S. J., D. J. Basford, and M. R. Robertson. 1990. The impact of hydraulic dredging for razor clams *Ensis* sp. on an infaunal community. Netherlands Journal of Sea Research 27:119–125.

Hall, S. J., M. R. Robertson, D. J. Basford, and S. D. Heaney. 1993. The possible effects of fishing disturbance in the northern North Sea: an analysis of spatial patterns in community structure around a wreck. Netherlands Journal of Sea Research 31:201–208.

Harper, D. E., Jr., and S. H. Hopkins. 1976. The effects of oyster shell dredging on macrobenthic and nektonic organisms in San Antonio Bay. Pages 232–279 in A. H. Bouma, editor. Shell dredging and its influence on Gulf coast environments. Gulf Publishing Company, Houston.

Heck, K. L. Jr., and R. J. Orth. 1980. Seagrass habitats: the roles of habitat complexity, competition and predation in structuring associated fish and motile macroinvertebrate assemblages. Pages 449–464 in V. S. Kennedy, editor. Estuarine perspectives. Academic Press, New York.

Holme, N. A. 1983. Fluctuations in the benthos of the western English Channel. Oceanol. Acta XX:121–124.

Horn, H. S. 1976. Succession principles and applications. Pages 187–204 in R. M. May, editor. Theoretical ecology. WB Saunders, Philadelphia.

Hutchings, P. 1990. Review of the effects of trawling on macrobenthic epifaunal communities. Australian Journal of Marine and Freshwater Research 41:111–120.

ICES (International Council for the Exploration of the Sea). 1988. Report of the study group on the effects of bottom trawling. ICES C.M. 1988/B:56.

ICES (International Council for the Exploration of the Sea). 1992. Report of the working group on ecosystem effects of fishing activities. Copenhagen, 7-14 Apr. 1992. ICES C.M. 1992/G:11 Ref.: Session T.

ICES (International Council for the Exploration of the Sea). 1996. Report of the working group on ecosystem effects of fishing activities. ICES Headquarters, 13-21 Mar. 1996. ICES CM 1996/Assess/Env:1 Ref.: Session G.

Industrial Science Division. 1990. The impact of commercial trawling on the benthos of Strangford Lough. Interim Report No. TI/3160/90. Industrial Science Division, 17 Antrim Rd., Lisburn, Co., Antrim B128 3AL.

Jennings, S., and M. J. Kaiser. 1998. The effects of fishing on marine ecosystems. Advances in Marine Biology 34.

Jones, J. B. 1992. Environmental impact of trawling on the seabed: a review. New Zealand Journal of Marine and Freshwater Research 26:59–67.

Kaiser, M. 1996. Starfish damage as an indicator of trawling intensity. Marine Ecology Progress Series 134:303–307.

Kaiser, M. J., and B. E. Spencer. 1994. Fish scavenging behavior in recently trawled areas. Marine Ecology Progress Series 112:41–49.

Kaiser, M. J., and B. E. Spencer. 1995. Survival of bycatch from a beam trawl. Marine Ecology Progress Series 126:31–38.

Kaiser, M. J., and B. E. Spencer. 1996a. The effects of beam-trawl disturbance on infaunal communities in different habitats. Journal of Animal Ecology 65:348–358.

Kaiser M. J., and B. E. Spencer. 1996b. Behavioural responses of scavengers to beam trawl disturbance. Pages 116–123 in S. P. R. Greenstreet and M. L. Tasker, editors. Aquatic predators and their prey. Blackwell Scientific Publications, Oxford.

Kaiser M. J., and K. Ramsay. 1997. Opportunistic feeding by dabs within areas of trawl disturbance: possible implications for increased survival. Marine Ecology Progress Series 152:307–310.

Kaiser, M. J., D. B. Edwards, and B. E. Spencer. 1996. Infaunal community changes as a result of commercial clam cultivation and harvesting. Aquatic Living Resources 9:57–63.

Kaiser, M. J., and six coauthors. In press. Changes in megafaunal benthic communities in different habitats after trawling disturbance. ICES Journal of Marine Science.

Kroger, R. L., and J. F. Guthrie. 1972. Effect of predators on juvenile menhaden in clear and turbid estuaries. Marine Fisheries Review 34:78–80.

Langton, R. W. 1994. Fishing effects on demersal fish habits. In R. W. Langton, J. B. Pearce, and J. A. Gibson, editors. Selected living resources, habitat conditions and human perturbations of the Gulf of Maine. NOAA (National Oceanic and Atmospheric Administration) Technical Memorandum NMFS-NE-106.

Langton, R. W., P. J. Auster, and D. C. Schneider. 1995. A spatial and temporal perspective on research and management of groundfish in the northwest Atlantic. Reviews in Fisheries Science 3:201–229.

Langton, R. W., R. S. Steneck, V. Gotceitas, F. Juanes, and P. Lawton. 1996. The interface between fisheries research and habitat management. North American Journal of Fisheries Management 16:1–7.

Lindholm, J., M. Ruth, L. Kaufman, and P. Auster. 1998. A modeling approach to the design of marine refugia for fishery management. Pages 138–168 in N. W. Munro and J. H. M. Willison, editors. Linking protected areas with working landscapes, conserving biodiversity. Science and Management of Protected Areas Association, Wolfville, Nova Scotia.

Lough, R. G., and six coauthors. 1989. Ecology and distribution of juvenile cod and haddock in relation to sediment type and bottom currents on eastern Georges Bank. Marine Ecology Progress Series 56:1–12.

MacDonald, D. S., M. Little, N. C. Eno, and K. Hiscock. 1996. Disturbance of benthic species by fishing activities: a sensitivity index. Aquatic Conservation: Marine and Freshwater Ecosystems 6:257–268.

MacKenzie, C. L., Jr. 1982. Compatibility of invertebrate populations and commercial fishing for ocean quahogs. North American Journal of Fisheries Management 2:270–275.

Magorrian, B. H. 1995. The impact of commercial trawling on the benthos of Strangford Lough. Doctoral dissertation. The Queen's University of Belfast, Northern Ireland.

Mann, K. H. 1982. Kelp, sea urchins and predators: a review of strong interactions in rocky subtidal systems of eastern Canada, 1970–1980. Netherlands Journal of Sea Research 16:414–423.

Mann, K. H., and P. A. Breen. 1972. The relation between lobster abundance, sea urchins, and kelp beds. Journal of the Fisheries Research Board of Canada 29:603–605.

Mayer, L. M., D. F. Schick, R. H. Findlay, and D. L. Rice. 1991. Effects of commercial dragging on sedimentary organic matter. Marine Environmental Research 31:249–261.

Medcof, J. C., and J. F. Caddy. 1971. Underwater observations on the performance of clam dredges of three types. ICES C.M. 1971/B:10.

Messieh, S. N., T. W. Rowell, D. L. Peer, and P. J. Cranford. 1991. The effects of trawling, dredging and ocean dumping on the eastern Canadian shelf seabed. Continental Shelf Research 11(8-10):1237–1263.

Meyer T. L., R. A. Cooper, and K. J. Pecci. 1981. The performance and environmental effects of a hydraulic clam dredge. Marine Fisheries Review 43(9):14–22.

Moser, M. L., P. J. Auster, and J. B. Bichy. 1998. Effects of mat morphology on large Sargassum-associated fishes: observations from a remotely operated vehicle (ROV) and free- floating video camcorders. Environmental Biology of Fishes 51:391–398.

Murawski, S. A. 1993. Climate change and marine fish distributions: forecasting from historical analogy. Transactions of the American Fisheries Society 122:647–658.

Murawski, S. A., and F. M. Serchuk. 1989. Environmental effects of offshore dredge fisheries for bivalves. ICES 1989 Statutory Meeting. The Hague, Netherlands.

National Research Council. 1994. Improving the management of U.S. marine fisheries. National Academy Press, Washington, D.C.

National Research Council. 1995. Understanding marine biodiversity: a research agenda for the nation. National Academy Press, Washington, D.C.

Overholtz, W. J., and A. V. Tyler. 1985. Long-term responses of the demersal fish assemblages of Georges Bank. Fishery Bulletin 83:507–520.

Pearson, T. H., A. B. Josefson, and R. Rosenberg. 1985. Petersen's benthic stations revisited. I. Is the Kattagatt becoming eutrophic? Journal of Experimental Marine Biology and Ecology 92:157–206.

Peters, D. S., and F. A. Cross. 1992. What is coastal fish habitat? Pages 17–22 in R. H. Stroud, editor. Stemming the tide of coastal fish habitat loss. Marine recreational fisheries, volume 14. National Coalition for Marine Conservation, Savannah, Georgia.

Peterson, C. H., H. C. Summerson, and S. R. Fegley. 1983. Relative efficiency of two clam rakes and their contrasting impacts on seagrass biomass. Fishery Bulletin 81:429–434.

Peterson, C. H., H. C. Summerson, and S. R. Fegley. 1987. Ecological consequences of mechanical harvesting of clams. Fishery Bulletin 85(2):281–298.

Phoel, W. C. 1986. Community structure of demersal fishes on the inshore U.S. Atlantic continental shelf: Cape Ann, Massachusetts to Cape Fear, North Carolina. Doctoral dissertation. College of William and Mary, Gloucester Point, Virginia.

Pickett, S. T. A., and P. S. White, editors. 1985. The ecology of natural disturbance and patch dynamics. Academic Press, New York.

Pilskaln, C. H., J. H. Churchill, and L. M. Mayer. 1998. Resuspension of sediment by bottom trawling in the Gulf of Maine and potential geochemical consequences. Conservation Biology 12(6):1223–1224.

Prena, J., T. W. Rowell, P. Schwinghamer, K. Gilkinson, and D. C. Gordon, Jr. 1996. Grand Banks otter trawling impact experiment: site selection process, with a description of macrofaunal communities. Canadian Technical Report of Fisheries and Aquatic Sciences 2094.

Ramsay, K., M. J. Kaiser, and R. N. Hughes. 1996. Changes in hermit crab feeding patterns in response to trawling disturbance. Marine Ecology Progress Series 144:63–72.

Ramsay, K., M. J. Kaiser, and R. N. Hughes. 1997a. Responses of benthic scavengers to fishing disturbance by towed gear in different habitats. Journal of Experimental Marine Biology and Ecology 224:73–89.

Ramsay, K., M. J. Kaiser, P. G. Moore, and R. N. Hughes. 1997b. Consumption of fisheries discards by benthic scavengers: utilization of energy subsidies in different marine habitats. Journal of Animal Ecology 66:884–896.

Reise, K. 1982. Long-term changes in the macrobenthic invertebrate fauna of the Wadden Sea: are polychaetes about to take over? Netherlands Journal of Sea Research 16:29–36.

Reiswig, H. M. 1973. Population dynamics of three Jamaican Demspongiae. Bulletin of Marine Science 23:191–226.

Rhoads, D. C., P. L. McCall, and J. Y. Yingst. 1978. Disturbance and production on the estuarine seafloor. American Scientist 66:557–586.

Riemann, B., and E. Hoffmann. 1991. Ecological consequences of dredging and bottom trawling in the Limfjord, Denmark. Marine Ecology Progress Series 69:171–178.

Riesen, W., and K. Reise. 1982. Macrobenthos of the subtidal Wadden Sea: revisited after 55 years. Helgoländer Meersunters 35:409–423.

Rijnsdorp, A. D., A. M. Buijs, F. Storbeck, and E. Visser. 1996. Micro-scale distribution of beam trawl effort in the southern North Sea between 1993 and 1996 in relation to the trawling frequency of the sea bed and the impact on benthic organisms. ICES CM 1996/Mini 11 Mini-Symposium Ecosystem Effects Fisheries.

Roberts, C. M. 1995. Effects of fishing on the ecosystem structure of coral reefs. Conservation Biology 9:988–995.

Rumohr, H., and P. Krost. 1991. Experimental evidence of damage to benthos by bottom trawling with special reference to *Artica islandica*. Meeresforsch 33:340–345.

Rumohr, H., H. Schomann, and T. Kujawski. 1994. Environmental impact of bottom gears on benthic fauna in the German Bight. Pages 75–86. NIOZ Rapport 1994-11, Netherlands Institute for Fisheries Research, Texel.

SAFMC (South Atlantic Fishery Management Council). 1991. Amendment 4 (gear restrictions and size limits), regulatory impact review, initial regulatory flexibility analysis and environmental assessment for the fishery management plan for the snapper grouper fishery of the south Atlantic region. SAFMC, Charleston, South Carolina.

Sainsbury, K. J. 1987. Assessment and management of the demersal fishery on the continental shelf of northwestern Australia. Pages 465–503 in J. J. Polovina and S. Ralston, editors. Tropical snappers and groupers: biology and fisheries management. Westview, Boulder, Colorado.

Sainsbury, K. J. 1988. The ecological basis of multispecies fisheries and management of a demersal fishery in tropical Australia. Pages 349–382 in J. A. Gulland, editor. Fish population dynamics, 2nd edition. John Wiley and Sons, London.

Sainsbury, K. J. 1991. Application of an experimental approach to management of a demersal fishery with highly uncertain dynamics. ICES Marine Science Symposium 193:301–320.

Sainsbury, K. J., R. A. Campbell, R. Lindholm, and A. W. Whitelaw. 1997. Experimental management of an Australian multispecies fishery: examining the possibility of trawl-induced habitat modification. Pages 107–112 in E. K. Pikitch, D. D. Huppert, and M. P. Sissenwine, editors. Global trends: fisheries management. American Fisheries Society, Symposium 20, Bethesda, Maryland.

Sale, P. F., editor. 1991. The ecology of fishes on coral reefs. Academic Press, New York.

Santbrink, J. W., and M. J. N. Bergman. 1994. Direct effects of beam trawling on macrofauna in a soft bottom area in the southern North Sea. Pages 147–178. NIOZ Rapport 1994-11, Netherlands Institute for Fisheries Research, Texel.

Sebens, K. P. 1986. Community ecology of vertical rock walls in the Gulf of Maine, U.S.A.: small-scale processes and alternative community states. Pages 346–371 in P. G. Moore and R. Seed, editors. The ecology of rocky coasts. Hodder and Stoughton Press, Kent, UK.

Smith, E. M., and 15 coauthors. 1985. A study of lobster fisheries in the Connecticut waters of Long Island Sound with special reference to the effects of trawling on lobsters. Connecticut Department of Environmental Protection, Marine Fisheries Program, Hartford.

Sogard, S. M., and K. W. Able. 1991. A comparison of eelgrass, sea lettuce macroalgae, and marsh creeks as habitats for epibenthic fishes and decapods. Estuarine Coastal and Shelf Science 33:501–519.

Steele, J. H. 1996. Regime shifts in fisheries management. Fisheries Research 25:19–23.

Suchanek, T. H. 1986. Mussels and their role in structuring rocky shore communities. Pages 70–96 in P. G. Moore and R. Seed, editors. The ecology of rocky coasts. Hodder and Stoughton Press, Kent, UK.

Szedlmayer, S. T., and J. C. Howe. 1997. Substrate preference in age-0 red snapper, *Lutjanus campechanus*. Environmental Biology of Fishes 50:203–207.

Thomas, C. J., and L. B. Cahoon. 1993. Stable isotope analyses differentiate between different trophic pathways supporting rocky-reef fishes. Marine Ecology Progress Series 95:19–24

Thrush, S. F., R. D. Pridmore, and J. E. Hewitt. 1994. Impacts on soft-sediment macrofauna: the effects of spatial variation on temporal trends. Ecological Applications 4:31–41.

Thrush, S. F., J. E. Hewitt, V. J. Cummings, and P. K. Dayton. 1995. The impact of habitat disturbance by scallop dredging on marine benthic communities: what can be predicted from the results of experiments? Marine Ecology Progress Series 129:141–150.

Thrush, S. F., and eight coauthors. In press. Disturbance of the marine benthic habitat by commercial fishing: impacts at the scale of the fishery. Ecological Applications.

Tupper, M., and R. G. Boutilier. 1995. Effects of habitat on settlement, growth, and postsettlement survival of Atlantic cod (*Gadus morhua*). Canadian Journal of Fisheries and Aquatic Sciences 52:1834–1841.

Valentine, P. C., and E. A. Schmuck. 1995. Geological mapping of biological habitats on Georges Bank and Stellwagen Bank, Gulf of Maine region. Pages 31–40 in Applications of side-scan sonar and laser-line systems in fisheries research. Alaska Department of Fish and Game, Special Publication 9.

Van Dolah, R. F., P. H. Wendt, and N. Nicholson. 1987. Effects of a research trawl on a hard bottom assemblage of sponges and corals. Fisheries Research 5:39–54.

Van Dolah, R. F., P. H. Wendt, and M. V. Levisen. 1991. A study of the effects of shrimp trawling on benthic communities in two South Carolina sounds. Fisheries Research 12:139–156.

Walters, C. J., and F. Juanes. 1993. Recruitment limitation as a consequence of natural selection for use of restricted feeding habitats and predation risk taking by juvenile fishes. Canadian Journal of Fisheries and Aquatic Sciences 50:2058–2070.

Watling, L., and E. A. Norse. 1998. Disturbance of the seabed by mobile fishing gear: a comparison to forest clearcutting. Conservation Biology 12(6):1180–1197.

Witbaard, R., and R. Klein. 1994. Long-term trends on the effects of the southern North Sea beamtrawl fishery on the bivalve mollusc *Arctica islandica* L. (Mollusca, bivalvia). ICES Journal of Marine Science 51:99–105.

Witman, J. D. 1985. Refuges, biological disturbance, and rocky subtidal community structure in New England. Ecological Monographs 55:421–445.

Witman, J. D. 1987. Subtidal coexistence: storms, grazing, mutualism, and the zonation of kelp and mussels. Ecological Monographs 57:167–187.

Witman, J. D., and K. P. Sebens. 1985. Distribution and ecology of sponges at a subtidal rock ledge in the central Gulf of Maine. Pages 391–396 *in* K. Rutzler, editor. New perspectives in sponge biology. Smithsonian Institution Press, Washington, D.C.

Witman, J. D., and K. P. Sebens. 1992. Regional variation in fish predation intensity: a historical perspective in the Gulf of Maine. Oecologia 90:305–315.

Witman, J. D., J. J. Leichter, S. J. Genovese, and D. A. Brooks. 1993. Pulsed phytoplankton supply to the rocky subtidal zone: influence of internal waves. Proceedings of the National Academy of Sciences of the United States of America 90:1686–1690.

American Fisheries Society Symposium 22:188–211, 1999

Fish Habitat: A Focus on New England Fishermen's Perspectives

JUDITH PEDERSON AND MADELEINE HALL-ARBER

Massachusetts Institute of Technology, Sea Grant College Program
292 Main Street E38-300, Cambridge, Massachusetts 02139, USA

Abstract.—This study sought input from fishermen on their knowledge of fish habitat and the effects of fishing gear to fill some gaps in the science. We looked for any documentation of habitats and effects to habitats from fishing gear or other causes that fishermen could or were willing to provide. This report summarizes documentation provided by fishermen of fish habitat, changes to habitat observed over time, and fishing gear effects. In addition, the report evaluates the effectiveness of different approaches to identify fishermen's knowledge and document their observations. To better represent fishermen and provide accurate information, we were interested in fishermen's responses to two questions: (1) How can we better solicit fishermen's knowledge of habitat, and (2) what would make it possible for fishermen to share that information? The results of this study were influenced by several factors, including the fact that methodologies for integrating fishermen's knowledge into fisheries scientific literature and fisheries management are at an embryonic stage. In addition, for this initial study, resources were limited, which gave the survey a strong New England bias. We also found that fishermen are reluctant to get involved in essential fish habitat identification for several reasons, including the perceived proprietary nature of their habitat information. This review represents an important first step toward making the crucial linkage between fisheries management and fishermen's local knowledge. This study and future similar studies will provide opportunities to bring fishermen's knowledge to the forefront as essential fish habitat management plans are being developed. The contribution of fishermen's knowledge should help managers design a balanced regulatory system that will lead to sustainable fisheries and fisheries communities.

The 1996 reauthorization of the Magnuson-Stevens Fishery Conservation and Management Act (Magnuson-Stevens Act) required the regional fishery management councils (Councils) and the Secretary of Commerce to describe and identify essential fish habitat (EFH), identify negative impacts to EFH from fishing and nonfishing activities, and identify means to conserve and enhance EFH in each of their fishery management plans by October 1998. This was a daunting requirement given the lack of systematic, long-term, scientific research on habitat—as well as the length of time Councils usually need to propose, discuss, present at public hearing, and vote on management proposals.

The new rule reflects a change in fisheries management by specifically requiring the inclusion of habitat definitions in fishery management plans. Congress has mandated that fisheries managers should move toward an ecosystem approach rather than rely exclusively on stock assessment-based management. The concern with habitat and effects on fish productivity is not new, but fisheries management relies heavily on stock-assessment approaches (Ryther 1969; Russell-Hunter 1970; Cushing 1975; Holt 1981; NEFSC 1998). Habitat and the relationship between habitat and fish population dynamics has not been integrated into stock-assessment approaches. Nor is the functioning of complex ecosystems at an individual species level well understood.

Although stock-assessment methods offer managers a tool for estimating fish productivity, few assessment models account for uncertainty, directional environmental change, impacts of recreational fisheries, and changes in catchability, selectivity, and mortality over time (NRC 1998). Yet with constant changes in navigational equipment, larger and faster boats, and improved fishing gear, for example, fishermen are able to harvest more fish and to fish in regions previously unexploited and unexplored. Data on such changes in fisheries practices are rarely reflected in stock-assessment models. Incomplete or inaccurate information, coupled with high-grading and misreporting of landings, can skew assessment results (NRC 1998). Furthermore, some models have a lag time that tends to overestimate exploitable biomass when stocks are declining (NRC 1998). Although a report by the National Research Council (NRC 1998) stressed the need to train stock-assessment and fisheries scientists, we further recommend that fishermen be trained to collect data on fish habitat and related environmental and biological data that could be used to improve stock-assessment models and assist fisheries management decisions.

As more and more targeted fish species become over- or fully exploited, there is greater awareness of the need to manage using all available information. The interim final rule to implement the EFH policy issued by National Marine Fisheries Service (NMFS) on 19 December 1997 noted that it is important to understand all of the roles of managed species, whether they be prey, competitors, links in the food web, or actors in the nutrient transfer between ecosystems (NMFS 1997). The rule also pointed out that the Councils will have to identify the habitats used by each stage in the life history (including breeding, spawning, feeding, and growth to maturity) of managed species and will have to note impacts of fishing on each habitat. Furthermore, nonfishing impacts are also to be considered because actions in upland and riparian areas may affect habitat conservation and enhancement efforts. In addition, the Magnuson-Stevens Act required NMFS to consult with stakeholders before submitting its recommendations and information to the Councils to assist in the description and identification of EFH.

Acceptance of the idea that local knowledge, or what has come to be known as traditional ecological knowledge, could be valuable to scientists and managers in the conservation and management of natural resources to achieve sustainability is relatively recent. In fact, it was in the 1980s that the International Union for Conservation of Nature and Resources established the Working Group on Traditional Ecological Knowledge with the goal of promoting this concept (Morren 1995). Although local knowledge in fishing communities has been described in various places in the Pacific, South America, Caribbean, and India, this knowledge rarely has been assessed with regard to management and sustainability (Ruddle 1994).

Nevertheless, customary marine tenure (Ruddle et al. 1991) and local-level management of fisheries in various small-scale fisheries (Acheson 1975; Davis 1984; McGoodwin 1984; Berkes 1986; Durrenberger and Palsson 1987; Dahl 1988; Johannes 1989; Palmer 1993) exists and has been successful in reaching the goal of sustainable fisheries for some time in some locations. The success of local fisheries management is necessarily dependent on fishermen's traditional ecological knowledge.

Evidence that local knowledge of fishermen in the United States was considered important in the past is offered in the book *American Fishes*, which was written by George B. Goode, former U.S. Commissioner of Fisheries, and published in 1887 (with a revised edition by Theodore Gill published in 1903). In his book, Goode frequently cited observations of fishermen as evidence for his descriptions of various species' stock sizes, feeding habits, location, and other related information. However, there is no analysis in the book of how useful this information was to fisheries managers. With the exception of halibut and river herring, fish were plentiful relative to fishing pressure during Goode's tenure, so management concerns could focus more on supporting "the interest of the American fishermen" than on rebuilding stocks (Goode 1887).

Until recently, little effort has been devoted to systematically collecting local knowledge about habitat from fishermen in the United States (Ames 1997; M. Hall-Arber, Massachusetts Institute of Technology Sea Grant College Program; K. St. Martin, Clark University; and C. Dyer, University of Rhode Island, unpublished data). Too often, fishermen say that their observations, which are solicited in the public hearing process associated with the Councils' fishery management plan development, are dismissed as "anecdotal" and therefore considered to be without scientific credence.

Because fishermen's traditional ecological knowledge has not been systematically collected and analyzed, managers have had no objective means to evaluate its content. Just as the NRC recommended independent peer review of fishery management methods, including stock-assessment procedures, so do we recommend formal collection and independent review of fishermen's local knowledge so that their contributions may be incorporated into the management process.

Initially, the collection of fishermen's knowledge will not be easy. At a 1997 conference on the effects of fishing gear on the seafloor in New England, several fishermen presented documentation of habitats, habitat types, and fishing gear effects in the form of videos; anecdotal observations; charts with tow lines; samples of plastics, algae, and invertebrates; and photographs (Dorsey and Pederson 1998). However, many fishermen are reluctant to share their detailed knowledge with fisheries managers, anticipating that the information "will be used against" them and that further limits on fishing will be imposed. Without detailed knowledge about fishing practices, landings, habitat observations, and bycatch, and without other documentation of where, when, and how much fish is caught, managers act on the best information they have available—information that may be incomplete or insufficient. Without appropriate limits or management, target fish production may be limited, nonpreferred species may proliferate, and low-end (both in trophic level and size) fishing is encouraged. A recent analysis of over 60 data sets with complete diet information suggested that global fisheries catches contain an increasing proportion of low-trophic-level animals (Pauly et al. 1998). This study suggested that fishing practices are creating ecological shifts that may be irreversible.

It is certain that "traditional knowledge cannot make a contribution to sustainable development without having a functional link to management" (Bellon 1995:264). By its requirement that the Councils seek information on habitat from local stakeholders as well as other information to augment scientific data, the Magnuson-Stevens Act implicitly recognizes the value of linking management and fishermen's local knowledge.

The Research Effort

As a first step in helping the Councils change their management focus to include habitat and ecosystem considerations, the NMFS supported two habitat studies through a collaborative agreement with the American Fisheries Society, World Wildlife Fund, and National Fish and Wildlife Foundation. One study reviewed scientific, peer-reviewed literature on gear impacts on habitat (Auster and Langton 1999, this volume), and the other study, the focus of this report, reviewed fishermen's knowledge of habitat and gear impacts.

This report summarizes a sample of fishermen's documentation of fish habitat, changes to habitat observed over time, and effects of fishing gear on habitat. Fishermen's knowledge is not neatly written in journals, articles, or technical reports for perusal and distillation. Instead, fishermen must be contacted directly. The results of our contacts with fishermen are presented as a preliminary indication of what documentation is available.

Although the initial purpose of this study was to compile a database of fishermen's documentation of observations about habitat, changes to habitat over space and time, and gear impacts, it became evident early on in the study that the following factors would influence the outcome:

- Methodologies for integrating fishermen's knowledge into fisheries scientific literature and fisheries management are at an embryonic stage.
- For this initial study, resources were limited, and what was to be a "national" survey has a strong New England bias.
- Fishermen are reluctant to get involved for several reasons that will be discussed later in this paper.

A secondary purpose of this study is to evaluate the effectiveness of different approaches to identify fishermen's knowledge and document their observations. For this project, we relied on interviews, focus groups, participation in public hearings, and the use of written questions.

Methodologies and Approach

To collect information from fishermen on their documentation of fishing gear effects and habitat observations, a general solicitation requesting information from a broad audience was sent to newsletters and media targeting fishermen and fishermen's organizations. The primary goal of this initial solicitation was to compile a list of the types of documentation that fishermen maintain about habitat, fishing gear effects, and favored fishing sites, which in turn could be used (to the extent that fishermen were willing to share this information) to support EFH identification and development of federal fishery management plans.

To understand the context of the initial responses about logbooks, videos, or other documentation, a questionnaire was prepared to collect additional information about fishing activities. This survey form was reviewed by fisheries managers, fishermen, and other knowledgeable individuals before distribution and served as the basis for individual discussions with fishermen. It also was used to stimulate focus-group meetings and give structure to the discussions. The survey instrument provided a standardized method for collecting and summarizing information. The questionnaire (Figure 1) requested information in three categories:

1. background information about fishermen, fishing vessel(s), and target species and habitats;
2. fishermen's perspectives on potential causes of change observed in target-fish populations and habitats; and
3. documentation of fishermen's observations.

**Interim Study of Available Information on
Bottom Habitat, Fishing Gear Effects and Natural Disturbances**

Background information about you

1. Name_____Street_____
City/town_____State_____Zip_____
F/V_____Phone_____FAX_____email_____

2.Please indicate the category or categories that best describe your fishing activities:
☐commercial fisherman ☐recreational fisherman ☐other ☐full time ☐part time
☐owner ☐captain ☐mate ☐engineer ☐deck hand ☐cook

3. Vessel information: F/V length_____Vessel tonnage_____Horsepower_____Hold capacity_____

Background information about your fishing gear type and targeted species

4. Please indicate the type or types of fishing gear and the years and seasons in which you use them:
CHECK AS MANY AS APPROPRIATE   SEASON   BOTTOM TYPES FISHED

Gear types	W	Sp	Su	F	from....to	Rocky	Gravel	Sand	Mud
Beam trawl	☐	☐	☐	☐	19___ to 19___	☐	☐	☐	☐
Otter trawl	☐	☐	☐	☐	19___ to 19___	☐	☐	☐	☐
Rock hopper/roller	☐	☐	☐	☐	19___ to 19___	☐	☐	☐	☐

(approximate rock hopper/roller size _____ inches)

	W	Sp	Su	F	from....to	Rocky	Gravel	Sand	Mud
Scallop dredge	☐	☐	☐	☐	19___ to 19___	☐	☐	☐	☐
Clam/hydraulic dredge	☐	☐	☐	☐	19___ to 19___	☐	☐	☐	☐
Midwater trawl	☐	☐	☐	☐	19___ to 19___	☐	☐	☐	☐
Factory trawler	☐	☐	☐	☐	19___ to 19___	☐	☐	☐	☐
Longline/tub trawl	☐	☐	☐	☐	19___ to 19___	☐	☐	☐	☐
Troll	☐	☐	☐	☐	19___ to 19___	☐	☐	☐	☐
Seine	☐	☐	☐	☐	19___ to 19___	☐	☐	☐	☐
Gillnet	☐	☐	☐	☐	19___ to 19___	☐	☐	☐	☐
Lobster/crab/fish pots	☐	☐	☐	☐	19___ to 19___	☐	☐	☐	☐
Other	☐	☐	☐	☐	19___ to 19___	☐	☐	☐	☐

5. Please indicate the species targeted and the years and seasons fished:
CHECK AS MANY AS APPROPRIATE   SEASON   BOTTOM TYPES FISHED

Target species	W	Sp	Su	F	from.....to	Rocky	Gravel	Sand	Mud
Shrimp	☐	☐	☐	☐	19___ to 19___	☐	☐	☐	☐
Lobsters/crab	☐	☐	☐	☐	19___ to 19___	☐	☐	☐	☐
Squid	☐	☐	☐	☐	19___ to 19___	☐	☐	☐	☐
Scallops	☐	☐	☐	☐	19___ to 19___	☐	☐	☐	☐
Clams/oysters	☐	☐	☐	☐	19___ to 19___	☐	☐	☐	☐
Tuna/swordfish	☐	☐	☐	☐	19___ to 19___	☐	☐	☐	☐
Salmon	☐	☐	☐	☐	19___ to 19___	☐	☐	☐	☐
Herring/mackerel	☐	☐	☐	☐	19___ to 19___	☐	☐	☐	☐
Halibut	☐	☐	☐	☐	19___ to 19___	☐	☐	☐	☐
Ocean perch	☐	☐	☐	☐	19___ to 19___	☐	☐	☐	☐
Whiting/hake	☐	☐	☐	☐	19___ to 19___	☐	☐	☐	☐
Sharks/dogfish	☐	☐	☐	☐	19___ to 19___	☐	☐	☐	☐
Rockfish	☐	☐	☐	☐	19___ to 19___	☐	☐	☐	☐
Sablefish	☐	☐	☐	☐	19___ to 19___	☐	☐	☐	☐
Bait fish	☐	☐	☐	☐	19___ to 19___	☐	☐	☐	☐
Groundfish/flatfish	☐	☐	☐	☐	19___ to 19___	☐	☐	☐	☐

(Type or types of groundfish/flatfish_____)
☐ Other ☐ ☐ ☐ ☐ 19___ to 19___ ☐ ☐ ☐ ☐
(Type or types of other fish_____)

Observations on habitats, changes, and possible causes

6. How do you define habitat? Structures on bottom (e.g. shipwrecks, canyon edges, rocks, plants, animals, etc.)?_____
_____
_____

7. What do you think is essential fish habitat for the species you target? Identify structures and other characteristics of habitat._____
_____
_____

8. What do you think is/are the most significant factor(s) affecting the habitat you fish? _____
_____
_____

FIGURE 1.—Survey form distributed to fishermen (revised May 1998).

9. Indicate which of the following you have observed over time for the target species that you fish:
☐no change   ☐increase   ☐decrease   ☐replaced by another species   ☐moved to other areas.
Please explain observations:_____
_____

10. Please indicate what, if any, biological changes you have noticed in the time you have been fishing e.g.
☐target species   ☐fish health   ☐type of bottom algae and creatures   ☐habitat productivity
☐bycatch   ☐other changes. Please specify:
_____
_____

11. Please indicate significant changes in the environment that you have noticed, e.g. ☐salinity   ☐currents
☐temperature. Please specify:_____
_____
_____

12. Please identify any signs of pollution that you observed, e.g. ☐sewage   ☐chemical waste   ☐plastics
☐gear debris ☐oil ☐bottom obstacles ☐other. Please explain:_____
_____
_____

13. If you observed a change to the habitats you fish or to specific species, please explain what you think is the
cause? ☐weather   ☐fishing gear   ☐pollution   ☐habitat loss   ☐overfishing
☐ fronts (upwelling/downwelling)   ☐changes in prey or food abundance   ☐other
_____
_____

14. Does your gear ever pick up bottom features? If yes, please describe how, how often (rarely,
occasionally,frequently), and general bottom-type where this may occur. Describe changes over time in this
location?_____
_____
_____
_____

15.Does your gear affect the habitat you normally fish? ☐ yes ☐no   If yes, how and how do you
know:_____
_____
_____
_____

Documentation of your observations
16. Do you have any of the following:
   ☐Videos of your fishing gear   ☐Logbooks
   ☐Fishing ground coordinates   ☐Plots of usual tows from 19____ to 19____
   ☐Charts with tows marked   ☐Others
Please explain how your documentation might be used to describe fish habitat._____
_____
_____
_____
_____

17. Are you willing to share this information with scientists or others?   ☐yes   ☐no

**Please return this form to: Interim Habitat Study, Massachusetts Institute of Technology Sea Grant
College Program, 292 Main Street, E38-300, Cambridge, MA 02139**

FIGURE 1.—(continued.)

The first section of the questionnaire asked for background information, which was used to distinguish between "day fishermen" and large-vessel fishermen, commercial and recreational fishermen, and target species and fishing gear used. A request for dates fished with different gear and species targeted was designed to provide an indication of how gear and target species have changed over time. To document fishermen's perspectives on what they perceive as the cause of fish population changes, the second section was made up of a series of questions that offered opportunities to elaborate on observations or to indicate possible causes of changes. The questions were designed to elicit observations on pollution, physical environment, biotic changes, and fishing effects (e.g., gear effects, overfishing, and habitat alterations). The second section of the questionnaire also requested information on habitat (although our initial survey form did not ask for fishermen's definitions of habitat and EFH) including changes to habitats and insights into possible causes of these changes. The final section of the questionnaire requested sources of documentation about habitats and fishing gear effects and asked whether fishermen were willing to share this information.

A request for study participants was distributed to all of the known New England fishing associations and selected associations in the southern and northwestern United States. In addition, a notice was sent to all Councils along with copies of the questionnaires, encouraging Council members and staff to distribute the forms to interested fishermen. A notice regarding the project was distributed electronically to listserves and several trade journals and by mail to individuals who had requested more information about the survey. In addition to the general distribution of project information, direct contact by phone or in person was used to encourage fishermen representing different gear sectors to respond. We solicited the support of Sea Grant Advisory and Extension colleagues in encouraging fishermen to respond and in holding focus-group meetings.

The most successful (although time-consuming) approach was to convene focus-group meetings. The questionnaires provided the framework for these meetings. One advantage of such face-to-face meetings was that the intent of each question could be discussed in detail. As they responded to the open-ended survey questions during the focus-group meetings, fishermen were not inhibited by a limited number of lines on a form and therefore provided additional insights. The focus-group meetings also

provided the opportunity for fishermen to identify significant habitats on maps. During the group discussions, National Oceanic and Atmospheric Administration nautical charts were provided, and fishermen were encouraged to highlight on the charts habitats of value to them. These hand-drawn areas of important habitats are being digitized for use in ArcView, a geographic information system. Data from the forms and transcribed tapes of the focus-group meetings were used in preparing the tables and graphs in this chapter. Additional information from the study has been summarized in narrative form for this chapter.

Results of the Focus-Group Meetings

The identification on maps of areas that are fished for specific species and associated with specific habitat structures suggests the importance and complexity of habitat (Figures 2–4). Because many details about habitat structures and species distributions were revealed through these relatively small-scale maps, measures smaller in scale than the 10-min squares (approximately 100 mi^2 each) used by the New England Fishery Management Council for their habitat maps may be necessary for the Council to accurately identify habitat areas of particular concern.

In the mapping process, on a large scale, fishermen identified areas of good fishing (Figure 2). In some cases, two or three species are associated with the same general region. Tilefish *Lopholatilus chamaeleonticeps*; hake (silver hake *Merluccius bilinearis,* red hake *Urophycis chuss*, and white hake *U. tenuis*); and American lobsters *Homarus americanus* can be found in deep waters off the southwest part of Georges Bank and to the west of that region between the 50- and 100-ft isobars. In other areas associated with ridges (e.g., Dwyers, Dimple, and Sherrer and Franklin Swell), fishermen catch Atlantic cod *Gadus morhua*, haddock *Melanogrammus aeglefinus*, and cusk *Brosme brosme*. Also of interest is the identification of areas where lobsters are found during August to October (when they shed) and in winter and spring. In one additional region, cusk were found.

As the scale gets larger, fine-scale partitioning gets lost. For example, both lobster and cod appear to be fished in the same area on the outer banks of Cape Cod. However, on a smaller scale, these two areas are separated (Figure 2). In an area off the coast of Cape

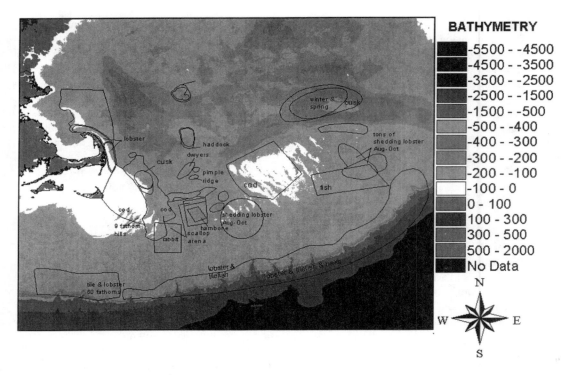

FIGURE 2.—Map showing habitat and fisheries characteristics off Cape Cod and on Georges Bank.

Cod, structural components include nine-fathom hills (near Davis Bank and within Nantucket Shoals), two areas with extensive mussel beds, a clay pipe region, crushed shells, and benthic organisms described as figs (Ascidians), lemons (*Boltenia ovifera*), and pumpkins (Ascidians) (Figure 3). Hook and line fishermen drew the outlines of the cod and haddock areas fished by both themselves and gillnetters. The area around the tip of Cape Cod, near Provincetown (Figure 4), is also used by different types of fishermen. The area is a spawning ground for fluke (also called summer flounder *Paralichthys dentatus*), which is fished by hook and line fishermen within the crook of Provincetown and fished by draggermen on the outer area (as fluke leave the crook). The area around the tip of Cape Cod is also used by lobstermen.

Results of the Written Survey

Fishermen and Vessels

There were 43 respondents to the questionnaire, of whom 27 were commercial fishermen from New England, except for 1 retiree and 1 recreational fisherman. The distribution of responses from New England were 14 from Massachusetts,

9 from New Hampshire, 3 from Maine, and 1 from Rhode Island. Other responses included 9 from North Carolina; 1 each from Texas, New Jersey, California, and Oregon; and 3 summaries from the Louisiana Intercoastal City representing 7 menhaden fishermen, 75 shrimp fishermen, and 45 crab pot fishermen. These three Intercoastal City responses were treated as single responses and are noted as such where appropriate. Most New England respondents were owners, captains, or owners and captains of their own boats and had fished commercially for 15–20 or more years. Distribution of fishermen, boat size, and hold capacity are summarized in Table 1.

As expected, recreational fishermen's boats were smaller than commercial fishermen's boats and had less horsepower. The size of commercial boats for the northeast region ranged from 23 to 185 ft with the majority in the 30–40-ft range. Horsepower ranged from 150 to 850 hp with the majority around 300–400 hp. For mid-sized boats, hold capacity was between 2,000 and 50,000 lbs with larger boats having capacities of up to 250,000 lbs. Based on boat size of respondents, most of the respondents were day fishermen who return to port each night.

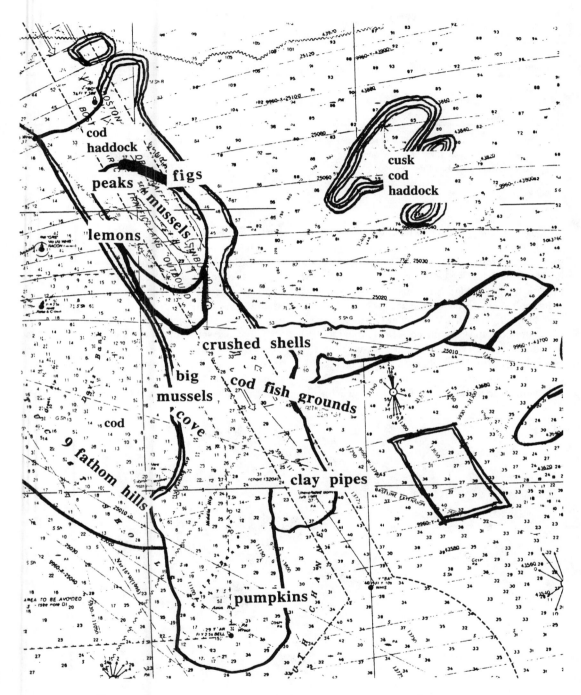

FIGURE 3.—Map showing areas off Cape Cod with habitat structure and associated fish species.

Gear Types

Approximately half of the northeast commercial fishermen (13 of 27 active New England fishermen) fished two or more gear types in their careers or throughout the year. Of the respondents, six New England fishermen trawled, and three former trawlers were using hooks, lobster pots, and gill nets, respectively. One other respondent may have been trawling, but the

TABLE 1.—Distribution of fishermen as owners and captains and boat sizes. A blank space means no answer was provided in the questionnaire. (California and Oregon are not included.)

Geographic region	Owners	Captains	Range of boat size (ft)	Horsepower	Hold capacity (lbs.)
Gulf of Mexico [a]			18–180 [b]	200 [c]	350 cubic ft [c]
Southeast Atlantic	1 of 9	1 of 9	19–33	90–900	
Northeast Atlantic [d]	20 of 28	23 of 28	23–185	150–850	1,500–250,000

[a] Three responses represented three different gear types with between 7 and 75 fishermen fishing each gear type.

[b] Boats ranged from 18 to 20 ft for crab fishermen, 60 to 75 ft for shrimp fishermen, and 180 ft for menhaden fishermen.

[c] Response of shrimp fisherman from Texas.

[d] States of Massachusetts, New Hampshire, Maine, Rhode Island, and New Jersey are represented.

response was ambiguous. Fifteen of the twenty-seven New England respondents used hook and line, and fourteen of those respondents were long-liners who used tub trawls or jigged. One of the respondents indicated using a scallop dredge, and three other respondents indicated having done so in the past.

The following discussion about gear types, seasons, and bottom types fished reflects previous experience (of retired fishermen), as well as the responses of active fishermen (Figure 5). Fishermen currently using various gear types are distinguished by shading from those who fished the gear in the past. The bar graphs in Figure 5 include responses from the Louisiana Intercoastal City, and these responses are treated as one response for each gear type. Other gear considered in Figure 5 includes gear used by recreational fishermen (several from the southwest Atlantic region) and unique gear (primarily recreational gear).

Because several fishermen used more than one gear type, the total number of fishermen for all gear types in Figure 5 exceeds 43, the number of respondents. Given the limited response to the questionnaire and the bias toward New England fisheries,

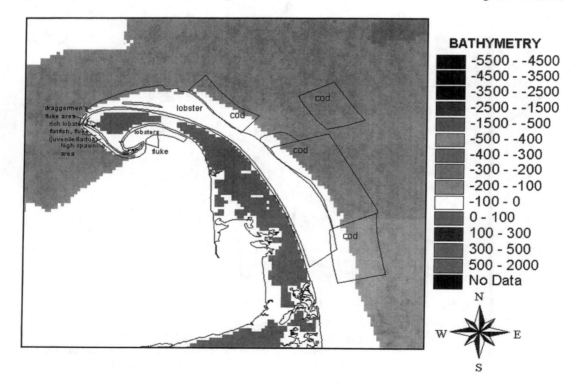

FIGURE 4.—Map showing fisheries characteristics in areas near Provincetown, Massachusetts.

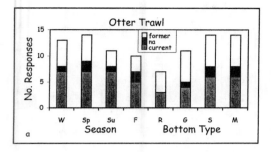

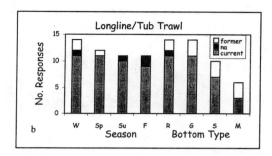

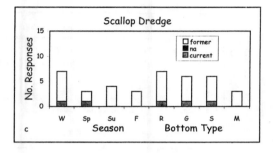

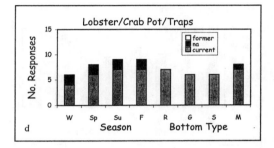

FIGURE 5.—Fishing gear as used by season and bottom type for current and former fishermen. Season is defined as W (winter), Sp (spring), Su (summer), and F (fall). Bottom types are indicated as R (rocky), G (gravel), S (sand), and M (mud). No answer is indicated by na.

the data should be cautiously interpreted and may not represent national trends, or even regional trends. Only two respondents had less than 10 years of experience fishing. In addition, 14 respondents had between 10 and 20 years of experience, 12 respondents had between 20 and 30 years of experience, and two respondents had between 30 and 40 years of experience. Finally, two retirees had 29 and 46 years of experience, respectively, and six respondents did not indicate how many years they had fished.

The data indicate that among fishermen who changed gear type, the greater percentage abandoned scallop dredging and trawling to adopt other fishing gear, which is perhaps a reflection of the change in New England fisheries over the past decade. The data also indicate a seasonal component to the employment of different fishing gear. Winter fishing is popular with trawlers (and those using "rockhoppers"), hook and line fishermen, and scallop dredgers (Figure 5a, 5b, and 5c), whereas other months are popular with those fishing with traps (lobsters and crabs), trolls, and "other" gear (Figure 5d). These differences reflect, in part, the winter weather that is inhospitable to recreational and other small boats.

Most fishermen switched gear types during their fishing careers, and many continue to fish more than one gear type during their annual round to take ad-

vantage of target species availability or fishing quotas. For example, trawlers often fish for lobsters during warm months, and several gear types fish for tuna and swordfish during summer and fall. There were not enough responses from the various regions to separate out seasonal trends by region.

Nor were there enough responses to correlate specific habitat types with specific gear types. Of the two gear types used by the most respondents, trawls (Figure 5a) and hook and line (Figure 5b), both sets of respondents indicated that they fished all habitats. Trawlers preferred sand and mud habitats, although rocky and gravel bottoms are also fished by trawlers. Hook and line fishermen preferred rocky and gravel bottoms, sand to a lesser extent, and mud bottoms least of all. The capability to fish all bottom types exists, which reveals the susceptibility of all fish habitat to human impacts. Respondents indicated that scallop dredges (Figure 5c), gill nets, and lobster traps (Figure 5d) fished all habitats, as did trollers and "other gear" (primarily recreational gear).

Targeted Fish Species

Fishermen were asked on the questionnaire to characterize habitat type (rocky, gravel, sand, mud) and to indicate during which seasons they

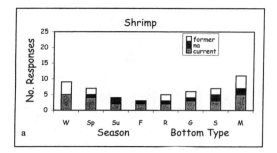

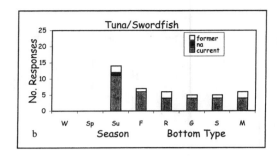

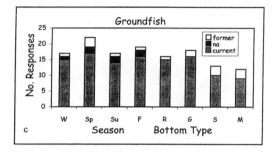

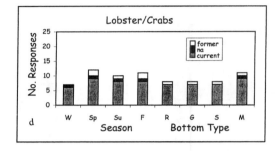

FIGURE 6.—Target fish species by season fished and bottom type for current and former fishermen. Season is defined as W (winter), Sp (spring), Su (summer), and F (fall). Bottom types are indicated as R (rocky), G (gravel), S (sand), and M (mud). No answer is indicated by na.

fished. These data reflect when and where fish aggregate or when they are available throughout the year (Figure 6). Some fisheries (e.g., squid) were noted as both site and season specific, reflecting spring spawning aggregations over sandy bottoms. Other target species, such as "groundfish," were generally fished over a variety of habitat types throughout the year (Figure 6c). Tuna and swordfish, groundfish, and lobsters and crabs (Figures 6b, 6c, and 6d) were the most popular fisheries among respondents, particularly in the northwest Atlantic Ocean. Shrimp (6a) was a popular fishery among respondents representing the Gulf of Mexico and northwest Atlantic Ocean, with a wide diversity of habitats fished. Because only one questionnaire was submitted to account for the 75 shrimp fishermen of the Louisiana Intercoastal City, the number of shrimp fishermen represented is larger than indicated in Figure 6a.

The questionnaire indicated that fewer scallop fishermen are active today (Figure 5c), which reflects, in part, closures on Georges Bank of scallop fishing grounds and lowered catch over the past several years (USDOC 1996)[1]. Groundfish

catch has also decreased over the past decade in New England, and although biomass appears to be recovering on Georges Bank, this recovery has not occurred throughout the Gulf of Maine (NEFSC 1998). Although dogfish are often cited as having replaced depleted groundfish stocks in terms of biomass, few fishermen responding to our survey targeted dogfish or other sharks. Whiting and hake, halibut, herring and mackerel, and squid were fished by some but not all respondents. A number of "other" fish species, such as rockfish, sablefish, and monkfish, were mentioned by only one of the respondents. As noted earlier, the responses are heavily weighted toward New England fisheries.

Questionnaire results indicated a stronger correlation between season and specific targeted species than fishing gear and specific targeted species, although for several species there were too few responses to draw definitive conclusions. Squid are most heavily fished in the spring and summer, and tuna and swordfish (Figure 6b) are heavily fished in the summer and fall. Fishermen also indicated that they fish some habitats for specific species, for example, fine-grained sediments for shrimp (Figure 6a), squid, and whiting. Most other species appear to be evenly distributed through all habitat categories, according to questionnaire results. Several lob-

[1] See also http://www.st.nmfs.gov/commercial/landings/qc_runc.html, an online database maintained by the National Marine Fisheries Service, Northeast Fisheries Science Center.

ster fishermen noted that they previously caught lobsters in rocky and gravel habitats but that they currently fish in sandy and muddy environments as well.

Groundfish, including cod, haddock, and flounder, are the fish species most often targeted by New England fishermen and fishermen from other regions. The distribution of fishing gear types used for capturing groundfish indicated that 16 respondents fished with hook and line, 9 trawled, and 5 used gill nets.

Habitat, Effects on Habitat, and Possible Causes

The next series of questions (questions 6–15) focused on fishermen's perspectives on habitat, changes in fish productivity, and changes in habitat over time. Recording fishermen's responses makes it possible to evaluate consistency in observations and general conclusions and compare these observations and conclusions to conventional wisdom. When information from fishermen is independently verified, opportunities for challenging conventional wisdom may arise, as well as suggestions for new scientific research directions. Differences between fishermen's local knowledge and scientific information may indicate a lack of sufficient scientific research or in some cases may suggest that educational outreach efforts are needed to offer fishermen a different explanation for their observations.

The questions solicited input on possible causes of physical (including climate and weather), biological (target species and bycatch), and human-induced (habitat alteration, pollution, and overfishing) changes observed. The questions provided a partial checklist of possible causes for each category and an opportunity to respond to a series of open-ended questions about perceived changes in fisheries and habitat.

Most respondents were consistent throughout the questionnaire in their identification of what they considered to be the significant factors affecting habitat. For example, if a fisherman thought that pollution was the primary cause of habitat alteration and fishery decline, he consistently noted this throughout the series of questions. Table 2 lists the "most significant factor(s)" that fishermen identified as affecting habitat (see question 8 in Figure 1). Because fishermen could indicate more than one response, the total number of responses is greater than the number of fishermen surveyed.

Of 42 respondents to this question, 22 identified mobile gear (including otter trawls, scallop dredges, and rockhoppers) as the most significant factor affecting habitat. Eleven respondents singled out habitat destruction and wetland loss separately from fishing gear effects. Eleven identified overfishing as the most significant factor affecting fishing, and eleven respondents also identified pollution (including lower water quality and nutrient loading) as the most significant. Additional factors cited reflected regional differences or an awareness on the part of individual fishermen. For example, freshwater discharge and changes in salinity and weather were cited by fishermen from the Gulf of Mexico or southeast United States, whereas chemical contaminants and noxious algae blooms were identified by fishermen from urban areas. Of the 13 current trawlers who responded, none identified mobile gear as a problem.

The next question (question 9 in Figure 1) asked fishermen to identify changes in target species over time. Of the 43 surveys returned, 27 noted a decrease in one or more target species (Table 3). Eight respondents thought fish had moved elsewhere, five thought target species were increasing, five reported no change, five thought target fish had been replaced by other species, two noted that the increases and decreases were cyclical over time, and two did not respond. One fisherman cited decrease in catch per unit effort as the criterion used to evaluate fish abundance. Two respondents (including the representative of the southern shrimpers) noted that changes

TABLE 2.—Most significant factors affecting habitat as identified by 42 fishermen. (Several fishermen identified more than one significant factor.)

Most significant factor	Responses
Trawls, roller gear, scallop dredges, and mobile gear	22
Habitat destruction and wetland loss	11
Pollution	11
Number of boats and technology (overfishing)	11
Ghost gill nets, drag and longlines	10
Freshwater discharge	4
Weather	3
Chemical pollutants	3
Bycatch	2
Noxious algae (*Pfiesteria, Desmarestia*)	2
Fish food availability (as bait)	1
Predation increase	1

TABLE 3.—Responses to question about observed changes in target species.

Response category	Respondents
Decrease	27
Moved	8
No increase	5
Increase	5
Replaced	5
No answer	2

in abundance varied with environmental conditions. New England fishermen observed that fish size has decreased over time such that large breeders are rarely caught these days. Longline fishermen in Massachusetts claimed that gillnetters were occupying areas that long-liners traditionally fished, thus restricting the access of long-liners to prime fishing areas and thereby limiting their catch.

Species identified as increasing were small flounder (graysole), monkfish, cod (attributed to conservation efforts), pollock, and haddock. Respondents that identified decreasing fish abundance did not always identify their target species, but rockfish were observed to decrease off California, with salmon and albacore tuna showing no change. Increases in lobsters on smooth bottoms were attributed to decreased cod and flatfish, and some of the decrease in cod and flatfish

was attributed to increased striped bass that prey on juvenile groundfish. Several respondents referred to overfishing, habitat degradation (especially of spawning areas), improved technology, and predation by seals and birds as additional causes for observed decreases in target species. In addition, incidences of sores and lesions on fish were increasing, according to some respondents.

The next series of questions (questions 10–13 in Figure 1) asked fishermen to focus on biological changes, environmental trends, signs of pollution, and causes of changes to the habitats of species they fish. The responses are presented in the following four sections (Figure 7). Respondents were fairly consistent in their responses regarding observed changes and their perceptions of causation.

Biological Changes

The top three biological changes identified by fishermen were habitat productivity, bycatch, and fish health followed by bottom organisms, target species, and "other" changes (Figure 7b). Written comments on the questionnaires elaborated on these responses. (See Appendix for comments excerpted from the open-ended questions on the survey.) Changes in fish health reported by respondents were based on observed increases in numbers of tumors,

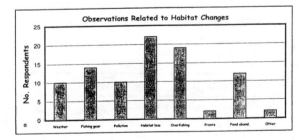

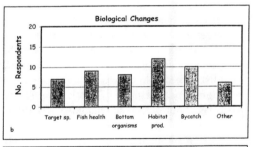

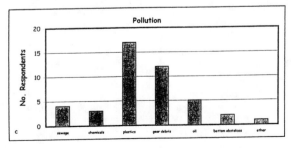

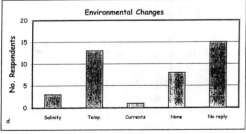

FIGURE 7.—Number of survey respondents who made observations related to (a) habitat, (b) biological, (c) pollution, and (d) environmental changes.

parasites, and lesions, and these changes were reported by fishermen from the southern and northern United States. The presence of slime eels was identified as an indicator of "featureless" habitats, and one respondent ascribed the term "desert" to areas where habitat features are lost. Loss of kelp and replacement of kelp by "green slime," presence of a noxious alga *Desmarestia viridis,* and absence of life or living creatures on rocks compared to previous observations were also noted. Several fishermen cited in their written comments bycatch, mortality, and loss of breeders as important biotic changes.

Environmental Changes

Over half the respondents did not reply or indicated no changes in salinity, temperature, currents, or other environmental factors (Figure 7d). Although 12 of the 43 respondents identified temperature as increasing over time, especially during the summer, only a few respondents suggested that fish productivity was related to temperature changes. Individuals had specific observations regarding temperature or offered reasons for temperature changes. One fisherman noted that temperatures have stayed about the same, another identified solar cycles of 33 years as affecting sea temperature, and another reported actual temperatures, e.g., in Cape Cod Bay during "hot" summers, temperatures ranged from 68 to 72°F during the months of July, August, and September. Some fishermen who indicated warmer temperatures (but did not report specific temperatures) related these changes to a lag in the onset of the normal fishing season, and some fishermen suggested that bluefish *Pomatomus saltatrix* presence may be related to temperature.

Four fishermen from the southern United States identified salinity changes, including freshwater discharge, as important environmental factors that affected their fisheries. Increases in siltation were noted by one fisherman. One of the fishermen who did not identify trends noted that major storms (e.g., gales and nor'easters) affect large areas of the Gulf of Maine and, consequently, fish populations. For example, according to one respondent, the Halloween storm (gale) of 1991 coated the bottom to 20 fathoms with marsh hay, and another fisherman, probably a nearshore fisherman, reported that the October 1996 rainstorm caused salinity levels to decrease by 50%, which affected fish and shellfish. Several fishermen noted that changes in salinity, temperature, and currents are normal and that those environmental factors change from year to year.

Pollution

Responses to questions about pollution issues exhibited consistency regardless of where in the United States the respondents fished. A majority identified plastics and marine debris as the predominant form of pollution (Figure 7c). Seventeen fishermen identified the presence of plastics as pervasive and increasing, although a few fishermen thought plastic and marine debris were not so pervasive. Fishermen from two different regions noted that plastics and a scummy sheen were noticeable on calm days. Twelve fishermen identified as problematic gear debris such as gill nets, dragger nets, lobster traps, and longlines. One southern fisherman noted illegal sludge dumping, and three fishermen from two different regions attributed reduced fish catch to "bad" algal blooms (*Pfiesteria* in North Carolina and *Desmarestia* in Narragansett Bay). Others suggested that land-based overdevelopment affected Georges Bank productivity. Loss of marsh areas and increases or decreases in freshwater flow were associated with diminished fish catch in the Gulf of Mexico. Several fishermen again mentioned draggers as being a primary cause of reduced catches and suggested that gill nets "cause" cod to leave certain areas of the ocean. One fisherman noted that chemical pollution is unseen and expressed concern that sex-hormone mimics and dioxins were affecting nearshore spawning areas.

Changes in Fish Habitat and Species

Although fishermen were not asked to rank different factors affecting fish habitat, responses to question 13 (see Figure 1) provide an indication of what is considered important (Figure 7a). Habitat loss, either anthropogenic (e.g., from gear impacts, human alteration of shorelines) or natural (environmental), and overfishing were most frequently cited as the two major reasons for fish habitat and species changes, with fishing gear and lowered prey abundance as the third and fourth most-cited reasons. Weather, one of the next most-mentioned causes, was cited as altering marshes in the south (important for shrimp fishing) and causing storms that killed lobsters in the north. Overfishing was specifically identified as problematic in the herring fishery and several other fisheries. Mobile gear was identified as causing changes in bottom features, for example, "smoothing" the bottom by reducing peaks from 10 fathoms to less than 2 fathoms and destroying pipe clay that serves as fish habitat.

Fishing Gear Effects

The last two questions of section two (numbers 14 and 15 in Figure 1) focused on observed habitat changes and asked fishermen to identify how their gear affects the seafloor, including bottom features. Of the 35 fishermen who responded to this question, 10 stated that their fishing gear affected the bottom, although minimally, and 25 stated their gear did not. Long-liners reported that they retrieved several types of bottom features including mussels, lemons (stalked sea squirts), pumpkins (sea squirts), figs (sea squirts) and rocks with barnacles and calcareous tubeworms, weeds, and other life. One fisherman noted that these features were returned to nearly the same area from which they were retrieved. Two groundfish fishermen noted that they picked up prey items including starfish, worms, clams, small fish (herring and mackerel), squid, and small bottom-dwelling invertebrates. All seven long-liners from New England noted that biota are less abundant than in the past and that rocks are nearly devoid of life in current hauls.

One trawler stated that he rarely picks up bottom features and identified plastics and debris as the material causing habitat problems. Louisiana fishermen observed oil debris and vegetation from storms in their trawls. Shrimp fishermen from Louisiana noted that their gear caused an increase in turbidity. Because tables and graphs do not adequately capture such perspectives and insights of fishermen, gear-related responses to the open-ended survey questions and questions at focus-group meetings are summarized in the Appendix.

Documentation of Observations

Not all fishermen answered questions 16 and 17 (Figure 1). Thirteen fishermen did not respond, and several fishermen responded to question 17 but did not indicate what if any documentation they had. Twenty-two fishermen noted that they had coordinate headings for habitat locations. Twenty-three fishermen indicated that they maintained logbooks. Eleven and ten fishermen, respectively, kept charts and tow plots, and nine had videos of habitat. Four fishermen that marked "others" in question 16 indicated that they had photographs, samples of algae, and invertebrate specimens. Of the respondents, 24 stated that they would share information with scientists and others, 11 did not answer, two stated that they would not share information, and four stated that they might share information.

Discussion

Collective Knowledge

Fishermen's nearly daily forays onto fishing grounds over the course of many years lead the more observant among them to notice changes over time, especially in their target species. Sometimes the passing on of logbooks from one generation to the next extends the time line of observations. Even fishermen who are not themselves observant are usually interested enough in their business to learn from fellow fishermen what they have noticed.

The collective knowledge of active fishermen generally includes observations about the extremes in their own and others' catch (e.g., largest examples of the species, physical or coloration oddities, sores or lesions). Changes in average sizes of their target species, size of their catch, migration patterns, and sites of successful harvests are also noted. Fishermen know when spawning occurs, and often they know where juveniles are found. They often know bottom features from their bathymetric recordings, know what features they retrieve with gear, and know how some of these bottom features have changed in time and space. For every noted change, fishermen have an explanation based on their observations, impressions, and perceptions of the change, which are colored by their values or culture and may or may not be scientifically defensible. The challenge is to develop a reporting mechanism that is consistent among fishermen and useful to fisheries managers.

This project has revealed that many fishermen have documented their observations about habitat and changes to habitat caused by fishing gear or other effects. The question still to be answered is to what extent can fishermen's data be used in the identification of EFH for fishery management plans (FMPs) as required under the Magnuson-Stevens Act. Specifically, we would like to know what data are needed and whether fishermen can provide these data.

Fishery management plans rely on quantitative data. Many of the fishermen's observations are qualitative. Examination of the questionnaire responses regarding biological components of the ecosystem, physical and climatological changes, and human-induced activities suggests that some observations lend themselves more than others to quantification and inclusion in FMPs. The following sections identify types of information currently available from fishermen that can be used to help identify EFH and stress the need to "train" a cadre of fishermen to record data in a standardized format for use by fisheries managers.

Seafloor Data

Fisheries managers attempting to identify EFH require habitat data for each life history stage of fishes. In New England, these data are being analyzed for 10-min squares, which will become the preliminary locus of EFH for each species. Fishermen, particularly fixed-gear fishermen, use a much smaller scale of reference than 10-min squares. Hook and line fishermen from Chatham, Massachusetts in a focus-group meeting drew areas on nautical charts indicating where they found cod, haddock, lobsters, and flounders. In addition, the fishermen were able to indicate specific habitat features such as peaks, pipe clay, large mussel beds, and other areas where specific invertebrate types were associated with the bottom. All of the different named areas fall within one of the 10-min squares, suggesting that the scope of EFH designations will ignore important details about significant habitat features.

Every fishing gear has some impact on seafloor habitat. Most types of gear pick up bottom features when retrieved, although fixed gear seems to be less intrusive than mobile gear. Some bottom features can be returned to the spots from which they were taken. Gill nets and trawls can pick up pipe clay, and hooks can pick up mussels, squirts, figs, barnacle-covered rocks, sea cucumbers, sponge coral, and lemons. Trawlers can pick up large pieces of bottom (e.g., rock) and a great variety of features depending on the vessel's size (weight), horsepower, and rigging.

Fixed-gear fishermen, especially those who use hook and line, noted changes in bottom features as particularly troublesome for their fishery because the formerly complex bottom attracted and provided pollock, catfish, monkfish, halibut, hake, cusk, and haddock to their gear. Several fishermen expressed concern over the diminishment of bottom features and noted that rocks brought up by their gear no longer are covered with living creatures and plant life as they once were. According to one respondent, "Hard, flat places don't produce any more."

Observations by fixed-gear fishermen most frequently focused on changes in bottom structure. Several fishermen reported that "peaks," that is, sea mounts of gravel material 10–12 fathoms in height, had been reduced to mounds of less than 2 fathoms. This type of information is particularly useful because smoothing of the seafloor can be verified by comparing depth soundings from the past with current depth soundings. Similarly, assuming fishing coordinates provided by fishermen are reasonably accurate, it should be possible to verify changes in benthic communities reported by fishermen. An example of an observation that could be verified is the loss of areas of stalked sea squirts (ascidians), nonstalked sea squirts, and anemones (referred to as figs and lemons) and the reduction in the reported "big mussels" bed. All of these areas off the coast of Cape Cod are regions where large breeder fish had been captured, but today are absent. Although such changes in fish size are verifiable, given the observational nature of the data it is not possible to demonstrate cause and effect. This is one of the limitations of anecdotal information.

The importance of identifying questions or hypotheses and requisite data as well as developing a methodology for gathering needed data cannot be overstated. Fishermen themselves are a valuable resource, and tapping their knowledge has potential benefits for science, for EFH, and ultimately for sustainable fisheries. One example of tapping the knowledge of fishermen is the work done by Madeleine Hall-Arber, Kevin St. Martin, and Christopher Dyer with the Gloucester Fishermen's Wives Association in 1997 to collect oral histories from fishermen (Ames 1997; Hall-Arber, St. Martin, and Dyer, unpublished data). These oral histories in part detailed what the fishermen knew about habitat. In addition, as has been mentioned, some fishermen involved in the habitat survey project described in this chapter exhibited a keen awareness of specific changes in the environment, biological changes in their target species, and changes in the amount of marine debris and plastics encountered, and these fishermen have come up with various explanations for the changes. Individual notations on charts made by focus-group participants are being digitized as of this writing for analysis by geographic information systems.

Biological Data

On the questionnaires, few of the fishermen identified bycatch as species other than nontarget or juvenile fish species. During the focus-group meetings, however, it was possible to expand the discussion so that fishermen could identify benthic organisms associated with fish habitat. Whether these communities of benthic organisms identified by fishermen serve as refuge areas, provide food, or contribute to some other component of fish habitat can be elucidated by research. Certainly, however, relationships between benthic organisms and fish are important habitat considerations, particularly if one can associate specific fish species or size classes with specific benthic organisms.

The survey did not ask fishermen to identify prey items, but anecdotal information offered during one of the focus-group meetings suggested that prey data could be gathered from fishermen. Fishermen who gut their fish and observe the contents of their catches' stomachs could preserve samples and record what they observe. Similarly, asking fishermen to identify invertebrate species caught by fishing gear is another potentially valuable source of information. There are several user-friendly identification books that fishermen can use as guides. Using a field guide, figs and lemons (fishermen's terms) can be identified to phyletic group as anemones and ascidians, if not to genus and species. Similarly, encrusting organisms on rocks and algae can be more accurately identified by fishermen using guides. Some fishermen could be trained to collect data quantitatively and record observations, for example, collecting otoliths or measuring, counting, and tallying nonfish bycatch.

Physical and Chemical Data

To the extent that meteorological and physical data are useful to fish habitat management, fishermen can add significantly to the database. Correlating physical oceanographic data with fishing success is complicated because of seasonal changes and annual variability. Fishermen participating in this study either did not observe any physical and chemical changes or noted changes and related them to seasonal, annual, or longer-term variability. One fisherman related changes in fish abundance to solar cycles, and a few related changes in fish abundance to El Niño. Several fishermen, particularly from the Gulf of Mexico and southeast United States, related changes in shrimp and fish abundance to meteorological events (e.g., rainfall and river flow) and land-based human activities (development and destruction of marshes). A project recently funded by a federal Saltonstall-Kennedy grant will address the feasibility of using fishing vessels as scientific platforms with a variety of equipment that will passively collect meteorological and physical oceanographic data (C. Goudey, Massachusetts Institute of Technology Sea Grant College Program, personal communication). Correlation of such data with productivity will require a long-term commitment to both passive data collection and active tallying of catch and other parameters dictated by working hypotheses.

Pollution and Productivity Data

Fishermen from the Louisiana Intercoastal City noted the relationship between runoff and fishing success. Fisheries biologists have also correlated runoff, salinity, currents, and fronts to biological productivity, but the majority of survey respondents did not make the same observations. The problem may be one of scale, both in time and space. Fishermen are apt to notice changes in parameters that are part of the fishing process and notable in their fishing cycle.

If scientists wished to test hypotheses examining on local, short-term scales the effects of physical parameters on fish productivity, fishermen could easily assist with data collection. Hypotheses that attempted to correlate environmental changes with productivity of fish that live 5–10 years and cover thousands of miles in range, however, would need a much longer time commitment on the part of both scientists and fishermen.

Whatever the premise, fishermen can record temperature, salinity, currents, and other meteorological conditions related to productivity with great precision today given the availability of sophisticated equipment. However, data collection is only useful if it is needed to answer questions and test hypotheses. Fisheries managers, the NMFS, and Councils must identify what data are needed.

Fishermen often tout pollution effects, especially plastics and gear debris, as a significant cause of declining fish populations. Oil, chemicals, and sewage are identified by fishermen as problems to a lesser extent. However, with the exception of catastrophic events such as major oil spills, observations of fishermen are difficult to use in correlating (either quantitatively or qualitatively) declining fish abundance with pollution.

The mandatory keeping of logbooks in current federal management regimes indicates an awareness of the potential value of fishermen's observations for management decisions related to pollution and fish productivity. The state of Maine has already begun to base management decisions in part on fishermen's local knowledge. The timing of the 1999 closures due to spawning and juvenile cod distribution, for example, is based, in part, on information gathered by Ted Ames (1997) during his efforts to collect Maine fishermen's oral histories.

Testing of fishermen's observations has been endorsed by several Maine scientists. Daniel Shick with the Maine Department of Marine Resources noted that shrimp fishermen's claims about the absence of small male shrimp in certain areas during certain months has proved correct (D. Shick, Maine Department of Marine Resources, personal communication). The University of Maine's Robert Steneck recently described learning from lobster fishermen that lobster larvae settle in rocky areas west of Penobscot, Maine, while mature females congregate east of Penobscot. Steneck said that he would not have known where to look for these larvae and females without having spoken to knowledgeable lobstermen (R. Steneck, University of Maine, personal communication).

Another area that offers potential for data collection involving fishermen, but no clear context, is the observation of marine debris and plastics in the ocean. Plastics and gear debris are tangible objects that are picked up with gear and observed visually. As society's awareness of the potential impacts of pollution has grown, individual observations may also have become more acute. This shift does not necessarily mean that there has been a measurable change in the amount of pollution but may simply reflect a change in observation due to awareness. Although such observations provide crude data, establishing a routine to quantify pollution observations (modeled on coastal cleanup efforts, for example) would result in more-reliable data.

Observations of sewage releases and increased turbidity that may directly or indirectly affect fish and prey items are types of data that are less easy to collect. Such observations warrant further examination, if not by the NMFS then by agencies that regulate water quality. Even when plumes are not visible, reports of noxious algal booms such as *Pfiesteria* and *Desmarestia* have been associated with increased nutrients. Fishermen can report on observed pollution sources and distribution of algae or on the effects of pollution and algae on habitat and fish.

Documentation of Fishermen's Knowledge

Several approaches were used in this project to solicit fishermen's knowledge and information on habitat, fishing gear effects, and changes in fish populations. Several types of documentation for this knowledge and information were identified, and the majority of fishermen involved with the project were willing to share that information. The following sections present several observations regarding the approaches that we used to document fishermen's knowledge. In addition, the following sections evaluate the effectiveness of these approaches in gathering data.

Focus Groups

We found that focus groups were the most useful technique used to gather habitat information from fishermen. As part of the focus-group meetings, we asked the fishermen to mark nautical charts to identify specific habitats, including juvenile areas, spawning areas, and bottom features. The primary difficulty associated with this technique was the time it took to gather fishermen together to attend focus groups. Time has become an issue for meetings with fishermen because proliferating meetings are likely to directly affect their fishing practices. The focus-group method itself was time-consuming as well compared to the distribution of questionnaires, but the product of focus-group meetings has potentially more management value.

Documentation

More fishermen than anticipated agreed to share their logbooks, marked nautical charts, and plotter charts with scientists. The difficulty in utilizing these types of information will be fully realized during the follow-up to these offers. Before tackling the diversity of types of documentation, decisions should be made about what information from these sources would be useful to science and what mechanism could be used to transfer the information to a data set that could be incorporated into both scientific analysis and management decision making.

Questionnaires

The questionnaires we used were particularly helpful in documenting time lines for individuals' participation in various fisheries, both in terms of years and seasons associated with different target species and gear. The questionnaires also helped us distinguish different points of view among the fishermen. In addition, the questionnaires aided in the quantification of observations that fishermen have made about environmental changes, particularly changes in bottom features. Such observations provide insights into what the various fishermen believe are significant factors in the fishing context. The quality of these observations has two-fold significance. The factors may or may not be truly important to fishing productivity, but they certainly suggest some areas of research that should be undertaken. In addition, the clarity of some of the fishermen's observations indicates that these individuals could be trained to collect data that would provide a welcome supplement to the less-than-optimal number of government assessment cruises that can be undertaken given the costs of such cruises.

Again, it is the follow-up to this project that will prove its value. Fisheries scientists, especially those serving the needs of managers, need to think seriously about what information would help improve predictive models and what kind of training fishermen would need to provide that missing information. In addition, a mechanism for handling data and incorporating data from fishermen into the science and management processes would be needed.

Outreach

In order for the techniques highlighted above to be applicable beyond the small segment of the fishing industry from which we were able to elicit information, it will be necessary to better publicize the new significance of habitat to management. In addition, fishermen must be assured that their data will be used in aggregate form to minimize revelations that would help competitors. Fishermen also must be convinced that their knowledge is considered valuable.

Fishermen's Reluctance to Get Involved

Both fishermen and those who work with fishermen have been very concerned about the Magnuson-Stevens Act's mandate for Councils to amend their fishery management plans to include EFH considerations by October 1998. Many have feared that the short amount of time allotted to identifying EFH and amending FMPs would result in haphazard regulation based on incomplete information that would address neither the needs of the fish stocks nor the fishing industry.

Nevertheless, many fishermen have been reluctant to volunteer information about bottom habitat because this knowledge is considered proprietary information upon which their success in fishing depends. As in any business, fishing industry members are competitive with each other and reluctant to divulge specialized knowledge that could provide their competitors with an advantage. In addition, some fishermen fear that habitat issues will be used to further restrict their fishing effort, making it impossible to survive financially. Therefore, they have little incentive to provide information that could be used against them.

For example, not far from Stellwagen Bank, inshore waters off Plymouth, Massachusetts are characterized by a complex mix of "good bottom" and boulders. The best fishermen among the small draggers of the Plymouth-based fleet weave in and out of the boulders, managing to avoid hanging up and still finding fish while recording their tows and movements on plotter charts. These charts become a kind of "currency" that is traded among friends and family (St. Martin, personal communication). The charts might also be said to function as a limited-entry mechanism, because without the detailed information about where to find the fish and how to avoid ripping nets, few newcomers can make a living.

Another problem with incorporating fishermen's knowledge is that not all fishermen are in accord with each other. For example, hook and line fishermen that were part of this study pointed out that they have often testified about the negative impacts on rocky habitat of mobile gear, but they feel that the New England Fishery Management Council is composed of too many representatives of mobile-gear fisheries and therefore will never restrict such gear.

A strong, coordinated, educational outreach effort for fishermen is needed. At the best of times, gathering fishermen is difficult and time-consuming, although there are many people around the country who, given time and financial support, would be able and willing to do so. We have found during other fieldwork projects that rapid assessment techniques work best in situations where there groundwork is already laid. The EFH issue is so new and its impacts (both positive and negative) are so poorly understood that the immediate reaction by fishermen to the EFH policy is antipathy, negativity, and suspicion. With time and effort, that reaction could be changed and valuable information could be obtained.

Conclusions and Recommendations

Based on our questionnaire responses and focus-group meetings, currently available information can be used to assist with the identification of essential fish habitat. If a framework for using and managing data were established, fishermen's local knowledge could be valuable to the management process of identifying habitat and could contribute to achieving sustainable fisheries. Fisheries managers, with the assistance of advisory groups, should identify the types of information needed. Without such a framework, data collected by fishermen or others have limited value. We envision a cadre of trained fishermen that can assist in the following six ways:

1. Fishermen have local knowledge of the seafloor, habitat structure, and fish distribution that complements NMFS surveys. We recommend that the NMFS, the Councils, and state marine fisheries agencies identify a process (e.g., focus-group meetings, workshops, and other opportunities) for fishermen to identify habitats and share knowledge about distribution of fish and the structure of habitats.
2. Some fishermen are willing to collect information that facilitates the identification of habitat. We recommend that protocols for identifying prey items, bycatch (including invertebrates), and other information be established to assist with EFH identification. For example, it might prove valuable to develop a one- or two-page protocol for collecting fish gut contents throughout the year in different locations.
3. Focus-group meetings and oral histories reveal information about the present and the past. Such knowledge is invaluable for understanding changes over time, including weather, climate, and human-induced changes.
4. Fishermen should have the opportunity to produce a video with underwater footage of habitat as they understand it. Habitat documentation provided by the video could be supplemented with information from focus-group meetings or interviews with individual fishermen.
5. The questionnaire used for this study can be modified to ask respondents to describe specific aspects of habitat to support EFH requirements. The questionnaire also can be supplemented with additional questions that broaden the survey's scope as well as with small charts for respondents to note where they fish, what they observe about habitats, and which habitats they fish for target species.
6. Fishermen's local knowledge should be formally collected and independently reviewed, and findings based on this knowledge should be incorporated into the management process.

Acknowledgments

The authors thank all the fishermen who participated in this study, especially members of the Cape Cod Fish and Hook Association; Tay Evans; and members of the Sea Grant Extension Service, especially Rollie Barnaby and James Murray. The project was supported by a grant from the American Fisheries Society.

References

Acheson, J. M. 1975. The lobster fiefs: economic and ecological effects of territoriality in the Maine lobster fishery. Human Ecology 3:183–207.

Ames, E. P. 1997. Cod and haddock spawning grounds in the Gulf of Maine. Island Institute, Rockland, Maine.

Auster, P. J., and R. W. Langton. 1999. The effects of fishing on fish habitat. Pages 150–187 in L. R. Benaka, editor. Fish habitat: essential fish habitat and rehabilitation. American Fisheries Society, Symposium 22, Bethesda, Maryland.

Bellon, M. R. 1995. Farmers' knowledge and sustainable agroecosystem management: an operational definition and an example from Chiapas, Mexico. Human Organization 54(3)263–272.

Berkes, F. 1986. Local level management and the commons problem: a comparative study of Turkish coastal fisheries. Marine Policy 10:215–229.

Cushing, D. H. 1975. Marine ecology and fisheries. Cambridge University Press, Cambridge, UK.

Dahl, C. 1988. Traditional marine tenure: a basis for artisanal fisheries management. Marine Policy 12:40–48.

Davis, A. 1984. Property rights and access management in the small boat fishery: a case study from Southwest Nova Scotia. Pages 133–164 in C. Lamson and A. J. Hanson, editors. Atlantic decision-making case studies. Dalhousie Ocean Studies Programme, Halifax, Nova Scotia.

Dorsey, E., and J. Pederson, editors. 1998. Effects of fishing on the sea floor in New England. Conservation Law Foundation, Boston.

Durrenberger, E. P., and G. Palsson. 1987. Ownership at sea: fishing territories and access to sea resources. American Ethnologist 14(3):508–523.

Goode, G. B. 1887. American fishes, a popular treatise upon the game, and food fishes of North America with especial reference to habits, and methods of capture. (Revised edition by Theodore Gill published in 1903) L.C. Page & Company, Boston.

Holt, S. J. 1981. The food resources of the ocean. Pages 201–213 in Life in the sea, readings from Scientific American. Freeman, San Francisco.

Johannes, R. E. 1989. Introduction. Pages 5–8 in R. E. Johannes, editor. Traditional ecological knowledge: a collection of essays. International Union for the Conservation of Nature, Gland, Switzerland.

McGoodwin, J. 1984. Some examples of self-regulatory mechanisms in unmanaged fisheries. FAO Fisheries Report 289, Supplement.

Morren, G. E. B. 1995. Book review of traditional ecological knowledge: wisdom for sustainable development. American Anthropologist 97(1):174–175.

NEFSC (Northeast Fisheries Science Center). 1998. Report of the 27th Northeast Regional Stock Assessment Workshop (27th SAW). Stock Assessment Review Committee Consensus of Summary Assessments, NEFSC Reference Document 98-03. National Marine Fisheries Service, Woods Hole, Massachusetts.

NMFS (National Marine Fisheries Service). 1997. Magnuson-Stevens Act provisions: Essential Fish Habitat: interim final rule and request for comments. Federal Register [Docket No. 961030300–7238–04; I.D. 120996A]: 66531–66559.

NRC (National Research Council). 1998. Improving fish stock assessments. National Academy Press, Washington, D.C.

Palmer, C. 1993. Folk management, "soft evolutionism," and fishers' motives: implications for the regulation of the lobster fisheries of Maine and Newfoundland. Human Organization 52(4):414–420.

Pauly, D., V. Christensen, J. Dalsgaard, R. Froese, and F. Torres, Jr. 1998. Fishing down marine food webs. Science 279:860–863.

Ruddle, K. 1994. Local knowledge in the folk management of fisheries and coastal marine environments. Pages 160–206 in C. L. Dyer and J. R. McGoodwin, editors. Folk management in the world's fisheries: lessons for modern fisheries management. University Press of Colorado, Boulder.

Ruddle, K., E. Hviding, and R. E. Johannes. 1991. Customary marine tenure: an option for small-scale fisheries management. Center for Development Studies, No. 10/91, University of Bergen, Norway.

Russell-Hunter, W. D. 1970. Aquatic productivity. Macmillan Publishing, New York.

Ryther, J. H. 1969. Photosynthesis and fish production in the sea. Science 166:72–80.

USDOC (U.S. Department of Commerce). 1996. Fisheries of the United States, 1995. National Oceanic and Atmospheric Administration, National Marine Fisheries Service, U.S. Government Printing Office, Washington, D.C.

Appendix: Responses to Open-Ended Questions and Focus-Group Discussion Topics

Not every respondent chose to elaborate on the questions, but those who did commented on fishing impacts to habitat, nonfishing impacts, and some positive changes in fisheries over time. Some of their responses repeat what has been recorded, and presented elsewhere in this chapter, but classifying the responses in the following manner reiterates major perceptions, and reveals additional insights. Furthermore, this section includes some of the lengthier observations recorded during the focus groups.

Habitat

Defining

Important, perhaps essential, habitat is anything that has some variability in it, and in its structure. "It's living stuff, it breathes..." Mussels, lemons, and kelp are included in the respondents' concept of habitat.

Resident Fish

There are residential fish, and there are fish that travel through. Once the residential fish are gone, they are never coming back; "that's why that spot won't produce much anymore."

"This isn't the nursery anymore because the draggers destroyed it, now it's just a little lump. You can catch a box if no one's been poking at it for a week or so, which tells you they still swim through there, and they would settle if there was anything to hold them, but they don't. There must be nothing to eat."

Fishing Impacts (Overfishing)

Overfishing has led to decreases in stock abundance, and size of individual fish. Selective fishing is breeding a slower-growing fish of smaller size.

Gear Impacts

Bottom Features

Smoothing out of humps, and pinnacles, and loss of bottom features have been attributed to repeated towing of heavy gear, notably scallop dredging, and otter trawling (particularly street-sweeper gear, and rollers). This smoothing, and loss have meant that some previously productive areas are no longer productive, and spawning areas are thought to have been reduced. Some hard-bottom areas are showing signs of soft bottom (e.g., slime eels are showing up).

"The ridges, they're flat, they're plateaus, they've just leveled right off. Like the Hill of Giants, I'm like, 'Where is it?'"

"But how do you explain [site], they can't ruin it no matter what they do. You can step right behind them, and still catch them. We need more of that, whatever it is. They can't ruin it, they've been trying for 20 years."

One fishermen suggested that fish "travel in their own little roads, meandering through valleys, and around ridges," but that when the bottom is flattened, the fish's usual pattern of movement changes. Another explained that the currents are very strong in certain areas, especially where the current races through a channel. The complex habitat is essential there to protect the fish from having to expend a lot of energy fighting the current.

"There's not enough habitat for those fish to make a residence all summer long. When they come through, there's a big school of them, and they keep going. There's nothing to hold them in place."

Breaking up of mussels with heavy mobile gear attracts starfish.

Changes are said to have started to occur when the draggers got roller gear in the late 1970s and early 1980s.

Technology

Changes in technology have led to gear that has become too effective, according to some respondents. One respondent noted that although the fishermen might be catching twice as many fish, they are also discarding twice as many.

There is a lack of good, unfishable areas such as man-made reefs, and shipwrecks (that could act as reserves or "safe havens") because the changes in technology allow trawling in areas that were previously unfishable by mobile gear.

Quantity of Gear

Proliferation of gear (e.g., gill nets) was thought to cause cod to change migration patterns. Ghost gear that continues to fish after being lost was also cited. Also, if too many nets are deployed for a fisherman to tend every 12 to 24 hours, sand fleas, and other predators can ruin the catch, and cause the bottom to sour. (Some respondents complained that some gillnetters wastefully set out their nets principally to reserve a piece of bottom for future use. "What gives them the right to own a piece of bottom?") Nondecaying gear was thought to be a problem, as were untended commercial nets.

Repeated trawling over the same area does not allow that area to replenish.

Shrimp trawls are killing bycatch, dragging in waterways, and in the ocean nearshore zone in 15 to 30 ft of water, and destroying bottom.

Gear Conflicts

"If you drag a piece of hard bottom, you make it more productive for scallops. There's no place for scalloping, and groundfishing in the same spot, they don't coexist very well. We depend on the habitat to have fish. They depend on eradicating the habitat in order for scallops to be plentiful, and to catch more. They need it flat to be able to harvest them."

Nonfishing Impacts

Changes in Predator–Prey Relationships

Increases in the stripped bass population have pushed bluefish offshore. Bass also feed on juvenile lobsters throughout the lobsters' range, and take a toll on flounders.

Presence or absence of krill affects the movement of fish.

Baitfish reduction from bycatch or directed catch (e.g., midwater trawling for herring) has reduced the presence of food fish in some areas (especially Jeffreys Ledge).

Reduction in scavengers is a problem, for example, the fishery on slime eels changed the balance resulting in sour bottom in some areas.

Marine mammal, and bird populations have increased.

Decline in menhaden during *Pfiesteria*-related fish kills has caused a change in food, and prey abundance.

Other Changes

"I think the more significant changes I have seen occurred in the bay. The crabs are not as big, and plentiful. In the mid-seventies there were many blowfish, now there are few. Also, fiddler crabs have dwindled."

Weather and Temperature

The October storm of 1991 changed the bottom and killed tens of thousands of small lobsters in New Hampshire. El Niño and global warming affected water temperature (staying warmer), causing a lag in fishing seasons. Temperature is thought to be the cause of a smaller size-class of groundfish being caught. (Cape Cod Bay is now 68–72°F in July, August, and September.)

The October storm of 1990 coated the bottom (out to 20 fathoms) with marsh hay, and the rain storm in October 1996 halved salinity; both of these incidents caused problems for fish and shellfish.

Storm debris can be a problem in the Gulf of Mexico.

Cyclical Change

"Changes reflect 32–33-year cycles. Two I have observed are the same: sea turtles and dolphins died 1957–1958, also died 1987–1989. Fisheries were the same [in each] cycle."

The effects of solar cycles, the 18.6-year tide, and the Russell cycle that is 15 to 20 years in the North Atlantic are all important.

"The only thing one can count on is a constant state of flux. We have seen abundance, and lean years time and again."

"I have seen dramatic changes in habitat over a few (2–3) years. For example, there are certain areas where sponges comprised 90% of the bottom for years, then I no longer saw the sponges, they were replaced by sand dollars. Then, a year or two later, the sponges returned."

Chlorine and Other Chemical Pollutants

Despite conservation efforts, blackback flounder are diminishing due to habitat degradation. Haddock are no longer found nearshore in the Gulf of Maine. Flounders (blackbacks, and dabs) with cancerous lesions have been found. Dioxins and chemicals that mimic sex hormones are thought to be affecting spawning in the nearshore Gulf of Maine. Cumulative impacts rather than individual pollutants are thought to be causing problems.

Estrogen and similar chemicals, chlorine, and dioxins are problems.

River Flows

Salinity, and temperature of estuaries are affected by water discharge of the Mississippi, and Atchafalaya Rivers, and a hypoxic zone there is related to the nutrients of the river water.

Water-Quality Problems

Respondents cited as problematic water quality, particularly in estuaries; oil spills; waste spills from treatment plants; hog farm runoff; groundwater contamination; and insufficient sewage treatment from municipalities.

Upper Cape Fear River has an odor, and shad and menhaden have declined there.

Increases and decreases of viable oyster reefs are a function of water quality.

Air Pollution

Film on water after two or three calm days was thought to be air pollution that could be affecting larval stages.

Atmospheric deposition of nitrogen is a problem.

Coastal Marsh Loss

Coastal marsh and wetland loss (particularly important for shrimp and crabs) occurs due to saltwater intrusion, ship channels, and wind and wake erosion.

Invasive Species

Before the early 1970s there were no signs of *desmarestia vividus* in Narragansett Bay, but now close to 15% of the bay is covered. Pebbly bottom, a prime winter flounder spawning area, is now devoid of fish. This weed's roots can hold fast to these pebbles. Trawlers cannot tow over one minute in these areas without slowing down to a halt from the filling of their nets with this weed. There are not any fish in these areas, which were once some of the most productive.

Algae Blooms

Blooms have been increasingly common in the past 10 to 12 years.

There have been increased algae, and fish kills due to overfertilization.

Decline in menhaden during *Pfiesteria*-related fish kills has caused a change in food and prey abundance.

Debris

Plastic garbage and other debris (especially during high tides of full or new moon) are present.

Oil field-related debris caught off Louisiana in nets. Garbage and plastics wash ashore.

Positive Changes

Gear Changes

The Nordmore grate and larger mesh sizes have led to increases in fish size, less bycatch, and more grey sole and other flounders.

Responsibility

More fishermen bring in plastics (including deflated balloons) that have come up in nets for disposal ashore.

Impacts of Closed Areas

Haddock, rarely caught in 1992, has been abundant in certain times of the year from 1996 to 1998. Cod also appears to be more abundant. Pollock has increased.

Impacts of Fishing

"I've seen times scalloping if we go back and forth in the same area for 12 or 14 hours, fish will come to the area that were not there in the earlier tows."

Views on Enforcement and Management

Inequity

Trip limits are not enforced in Boston. Disagreement was expressed about the possibility of opening closed areas to scallopers: "If you disagree with closed area boundaries, just go in there enough and eventually they'll let you in." Gillnetters do not get charged for the time their nets are in the water (against their days-at-sea allocation), but "nets catch the fish, not the boats."

Habitat

"Don't let anyone into the closed areas until the whole habitat thing is figured out."

"I would also say the closures of thousands of square miles of bottom put undue pressure on the bottom that remains open, throwing off the natural balance. I would also argue that the closed habitat balance becomes overpopulated in some cases."

Economics

The fishermen recognize that there is a limit to the amount of fish that can be sustainably caught. Now, one noted, it is a question about "whether you want a few guys to make a lot or a lot of guys to make enough for a living." Another commented that "NMFS would like to put the small boats out of business, since management would be easy with maybe 15 big boats that they could track all the time."

Science

Single-species management is the greatest problem. No true science exists in current fishery management.

American Fisheries Society Symposium 22:212–223, 1999
© Copyright by the American Fisheries Society 1999

Importance of Benthic Habitat Complexity for Demersal Fish Assemblages

MICHEL J. KAISER

School of Ocean Sciences, University of Wales-Bangor
Menai Bridge, Gwynedd, LL59 5EY, UK

STUART I. ROGERS AND JIM R. ELLIS

The Centre for Environment, Fisheries and Aquaculture Science
Lowestoft Laboratory, Lowestoft, NR33 0HT, UK

Abstract.—Major amendments in 1996 to the Magnuson-Stevens Fishery Conservation and Management Act require fisheries managers to define "essential" fish habitat and address the impact of fishing gear in their management plans. However, before considering what might qualify as essential fish habitat, it is necessary to first understand the association between fish and their habitat. Some studies have already revealed subtle relationships between fishes and sediment type; however, this approach does not quantify habitat complexity. We undertook a large-scale survey of demersal fish populations and benthic communities in the southern North Sea and eastern English Channel. As in other studies, water depth was closely linked to the main dichotomy in assemblage composition. Flatfishes occurred in shallow water, whereas roundfishes and small shark species were found in deeper habitats. Within each of these two sample station groupings, the assemblages dichotomised further on the basis of habitat type and benthic faunal associations. Three further groupings were identified within the deepwater habitat. These groupings were characterized by the presence of rocks, broken shells, or a large biomass of sessile epibenthos. Small shark species were almost exclusive to habitats with shelly substrata. In contrast, the shallow-water habitats were topographically less complex with sessile epibenthos of a smaller biomass. Flatfishes that were visual predators were most closely associated with habitats with some sessile epibenthos, whereas sole *Solea solea*, which largely locate their prey using chemosensory cues, were more closely associated with the least complex habitat. Although these flatfish habitats are intensively fished by bottom trawls, the characteristic sessile epifauna are relatively fast growing and are probably able to withstand such disturbance. In contrast, the deepwater sessile communities had sessile epifauna of a greater biomass with some slow-growing species that would be more vulnerable to fishing disturbance. However, these habitats are seldom fished using invasive techniques.

Recent studies have demonstrated that fishing gears that are towed across the seabed lead to the perturbation of benthic fauna and habitats (for reviews see de Groot 1984; Messieh et al. 1991; Jones 1992; Dayton et al. 1995; Jennings and Kaiser 1998; Auster and Langton 1999, this volume). Towed bottom fishing gears are used to catch species that live in, on, or in association with the seabed. Typically, these gears are designed or rigged to remain in close contact with or dig into the seabed such that the catch rate of the target species is maximized. At the same time, benthic fauna are removed directly from the seabed or are killed, damaged, and exposed on the seabed, whereupon they are consumed by predators and scavengers (Kaiser and Spencer 1994; Ramsay et al. 1996, 1997). In the short term (days to months), fishing can result in a decrease in the abundance and diversity of benthic organisms and reduction in habitat complexity (Thrush et al. 1995; Currie and Parry 1996; Kaiser and Spencer 1996; Collie et al. 1997; Tuck et al. 1998). These effects are mani-

fested most clearly in stable habitats in which large emergent species such as sponges, corals, and bryozoans tend to predominate (Sainsbury 1987; Auster et al. 1996; Collie et al. 1997). These organisms increase the structural complexity of habitats and provide important refuges and feeding sites for juveniles and adults of some commercial species (Walters and Juanes 1993). Conversely, fishing activities cause relatively few changes to the structure of less-complex habitats. These habitats are typically found in shallow inshore waters and tend to have a sandy substratum with few large sessile epifauna. Although it is possible to detect short-term community changes in such habitats (Currie and Parry 1996; Kaiser and Spencer 1996), they recover relatively quickly from the effects of fishing disturbance (Kaiser et al. 1998). There is now evidence to show that the magnitude of the effects of fishing in different habitats varies relative to the background of natural disturbances encountered within each habitat (Sainsbury 1987; Auster et al. 1996; Kaiser and Spencer 1996;

Collie et al. 1997). As a result, the consequences of fishing disturbance for fish assemblages may vary depending upon how closely they are associated with a particular habitat and its vulnerability to that disturbance.

Recent amendments to the Magnuson-Stevens Fishery Conservation and Management Act require fisheries managers to define "essential fish habitat" (EFH) and address the impact of fishing gear in fishery management plans. In some instances, it is fairly simple to identify habitats that might be considered essential to the life history of some species. Such habitats include spawning and nursery areas, many of which are already protected (e.g., in the United Kingdom, see Rogers 1997). However, spawning activities and early development constitute a relatively small proportion of fish life histories, of which the remainder is spent acquiring energy and avoiding predators. Hence there is an urgent need to identify habitats that have an important or essential functional role for particular species or types of fish (e.g., piscivores, herbivores, and omnivores, or flatfish and roundfish) at other stages of their life history. Equally, we contend that it is important to identify the nonessential elements of fish habitat. A number of studies have examined the relationship between fish and shellfish assemblages and environmental variables (e.g., Overholtz and Tyler 1985; Smale et al. 1993). Although such environmental parameters are good correlates of certain fish assemblages, they do not necessarily define the essential features of a specific habitat; rather, they constitute a component of that habitat. Habitat structure and composition appear to be important criteria for some fish species (e.g., Sainsbury 1987; Gibson and Robb 1992). Many studies have already demonstrated the relationship between flatfish species and sediment particle composition of the seabed, which may be more important than the occurrence of associated epibenthic structures or fauna that occur in that habitat (e.g., Gibson and Robb 1992; Rogers 1992). Hence, a specific particle-size composition may be essential for flatfish, whereas the presence of large sessile epifauna or rocky substrata might be considered nonessential. In contrast, there is good evidence to suggest that structural complexity can have important implications for the survival of roundfishes (e.g., Walters and Juanes 1993).

Habitat complexity is a product of the surface topography of the substratum and the sessile epifauna that grow upon it. Reef-forming organisms can result in habitats of very high complexity providing a multitude of refuges for a diverse range of species (e.g., Peattie and Hoare 1981; Kaiser et al. 1998). More subtle features such as sand ridges and pits created by the feeding or burrowing action of benthic fauna may provide shelter for bottom-dwelling fish species (e.g., Auster et al. 1997). Bottom-fishing activities are capable of greatly reducing habitat complexity by either direct modification of the substratum or removal of the fauna that contribute to surface topography (Jennings and Kaiser 1998; Auster and Langton 1999). Hence, degradation of habitat complexity by fishing activities may lead to changes in the associated fish assemblages (e.g., Sainsbury et al. 1997).

Surprisingly, there have been few attempts to investigate the relationships between fish and benthic assemblages and habitat structure. The sampling gear used on fisheries surveys (usually an otter trawl) is generally considered unsuitable for sampling benthic invertebrates. However, surveys of flatfish communities in the seas of northwestern Europe are undertaken using beam trawls (Rogers et al. 1998). Beam trawls are highly efficient sampling devices for both flatfishes and mobile and sessile invertebrates (Cruetzberg et al. 1987; Rogers and Lockwood 1989; Kaiser et al. 1994) and thus provide an opportunity to quantitatively investigate the relationships between fish and benthic fauna.

We have analyzed data collected as part of a standard groundfish survey that included an analysis of the associated benthic community at each sampling station. The main purpose of this study is to explore the relationships between fish and benthic assemblages and environmental variables that may reveal essential habitat characteristics with which fish are closely associated. We suggest that this is the first step toward identifying what might constitute EFH.

Methods

Habitat and Community Survey

The Center for Environment, Fisheries and Aquaculture Science undertakes an annual beam trawl survey of the eastern English Channel to provide data used for the stock assessment of flatfish species (Figure 1). At each of the 72 stations, a single sample was collected with a 4-m beam trawl towed (in the same direction as the tide) for 30 min at a speed of 4 knots. The beam trawl was fitted with a chain mat, flip-up gear, and an 80-mm diamond mesh cod end net with a 20-mm square mesh liner (Kaiser and Spencer 1994; Rogers et al. 1998). The distance covered by the net over the ground was ascertained by recording the positions (ship's position given by differential global positioning system) of the vessel when the net was shot and hauled.

Each catch was sorted for commercially important fish and shellfish, and these were identified to species, weighed, and enumerated. The remaining bycatch of benthic invertebrates was treated in a similar way. When the catch exceeded one basket in volume, a subsample of one basket (c. 25 kg) was taken at random. Encrusting organisms such as the soft coral *Alcyonidium digitatum* were removed from their inert substratum before weighing wet. Very small organisms such as encrusting worms were excluded from the analyses, except when they formed substantial structures as in the case of *Sabellaria* spp. Catches were standardized to weight per 1,000 m^2 using a correction factor based on the size of the subsample. The motion-compensated balance had a resolution of 5 g; hence this was the minimum weight recorded for any organism. The presence of inert materials was also recorded. The total weight of stones from the entire catch and broken shell from one basket of bycatch were also recorded and raised to the total catch where

appropriate. Water depth and surface water salinity were recorded from an echo sounder and continuous data logger, respectively.

Although this particular survey represents a snapshot of the relationship between the benthic fauna and associated fish assemblages sampled, analyses of historical fish surveys indicated that the distribution of fish species is relatively constant through time (Rogers and Millner 1996). Although it would have been desirable to try to relate fishing intensity to assemblage structure or station depth, fishing effort data are currently collected on a scale of insufficient accuracy to make such comparisons meaningful.

Statistical Analyses

Multivariate analyses were conducted on community data using the PRIMER analytical package (Clarke and Warwick 1994). Only demersal fish and invertebrates were included in the data set. Pelagic species such as herring *Clupea harengus* were excluded from the analyses as beam trawls do not sample these species representatively. A cluster analysis was undertaken using the Bray-Curtis index of similarity and the group-average method of linkage on root-root transformed data of the fish and invertebrate assemblages. Once groups of similar stations had been identified, the two-dimensional

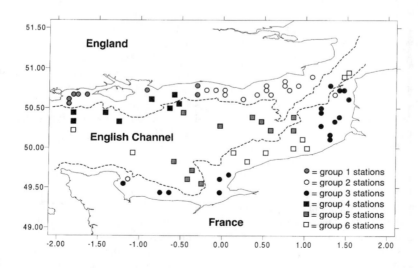

FIGURE 1.—The location of each station sampled with a 4-m beam trawl in the English Channel. The stations are grouped according to cluster analysis on community data (see Figure 2). Stations that have the same symbol are most similar. The communities sampled fell into six distinctly different groups. The 30-m depth contour is shown by a dashed line.

relationship between these different groups was investigated using multidimensional scaling (MDS). Indicator species for each separate group were identified using a similarity of percentages (SIMPER) procedure. The SIMPER procedure examines the contribution each species makes to the average similarity within a group as identified by the cluster analysis. The more evenly a species is distributed between similar samples and the more abundant a species is within a group, the more the species will contribute to the intra-group similarity. A species typifies that group if it is found at a consistent abundance throughout so that the standard deviation (SD) of its contribution is low and the ratio of average contribution/average SD of contribution (Ave_{con}/SD_{con}) is high. The relationships between the separate groups of stations and environmental variables (water depth, salinity, weight of broken shell, and weight of rocks) were analyzed using the BIOENV procedure with a weighted Spearman's correlation coefficient (r_w) (Clarke and Warwick 1994). Differences in mean salinity between each group of stations were tested using one-way analysis of variance (ANOVA) on log-normal (i.e., log to the power e or log e) transformed data. Differences in depth and total weight of rocks, broken shell, and sponges for each group of stations were tested using a Kruskal–Wallis test. For each sample, the assemblage data were then split into the following subsets of fauna: commercial flatfish, noncommercial flatfish, commercial demersal nonflatfish, noncommercial demersal nonflatfish, sessile infauna, mobile infauna, sessile epifauna, and mobile epifauna. Then their total biomass was calculated. The relationship between the biomass of each subset of animals and station groupings was explored by plotting the relative biomass of each subset of animals using the x and y coordinates of the appropriate sample as given

by the MDS ordination of the total assemblage data. No statistical analysis of these relationships was conducted due to autocorrelation between them, and the relationships should be regarded as an exploratory tool as used within this paper.

Results

Cluster analysis and subsequent multidimensional scaling indicated two major groupings of stations within which there were three further groupings (Figure 2). The two major groupings relate to their geographic position: one group of stations (identified by circles) is found close inshore in close proximity to major estuaries, and the other group of stations is found further offshore or in areas away from the influence of estuaries (Figure 1). The relationship between salinity and the station groupings was poor (r_w = -0.032; Figure 3), although salinity for group-3 stations was significantly lower than stations in groups 1, 2, and 4 (Table 1; ANOVA, $F_{5,48}$ = 6.03, $P < 0.0001$). The BIOENV procedure revealed that the combination of water depth and weight of rocks in the catch gave the best correlation with the biotic data (r_w = 0.307). Groups 1, 2, and 3 were found in more shallow water than groups 4, 5, and 6 (Table 1; K-W, H = 25.37, df = 5, $P < 0.0001$). There was significantly more broken shell in the catches from group-5 samples (Table 1; K-W, H = 24.93, df = 5, $P < 0.0001$), whereas a significantly greater weight of rocks was caught from group-4 stations (Table 1; K-W, H = 16.16, df = 5, $P < 0.005$).

The SIMPER procedure identified species that contributed most to the similarity between samples within each separately identified group. Those species or taxa that typify each group are indicated in Table 2. Flatfish species were all typical of groups 1, 2, and 3, whereas no flatfish were typical of the

TABLE 1.—Mean (±95% Cl) of four environmental or habitat characteristics and sponge biomass for each separate group of stations. Groups that are not significantly different from each other share the same letter. Pair-wise comparisons were undertaken using the Tukey–Kramer multiple comparison test for salinity and the Kruskal–Wallis test for all other variables. Across a row means without a letter in common are significantly different (P < 0.05).

Characteristic	Group 1	Group 2	Group 3	Group 4	Group 5	Group 6
Salinity (psu)	34.64±0.12z	34.79±0.13z	33.17±0.97y	34.86±0.05z	33.99±0.76zy	34.16±0.31zy
Depth (m)	18.67±8.09z	24.07±5.96z	21.71±2.12z	32.00±7.02y	38.55±5.49y	34.70±9.34y
Weight of rocks (kg/1,000 m²)	5.73±6.74z	4.30±3.84z	0.83±0.71z	28.68±20.55y	7.48±5.07z	7.22±6.97z
Weight of broken shell (kg/1,000 m²)	0.12±0.09z	0.48±0.61z	0.88±0.62z	0.21±0.22z	15.82±8.87y	0.49±0.70z
Weight of sponges (kg/1,000 m²)	0.23±0.22z	0.00±0.00z	0.54±0.49z	2.43±3.54z	0.11±0.09z	39.90±50.29y

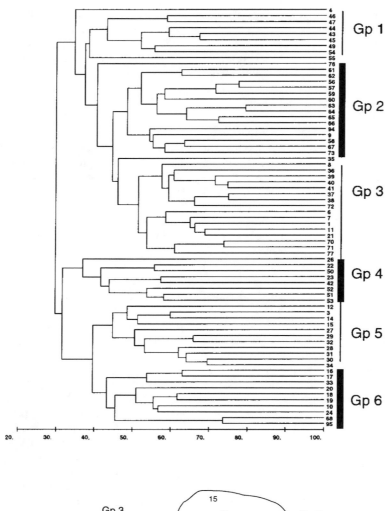

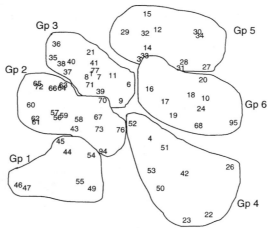

FIGURE 2.—(Top) Cluster diagram and (Bottom) subsequent two-dimensional multidimensional scaling (MDS) plot of the stations sampled. Each station has a numerical code from 1 to 72. The bars in the cluster diagram highlight the 6 different groupings of stations (Gp 1–6). Each group is separated in the MDS ordination by the solid lines.

other groups. Plaice *Pleuronectes platessa* and sole *Solea solea* were typical of groups 1, 2, and 3; however, dabs *Limanda limanda* were only typical for groups 2 and 3. Groups 1, 2, and 3 were also typified by a relatively low biomass of sessile epibenthic fauna such as hydroids (groups 2 and 3); *Alcyonium digitatum* (group 3); *Flustra foliacea* (groups 1 and 2); *Alcyonidium diaphanum* (group 2); and mobile

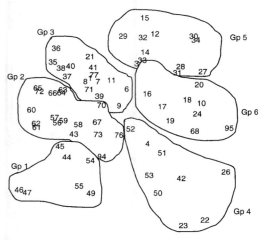

ALL STATIONS

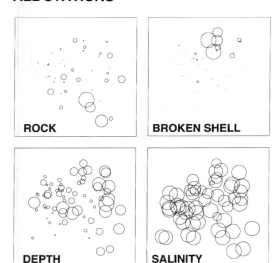

FIGURE 3.—The relative salinity, water depth, weight of rocks, and broken shells per 1,000 m² overlaid on the MDS plot (all stations) of the assemblage data. The larger the radius of the circle, the larger the value of that variable. The ordination of the community data for all stations is the same as Figure 2B. This acts as a reference point for the superimposed plots of the environmental variables shown. For example, the greatest weight of broken shells occurs in 7 of the stations clustered in group 5.

epibenthic taxa such as *Liocarcinus holsatus* (groups 2 and 3), *Asterias rubens* (group 3), and *Psammechinus miliaris* (group 3). In contrast, groups 4, 5, and 6 were all typified by round fishes such as pogges, dragonets and gurnards. Gadoids were typical of groups 4 and 6, whereas dogfish were typical of group 5. A large biomass of sessile structural epifauna (*F. foliacea*, *A. digitatum*, or Porifera) typically occurred in groups 4, 5, and 6.

The prevalence of certain subsets of organisms (e.g., sessile epifauna, mobile epifauna, etc.) at each station was investigated by overlaying their summed biomass on the MDS plot of the community data. Although the communities in deeper water may be typified by a large biomass of several sessile epifaunal taxa (Table 1), the total biomass of all sessile epifaunal species is highest in shallower areas (Figure 4). In contrast, the highest biomass of mobile epifauna was found for groups 3 (shallow) and 5 and 6 (deep). Few stations had a relatively large biomass of either mobile or sessile infauna. The biomass of sessile infauna was highest in group 2 and was dominated by the burrowing heart urchin *Echinocardium cordatum* and the large tube dwelling polychaete *Chaetopterus* sp. *Ophioderma longicauda* accounted for the large biomass of mobile infauna at some of the stations from group 5. It must be remembered that the beam trawl could only retain large infaunal organisms, whereas most infauna are smaller than the mesh used in the cod end liner. The highest biomass of both commercial and nontarget flatfish occurs in groups 2 and 3 (Figure 5). Commercial demersal (nonflatfish) species were fairly uniformly distributed among all stations, whereas there was a tendency for the highest biomass of nontarget demersal (nonflatfish) species to occur in group 3. Small shark species were most prevalent in group 5.

Discussion

Past studies have related the distribution of fish assemblages to environmental variables such as depth, salinity (as in this study), temperature, and sediment type (Gibson and Robb 1992; Smale et al. 1993). However, although these variables are useful general descriptors of some of the physical habitat characteristics associated with certain fish assemblages, they do not provide a useful basis for the formulation of conservation policy with respect to essential fish habitat. Features that constitute a particular habitat include both physical and biotic ele-

TABLE 2.—The average biomass (kg) of the 10 species or taxa that contributed most to the Bray–Curtis similarity for each separate group of stations. Taxa considered to be indicator species are indicated by a ratio >1.5. The ratio is the product of the average contribution of that species to the similarity within that group/the standard deviation of the average contribution.

Taxon	Common name	Group 1 Ave. bio	Group 1 Ratio	Group 2 Ave. bio	Group 2 Ratio	Group 3 Ave. bio	Group 3 Ratio	Group 4 Ave. bio	Group 4 Ratio	Group 5 Ave. bio	Group 5 Ratio	Group 6 Ave. bio	Group 6 Ratio
Laminaria spp.	algae	73.6	0.9					6.4	0.7				
Porifera	sponges							2.4	1.8			39.9	1.5
Hydrozoa	sea ferns			0.3	1.8	0.3	2.8	0.6	5.3				
Nemertesia spp.	sea ferns							0.1	3.8				
Alcyonium digitatum	soft coral					2.6	2.0			11.4	2.2	43.4	1.4
Liocarcinus holsatus	swimming crab			0.5	2.6	2.6	1.6	0.1	1.5				
Maja squinado	spider crab	2.5	1.1	1.7	2.2			3.5	3.8	0.7	1.0	1.3	1.7
Cancer pagurus	edible crab							0.7	1.0				
Aequipecten opercularis	queen scallop									16.1	2.7		
Sepia officianalis	cuttlefish	0.3	1.8			3.4	2.1						
Crossaster papposus	common sunstar									1.1	0.9	2.8	1.2
Asterias rubens	common starfish					56.7	2.5			25.0	1.8	37.7	4.9
Psammechinus miliaris	sea urchin					2.0	1.7			3.4	1.9		
Flustra foliacea	foliose bryozoan	1.3	1.5	0.6	2.2			14.8	2.6			28.5	1.7
Alcyonidium diaphanum	gelatinous bryozoan	9.6	1.0	3.5	1.9	0.8	1.3						
Ascidia mentula	sea squirt											3.4	1.1
Scyliorhinus canicula	dogfish									5.5	0.7		
Raja clavata	thornback ray	0.9	1.1										
Pleuronectes platessa	plaice	11.5	4.6	5.9	6.4	13.8	2.4						
Solea solea	sole	1.2	5.1	1.5	2.2	2.1	2.4						
Limanda limanda	dab			1.6	2.0	2.8	4.0						
Buglossidium luteum	solenette	1.2	1.3	1.4	0.9								
Callionymus lyra	dragonet	0.3	4.6	0.4	7.0	4.1	4.7			1.6	3.9	0.4	3.1
Agonus cataphractus	pogge									0.3	3.5		
Triglidae	gurnard									0.8	1.9	0.7	3.3
Trisopterus minutus	poor cod							1.1	1.5			0.5	3.6
Trisopterus luscus	pouting							0.8	0.9				

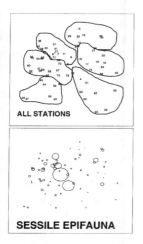

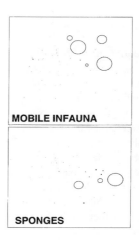

FIGURE 4.—The relative biomass per 1,000 m² of various categories of benthic fauna related to the MDS ordination of the entire assemblage data (as in Figure 3).

ments. Important physical components include water quality; salinity and depth; substratum type (e.g., bedrock, gravel, mud, or sand); tidal scour; and exposure to wave action. Biotic features of a habitat include the resident prey assemblage and organisms that increase the topographic complexity of the environment. The latter group of organisms consists of fauna that modify habitat through their feeding and burrowing activities (e.g., Thrush 1986; Thrush et al. 1991; Auster et al. 1996) and emergent sessile organisms that increase surface topography by their presence (Auster et al. 1996; Auster and Langton 1999). Physical descriptors provide a good indication of very general habitat features, for example, European flatfish species tend to occur in shallow water (Figure 3). In the present study, the six distinct assemblages were divided equally among either shallow or deeper-water environments that were either greater or less than 30 m deep. This simple distinction accurately predicts the presence or absence of significant populations of either flatfishes in shallow water or round fish or small shark species in deeper water. However, to resolve the finer elements of what constitutes the important features of a habitat for a particular species of fish, it is also necessary to examine the habitat's biotic features. Within both the shallow and deeper-water habitats studied there are three further distinct assemblages, each related to different physical or biological characteristics (Figures 3 and 4).

The distinctions among the three assemblages found in deeper water were related to either the characteristics of the substratum or the presence of certain benthic epifauna. The substratum at group-4 stations was characterized by the presence of occa-

sional rocks, hydroids, and some sponges that increase habitat heterogeneity. This habitat was typically inhabited by small gadoid species. Although few rocks were caught at group-6 stations, habitat complexity was increased by a wide selection of structural fauna such as soft corals, hydroids, bryozoans, and sponges. These sponges greatly increase habitat complexity as some specimens measured in excess of 30 cm in diameter. Small gadoid species and gurnards were the most important fish species associated with group 6. Group-5 stations had few rocks or sponges. This habitat was characterized by a relatively high content of broken shell within the sediment, which is typical of an assemblage associated with queen scallops. Small shark species were almost exclusively found in this habitat, and a similar relationship exists in the Irish Sea (Kaiser and Spencer 1994). Although it is difficult to infer what the important associations may be in broken-shell habitat, associations may relate to enhanced feeding opportunities for species such as the dogfish *S. canicula* on coarse broken-shell substrata (Ellis et al. 1996). In addition, dogfish egg cases are often found attached to erect biota, and this type of habitat may also provide an important role in reproduction (Ellis and Shackley 1997). Our data would seem to indicate that small gadoids are among the most important fish taxa found in structurally complex habitats in relatively deep water. Gotceitas and Brown (1993) have demonstrated that juvenile cod sheltering in complex habitats suffer lower predation rates than those in less-structured environments. Auster et al. (1997) found that juvenile silver hake are strongly attracted to microtopographic features that provide a foil for their camouflaged pigmentation.

The three assemblages found in shallower water were all dominated by flatfish species. Plaice and sole occurred in all three groups whereas dab only occurred in group 2 and 3. Sole were most important for group 1 as indicated by the high ratio of Ave_{con}/SD_{con}. The habitat typically associated with groups 2 and 3 had more structural fauna such as hydroids, soft corals, or gelatinous or foliose bryozoans than group 1 stations. Sole generally predate on infaunal invertebrates that occupy soft substrata, and sole locate their prey using chemosensory papillae near the mouth. Presumably, therefore, sole are best adapted to forage in relatively simple habitats, and, indeed, emergent fauna may reduce the their feeding efficiency. In contrast, plaice and dab are both visual feeders that consume small fishes and crustacea associated with epibenthic structures (Basimi and Grove 1985; Auster et al. 1997), as well as small infaunal polychaetes and crustacea. Of the three flatfish species, dab appear to be most closely associated with assemblages containing structural epifauna (Table 2).

The present study has demonstrated links between certain fishes and different levels of habitat complexity. Fishing activities using mobile bottom gears are the greatest potential threat to sessile epifauna that increase the topography of the seabed. In the eastern English Channel, the most important commercially exploited demersal species (sole and plaice) are landed from beam and otter trawl fisheries in the coastal waters of England and France (Pawson 1995). In these shallow-water environments, dab and plaice populations might be expected to suffer most in areas of more-

intense trawling activity that will reduce habitat complexity. These less-complex habitats may then become more suitable for sole, which prefer a simpler habitat. However, dab and plaice continue to populate the southern North Sea even though it is intensively fished by beam trawls (Heessen and Daan 1996; Rogers et al. 1998). There are several possible explanations for this observation. First, bottom-fishing activity promotes the food supply of small dab, plaice, and all size classes of sole by maintaining the benthic community in a high state of productivity (Rijnsdorp and van Leeuwen 1996; Kaiser and Ramsay 1997). Second, fishing has removed the major predators (such as cod) of juvenile flatfish (Rijnsdorp and van Leeuwen 1996). Although bottom fishing removes large quantities of structural fauna (Kaiser et al. 1998), fauna found in flatfish habitats have relatively short generation times. Kaiser et al. (1998) found that an area disturbed by beam trawling was recolonized by soft corals, hydroids, and bryozoans after six months. Collie et al. (1997) studied the effects of scallop dredging on a similar community on Georges Bank, although the environment studied was more stable than that studied by Kaiser et al. (1998) (cobble and gravel substratum in deep water c.f. shelly gravel in relatively shallow water). As a result, Collie et al. (1997) observed a dense turf of epifaunal organisms in undisturbed areas that only began to recover 2–3 years after dredging disturbance.

The present study also has identified links between certain fish taxa or types (flatfish c.f. round fish) and both physical and biotic habitat features of the English Channel including depth, sediment type,

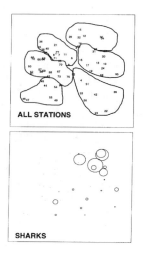 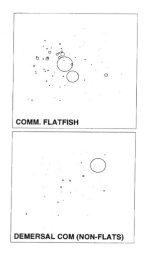 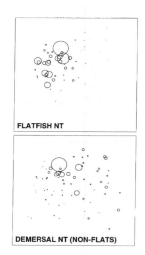

FIGURE 5.—The relative biomass per 1,000 m² of various categories of fishes related to the MDS ordination of the entire assemblage data (as in Figure 3). COMM./COM = commercial species, NT = nontarget species.

and biomass of sessile invertebrates. Many of the sessile epifauna increase the topographic complexity of the seabed habitat (Table 2). However, the biomass of sessile epifauna was higher in shallow water compared with deeper-water habitats. In addition, populations of fish species that occurred in shallow water would appear to be relatively resilient to bottom-fishing disturbances (Kaiser et al. 1998). In contrast, larger and less-abundant epifauna such as sponges occurred in the deepwater environment. Slow-growing organisms such as sponges are more sensitive to physical disturbance, and the removal of these slow-growing organisms may lead to a decline in fish species that are closely associated with them (Bradstock and Gordon 1983; Sainsbury 1987). However, few commercially important species were associated with these deeper-water communities of the English Channel, and less effort is deployed in these deeper-water communities by trawl fisheries than in coastal areas (Pawson 1995). Species that did occur in the deeper-water communities (for example, gurnards and dogfish) are not targeted by demersal fleets in the eastern English Channel and are of limited commercial value. It is possible that populations of demersal gadoids were present in these deeper areas but were poorly sampled by the gear used in this study. However, the presence of long-lived fauna such as large sponges tends to confirm that these deepwater habitats currently experience little bottom trawling or dredging activity.

Summary

There are subtle habitat preferences among the flatfish species sampled in this study. Sole appear to prefer structurally simple habitats whereas plaice and dabs prefer habitats with some sessile epifauna that increases surface topography. Although these habitats and communities are heavily fished with bottom gears, they are unlikely to be degraded permanently by such disturbance, although chronic fishing disturbance may reduce habitat complexity in favor of sole. The structurally more-complex habitats found in deep water were not an important habitat for flatfishes. As such, these habitats might be described as "nonessential fish habitats" with respect to flatfish. These deepwater habitats were associated with roundfish and small shark species. Although sensitive to physical disturbance, these communities are currently fished at relatively low intensity. On a scale of increasing habitat complexity, the habi-tats studied in our survey are relatively simple when compared with complex habitats reported elsewhere (Auster et al. 1996; Collie et al. 1997; Sainsbury et al. 1997). Habitats of greater complexity, that is, habitats with large-scale rocky reefs and much larger and more abundant sessile epifauna, did not occur in our study region. Bottom fishing with trawls and dredges in complex habitats leads to long-term changes (Auster et al. 1996; Collie et al. 1997), and Sainsbury et al. (1997) report that recovery is predicted to take between 10 and 15 years for some soft coral and gorgonian communities. The present study of relatively simple habitats emphasizes the importance of considering subtle differences in habitat structure and assemblage composition if we are to understand the consequences of impacts by fishing activity.

Acknowledgments

We thank Kathryn Turner for assistance with fieldwork. This project was part funded by the Ministry of Agriculture, Fisheries, and Food, contract number MF0716, and the UK Department of the Environment, Transport, and the Regions as a contribution to its coordinated program of marine research for the Northeast Atlantic.

References

Auster, P. J., and R. W. Langton. 1999. The effects of fishing on fish habitat. Pages 150-187 in L. R. Benaka, editor. Fish habitat: essential fish habitat and rehabilitation. American Fisheries Society, Symposium 22, Bethesda, Maryland.

Auster, P. J., R. Malatesta, and C. Donaldson. 1997. Distributional responses to small-scale habitat variability by early juvenile silver hake, *Merluccius bilinearis*. Environmental Biology of Fishes 50:195–200.

Auster, P. J., and eight coauthors. 1996. The impacts of mobile fishing gear on seafloor habitats in the Gulf of Maine (Northwest Atlantic): implications for conservation of fish populations. Reviews in Fisheries Science 4:185–202.

Basimi, R. A., and D. J. Grove. 1985. Studies on feeding, growth and production of a recruited inshore population of *Pleuronectes platessa* (L.) at East Anglesey, North Wales. Journal of Fish Biology 27:765–783.

Bradstock, M., and D. P. Gordon. 1983. Coral-like bryozoan growths in Tasman Bay, and their protection to conserve local fish stocks. New Zealand Journal of Marine and Freshwater Research 17:159–163.

Clarke, K., and R. Warwick. 1994. Change in marine communities: an approach to statistical analysis and interpretation. Natural Environmental Research Council, Plymouth Marine Laboratory, Plymouth, Devon, UK.

Collie, J. S., G. A. Escanero, and P. C. Valentine. 1997. Effects of bottom fishing on the benthic megafauna of Georges Bank. Marine Ecology Progress Series 155:159—172.

Cruetzberg, F., G. C. A. Duineveld, and G. J. van Noort. 1987. The effect of different numbers of tickler chains on beam trawl catches. Journal du Conseil International pour l'Exploration de la Mer 43:159–168.

Currie, D. R., and G. D. Parry. 1996. Effects of scallop dredging on a soft sediment community: a large-scale experimental study. Marine Ecology Progress Series 134:131–150.

Dayton, P. K., S. F. Thrush, M. T. Agardy, and R. J. Hofman. 1995. Environmental effects of marine fishing. Aquatic Conservation: Marine and Freshwater Ecosystems 5:205–232.

de Groot, S. 1984. The impact of bottom trawling on the benthic fauna of the North Sea. Ocean Management 10:21–36.

Ellis, J. R., M. G. Pawson, and S. Shackley. 1996. The comparative feeding ecology of six species of shark and four species of ray (Elasmobranchii) in the Northeast Atlantic. Journal of the Marine Biological Association of the United Kingdom 76:89–106.

Ellis, J. R., and S. Shackley. 1997. The reproductive biology of *Scyliorhinus canicula* in the Bristol Channel, UK. Journal of Fish Biology 51:361–372.

Gibson, R. N., and L. Robb. 1992. The relationship between body size, sediment grain size and the burying ability of juvenile plaice *Pleuronectes platessa* L. Journal of Fish Biology 40:771–778.

Gotceitas, V., and J. Brown. 1993. Substrate selection by juvenile Atlantic cod (*Gadus morhua*): effects of predation risk. Oecologia 93:31–37.

Heessen, H. J. L., and N. Daan. 1996. Long-term trends in ten non-target North Sea fish species. ICES Journal of Marine Science 53:1063–1078.

Jennings, S., and M. Kaiser. 1998. The effects of fishing on marine ecosystems. Advances in Marine Biology 34:201–352.

Jones, J. 1992. Environmental impact of trawling on the seabed: a review. New Zealand Journal of Marine and Freshwater Research 26:59–67.

Kaiser, M. J., and six coauthors. 1998. Changes in megafaunal benthic communities in different habitats after trawling disturbance. ICES Journal of Marine Science 55:353–361.

Kaiser, M. J., and K. Ramsay. 1997. Opportunistic feeding by dabs within areas of trawl disturbance: possible implications for increased survival. Marine Ecology Progress Series 152:307–310.

Kaiser, M. J., S. I. Rogers, and D. T. McCandless. 1994. Improving quantitative surveys of epibenthic communities using a modified 2m beam trawl. Marine Ecology Progress Series 106:131–38.

Kaiser, M. J., and B. E. Spencer. 1994. Fish scavenging behaviour in recently trawled areas. Marine Ecology Progress Series 112:41–49.

Kaiser, M. J., and B. E. Spencer. 1996. The effects of beam-trawl disturbance on infaunal communities in different habitats. Journal of Animal Ecology 65:348–358.

Messieh, S., T. Rowell, D. Peer, and P. Cranford. 1991. The effects of trawling, dredging and ocean dumping on the eastern Canadian continental shelf seabed. Cont. Shelf Research 11:1237–1263.

Overholtz, W., and A. Tyler. 1985. Long-term responses of demersal fish assemblages of Georges Bank. U.S. Fisheries Bulletin 83:507–520.

Pawson, M. G. 1995. Biogeographical identification of English Channel fish and shellfish stocks. Fisheries Research Technical Report No. 99. Ministry of Agriculture, Fisheries and Food, Directorate of Fisheries Research, Lowestoft, UK.

Peattie, M., and R. Hoare. 1981. The sublittoral ecology of the Menai Strait II. The sponge Halichondria panicea (Pallas) and its associated fauna. Estuarine, Coastal and Shelf Science 13:621–633.

Ramsay, K., M. J. Kaiser, and R. N. Hughes. 1996. Changes in hermit crab feeding patterns in response to trawling disturbance. Marine Ecology Progress Series 144:63–72.

Ramsay, K., M. J. Kaiser, P. G. Moore, and R. N. Hughes. 1997. Consumption of fisheries discards by benthic scavengers: utilisation of energy subsidies in different marine habitats. Journal of Animal Ecology 66:884-896.

Rijnsdorp, A. D., and P. I. van Leeuwen. 1996. Changes in growth of North Sea plaice since 1950 in relation to density, eutrophication, beam-trawl effort, and temperature. ICES Journal of Marine Science 53:1199–1213.

Rogers, S. I. 1997. A review of closed areas in the United Kingdom exclusive economic zone. Science Series Technical Report No. 106. The Centre for Environment, Fisheries and Aquaculture Science, Lowestoft. UK.

Rogers, S. I., and S. Lockwood. 1989. Observations on the capture efficiency of a two-metre beam trawl for juvenile flatfish. Netherlands Journal for Sea Research 23:347–352.

Rogers, S. I. 1992. Environmental factors affecting the distribution of Dover sole (Solea solea L.) within a nursery area. Netherlands Journal of Sea Research 29:151–159.

Rogers, S. I., and R. S. Millner. 1996. Factors affecting the annual abundance and regional distribution of English inshore demersal fish populations: 1973 to 1995. Journal of Marine Science 53:1094–1112.

Rogers, S. I., A. D. Rijnsdorp, U. Damm, and W. Vanhee. 1998. Demersal fish populations in the coastal waters of the UK and continental N.W. Europe from beam trawl survey data collected from 1990 to 1995. Journal of Sea Research 37:79–102.

Sainsbury, K. J. 1987. Assessment and management of the demersal fishery on the continental shelf of northwestern Australia. Pages 465–503 in J. J. Polovina and S. Ralston, editors. Tropical snappers and groupers—biology and fisheries management. Westview Press, Boulder, Colorado.

Sainsbury, K. J., R. A. Campbell, R. Lindholm, and A. W. Whitlaw. 1997. Experimental management of an Australian multispecies fishery: examining the possibility of trawl-induced habitat modification. Pages 107–112 in E. K. Pikitch, D. D. Huppert, and M. P. Sissenwine, editors. Global trends: fisheries management. American Fisheries Society, Symposium 20, Bethesda, Maryland.

Smale, M., B. Roel, A. Badenhorst, and J. Field. 1993. Analysis of the demersal community of fish and cephalopods on the Agulhas Bank, South Africa. Journal of Fish Biology 43A:169–191.

Thrush, S. F. 1986. Spatial heterogeneity in subtidal gravel generated by the pit-digging activities of *Cancer pagurus*. Marine Ecology Progress Series 30:221–227.

Thrush, S. F., J. E. Hewitt, V. J. Cummings, and P. K. Dayton. 1995. The impact of habitat disturbance by scallop dredging on marine benthic communities: what can be predicted from the results of experiments? Marine Ecology Progress Series 129:141–150.

Thrush, S. F., R. D. Pridmore, J. E. Hewitt, and V. J. Cummings. 1991. Impact of ray feeding on sandflat macrobenthos: do communities dominated by polychaetes or shellfish respond differently? Marine Ecology Progress Series 69:245–252.

Tuck, I., S. Hall, M. Roberston, E. Armstrong, and D. Basford. 1998. Effects of physical trawling disturbance in a previously unfished sheltered Scottish sea loch. Marine Ecology Progress Series 162:227–242.

Walters, C. J., and F. Juanes. 1993. Recruitment limitation as a consequence of natural selection for use of restricted feeding habitats and predation risk taking by juvenile fishes. Canadian Journal of Fisheries and Aquatic Sciences 50:2058–2070.

American Fisheries Society Symposium 22:224–237, 1999

The Significance of Seabed Disturbance by Mobile Fishing Gear Relative to Natural Processes: A Case Study in Narragansett Bay, Rhode Island

JOSEPH DEALTERIS, LAURA SKROBE, AND CHRISTINE LIPSKY

Department of Fisheries and Aquaculture, University of Rhode Island
Fisheries Center, East Farm, Kingston, Rhode Island 02881, USA

Abstract.—Seabed disturbance by mobile bottom-fishing gear has emerged as a major concern related to the conservation of essential fish habitat. Unquestionably, dredges and trawls disturb the seabed. However, the seabed is also disturbed by natural physical and biological processes. The biological communities that utilize a particular habitat have adapted to that environment through natural selection, and, therefore, the impact of mobile fishing gear on the habitat structure and biological community must be scaled against the magnitude and frequency of seabed disturbance due to natural causes. Fishers operating in the mouth of Narragansett Bay, Rhode Island use trawls to harvest lobsters, squid, and finfish and dredges to harvest mussels. These mobile fishing gears impact rock, sand, and mud substrates. Side-scan sonar data from 1995 with 200% coverage were available from the National Oceanic and Atmospheric Administration for the mouth of Narragansett Bay. Analysis of these data indicates that evidence of bottom scarring by the fishing gear is restricted to deeper waters with a seabed composition of soft cohesive sediments, despite the observation that fishing activity is ubiquitous throughout the bay mouth. A quantitative model has been developed to compare the magnitude and frequency of natural seabed disturbance to mobile fishing gear disturbance. Wave and tidal currents at the seabed are coupled with sediment characteristics to estimate the degree of seabed disturbance. Field experiments designed to compare the longevity of bottom scars indicate that scars in shoal waters and sand sediments are short-lived, as compared to scars in deep water and mud sediments, which are long-lasting. Finally, the model results are compared to the recovery time of sediments disturbed by the interaction of the fishing gear with the seabed. The impact of mobile fishing gear on the seabed must be evaluated in light of the degree of seabed disturbance due to natural phenomena. The application of this model on a larger scale to continental shelf waters and seabed sediment environments will allow for the identification of problematic areas relative to the degradation of essential fish habitat by mobile fishing gear.

The 1996 amendments to the Magnuson-Stevens Fishery Conservation and Management Act (Magnuson-Stevens Act) require the National Marine Fisheries Service (NMFS) and the regional fishery management councils (FMCs) to protect and conserve the habitat of fishery resources under their jurisdiction. This habitat is referred to as "essential fish habitat" (EFH) and is defined as "those waters and substrate necessary to fish for spawning, breeding, feeding and growth to maturity." The Magnuson-Stevens Act further requires the FMCs to amend federal fishery management plans (FMPs) to describe and identify EFH, minimize adverse fishing effects on EFH, and identify other actions to conserve and enhance EFH.

Marine fishing activity in general has been identified as causing harmful environmental effects (Dayton et al. 1995; Auster and Langton 1999, this volume). Finfish and shellfish bycatch; incidental take of mammals, turtles, and seabirds; habitat damage; secondary effects of discards; indirect effects

of reduction of target species; and generation of marine debris are major concerns. Within this context, seabed disturbance by commercial mobile fishing gear has emerged as a major concern related to the conservation of EFH. However, the seabed is also disturbed by natural physical and biological processes. Bioturbation of sediments by benthic infauna mixes subsurface sediments with the surficial sediment layer (Rhoads et al. 1978). Bottom currents associated with surface waves and wind, tidal, and geostrophic forces also move bottom sediments, creating bedforms and causing erosion and accretion (Wright 1995). The biological communities that utilize a particular habitat have adapted to that environment through natural selection (Krebs 1994). As a result, animals naturally adapted to a highly dynamic seabed environment may not be affected by seabed disturbance due to fishing. Conversely, animals adapted to a stable, quiescent seabed environment may take a long time to recover if disturbed by fishing gear.

Therefore, we argue that the relative significance of seabed disturbance by mobile fishing gear to habitat structure and biological communities must be scaled against the magnitude and frequency of seabed disturbance due to natural causes. We have selected the mouth of Narragansett Bay, Rhode Island as a case study wherein the mobile gear fisheries are described and evidence of seabed disturbance by mobile gear is presented. In addition, the bottom hydrodynamic environment and sediment transport processes in two settings in the lower bay are characterized, and we present the results of a field experiment to compare the longevity of mobile gear bottom scars as a measure of habitat recovery time. Based on the results of these studies, we demonstrate that seabed disturbance by mobile fishing gear must be evaluated in light of natural processes and propose that a similar analysis for all continental shelf waters and seabed sediment environments would allow for the identification of problematic areas relative to the degradation of essential fish habitat by mobile fishing gear.

Effects of Mobile Fishing Gear on the Seabed

Understanding the extent and role of mobile fishing gear impacts is particularly important because of large increases in fishing effort over the last decade. For centuries, fishermen have used various kinds of mobile gear to capture bottom-dwelling finfish and shellfish (von Brandt 1984). Mobile fishing gear types include otter trawls, beam trawls, mussel and scallop rakes, and clam dredges. Some mobile gear can change the physical properties of surficial sediments, influence chemical exchanges between sediments and water, and alter the composition of benthic communities. Trawling and dredging can be expected to cause a number of direct and indirect changes in an ecosystem (Messieh et al. 1991; Riemann and Hoffmann 1991; Jones 1992). Direct, immediate effects include scraping and plowing of the substrate, sediment resuspension, destruction of benthos, and dumping of processing waste. Indirect, delayed, or long-term effects include postfishing mortality and long-term changes to the benthic community structure.

Most experimental studies to date have been restricted to evaluating only the immediate impacts of mobile gear. However, intensive and repeated trawling in the same area may lead to long-term changes in both benthic habitat and communities. The magnitude of the gear effect depends on the (de Groot 1984; Redant 1987; Churchill 1989; Krost et al. 1990; Jenner et al. 1991; Mayer et al. 1991; Jones 1992; ICES 1995; Prena et al. 1996):

- type of gear employed;
- depth of penetration of the gear into the sediment;
- water depth;
- nature of the substrate (mud, sand, pebbles, or boulders);
- kind of benthic communities being impacted (i.e., epibenthic versus infauna);
- frequency with which the area is fished;
- weight of the gear on the seabed;
- towing speed;
- strength of the tides and currents; and
- time of year.

The parts of a trawl that leave the most distinctive marks are the otter boards. Single otter-board tracks range in width from approximately 0.2–2.0 m, and their depths can vary from 3 to 30 cm deep (Caddy and Iles 1972; Krost et al. 1990). Sediment type is one of the more important factors affecting longevity of otter-board tracks. In sandy sediment, otter boards cannot penetrate deeply due to the high mechanical resistance of the sediment, and the seabed in sandy areas is more rapidly restored by waves and currents. Therefore, on sand bottoms, tracks are short-lived, whereas in mud bottoms tracks will be deeper and will last longer (Caddy 1973; Werner et al. 1976; Krost et al. 1990).

Studies have indicated that dredges (Langton and Robinson 1990; Auster et al. 1996); bottom trawls (Auster et al. 1996); and beam trawls (Kaiser and Spencer 1996) can alter the physical characteristics of the substratum, and Riemann and Hoffmann (1991) noted that particulate material is resuspended from the bottom into the water column due to dredging and bottom trawling. Kaiser et al. (1998) investigated changes in the megafaunal benthic community in different habitats after trawling disturbance and found that in mobile sediments, effects of fishing were not even immediately detectable, and in stable sediments, after six months, seasonal changes in the benthic community masked an effect of fishing. On pebble and cobble bottoms, mobile fishing gear eliminates or severely damages the epifaunal species present before the gear passing the

area (Eleftheriou and Robertson 1992; Auster et al.
1996; Collie et al. 1997) and reduces habitat complexity, species diversity, and abundance of some
taxa that live in stable sediments (Auster et al. 1996;
Kaiser and Spencer 1996).

Technology of Mapping the Seabed

The use of sound in the sea dates to the fifteenth
century when Leonardo da Vinci noted that the sound
of approaching sailing vessels could be heard in the
sea before the vessels were observed over the horizon. The modern age of sound navigation and ranging (sonar) began with World War II, as did the
development of electronic instruments that utilized
hydroacoustics (underwater sound) to determine
water depth and the distance and bearing of objects
under the sea (Urick 1983). Since 1970,
hydroacoustic methods have been used for the estimation of pelagic fishery resource abundance
(MacLennan and Simmonds 1992). The most advanced technology is capable of identifying, counting, and tracking individual fish as they pass around
and through hydroelectric plants. The technology of
using hydroacoustics to map the seabed with trans-
ducers that scan to the sides of a survey vessel was
developed in the 1960s and has been in commercial
application since the 1970s. In the 1990s, side-scan
sonar is standard equipment aboard coastal survey
vessels that map navigable waterways, and it is also
used in nautical archeology, seabed resource mapping, and environmental surveys (Anonymous 1996).
Side-scan sonar was used to map oyster reefs in the
James River, Virginia and to identify scars in the
reefs made by the propeller wash of tugboats passing over shallow reefs (DeAlteris 1988).

Side-scan sonar has also been used as a technique to demonstrate physical impacts of fishing
trawls and dredges by recording and documenting
tracks (Amos and King 1984; Fader and Pecore
1988). Moreover, side-scan sonar is a fast method
of data recording and is therefore well-suited for
mapping large areas of the seafloor (Krost et al.
1990). Previous studies (e.g., Krost et al. 1990;
Harrison et al. 1991; Jenner et al. 1991) have clearly
demonstrated that side-scan sonar can be used to
determine whether the seafloor has recently been
disturbed by mobile fishing gear. Krost et al. (1990)
identified otter trawl tracks in Kiel Bay (Western
Baltic) using side-scan sonar and found that the frequency of trawl tracks was highest in mud areas.

Coastal Sediment Transport Processes

Sediments of the coastal seabed are subject to
erosion, transport, and deposition as a function of
the hydrodynamic environment. Early work on sediment transport processes was restricted to freshwater environments where unidirectional currents
transport sediments downstream based on the velocity of the water and the grain size of the sediment (Graf 1971). Hjulstrom (1939) investigated the
erosion, transport, and deposition of uniformly sized
particles in a steady current. He demonstrated that
fine-grain-size sand with a diameter of 0.25 mm was
eroded at the lowest average velocity (about 25 cm/
s), whereas finer and coarser sediments required
substantially greater velocities. Hjulstrom also noted
that silt and clay-size sediments, because of their
cohesive nature, were considerably more resistant
to erosion and required average velocities greater
than 125 cm/s to erode. Hjulstrom's research was
based on average velocities in channels, and therefore the critical velocities for erosion measured at 1
m above the seabed must be adjusted downward to
account for a turbulent, logarithmically decaying
velocity profile (Munson et al. 1994).

Research by Shields (1936) and others on the
mechanics of sediment transport in steady, unidirectional flows developed the concepts of friction
velocities and critical sheer stresses for erosion of
cohesionless sediments. Research on the erosion,
transport, and deposition of fine, cohesive sediments
was lead by Partheniades (1965) and others. In the
1970s, Sternberg (1972) and Madsen and Grant
(1976) investigated coastal sediment transport processes, combining wave-generated oscillatory bottom currents with steady, unidirectional currents due
to wind, tides, and other forces. Cacchione and Drake
(1990), Metha and Dyer (1990), and Sleath (1990)
provided up-to-date research reviews of shelf sediment dynamics, cohesive sediment transport in
coastal waters, and seabed boundary layer dynamics, respectively.

A practical application of this research is to
predict the seaward limit of significant sediment
transport as related to the potential dispersal of disposed dredge material after disturbance of the sediment cap, or to compare natural seabed disturbance
to seabed disturbance by fishing gear. Estimates of
the seaward limit of sediment transport depend on
the local wave and current environment, water depth,
and sediment type. The Shore Protection Manual
(CERC 1984) of the U.S. Army Corps of Engineers

recommended estimating the local wave climate based on hindcast analysis of the wind climate, then determining the maximum wave orbital velocity 1 m above the seabed using linear (Airy) wave theory, and finally comparing this maximum bottom current to a tabulated threshold value for sediment motion. Sherwood (1989) described a more sophisticated analysis based on the Madsen and Grant (1976) model.

Description of the Study Area and Mobile Gear Fisheries

Lower Narragansett Bay is a well-mixed (vertically homogenous) estuary located in southern New England, USA. It is approximately 40 km in length and 10 km in width, and it discharges into Rhode Island Sound (Figure 1). Sediments in the bay range from sandy mud in the deeper portions of the bay, to pebbles and cobbles along portions of the shore and shoal areas, to sand in other shore and shallow areas (McMaster 1960). Tides are semidiurnal with a mean range of 1.2 m, and tidal currents at the surface reach maximum velocities in excess of 70 cm/s (Hicks 1959). Narragansett Bay is exposed to wind and waves of unlimited fetch from the southern quadrant (Hicks et al. 1956). The study area is located in the lower portion of the West Passage of Narragansett Bay and is approximately 7 km in length and 4 km in width (Figure 1). Dutch Island is located in the middle of the study area.

The mobile gear fisheries of Narragansett Bay include bottom trawls that harvest finfish, lobster, and squid (Figure 2) and dredges that harvest mussels (Figure 3). The dredges work primarily in the pebble and cobble environments along the peripheral edges of the bay, and the trawls work primarily in the sand and mud environments.

The state of Rhode Island issues a multipurpose commercial fishing license, and there is no trip-ticket or log reporting system. Therefore, this description of Rhode Island mobile-gear fisheries is based on anecdotal information provided by state regulatory agency personnel and leaders of local fishermen's organizations. It is estimated that there have been approximately 22 mobile-gear vessels annually working the lower bay for the last decade. This includes both part-time and full-time vessels but is about equal to 15 full-time equivalent (FTE) vessels. These FTE vessels range in length from 12 to 20 m and operate for 6 months of the year, 5 d per week. Each FTE vessel makes 4–5 tows per day. Thus, Narragansett Bay experiences about 8,000 tows annually, and it is estimated that the study area, the lower portion of West Passage, experiences about 10% of the total effort or about 800 tows annually. The average tow is 1.5 h in duration at a speed of about 4 km/h. Therefore, the length of the average tow is 6 km.

Observations by divers of bottom trawls operating on the seabed indicate that the otter boards principally impact the seabed, smoothing an area along their path and creating a small ridge at the trawling edge of the otter board shoe (Wardle 1993). The width of the smoothed area depends on the angle of attack of the otter board but is generally about ½ the length of the otter board. The depth of the smoothed area and the height of the ridge depend on the weight of the board and the sediment type, but in Narragansett Bay, our observations indicate the height of the ridge to be between 10 and 20 cm and the depth of the smoothed area to be 5–10 cm. The effect of the trawl on the seabed is dependent on the design of the sweep and the sediment type. A properly fishing trawl net skims the seabed and therefore only resuspends the fine surficial sediment layer and minimally impacts the micro-topography of the seabed. Video surveillance shows that dredging causes considerably more disturbance of the seabed than the bottom trawl. The dredge rolls over gravels, pebbles, and boulders; flattens bedforms on soft sand and mud sediments; and resuspends fine sediments. In Narragansett Bay, dredge activity is less than 5% of the total effort, and when it occurs, the disturbance is limited to the 2–3-m width of the single dredge towed by the local vessels.

Methods

Evidence of Seabed Disturbance by Mobile Fishing Gear

Side-scan sonar data were obtained from the National Oceanic and Atmospheric Administration (NOAA). Surveys were performed from 31 August– 25 September 1995 aboard the NOAA S/V Rude, a 27.4-m vessel equipped with an EdgeTech 262 side-scan sonar and P-code Global Positioning System. The system was adjusted to record a 50-m-wide range on either side of the trackline. Two duplicate surveys were performed within weeks of each other, and each of the surveys had 110% coverage (10%

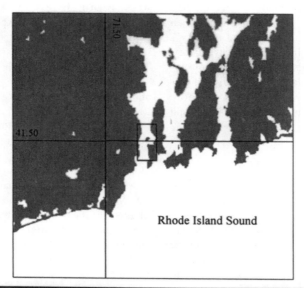

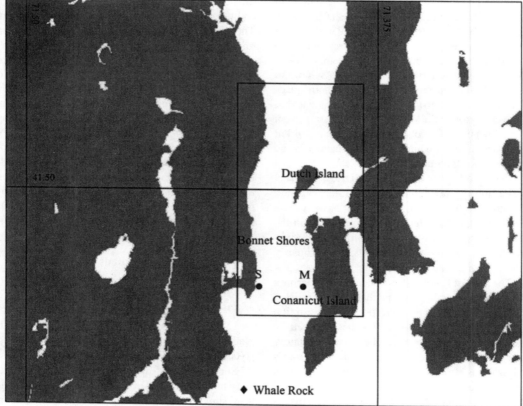

FIGURE 1.—Maps of the study area: (top) Lower Narragansett Bay and Rhode Island Sound and (bottom) the West Passage with Dutch Island in the center of the study area. The two study sites are indicated as S (sand site) and M (mud site).

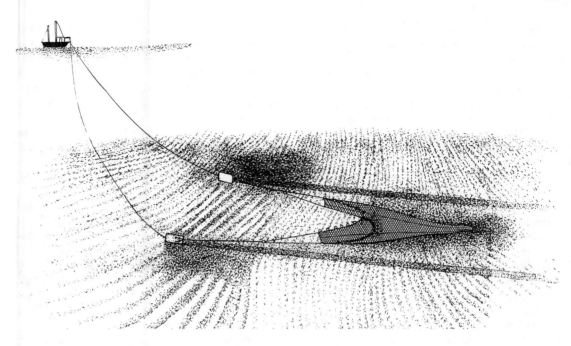

FIGURE 2.—Eastern rig fishing vessel towing a bottom trawl over the seabed. Note the clouds of suspended sediment downstream of the otter boards, the pair of bottom scars caused by the otter boards, and the smoothing of sediment in the wake of the trawl net.

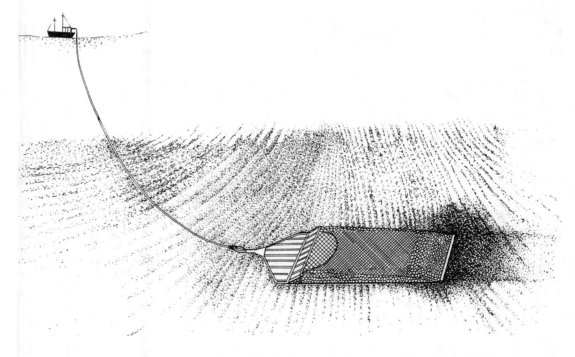

FIGURE 3.—Eastern rig fishing vessel towing a scallop-and-mussel dredge over a soft-bottom seabed. Note the smoothing of the micro-relief on the seabed by the dredge.

overlap in track lines). The track lines for the two surveys were offset from each other by 50 m. The two surveys were combined into one data set.

Analysis of the side-scan sonar records was conducted by creating an interpretation scheme and applying the scheme to all of the data obtained from NOAA. The records were interpreted at approximately 50-m spacing along each track line, thereby creating an interpretive data-point area of 50 m × 100 m. Trawl and dredge scars were noted and divided into 7 categories from 0 to 6, where 0 is the absence of scars and 6 is the presence of greater than 10 scars. Sediment type was interpreted based on acoustic backscatter and was divided into mud, sand, pebble and cobble, and boulder categories. Finally, structures were noted (if present), which included single boulders by sizes, shipwrecks, anchors, moorings, and lobster pots. Data were recorded in Excel, imported into Surfer, and plotted. Post plots were created of the interpretive points, bottom type, and distribution of scars. A detailed depth contour chart was constructed based on the bathymetric data (corrected to mean low water) collected concurrently with the side-scan sonar data.

Total area sampled was estimated by multiplying the area of each interpretive data point (50 m × 100 m) by the total number of interpretive points. This total was divided by 2.2 to account for the two surveys, each with 10% overlap. The total area that was scarred was estimated by assuming that the width of each scar was 0.5 m (a weighted average for trawls and dredges), multiplying the width by the length of each scar at each interpretive point (50 m) and by the number of scars recorded at each interpretive point, and dividing by 2.2 for duplication.

Characterization of the Bottom Hydrodynamic Environment and Sediment Transport Processes

The hydrodynamic environment at 1 m above the seabed was estimated for two experimental sites in the southern portion of Narragansett Bay using a methodology based on the Shore Protection Manual (CERC 1984) but using a Hjulstrom diagram to estimate the critical velocity for sediment erosion. The two sites included a shallow (7 m) sand area located at 41°28.636′ N, 71°25.027′ W and a deep (14 m) mud area located at 41°28.173′ N, 71°24.048′ W. Both of the sites were within the study area (Figure 1). A surface wave climate for the mouth of Narragansett Bay was developed based on four information sources. Hicks et al.

(1956) provided daily observations of wave height and period for two locations in the mouth of Narragansett Bay (Fort Varnum and Scarborough). Naval ship observations (Sea State Meteorological Observations, or SSMO) in southern New England waters (Quonset Marsden Square) for a 5-year period (1963–1968) were summarized in the final report of a dredge material disposal study (Anonymous 1975). In addition, hindcast wave climate data for station 83 in Rhode Island Sound for the 20-year period 1956–1975 (Wave Information Studies, or WIS) were taken from Hubertz et al. (1993). These data were analyzed, plotted as wave height versus cumulative probability greater than, and correlated for period and height. Regression models were best fit to both data sets. Tidal currents at 1 m above the seabed for the two sites were derived from average tidal currents provided by a vertically integrated numerical model (Spaulding and Swanson 1984) and were adjusted to 1 m above the seabed using a power-law velocity profile with $n = 7$ (Munson et al. 1994). Linear wave theory was used to estimate the maximum orbital velocity at 1 m above the seabed for the bay mouth wave climate at the two experimental sites' water depths. Critical velocities for erosion of sand and mud were conservatively taken from the Hjulstrom diagram.

Field Verification of the Longevity of Bottom Scars

Field studies to determine the longevity of bottom scars were conducted between June and July of 1998. The longevity of a scar is interpreted as a measure of both frequency of natural seabed disturbance and the recovery time of the substrate. Experiments were conducted at the two sites used in the hydrodynamic model analysis. (These sites are described in the preceding paragraph; see also Figure 1.) Sampling was conducted from a 6.4-m Boston Whaler. A stake field (DeAlteris et al. 1975) was established at both sites using two 1.8-m-long iron stakes; the stakes were driven into the sediment so that half was in the sediment and half was left exposed. The stakes were spaced 1.2 m apart. Each site was marked with a buoy at the surface attached to a concrete anchor. Divers scarred the bottom using a hand-held shovel, and the scars were approximately 15 cm deep and 1.2 m long. At both sites, the scars were made parallel and perpendicular to the two stakes. Divers visually checked the sites routinely (daily for the first week, and then weekly for two months) to monitor the longevity of the scars.

Results

Evidence of Seabed Disturbance by Mobile Fishing Gear

The results of the analysis of the side-scan sonar data are presented in Figures 4a–4d. The survey track lines with the individual interpretative data points are shown in Figure 4a. A total of 6,163 interpretive data points were included in the analysis, incorporating an area of 14 km². The contoured bathymetric data show a deep channel on the east side of the southern portion of West Passage that diverges into two channels around Dutch Island, and these channels converge into a single deep channel again on the eastern side of the northern portion of West Passage (Figure 4b). The bottom sediment types were predominantly mud with boulder fields along the shallow shoreline areas and sand with sand waves in the shallow southwestern portion of the study area (Figure 4c). This spatial bottom-type pattern corresponds reasonably well with the sediment grain size distribution reported by McMaster (1960) based on grab samples. The distribution of scars on the seabed attributable to the activity of mobile fishing gear is shown in Figure 4d. The number of scars evident in a single interpretive data point (50 m × 100 m) varied from 0 to more than 10. The spatial distribution of the scars was limited to the deep mud channels within the study area. A digital image of an original side-scan sonar interpretive data point from the lower bay is shown in Figure 5. The scars of individual otter boards are clearly evident, and when the original records were mosaiked, individual track pairs were observed, with two start and end points. The total area observed to be scarred by otter boards is estimated to be 0.12 km², or 0.9% of the area surveyed.

Characterization of the Bottom Hydrodynamic Environment and Sediment Transport Processes

The results of the characterizations of the hydrodynamic environment and sediment transport processes are presented in Figures 6a–6d. The four data sources provide a wave climate at the mouth of Narragansett Bay that indicates that waves greater than 1 m with a period of 8 s occur 20% of the time, and waves greater than 2 m with a period of 10 s occur only 5% of the time (Figures 6a and 6b). Maximum tidal currents 1 m above the bed at the sand and mud experimental sites were different, with the ebb current at the mud site being about 8 cm/s greater than at the sand site (Figure 6c). The maximum ve-

locity 1 m above the bed was determined by adding the maximum daily ebb tidal velocity at each site to the maximum wave orbital velocity calculated for the wave conditions (height and period) at the bay mouth at each site (7- and 14-m depths). The critical erosion velocities for sand and mud were estimated at 20 and 100 cm/s, respectively. Based on these methods, sediments in the sand location are eroded 100% of the time or every day, whereas at the mud site, erosion is predicted to occur less than 5% of the time (Figure 6d).

Field Verification of the Longevity of Bottom Scars

At the mud site, the two scars were monitored periodically and were observed to be unchanged for a period greater than 60 d. At the sand site, the first two scars lasted four days. Then the site was rescarred by the divers, and the scars lasted three days. In the third and final experiment at the sand site, the two scars lasted only one day. The divers made the following observations during the field work:

1. Large Atlantic rock crabs *Cancer irroratus* were observed inhabiting the scars in the mud area.
2. Sediments were observed in motion on all dives at the sand site.
3. Although both areas experience the activity of mobile fishing gear during certain seasons, lobster pots were found at both sites during the experimental period.

Discussion and Conclusions

With the emerging interest in essential fish habitat relative to the conservation and management of marine resources, mobile fishing gear is being scrutinized as contributing to the degradation of marine habitat. Seabed disturbance by mobile fishing gear is recognized as an important issue; however, we argue that seabed disturbance by mobile fishing gear must be evaluated relative to seabed disturbance due to natural physical and biological causes. We selected the lower portion of Narragansett Bay, Rhode Island as a case study area to compare seabed disturbance due to mobile fishing gear to seabed disturbance due to natural physical processes alone.

A small fleet of inshore mobile-gear vessels tow bottom trawls and dredges across the seabed in Narragansett Bay: approximately 15 FTE vessels make about 8,000 tows annually in the bay. The study area is

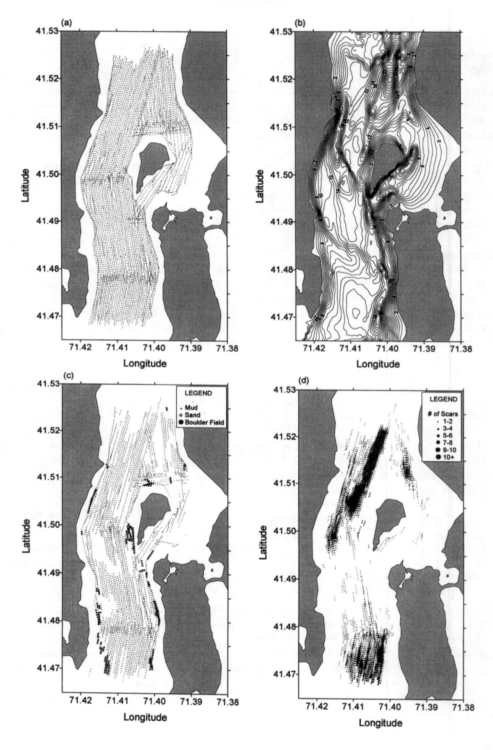

FIGURE 4.—Results of side-scan sonar data analysis, showing (a) interpretative data points; (b) high-resolution bathymetry in meters, contoured at 1-m intervals; (c) bottom type; and (d) abundance and distribution of bottom scars.

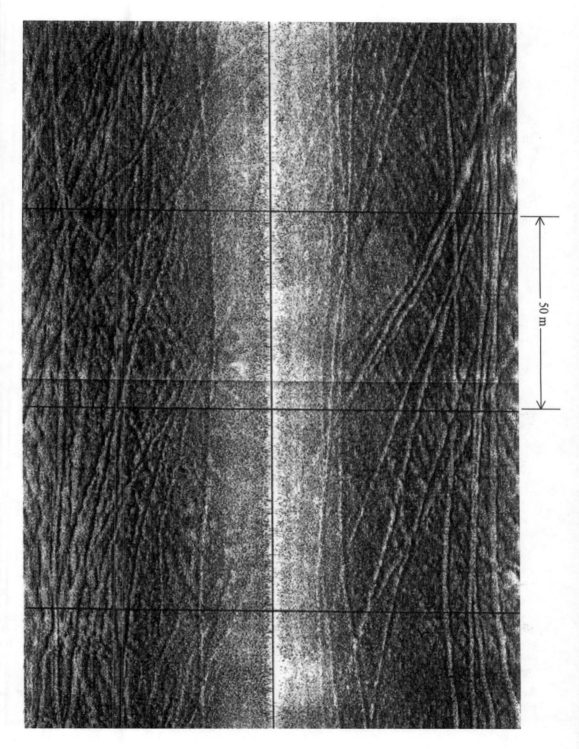

FIGURE 5.—Digital image of an interpretative data point (50 m × 100 m) from the side-scan sonar records showing 10 + bottom scars due to mobile fishing gear.

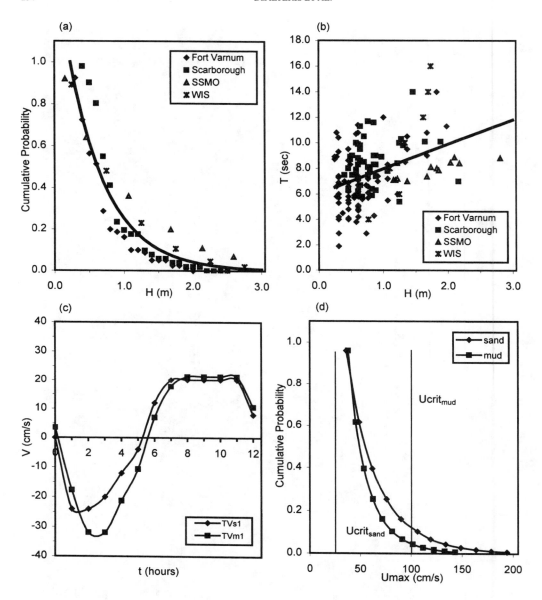

FIGURE 6.—Results of hydrodynamic and sediment transport process analysis, showing (a) wave climate for the mouth of Narragansett Bay, wave height versus cumulative probability greater than; (b) wave climate of the mouth of Narragansett Bay, wave period versus wave height; (c) tidal currents (cm/s) at 1 m above the bed for the sand (TVs1) and mud (TVm1) experimental sites; and (d) probability of sediment erosion at the sand and mud experimental sites based on the critical erosion velocities (cm/s) and maximum bottom velocities (cm/s) versus the cumulative probability greater than.

the lower portion of the West Passage in Narragansett Bay. This area experiences about 10% of the total mobile-gear effort, or 800 tows annually, with each tow estimated at 6 km in length. Mobile-gear activity occurs on mud, sand, and rock substrates, but we have restricted our analyses to the soft sediment bottoms (sand and mud).

The results of our analysis of side-scan sonar data available for the study area indicate that bottom scarring due to trawl doors is restricted to the relatively deep sandy mud substrates, despite observations that trawling activity occurs in all the habitat types in Narragansett Bay. Our estimate of the area impacted by bottom scars is less than 1% of the total area surveyed.

The model analysis of the bottom hydrodynamic and sediment transport processes of the two experimental sites in the lower portion of the study area indicates that sediment transport occurs daily in the shallow (7 m) sand substrate but less than 5% of the time in the deep (14 m) mud substrate. This suggests that bottom scars will be short-lived in the shallow sand site and long-lived in the deep mud site.

The actual longevity of bottom scars in these two experimental sites was measured in a field study. Bottom scars dug and monitored by divers lasted only 1–4 d in the shallow sand substrate as compared to greater than 60 d in the deep mud substrate. Thus, this difference in scar longevity is also a measure of a difference in substrate recovery time.

From these analyses, we conclude that although mobile fishing gear disturbs the seabed, the significance of that disturbance must be compared to the magnitude and frequency of natural seabed disturbance. In this study, our analyses indicate that in a shallow, sand substrate, natural physical processes are disturbing the seabed regularly. Thus, the substrate's recovery from fishing-gear–related disturbance is almost immediate. However, in the deep, mud substrate, the results of our analyses indicate that natural processes are rarely capable of disturbing the seabed, and therefore recovery from fishing-gear-related disturbance is slow. These results correspond well with the conclusions of Kaiser et al. (1998) in their study of megafaunal benthic communities in different habitats after trawling disturbance.

Our analysis of fishing effort suggests that potentially 4.8 km^2 of the seabed within the study area may be disturbed annually by mobile gear scars (6.0-km tow length x [0.5 + 0.5]m width disturbed x 800.0 tows). However, we identified only 0.1 km^2 of scars in the side-scan sonar data. This indicates that habitat recovery, albeit slow, must occur even in the mud substrate.

We recommend that an analysis of the seaward extent of active sediment transport for the continental shelf would be helpful in the evaluation of seabed disturbance by mobile fishing gear. The U.S. Army Corps of Engineers has available hindcast wave climates for the shelf region, and the U.S. Geological Survey has water depth and sediment grain size data for the shelf region; an analysis of fishing activity by gear type and location based on a NMFS database could be conducted for the same region. Comparison of these analyses would allow for the identification of areas that may be problematic with respect to seabed disturbance by mobile fishing gear, that is, areas with substantial fishing activity and minimal natural physical disturbance.

Acknowledgments

The authors thank the Rhode Island Sea Grant College Program for the support of this research. N. Perugini of the NOAA Corps graciously provided the raw side-scan sonar records and the navigational track data.

References

Amos, C. L., and E. L. King. 1984. Bedforms of the Canadian eastern seaboard: a comparison with global occurrences. Marine Geology 57:167–208.

Anonymous. 1975. Environmental assessment of Fall River Harbor dredging and Browns Ledge disposal. volume 2, appendices. Narragansett Marine Laboratory, University of Rhode Island, Kingston.

Anonymous. 1996. Side-scan sonar record interpretation. Klein Associates, Salem, New Hampshire.

Auster, P. J., and nine coauthors. 1996. The impacts of mobile fishing gear on seafloor habitats in the Gulf of Maine (Northwest Atlantic): implications for conservation of fish populations. Reviews in Fisheries Science 4(2):185–202.

Auster, P. J., and R. W. Langton. 1999. The effects of fishing on fish habitat. Pages 150–187 in L. R. Benaka, editor. Fish habitat: essential fish habitat and rehabilitation. American Fisheries Society, Symposium 22, Bethesda, Maryland.

Cacchione, D. A., and D. E. Drake. 1990. Shelf sediment transport: an overview with applications to the northern California continental shelf. Pages 729–773 in B. LeMehaute and D. M. Hanes, editors. The sea, volume 9, part B, ocean engineering science. Wiley, New York.

Caddy, J. F. 1973. Underwater observations in tracks of dredges and trawls and some effects of dredging on a scallop ground. Journal of the Fisheries Research Board of Canada 30:173–180.

Caddy, J. F., and T. D. Iles. 1972. Underwater observations on herring spawning grounds on Georges Bank. International Commission for the Northwest Atlantic Fisheries Research Bulletin.

CERC (Coastal Engineering Research Center). 1984. Shore protection manual volume 1. Department of the Army, Waterway Experiment Station Corps of Engineers, Coastal Engineering Research Center, Vicksburg, Mississippi.

Churchill, J. H. 1989. The effect of commercial trawling on sediment resuspension and transport over the Middle Atlantic Bight continental shelf. Continental Shelf Research 9(9):841–864.

Collie, J. S., G. A. Escanero, and P. C. Valentine. 1997. Effects of bottom fishing on the benthic mega-fauna of Georges Bank. Marine Ecology Progress Series 155:159–172.

Dayton, P. K., S. F. Thrush, M. T. Agardy, and R. J. Hofman. 1995. Viewpoint: environmental effects of marine fishing. Aquatic Conservation: Marine and Freshwater Ecosystems 5:205–232.

DeAlteris, J. T. 1988. Application of hydroacoustics to the mapping of subtidal oyster reefs. Journal of Shellfish Research 7(1):41–45.

DeAlteris, J. T., C. Carr, J. Roney, and L. Stahl. 1975. A sediment transport study, offshore, New Jersey. Pages 225–244 in Proceedings of civil engineering in the oceans III. American Society of Civil Engineers, New York.

de Groot, S. J. 1984. The impact of bottom trawling on benthic fauna of the North Sea. Ocean Management 9:177–190.

Eleftheriou, A., and M. R. Robertson. 1992. The effects of experimental scallop dredging on the fauna and physical environment of a shallow sandy community. Netherlands Journal of Sea Research 30:289–299.

Fader, G. B., and S. S. Pecore. 1988. Surficial geology of the Abegweit Passage area of Northumberland Strait, Gulf of St. Lawrence. Atlantic Geoscience Centre, Open File No. 2087, Bedford Institute of Oceanography, Dartmouth, Nova Scotia.

Graf, W. H. 1971. Hydraulic of sediment transport. McGraw-Hill, New York.

Harrison, P. H., K. W. Strong, and K. A. Jenner. 1991. A review of fishery related seabed disturbance on the Grand Banks of Newfoundland. Final contractors report to the Department of Fisheries and Oceans from Maritime Testing (1985) Ltd., Dartmouth, Nova Scotia.

Hicks, S. D. 1959. The physical oceanography of Narragansett Bay. Limnology and Oceanography 4(3):316–327.

Hicks, S. D., D. E. Frazier, and A. F. Taylor. 1956. Wind wave characteristics of Rhode Island Waters. Interim Report 4, Ref. No. 56-3, Hurricane Protection Project. Narragansett Marine Laboratory, University of Rhode Island, Kingston.

Hjulstrom, F. 1939. Transport of detritus by moving water. Pages 5–31 in P. B. Trask, editor. Recent marine sediment. The American Association of Petroleum Geologists, Tulsa, Oklahoma.

Hubertz, J. M., R. M. Brooks, W. A. Brendan, and B. A. Tracey. 1993. Hindcast wave information for the U.S. Atlantic coast. Wave Information Studies Report 30, U.S. Army Engineers Waterways Experiment Stations. Coastal Engineering Research Center, Vicksburg, Mississippi.

ICES (International Council for the Exploration of the Sea). 1995. Report of the study group on ecosystem effects of fishing activities, 1992. International Council for the Exploration of the Sea Cooperative Research Report 200.

Jenner, K., K. W. Strong, and P. Pocklington. 1991. A review of fishery related seabed disturbance in the Scotia-Fundy region. Industry Services and Native Fisheries Branch, Project Report 166. Maritime Testing (1985) Ltd., Dartmouth, Nova Scotia.

Jones, J. B. 1992. Environmental impact of trawling on the seabed: a review. New Zealand Journal of Marine and Freshwater Research 26:59–67.

Kaiser, M. J., and six coauthors. 1998. Change in megafaunal benthic communities in different habitats after trawling disturbance. ICES Journal of Marine Science 55:353–361.

Kaiser, M. J., and B. E. Spencer. 1996. The effects of beam-trawl disturbance on infaunal communities in different habitats. Journal of Animal Ecology 65:348–358.

Krebs, C. J. 1994. Ecology. Harper-Collins, New York.

Krost, P., M. Bernhard, F. Werner, and W. Hukriede. 1990. Otter trawl tracks in Kiel Bay (Western Baltic) mapped by side-scan sonar. Meeresforsch 32:344–353.

Langton, R. W., and W. E. Robinson. 1990. Faunal associations on scallop grounds in the western Gulf of Maine. Experimental Marine Biology and Ecology 144:157–171.

MacLennan, D., and E. J. Simmonds. 1992. Fisheries acoustics. Chapman and Hall, London.

Madsen, O. S., and W. D. Grant. 1976. Sediment transport in the coastal environment. Ralph M. Parsons Laboratory. Massachusetts Institute of Technology Report 209, Cambridge, Massachusetts.

Mayer, L. M., D. F. Schick, R. H. Findlay, and D. L. Rice. 1991. Effects of commercial dragging on sedimentary organic matter. Marine Environmental Research 31:249–261.

McMaster, R. L. 1960. Sediments of the Narragansett Bay system and Rhode Island Sound, RI. Journal of Sedimentary Petrology 39:249–274.

Messieh, S. M., T. W. Rowell, D. L. Peer, and P. J. Cranford. 1991. The effects of trawling, dredging and ocean dumping on the eastern Canadian continental shelf seabed. Continental Shelf Research 11:1237–1263.

Metha, A. J., and K. R. Dyer. 1990. Cohesive sediment transport in estuarine and coastal waters. Pages 815–839 in B. LeMehaute and D. M. Hanes, editors. The sea, volume 9, part B, ocean engineering science. Wiley, New York.

Munson, B. R., D. F. Young, and T. H. Okiishi. 1994. Fundamentals of fluid mechanics. Wiley, New York.

Partheniades, E. 1965. Erosion and deposition of cohesive soils. Journal of Hydraulics Division, American Society of Civil Engineers (91)HY1:105–138.

Prena, J., T. W. Rowell, P. Schwinghamer, K. Gilkinson, and D. C. Gordon, Jr. 1994. Grand Banks otter trawling impact experiment: I. site selection process, with a description of macrofaunal communities. Canadian Technical Report of Fisheries, and Aquatic Sciences 2094.

Redant, F. 1987. A bibliography on the effects of bottom fishing gear and harvesting techniques on benthic biota. Benthos Ecology Working Group, International Council for the Exploration of the Sea, C. M. 1987/L:26. ICES, Copenhagen, Denmark.

Rhoads, D. C., P. L. McCall, and J. Y. Yingst. 1978. Disturbance and production on the estuarine seafloor. American Scientist 66:577–587.

Riemann, B., and E. Hoffmann. 1991. Ecological consequences of dredging and bottom trawling in the Limfjord, Denmark. Marine Ecology Progress Series 69:171–178.

Sherwood, C. R. 1989. Use of sediment transport calculations in dredged material disposal site selection. Pages 326–332 in Oceans '89: the global ocean. volume 2: ocean pollution. MTS/IEEE, New York.

Shields, A. 1936. Anwendung der ahnlichkeitsmechanik und turbulenzforschung anf die geschiebebewegung. Mitteil Preuss. Uersuchsanst. Wasser, Erd, Schiffsbau, Berlin.

Sleath, J. F. 1990. Seabed boundary layers. Pages 693–729 *in* B. Le Mehaute and D. M. Hanes, editors. The sea, volume 9, part B, ocean engineering science. Wiley, New York.

Spaulding, M., and C. Swanson. 1984. Tides and tidal currents of Narragansett Bay, RI. Marine Technical Report 35, University of Rhode Island, Narragansett.

Sternberg, R. W. 1972. Predicting initial motion and bedland transport of sediment particles in the shallow marine environment. Pages 61–82 *in* D. P. Swift, D. B. Duane, and O. H. Pilky. Shelf sediment transport: processes and patterns. Dowden, Hutchinson, and Ross, Stroudsburg, Pennsylvania.

Urick, R. J. 1983. Principles of underwater sound. Peninsula Publishers, Los Altos, California.

von Brandt, A. 1984. Fish catching methods of the world. Fishing News Books, Farnham, UK.

Wardle, C. 1993. Fish behavior and fishing gear. Pages 609–643 *in* T. J. Pitcher, editor. Behavior of teleost fishes. Chapman and Hall, London.

Werner, F., J. Altenkirch, R. S. Newton, and E. Seibold. 1976. Sediment patterns and their temporal variation on abrasion ridges in a moderate flow regime (Stoller Grund, Western Baltic). Meyniana 28:95–105.

Wright, L. D. 1995. Morphodynamics of inner continental shelves. CRC Press, Boca Raton, Florida.

American Fisheries Society Symposium 22:239, 1999

Part Four:
Nonfishing Impacts on Fish Habitat

Robert R. Stickney

Director, Texas Sea Grant College Program
1716 Briarcrest Drive, Suite 702, Bryan, Texas 77802, USA

It only takes a small amount of thought to come up with an extensive list of nonfishing impacts on fish habitat. My "off-the-top-of-the-head" list includes point and nonpoint source pollution, noxious algal blooms, exotic species invasions, dredging and filling projects, global climate variation, storm activity, wetland restoration, artificial-reef-building projects, tectonic events, boating activity, and mining projects. I immediately added war to my list because bombs and torpedoes can have an ugly impact on ecosystems. Many of the preceding impacts are negative. At least two of the preceding impacts, wetland restoration and artificial-reef-building projects, can be very positive. And at least one of the impacts, war, can have both positive and negative effects.

This particular part of the symposium took both the broad and narrow view but overall considered many of the possible nonfishing impacts on fish habitat. A presentation at the American Fisheries Society's (AFS's) August 1998 Annual Meeting in Hartford, Connecticut by Bob Francis (not included in this volume) on interdecadal climate variations in the North Pacific on various fish species distribution patterns took into consideration a big chunk of the world's marine environment. Taking a narrower view are discussions in the following chapters of the restoration of portions of the extensive Louisiana wetlands by R. Glenn Thomas and of community involvement with agencies to help restore an Oregon watershed by Paul Heikkila. Focusing even further, J. Stanley Cobb et al. describe the impacts of an oil spill on a New England lobster community.

One of the items that should have made my list of nonfishing impacts but did not was land-use practices. That topic, with respect to forestry, is covered by Nina Kelly et al. Finally, a chapter by Anthony Wilbur and Michael Pentony, based on a poster presentation at the AFS meeting, provides a compilation of various human activities that can impact fish habitat. Again, Wilbur and Pentony's chapter contains items that I had not considered.

These chapters demonstrate not only some different approaches to habitat research but also the potential for successful outreach program development to engage the public in habitat issues. There seems to have been at least one consensus arising from the symposium in Hartford: the public will need to become engaged if the goal of taking habitat into consideration in the management of our fisheries is to be attained. Everyone has a stake in maintaining or improving habitat. One of our challenges now is to make the public aware of that fact.

American Fisheries Society Symposium 22:240–251, 1999

Fish Habitat and Coastal Restoration in Louisiana

R. GLENN THOMAS

Louisiana Department of Wildlife and Fisheries
Post Office Box 98000, Baton Rouge, Louisiana 70898-9000, USA

Abstract.—The magnitude of changes occurring in Louisiana's estuaries creates a unique set of challenges in fish habitat management. Louisiana leads the nation in rate of coastal land loss, with some 70% of national losses. Both natural and anthropogenic factors are involved in coastal land loss in Louisiana: subsidence, erosion, sediment and freshwater deficits, channelization, and rising mean sea level. Disruption of the natural deltaic cycles of the Mississippi River has been particularly detrimental to estuarine fish habitat. Navigation and flood control needs have resulted in the near-total leveeing of the river, preventing normal overbank flooding, channel filling and switching, delta and subdelta development, and sediment nourishment of adjacent and down-current marshes. The resulting system is one in which the quantity and quality of estuarine habitat are linked to rapidly degrading wetland environments. Although the relative production value of subsiding marsh surfaces is often very high, this condition is not sustainable. Steep declines in fish production have been forecast for the next century. Federal, state, and local coastal restoration projects are attempting to address the loss of estuarine habitat with a number of techniques that may produce localized changes in fisheries production and distributions. Temporary resource displacements can result in increased harvest costs, and basin-scale changes may be particularly hard to accept for resource users who are satisfied with current conditions. Harvesters have demonstrated reluctance, and may lack the financial flexibility, to forfeit expected current catches for predicted enhancement of long-term fisheries production. In some instances, both sportfishers and commercial resource users have expressed concern over estuarine freshening and turbidity from restoration inputs from riverine sources. Additional public perception difficulties with restoration efforts arise from misunderstandings of the nature of estuarine functions, particularly of the importance of nursery habitat and of the value of low-salinity marshes as nursery habitat. Significant improvement in the outlook for estuarine fish habitat in Louisiana will require long-term and large-area vision from resource managers and the public.

Coastal Louisiana is often divided into two provinces or depositional categories: the chenier plain (from the Texas line to Vermilion Bay) and the deltaic zone (the eastern coast from Vermilion Bay to the Mississippi state line) (Figure 1; Gagliano and Van Beek 1990). Many aspects of the physical nature of these provinces and subsequent fisheries habitat problems are distinctive.

Deltaic Louisiana was created in large degree by the successive formation of Mississippi River delta complexes after each major shift of the lower river. Several models for this evolution have been projected. All models report the development of a series of deltas during the Holocene epoch, with each delta being active for 1,000–1,500 years. Kolb and Van Lopik (1958) described the creation of seven delta complexes; Penland et al. (1988) described six complexes forming over the last 7,000 years (Figure 2). The Teche and Maringouin deltas were the farthest westward, overlying the area now occupied by the Vermilion-Cote Blanche system. The St. Bernard lobe developed farthest to the east, well into what is now Mississippi Sound. Natural degradation begins to act on a delta lobe

immediately upon its abandonment by the river channel, but the chronology of this process can be obscured by the overlap of delta systems and the presence of short-lived distributary channels.

The chenier plain of western Louisiana was created by the deposition of Mississippi River sediments by prevailing longshore currents. The coastal plain that formed below the Pleistocene uplands is not as broad as the deltaic plain and is characterized by a series of transverse, parallel ridges composed largely of shell. These ridges were formed when erosion exceeded deposition during periods when the mouth of the Mississippi switched to the easternmost cycles. The cheniers (named for the characteristic live oaks) slowed freshwater drainage and formed a barrier to Gulf processes, creating and protecting the largely freshwater marshes behind them (Gagliano and Van Beek 1993).

Status of the Estuaries

The magnitude of changes occurring in Louisiana's estuaries is creating unique challenges in fish habitat management. Louisiana leads the na-

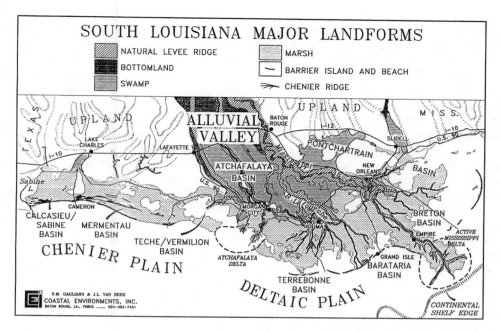

FIGURE 1.—Major landforms of coastal Louisiana. Evidence of direct deltaic formation is demonstrated in splay effects, with prominent interdistributary ridges. Sediment subsequently transported westward to the chenier plain shows transverse, reworked coastal ridges (reprinted with permission from Gagliano and Van Beek 1990).

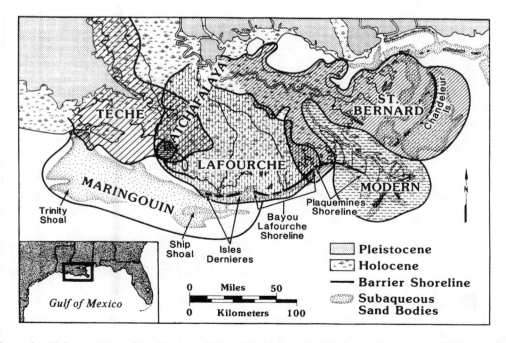

FIGURE 2.—Holocene deltas of the Mississippi River. The Maringouin delta began forming about 7,000 years before present, followed by the Teche, St. Bernard, Lafourche, Modern, and Atchafalaya deltas (as redrawn from Frazier 1967 by Penland et al. 1988; reprinted with permission from the Louisiana Geological Survey, Baton Rouge).

tion in rate of coastal land loss, with nearly 70% of national losses (Johnson et al. 1995). Wetland loss peaked during the 1970s at over 100 km²/year (Penland et al. 1990), continued at a rate of about 90 km²/year for the period 1978–1990, and dropped to about 65 km²/year by 1993. Between the 1930s and 1990, over 3,950 km² of wetlands were lost (Britsch and Dunbar 1993). The most recent estimates of ongoing loss rates are somewhat lower, due in part to the fact that many susceptible habitats have already converted to open water.

A number of factors, both natural and anthropogenic, are involved in coastal land loss in Louisiana. Subsidence, erosion, sediment and freshwater deficits, channelization, and rising mean sea level are most often listed as the principal causes. All or most of these processes are typically in operation at any given coastal location. Restoration efforts most often are directed toward correcting problems clearly created by human activity, but success will ultimately depend on the ability to counteract the majority of the effects from every process causing habitat degradation in an area.

Subsidence is the result of geologic faulting, crustal downwarping, sediment compaction, and extraction of subsurface fluids (Gagliano and Van Beek 1970; Coleman 1981; Suhayda 1987). Sediment compaction is generally believed to be the most significant contributor to Louisiana's coastal subsidence. The highest subsidence rates in Louisiana are greater than 1.5 cm/year at the Balize (modern) delta, where Holocene sediment deposits are thickest (120 m) (Figure 3). The next highest rates occur where the river incised a deep valley across the continental shelf during lowered sea levels in the early Holocene epoch (>18,000 years before present). Subsequent sea level rise caused the infilling of this valley with sediment, which is now about 60 m thick and subsides at 0.5–1.0 cm/year (Roberts 1985). Recent radiocarbon dating shows that younger sediments subside more rapidly than older sediments due to dewatering and compaction. The normal degasification process of organic-rich sediments is yet another component of subsidence (Penland et al. 1996). Across coastal Louisiana, subsidence averages 3–10 mm/year (Suhayda 1987; Penland et al. 1988).

Increase in mean sea level is another factor in coastal inundation (Coleman 1988). Over the last 80 years, eustatic sea level rise has been about 2.3–2.8 mm/year, with periods of up to 10 mm/year

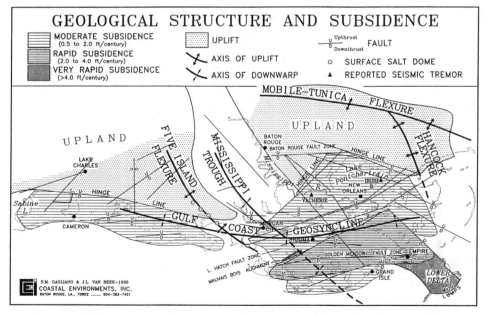

FIGURE 3.—General subsidence rates in relation to the geologic structure of south Louisiana. Subsidence is classified as moderate (0.5–2.0 ft/century; 0.15–0.61 m/century); rapid (2.0–4.0 ft/century; 0.61–1.22 m/century); or very rapid (over 4 ft/century; over 1.22 m/century) (reprinted with permission from Gagliano and Van Beek 1992).

(Suhayda 1987). When added to subsidence effects, the rate of relative sea-level rise across the coast of Louisiana averages over 1 cm/year (Penland and Ramsey 1990). Recent estimates for global warming and sea-level effects (Wigley and Raper 1992) forecast increases in rate of eustatic sea-level rise resulting in about 17.5 cm of increase from 1998 to 2050.

Geologic processes also contribute to marsh loss in Louisiana. The Gulf Coast Geosyncline is an area of coastal downwarping that extends from the inland Pleistocene terrace to the 183-m contour and from Grand Lake to Mississippi Sound (Frazier 1967). Kolb and Van Lopik (1958) estimated that basement sinking below southeast Louisiana contributed about 18% to total subsidence. A number of geologic faults underlie coastal Louisiana and produce increased local subsidence along thrust lines (Figure 3; Gagliano and Van Beek 1992).

Extractions (most often oil, gas, sulfur, and formation water) probably contribute least to total subsidence rates. Suhayda (1987) estimated that subsidence of over 10 cm due to oil and gas extraction in Louisiana can be expected over about 400 km^2 and that 80 cm of settlement can occur directly above depleted reservoirs.

Man has virtually eliminated the natural delta-building processes of the Mississippi River. Leveeing of New Orleans began in 1717, and by 1935 levees lined 3,427 km of the Mississippi (Russell et al. 1936). Expanding navigation and flood-control needs have since resulted in the near-total leveeing of the river, preventing normal overbank flooding, channel filling and switching, delta and subdelta development, and sediment nourishment of adjacent marshes (Viosca 1927; Saucier 1963; Baumann et al. 1984; Templet and Meyer-Arendt 1988). Concurrent changes in land-use practices and the damming of major upstream tributaries have also lowered the suspended sediment load of the lower Mississippi by almost 80% since the latter half of the 19th century (Kesel 1989). Today, most of the sediment load of the river is carried between levees to the modern "birdfoot" delta, which is dominated by several large passes. Navigation maintenance of the passes halts the natural cycle of shoaling, crevassing, and subdelta development, producing high efficiency of sediment transport into very deep Gulf waters with minimal deltaic aggradation. Effective delta-building is occurring in Louisiana only at the mouths of the Atchafalaya River, which now carries about one-third of the flow of the Mississippi River into shallow coastal waters.

In Louisiana, the construction of canals for general navigation and mineral extraction began in earnest in the 1930s. By 1970 there were 7,360 km of canals south of the Intracoastal Waterway (Barrett 1970). Direct wetland loss from canal dredging accounted for 120 km^2 of the total loss (about 16%) between 1955 and 1978. This massive alteration of coastal hydrology has produced ecological consequences far beyond the significant direct loss of habitat. Canals contribute indirectly to additional marsh loss by allowing increased erosive energy, salinity intrusion, and disruption of flow effects, producing areas of excessive sediment drying as well as areas of waterlogging (Turner and Cahoon 1988). Several natural processes are immediately disrupted wherever canals are cut between the Gulf and inland marshes. Freshwater storage effects, where freshwater inputs are held for gradual release through the seaward marshes, are subverted, and water of higher salinity and tidal energy can more frequently enter the upper marshes. Where canals are constructed "across the grain" of basin and interbasin ridges, most sheet flow effect becomes channelized (Gagliano 1973). Storms and floods that would have evenly overwashed marsh surfaces, depositing sediment and exporting detritus, may instead result only in high flows in certain waterways. The combined contribution of direct and indirect effects from canal building is postulated to be from 30% to 59% of all marsh loss (Turner and Cahoon 1988).

Marsh loss has also been caused by various attempts toward development. Perret et al. (1971) documented over 300 km^2 of coastal wetlands that had been filled and drained for all types of development; by 1990 over 2,000 km^2 had been developed (Day et al. 1990). Additionally, efforts to "reclaim" wetlands for agriculture during the period 1900–1920 resulted in near-universal failure. Sediments in these areas dried, oxidized, and subsided, and increasing costs to keep them dewatered eventually resulted in over 400 km^2 of shallow, open-water impoundments (Gagliano 1973).

Implications for Fish Production

The link between the riverine development of Louisiana's extensive coastal wetlands and the state's remarkable fisheries production has long

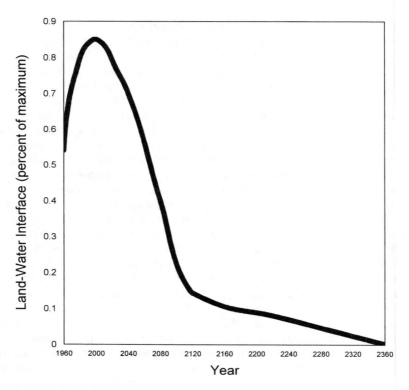

FIGURE 4.—Projected land–water interface length, expressed as percent of maximum, for the Lafourche delta (adapted from Browder et al. 1989).

been recognized (Viosca 1928; Kutkuhn 1966; Gunter 1967). More recently, the area of land–water interface has been tied more directly to fishery production than has general wetland acreage (Faller 1979; Gosselink 1984; Zimmerman et al. 1984). Turner (1977) related shrimp yield to total acreage of intertidal vegetation present in adjacent estuaries but noted that assessments of total intertidal area may actually have produced indices of the most valuable habitat: marsh "edge." Peterson and Turner (1994) showed that flooded marsh vegetation is important habitat for resident fauna (especially Cyprinodontiformes and *Paleomonetes* sp.) but that marsh transient species use primarily the edge habitats during regular tidal cycles. Morris et al. (1990) correlated shrimp and menhaden production with high mean sea levels during certain months, proposing that higher water levels resulted in increased time for juveniles to forage in vegetated habitats with reduced exposure to predation. This effect is functionally similar to that of submergence of coastal

marsh described by Rozas and Reed (1993), where habitat value of badly deteriorated marsh is maximized, at least until a certain point of marsh loss is reached (Zimmerman et al. 1991). Thus subsiding marshes flooded above sustainable levels may be accounting for some portion of continued high fisheries production in the face of Lousiana's massive marsh loss.

In a study of marshes in three Louisiana coastal basins, Browder et al. (1989) found a parabolic relationship between land–water interface and marsh disintegration. Aggregated simulation data suggested that interface area would be near maximum at about the year 2000, with a steep decline to follow. A significant positive linear relationship was found between brown shrimp *Penaeus aztecus* catch and interface length over 28 years, again attesting to the high production value of degraded marshes. Declining interface length and associated production can be expected when open water area exceeds 50% of total marsh surface (Browder et al. 1985). These data forecast dramatic declines in brown shrimp harvest (and possibly harvests of several other species) in relation to predicted interface losses over the next 75 years (Browder et al. 1989; Figure 4).

Coastal Restoration

Louisiana's coastal restoration efforts began in earnest in 1981 with passage of Legislative Act 41: The Coastal Protection Trust Fund. In 1989, Act 6 created the State Wetlands Conservation and Restoration Fund, for which monies were allocated by public referendum via constitutional amendment. The campaign shifted to a higher level in 1990 with enactment of the federal Coastal Wetlands Planning, Protection, and Restoration Act (CWPPRA). The CWPPRA established a federal cost-sharing mechanism and a task force of five federal agencies to work with the state to develop a "comprehensive approach to restore and prevent the loss of coastal wetlands in Louisiana." Sixty-two major coastal restoration projects have since been selected for implementation. Expected benefits over the 20-year life of the projects include the direct compensation of 298 km² of lost wetlands and enhancement of an additional 3,560 km² (LCWCRTF 1997). Project types currently range from barrier island restoration to vegetation plantings (Table 1). Although fisheries managers generally concur with the underlying con-

TABLE 1.—Total areas of active Coastal Wetland Planning, Protection, and Restoration Act projects in Louisiana, by project type. (Data provided by the Louisiana Department of Natural Resources, Coastal Restoration Division, Baton Rouge.)

Project type	Number of projects	Total area (km²)
Barrier island restoration	4	10.0
Beneficial use of dredged material	7	33.6
Freshwater diversion	4	301.3
Hydrologic restoration	16	1,032.2
Marsh creation	2	0.1
Marsh management	5	223.3
Sediment trapping	2	21.5
Shoreline protection	13	198.3
Terracing	1	12.9
Vegetation plantings	3	18.5
Total	57	1,851.7

cept that vegetated wetlands are more productive estuarine habitats than open water, there is disagreement over the relative merits of the various restoration project types. Marsh management projects in particular draw criticism for the potential to interfere with sediment transport (Reed 1992; Boumans and Day 1994; Cahoon 1994; Reed et al. 1997) and limit fish access (Rogers et al. 1992; Herke et al. 1992) to the marshes that are protected from increased salinity and erosive forces. Marsh management is most widespread in the chenier plain (Gosselink et al. 1979), where the low-salinity marshes north of the cheniers have become exposed to marine processes primarily from navigation canals. Over 1,100 km² of marshes (Day et al. 1990) have come under management programs developed by private, local, state, and federal entities.

The next phase for Louisiana's coastal restoration effort is the Coast 2050 initiative. This effort by the CWPPRA Task Force, State Wetlands Authority, and Louisiana Department of Natural Resources Coastal Zone Management Authority seeks to produce an overarching strategic plan to sustain coastal resources. Public acceptance and ecosystem needs will receive equal consideration in the strategies being considered (Table 2) for achieving a sustainable system by the year 2050 (Figure 5). An exhaustive effort is underway to compile all necessary information (including subsidence rates, historic and predicted land losses and causes, fisheries trends and forecasts, human infrastructure, and permitted activities) and gather input from coastal stakeholders. The resulting plan (scheduled for December 1998 completion) will attempt to mesh stakeholders' needs with restoration strategies.

Issues at the Forefront

The recapture and management of freshwater and sediment inputs from the Mississippi and Atchafalaya rivers is widely viewed as a critical component of any restoration plan (Viosca 1927; Gagliano 1989; Kesel 1989; Boesch et al. 1994; Day et al. 1997). Apprehension toward freshwater reintroduction efforts is sometimes based on the perception that only salt marsh is prime habitat for estuarine species. The public is often unaware of the importance of nursery habitat and the importance of low-salinity areas as nursery habitat (Parker 1970; Perret et al. 1971; Connor and Truesdale 1972; Chambers 1980; Zein-Eldin and Renaud 1986). The results of statewide small-mesh sampling from

TABLE 2.—Some of the principal strategies under consideration in the development of Louisiana's Coast 2050 plan. Selected strategies will be combined for each coastal planning unit to meet ecosystem and infrastructure needs.

Strategy	Examples
Hurricane and flood protection	Increase size, length of levees; realign levee systems; construct new levees.
Wastewater treatment	Require higher treatment levels; induce improved compliance rates; route outflows through wetland areas.
Beneficial use of dredged material	Use dredged material to maintain levees, create marshes, build terraces, create islands.
Hydrological management	Maintain or restore sheet flows; gap spoil banks; improve drainage; plug canals; install control structures.
Herbivory control	Protect plantings with barriers; encourage harvest of nuisance populations.
Tidal prism reduction	Re-establish integrity of natural ridges; increase sediment accretion; construct tidal barriers.
Reef zone creation and re-creation	Create reefs with stone or shell; replant oyster reefs; place oyster cultch (substrate).
Marsh bay and lake shoreline protection	"Armor" shorelines with hard materials; plant vegetation; install soft-structure mats, bales.
Freshwater diversion	Increase freshwater flows to create or improve marsh and swamp habitats.
Barrier island restoration	Increase island size, elevation by hauling or pumping sediment; restore back marshes.
Sediment delivery	Manage dredged material use and riverine inputs; add sediment delivery systems to freshwater diversion; optimize diversion flow rates.
Submerged aquatic vegetation (SAV) improvement	Protect existing SAV by excluding activity; plant new beds; increase production by improving water quality.
Navigation channel impact reduction	Control flows with structures; gap and degrade spoil banks; plug and refill unused canals.
Marsh re-creation	Create islands or terraces in shallow, open water with sediment from dedicated dredging or channel maintenance.
Regulatory improvements	Reduce speeds and wakes in eroding waterways; augment mitigation banking opportunities; limit construction of new canals and other detrimental activities.
Pump outfall management	Improve retention time of pumped flows in marshes to increase productivity while utilizing filtration effects.

Louisiana Department of Wildlife and Fisheries programs often contradict the conventional wisdom about species generally associated with high-salinity zones (such as brown shrimp and spotted seatrout *Cynoscion nebulosus*; Figures 6 and 7). The highest catch rates for juveniles of these species are—like those for species commonly associated with freshwater zones (blue crab *Callinectes sapidus* and white shrimp *P. setiferus*; Figures 8 and 9)—in waters of less than 10 ppt salinity.

Another obstacle to coastal restoration efforts has been the resource harvesters' demonstrated reluctance and in some cases lack of financial flexibility to forfeit expected current catches for predicted enhancement of long-term fisheries production. Even temporary resource displacements can be an economic burden, and basin-scale changes may be particularly hard to accept for resource users who are satisfied with current conditions. Class-action lawsuits have been filed by oyster leaseholders over possible uncompensated impacts from active freshwater diversion projects. The same sediment, nutrients, and freshwater that are needed for marsh restoration have in some instances been concerns for sportfishers. Where input from riverine sources has muddied areas of estuarine bay systems, user groups have equated poor fishing success with poor fish production.

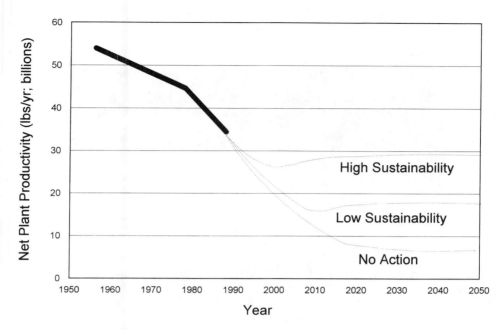

FIGURE 5.—Examples of hypothetical levels of wetland sustainability, based on the rate of loss of plant productivity in the Barataria–Terrebonne basins, 1956–1988 (solid line; Day et al. 1997). The primary goal of the Louisiana Coast 2050 initiative is to achieve the highest possible level of wetland sustainability for every coastal wetland planning unit; the three broken lines represent hypothetical outcomes from improving systems and taking no action.

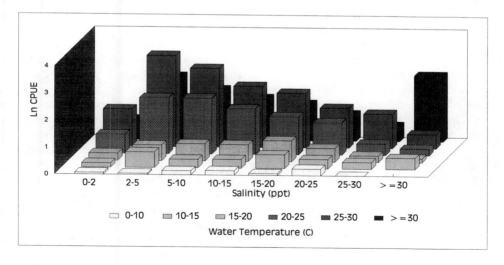

FIGURE 6.—Log-transformed catch per unit effort (CPUE) of brown shrimp *Penaeus aztecus* at the ranges of salinity (ppt) and water temperature encountered from 1991 to 1996 across coastal Louisiana. Samples ($N = 7,637$) were collected with 4.9-m trawls (6.4-mm mesh tail) by Louisiana Wildlife and Fisheries Department personnel during regular sampling.

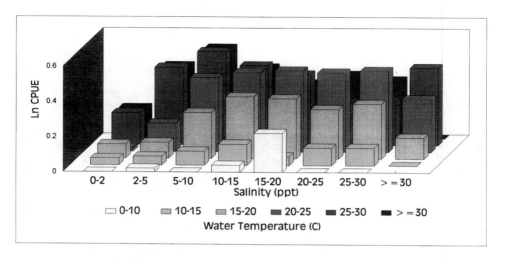

FIGURE 7.—Log-transformed catch per unit effort (CPUE) of spotted seatrout *Cynoscion nebulosus* at the ranges of salinity (ppt) and water temperature encountered from 1986 to 1996 across coastal Louisiana. Samples ($N = 6,219$) were collected with 15.25-m seines (6.4-mm mesh) by Louisiana Wildlife and Fisheries Department personnel during regular sampling.

Those faced with preserving essential fish habitat in Louisiana do not have an easy task. Although the overall coastal restoration effort is expected to help preserve fishery productivity over a wide area and over a considerable period of time, there will be many cases where this effort will require activities that may affect production negatively in a localized area for the short term and that will often change the spatial distribution of fisheries harvest zones. Additional conflicts will arise in areas where management procedures are conducted for waterfowl and furbearers, agricultural and municipal water supplies, transportation, and mineral extraction. Decision makers will often be confronted with situations where conclusive data are lacking and where strong opinions abound. In many cases, those tasked with maintaining essential fish habitat in Louisiana will have to use the best available information and submit habitat-improvement efforts to a triage process to accomplish habitat goals first in areas with the best outlook for environmental benefits and social acceptance.

Needs and Recommendations

Fisheries habitat enhancement in Louisiana can be facilitated by improvements in available information and in public understanding of habitat val-ues. Much work remains to be done on quantification of changes in fish production from habitat changes. At present, coastal fisheries managers often have only general population trend analyses and a few coarse paradigms on which to base decisions. The collection of specific information on the short- and long-term results of each type of proposed habitat modification should be a fundamental goal of resource managers. No less important are the goals of public education and consensus building. Every action toward coastal habitat protection or restoration should involve an extensive effort to achieve consensus among stakeholders. Such consensus can be unobtainable if pursued too late in the planning and implementation process. Public outreach must also include an education component. Ensuring a high level of public understanding of habitat-improvement goals is important, but perhaps more important is the promotion of a general understanding of the importance of habitat quality and availability to aquatic production. The link between estuarine ecosystem health and productivity should be understood by the public just as the need to preserve endangered species is generally understood. Without significant intervention, continued loss of Louisiana's estuaries will result in drastic and wide-ranging reduction in economic, esthetic, and biodiversity values.

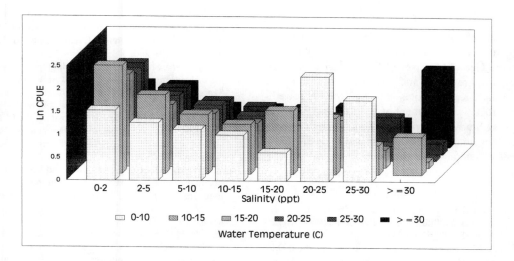

FIGURE 8.—Log-transformed catch per unit effort (CPUE) of blue crab *Callinectes sapidus* at the ranges of salinity (ppt) and water temperature encountered from 1991 to 1996 across coastal Louisiana. Samples (N = 7,637) were collected with 4.9-m trawls (6.4-mm mesh tail) by Louisiana Wildlife and Fisheries Department personnel during regular sampling.

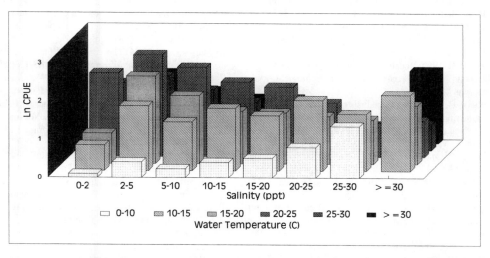

FIGURE 9.—Log-transformed catch per unit effort of white shrimp *Penaeus setiferus* at the ranges of salinity (ppt) and water temperature encountered from 1991 to 1996 across coastal Louisiana. Samples (N = 7,637) were collected with 4.9-m trawls (6.4-mm mesh tail) by Louisiana Wildlife and Fisheries Department personnel during regular sampling.

Acknowledgments

I am grateful to Bryan Piazza of the Louisiana Department of Natural Resources for graphics and data, to Gerald Morrisey of Coastal Environments, Inc., for graphics, and to Janet Abbott, Frank Truesdale, Karen Foote, and John Roussel for editorial review. Department of Wildlife and Fisheries Coastal Study Area personnel are appreciated for their long hours spent collecting and analyzing thousands of samples over the years.

References

Barrett, B. 1970. Water measurements of coastal Louisiana. Louisiana Wildlife and Fisheries Commission, Report 2-22-R/88-309, for the Bureau of Commercial Fisheries, U.S. Department of the Interior, Washington, D.C.

Baumann, R. H., J. W. Day, and C. H. Miller. 1984. Mississippi deltaic wetland survival: sedimentation versus coastal submergence. Science 224:1093–1095.

Boesch, D. F., and six coauthors. 1994. Scientific assessment of coastal wetland loss, restoration and management in Louisiana. Journal of Coastal Research, Special Issue 20.

Boumans, R. M., and J. W. Day, Jr. 1994. Effects of two Louisiana marsh management plans on water and materials flux and short-term sedimentation. Wetlands 14:247–261.

Britsch, L. D., and J. B. Dunbar. 1993. Land loss rates: Louisiana coastal plain. Journal of Coastal Research 9:324–338.

Browder, J. A., H. A. Bartley, and K. S. Davis. 1985. A probalistic model of the relationship between marshland-water interface and marsh disintegration. Ecological Modelling 29:245–260.

Browder, J. A., L. N. May, A. Rosenthal, J. G. Gosselink, and R. H. Baumann. 1989. Modeling future trends in wetland loss and brown shrimp production in Louisiana using thematic mapper imagery. Remote Sensing of Environment 28:45–59.

Cahoon, D. R. 1994. Recent accretion in two managed marsh impoundments in coastal Louisiana. Ecological Applications 4:166–176.

Chambers, D. G. 1980. An analysis of nekton communities in the upper Barataria basin, Louisiana. Master's thesis. Louisiana State University, Baton Rouge.

Coleman, J. M. 1981. Deltas. Burgess Publishing, Minneapolis, Minnesota.

Coleman, J. M. 1988. Dynamic changes and processes in the Mississippi River delta. Bulletin of the Geological Society of America 100:999–1015.

Connor, J. V., and F. M. Truesdale. 1972. Ecological implications of a freshwater impoundment in a low-salinity marsh. Pages 259–276 in R. H. Chabreck, editor. Proceedings of the second coastal marsh and estuary management symposium. Louisiana State University, Baton Rouge.

Day, J. W., Jr., J. F. Martin, L. Cardoch, and P. H. Templet. 1997. System functioning as a basis for sustainable management of deltaic ecosystems. Coastal Management 25:115–153.

Day, R. H., R. K. Holz, and J. W. Day, Jr. 1990. An inventory of wetland impoundments in the coastal zone of Louisiana, USA: historical trends. Environmental Management 14(2):229–240.

Faller, K. H. 1979. Shoreline as a controlling factor in commercial shrimp production. National Atmospheric and Space Administration Report 208. Earth Research Laboratory, Stennis Space Center, Mississippi.

Frazier, D. E. 1967. Recent delataic deposits of the Mississippi River; their development and chronology. Transactions of the Gulf Coast Association of Geological Societies 17:287–315.

Gagliano, S. M. 1973. Canals, dredging, and land reclamation in the Louisiana coastal zone. Hydrologic and geologic studies of coastal Louisiana. Report 14. Center for Wetland Resources, Louisiana State University, Baton Rouge.

Gagliano, S. M. 1989. Controlled diversions in the Mississippi River deltaic plain. Pages 257–268 in J. A. Kusler and S. Daly, editors. Proceedings of the symposium for wetlands and river corridor management. Association of Wetlands Managers, Charleston, South Carolina.

Gagliano, S. M., and J. L. Van Beek. 1970. Geologic and geomorphic aspects of deltaic processes, Mississippi delta system. Hydrologic and geologic studies of coastal Louisiana. Report 1. Center for Wetland Resources, Louisiana State University, Baton Rouge.

Gagliano, S. M., and J. L. Van Beek. 1990. Map of south Louisiana major landforms. Coastal Environments, Inc., Baton Rouge.

Gagliano, S. M., and J. L. Van Beek. 1992. Map of Louisiana geological structure and subsidence. Coastal Environments, Inc., Baton Rouge.

Gagliano, S. M., and J. L. Van Beek. 1993. A long-term plan for Louisiana's coastal wetlands. Report by Coastal Environments, Inc. to the Office of Coastal Restoration and Management, Louisiana Department of Natural Resources, Baton Rouge.

Gosselink, J. G. 1984. The ecology of the delta marshes of coastal Louisiana: a community profile. FWS/OBS-84/09. U.S. Fish and Wildlife Service, Washington, D.C.

Gosselink, J. G., C. L. Cordes, and J. W. Parsons. 1979. An ecological characterization of the Chenier Plain coastal ecosystem in Louisiana and Texas. Volume 1. FWS/OBS-78-09. Biological Services Program, U.S. Fish and Wildlife Service, Washington, D.C.

Gunter, G. 1967. Some relationships of estuaries to the fisheries of the Gulf of Mexico. Pages 621–638 in G. H. Lauff, editor. Estuaries. No. 83. American Association for the Advancement of Science, Washington, D.C.

Herke, W. H., E. E. Knudsen, P. A. Knudsen, and B. D. Rogers. 1992. Effects of semi-impoundment of Louisiana marsh on fish and crustacean nursery use and export. North American Journal of Fisheries Management 12:151–160.

Johnson, J. B., M. C. Watzin, J. B. Barras, and L. R. Handley. 1995. Gulf of Mexico coastal wetlands: case studies of loss trends. Pages 269–272 in E. T. Laroe, G. S. Farris, C. E. Puckett, P. D. Doran, and M. J. Mac, editors. Our living resources: a report to the nation on the distribution, abundance, and health of U.S. plants, animals, and ecosystems. U.S. Department of the Interior, National Biological Service, Washington, D.C.

Kesel, R. H. 1989. The role of the Mississippi River in wetland loss in southeastern Louisiana, U.S.A. Environmental Geology and Water Sciences 13(3):183–193.

Kolb, C. R., and J. R. Van Lopik. 1958. Geology of the Mississippi River deltaic plain, southeastern Louisiana. Technical Report 3-483. Waterways Experiment Station, U.S. Army Corps of Engineers, Vicksburg, Mississippi.

Kutkuhn, J. H. 1966. The role of estuaries in the development of and perpetuation of commercial shrimp resources. Pages 16–36 in R. F. Smith, A. H. Swartz, and W. H. Massman, editors. A symposium on estuarine fisheries. American Fisheries Society, Special Publication 3, Bethesda, Maryland.

LCWCRTF (Louisiana Coastal Wetlands Conservation, and Restoration Task Force). 1997. The 1997 evaluation report to the U.S. Congress on the effectiveness of Louisiana coastal wetland restoration projects. Louisiana Department of Natural Resources, Coastal Restoration Division, Baton Rouge.

Morris, J. T., B. Kjerfve, and J. M. Dean. 1990. Dependence of estuarine productivity on anomalies in mean sea level. Limnology and Oceanography 35(4):926–930.

Parker, J. C. 1970. Distribution of juvenile brown shrimp (Penaeus aztecus Ives) in Galveston Bay, Texas, as related to certain hydrographic features and salinity. Contributions in Marine Science 15:1–12.

Penland, S., I. Mendelssohn, L. Wayne, and D. Britsch. 1996. Natural and human causes of coastal land loss in Louisiana. Coastal Studies Institute, Wetland Biogeochemistry Institute, Louisiana State University, Baton Rouge.

Penland, S., and K. E. Ramsey. 1990. Relative sea-level rise in Louisiana and the Gulf of Mexico: 1908–1988. Journal of Coastal Research 6:323–342.

Penland, S., K. E. Ramsey, R. A. McBride, J. T. Mestayer, and K. A. Westphal. 1988. Relative sea level rise and delta plain development in the Terrebonne Parish region. Coastal Geology Technical Report Number 4. Louisiana Geological Survey, Baton Rouge.

Penland, S., and six coauthors. 1990. Coastal land loss in Louisiana. Transactions of the Gulf Coast Association of Geological Sciences 90:685–699.

Perret, W. S., and seven coauthors. 1971. Cooperative Gulf of Mexico estuarine inventory and study, Louisiana. volume 1, phase IV, biology. U.S. Department of Commerce, National Marine Fisheries Service, Project Report 2-22-R. Louisiana Wildlife and Fisheries Commission, New Orleans.

Peterson, G. W., and R. E. Turner. 1994. The value of salt marsh edge vs interior as a habitat for fish and decapod crustaceans in a Louisiana tidal marsh. Estuaries 17(1B):235–262.

Reed, D. J. 1992. Effect of weirs on sediment deposition in Louisiana coastal marshes. Environmental Management 16(1):55–65.

Reed, D. J., N. DeLuca, and A. L. Foote. 1997. Effect of hydrologic management on marsh surface sediment deposition in coastal Louisiana. Estuaries 20(2):301–311.

Roberts, H. H. 1985. A study of sedimentation and subsidence in the south-central coastal plain of Louisiana: summary report. U.S. Army Corps of Engineers, New Orleans.

Rogers, D. R., B. D. Rogers, and W. H. Herke. 1992. Effects of a marsh management plan on fishery communities in central Louisiana. Wetlands 12:53–62.

Rozas, L. P., and D. J. Reed. 1993. Nekton use of marsh-surface habitats in Louisiana (USA) deltaic salt marshes undergoing submergence. Marine Ecology Progress Series 96:147–157.

Russell, R. J., and six coauthors. 1936. Lower Mississippi River delta; reports on the geology of Plaquemines and St. Bernard Parishes. Geological Bulletin Number 13. Louisiana Department of Conservation, Louisiana Geological Survey, New Orleans.

Saucier, R. T. 1963. Recent geomorphic history of the Ponchartrain Basin. Coastal studies series number nine. Louisiana State University, Baton Rouge.

Suhayda, J. N. 1987. Subsidence and sea level. Pages 187–202 in R. E. Turner and D. R. Cahoon, editors. Causes of wetland loss in the coastal central Gulf of Mexico. Volume II: technical narrative. Outer Continental Shelf Study MMS 87–0120. U.S. Minerals Management Service, New Orleans.

Templet, P. H., and K. J. Meyer-Arendt. 1988. Louisiana wetland loss: a regional water management approach to the problem. Environmental Management 12(2):181–192.

Turner, R. E. 1977. Intertidal vegetation and commercial yields of penaeid shrimp. Transactions of the American Fisheries Society 106:411–416.

Turner, R. E., and D. R. Cahoon. 1988. Causes of wetland loss in the coastal central Gulf of Mexico. Volume I: executive summary. Outer Continental Shelf Study MMS 87–0120. U.S. Minerals Management Service, New Orleans.

Viosca, P., Jr. 1927. Flood control in the Mississippi valley and its relation to Louisiana fisheries. Transactions of the American Fisheries Society 57:49–61.

Viosca, P., Jr. 1928. Louisiana wet lands and the value of their wild life and fishery resources. Ecology 9(2):216–229.

Wigley, T. M. L., and S. C. B. Raper. 1992. Implications for climate and sea level of revised IPCC emission scenarios. Nature (London) 357:293–300.

Zein-Eldin, Z. P., and M. L. Renaud. 1986. Inshore environmental effects on brown shrimp, Penaeus aztecus, and white shrimp, P. Setiferus, populations in coastal waters, particularly of Texas. Marine Fisheries Review 48(3):9–19.

Zimmerman, R. J., T. J. Minello, E. F. Klima, and J. M. Nance. 1991. Effects of accelerated sea-level rise on coastal secondary production. Pages 110–124 in H. S. Bolten and O. T. Magoon, editors. Coastal wetlands: coastal zone '91. American Society of Civil Engineering, New York City.

Zimmerman, R. J., T. J. Minello, and G. Zamora. 1984. Selection of vegetated habitat by brown shrimp, Penaeus aztecus, in a Galveston Bay saltmarsh. United States Fishery Bulletin 82:325–336.

American Fisheries Society Symposium 22:252–267, 1999
© Copyright by the American Fisheries Society 1999

Remote Sensing of Forest-Clearing Effects on Essential Fish Habitat of Pacific Salmon

Nina M. Kelly

Department of Geography, San Diego State University
San Diego, California 92182-4493, USA

Don Field

National Marine Fisheries Service, Beaufort Laboratory
101 Pivers Island, Beaufort, North Carolina 28516, USA
and
National Ocean Service, Coastal Services Center
2234 South Hobson Avenue, Charleston, South Carolina 29405, USA

Ford A. Cross

National Marine Fisheries Service, Beaufort Laboratory
101 Pivers Island, Beaufort, North Carolina 28516, USA

Robert Emmett

National Marine Fisheries Service, Hatfield Marine Science Center
Newport, Oregon 97365, USA

Abstract.—The rivers and streams that drain into the lower Columbia River estuary in Oregon contain essential fish habitat (EFH) for several species of Pacific salmon. Seven subwatershed basins in the Columbia River drainage basin, each containing salmon spawning and nursery habitat, were examined using remote sensing and geographic information system techniques to measure the amount and pattern of upland forest clearing. Landsat Thematic Mapper imagery from 1989 and 1992 was used to determine the cleared forest patches produced by clear-cutting. Digital Elevation Models were used to determine slope underlying cleared patches. A digital coverage (or map layer) of streams containing EFH was used to measure proximity of cleared patches to streams. The size and slope of cleared forest patches and the proximity of cleared forest patches to streams can greatly exacerbate the deposition of sediment in streams, altering stream environments and the quality of EFH. Size, slope, and proximity of cleared forest patches to streams containing EFH were calculated for the seven subwatershed basins. This analysis was performed at a landscape scale and utilized readily available broadscale data to (1) compare forest-clearing patterns across basins and (2) locate critical areas for further analysis using finer-scale data. Once critical areas had been located, a second analysis was performed using finer-scale data. The landscape-scale results indicated major differences in the spatial pattern of forest-clearing change across the lower Columbia River estuary drainage basin, with some subwatershed basins significantly altered in the three-year period. Three subwatershed basins showed a pattern of large cleared patches close to streams containing EFH. Some of these cleared forest patches were situated at least partially on steep slopes. In the three basins, Milton Creek, Young's River, and the Claskanie River run directly through large areas of cleared forest. The pattern evidenced in these critical areas is consistent with increased sedimentation and decreased stream shading characteristics, both of which can have a detrimental effect on fish habitat. Milton Creek was examined with finer-scale data, and these results showed an increased number of cleared forest patches and increased total area of cleared forest draining into streams. More cleared forest patches on steep slopes were also shown with the finer-scale data. These results provide an initial justification for performing searches for critical areas at a synoptic or landscape scale, with further research performed at a finer scale. These techniques provide a practical method to evaluate upland land-use activities and essential fish habitat.

Increasing human population and concentrated economic activities along the coasts of the United States have made coastal areas the focus of critical natural resource issues including losses of anadromous fish habitat, increases in pollution, and declines in fisheries. Although linkages between upland land-cover changes and these living resource issues have been recognized scientifically (Chamberlin et al. 1991; Beechie et al. 1994), recognition of this linkage has only recently been codified in federal law in the 1996 Magnuson-Stevens Fishery Conservation and Management Act (Magnuson-Stevens Act). Although the Magnuson-Stevens Act defined essential fish habitat (EFH) to include only "waters," the Interim Final Rule (IFR) to implement the EFH provisions (NMFS 1997) published in the Federal Register on 19 December 1997 explicitly recognizes the linkages between land-cover changes and downstream effects (62 FR 66535). The IFR advises fishery management plans to analyze the cumulative impacts of individually minor but collectively significant alterations within a watershed that impact EFH (62 FR 66553). Because of its requirements that analysis of habitat function should take place at the watershed scale, the Magnuson-Stevens Act seems to be influenced by recent research that examines habitat change at a landscape or synoptic scale. Such a synoptic approach is a precursor to addressing multiple scales of ecosystem and resource interaction, and the approach addresses two objectives. First, a synoptic approach can address cumulative impacts by simultaneously examining many watersheds in various stages of change (Chamberlin et al. 1991). Second, the quantification of regional patterns and conditions of specific environmental properties, as well as changes in specific environmental properties, allows targeting of areas of concern requiring intensive field-based research (Brickner and Ruggiero 1998).

The Columbia River estuary drainage area in northern Oregon is an excellent locale in which to examine the linkages between upland land-cover changes and effects on EFH at a landscape scale. Northwest coho salmon *Oncorhynchus kisutch* populations have been declining for the last two decades (Beechie et al. 1994), and there are definite landscape-scale changes in watersheds where streams serve as spawning and nursery habitat to coho salmon. In particular, links among forest clearing in watershed basins, increased erosion, and decline in salmon spawning and nursery habitat have been suggested (Meehan 1991; Beechie et al. 1994; Waters 1995). Forest clearing at the landscape scale in areas draining directly into lower Columbia River salmon spawning and nursery streams have been observed from remotely sensed imagery. Large patches of closed-canopy forest are cleared each year by logging practices (Cohen et al. 1998), and the size, location, and slope of cleared patches can exacerbate erosion and increase sediment in streams (Chamberlin et al. 1991). The effect of these watershed activities on EFH needs to be examined, and satellite imagery and geographic information systems (GISs) provide effective tools to measure patterns across watershed basins and to locate further study areas.

Although overall amounts of forest clearing have been measured in the Pacific Northwest (Cohen et al. 1998), our work provides a quantitative description of important spatial patterns of upland forest-clearing activities. We describe seven subwatershed basins of the lower Columbia River drainage basin that contain EFH for several salmon species. Our first objective was to characterize forest clearing in each of the seven subwatershed basins based on the following spatial variables relevant to increased erosion: size of cleared forest patch, proximity of cleared forest patch to a stream containing EFH, and slope of cleared forest patch. The analysis was performed at a landscape scale, using readily available digital data that covered the entire study area. These data were at a coarse spatial resolution and provided only medium amounts of detail. Once areas of concern were located, our second objective was to perform similar analyses with large-scale data for a small area with finer spatial resolution and more detail.[1] Large-scale data are less easily available, however. Thus a method is presented that at a landscape scale characterized differences between upland land cover changes in watershed basins and identified areas with potential erosion problems. The method highlights some of the effects on measurement associated with analyses using multiple-source scales. This analysis is based on simple, generally accepted concepts regarding the effects of forest clearing on stream water quality (i.e., clearing of large patches of forest, clearing of forest patches on steep slopes, and clearing of forest patches that drain into streams can increase the deposition of sediment into streams, which can be detrimental to EFH). In addition, this analysis is considered to be the initial step in modeling functional change to EFH based on upland alterations.

Forest Clearing and Salmon Habitat

Coho salmon utilize streams in the lower Columbia River area during several stages of their reproductive and early life history. In this area, adult coho salmon usually enter spawning streams from

---

[1] This paper distinguishes between cartographic scale, which refers to data, and geographic scale, which refers to geographic extent of coverage. Large-scale data refers to data with more detail and less data generalization, and small-scale data refers to data with less detail and more generalization. Landscape-scale or synoptic-scale analysis refers to analysis that covers broad areas, that is, watersheds or regions.

September to January, during periods of high run-off. For spawning adults, essential fish habitat is composed of pools and riffles with pea- to orange-size gravel in which adult females create redds and spawn (Chapman 1988). Eggs residing in the redds develop during the winter and hatch in early spring, and the embryos remain in the gravel until they emerge in May or June. The emergent fry occupy pools and shallow stream margins among submerged woody debris while they grow into juveniles during the fall and winter. The juveniles usually spend one winter in streams before migrating to the sea in spring (Meehan and Bjornn 1991). During these stages of growth, salmon EFH consists of complex stream habitat that is shaded with tree-lined banks (promoting appropriate stream temperature levels) and contains large and small woody debris. Coho stock numbers have plummeted in this century due to a number of factors including ocean conditions, overfishing, and loss of freshwater habitat essential for spawning and rearing (Baker 1995). The National Marine Fisheries Service considered listing wild Columbia River coho as "threatened" under the Endangered Species Act in 1998, and wild Columbia River coho are considered to be extinct above the Bonneville Dam.

Much research on the relationship among forest practices, sediment, and salmonid reproduction has been applied to anadromous salmon in the Pacific Northwest. We are indebted to reviews provided by Meehan (1991) and Waters (1995). The effects of forest clear-cutting on stream ecosystems are complex. Clear-cutting can produce changes in stream temperature, dissolved organic content, nutrient loads, and suspended and deposited sediment (Meehan 1991). Forest clear-cutting exacerbates surface erosion as a result of changes in the distribution of precipitation that reaches the ground, the amount of precipitation intercepted or evaporated by vegetation, and the amount of water stored in the soil (Waters 1995). Clear-cutting also eliminates root structures and exposes mineral soil to accelerated surface erosion. In addition to surface erosion from cleared slopes, there is extensive evidence that logging roads increase mass movement of soil to streams, and clearing near streams increases the likelihood of bank failures and landslides (Reid and Dunne 1984).The effects of forest clearing and altered suspended and deposited sediment loads on the composition and quality of spawning gravel, and the influence of clearing and sediment loads on the survival and condition of emerging fry, are also com-plex. Although many studies indicate that sediment can have both a positive and negative effect on salmonid growth and reproduction, excessive fine-grain (<2 mm) sedimentation from clear-cut areas and logging roads in the Pacific Northwest is detrimental to salmon (Reid and Dunne 1984; Chamberlin et al. 1991; Meehan 1991). As sediment yield from logged areas increases, several stream characteristics change. Stream turbidity fluctuates with deposition events (Newcombe and MacDonald 1991). As suspended sediment settles, stream gravel permeability decreases (Moring 1982; Scrivener and Brownlee 1982), and the mean particle size of material decreases as fine particles are deposited in upper layers of the streambed (Ringler and Hall 1988). The response of coho salmon to these changes varies. Coho salmon are known to avoid highly turbid or silty water and to avoid potential redd sites covered by fine particles (Waters 1995). Once eggs are laid, a layer of fine particles from upland erosion can reduce interstitial space between gravel, slow water movement through the redd, and reduce oxygen, sometimes causing suffocation (Waters 1995). Excess deposited sediment can prevent fry from emerging through overhead stratum once hatched (Hartman and Scrivener 1990). In some cases, excessive suspended sediment can impair adult salmon respiration (Waters 1995).

The size and slope of cleared forest patches and the proximity of cleared patches to streams can greatly exacerbate the deposition of sediment in streams, altering stream environments and the quality of essential fish habitat (Chamberlin et al. 1991; Meehan 1991; Desbonnet et al. 1995). Small patches of cleared forest are less likely to produce landslides and debris flows than large patches. Cleared forest patches in contact with streams weaken stream banks and can cause stream bank failure. Cleared patches on steep slopes increase surface erosion and soil movement. Slope becomes an important factor in soil erosion when slopes are steep (>25%) (Heidtke and Auer 1993), and, as is mentioned in the following sections, many of the slopes associated with the study area are steep.

Study Area

The seven subwatershed basins that comprise the study area in the lower Columbia River drainage basin are in mountainous terrain, with elevations ranging from sea level to 978 m. Each basin contains creeks, streams, or rivers that contain essential fish habitat for salmon, and all basins drain into the lower Columbia River with the exception of basin 3, which contains the Necanicum River (Figure 1).

Modeling Upland Changes at the Landscape Scale Using GIS

A geographic information system was used to manage, manipulate, and analyze a series of geospatial data layers from the lower Columbia River basin. Landscape-scale analyses of spatially distributed data benefit from the efficient storage and analytical capabilities of GIS (Stow 1994; Burrough and McDonnell 1998), and GIS techniques have been used in the Pacific Northwest for modeling salmon habitat (Lunetta et al. 1997). However, integration

of multiple layers of digital data requires consideration of data accuracy (Gong 1994). The following sections describe data uncertainty related to this study and the data sources used.

Accuracy and Data Uncertainty

Uncertainty can be introduced into data at the data source (Lunetta et al. 1991). Several standard measurements have been developed to describe this error. The positional and vertical accuracy of digital spatial data are modeled by using vertical and horizontal root mean squared error (RMSE), which assumes a random normal distribution of error. Root mean squared error is usually reported with raster and vector format data, but vector data are also subject to National Map Accuracy

FIGURE 1.—The study area in the lower Columbia River estuary drainage area in Oregon. The study area includes seven subwatershed basins that have streams containing essential fish habitat.

TABLE 1.—Projection information and data uncertainty measures for spatial data layers (NAD27 = North American Datum 1927; NAD83 = North American Datum 1983).

Data [a]	Source scale or spatial resolution	Root mean squared error	Projection system [b]	Datum; units
C-CAP land-cover change	27.5-m spatial resolution	Horizontal: 0.47 pixels or 11–12 m	UTM	NAD27; meters
1:24,000-scale USGS DEM	30.0-m spatial resolution	Vertical: 15 m Horizontal: 3–5 m	UTM	NAD83; meters
1-degree USGS DEM	90.0-m spatial resolution	Vertical: 45 m Horizontal: 120–130 m	Geographic	NAD83; decimal seconds
Watersheds	1:24,000	Horizontal: 10–15 m	UTM	NAD83; meters
Rivers and streams	1:250,000	Horizontal: 120–130 m	Lambert conformal conic	NAD83; international feet
Rivers and streams	1:24,000	Horizontal: 10–15 m	UTM	NAD83; meters
Final projection format			Lambert conformal conic	NAD83; meters

[a] DEM = digital elevation model.
[b] UTM = universal transverse mercator.

Standards (NMAS), which determine the threshold of acceptable error for a map or data layer. The NMAS state that 90% of all points on a map shall be within 0.05 cm of their true location (Bolstad and Smith 1995). These standards are scale dependent, meaning that as scale increases, error decreases. Table 1 lists data source scales, projection information, and levels of uncertainty expressed as RMSE. The integration of digital spatial data layers also introduces error in the processing flow (Davis et al. 1991; Lunetta et al. 1991; Gong 1994; Congalton 1997). The geometric rectification, projection, data conversion, and co-registration processes described below can introduce additional data uncertainty that can be measured with in-the-field verification. With the exception of the land-cover data, ground verification of introduced error was not performed for this analysis. Specific data uncertainty figures are expressed in the discussion below.

Data Sources

We used four digital data sets or layers for this analysis, with varying source scales. The term "small-scale" refers to data with less detail than "large-scale" data. The digital data consist of data layers in either raster (regular grid or cell based—

usually used to depict continuous variables) or vector (linear representation—usually used to represent discrete variables) format (Burrough and McDonnell 1998). All data layers are available to the public, either from the Internet or from a free CD-ROM. Our intention was to perform the analysis using readily available data so that the method could be repeated.

Land cover.—The Coastal Change Analysis Program (C-CAP), part of the National Oceanic and Atmospheric Administration's (NOAA's) Coastal Services Center in Charleston, South Carolina, monitors change in terrestrial land cover and nearshore benthic habitats within coastal environments of the United States. The C-CAP classifies types of land cover and analyzes and monitors changes in coastal submersed habitats, wetland habitats, and adjacent uplands using remote sensing techniques (satellite imagery and aerial photography). The long-term goal of the C-CAP is to correlate changes in terrestrial regions with changes in coastal aquatic habitats and relate habitat changes to population fluctuations in living marine resources.

The change analysis used in this study is part of a C-CAP project to detect land-cover change for the area surrounding the Columbia River estuary.

This project was carried out in cooperation with the Oak Ridge National Laboratory, the Columbia River Estuary Study Task Force (CREST), the National Marine Fisheries Service (NMFS) Point Adams Field Station, and Pacific Meridian Resources. Changes were detected by comparing Landsat Thematic Mapper (TM) satellite imagery (Path 47, Row 28) for 10 September 1989 and 18 September 1992. As per C-CAP protocols (Dobson et al. 1995), the 1992 imagery was georectified and then classified by a combination of supervised and unsupervised classification techniques. Pixels that exhibited change between 1989 and 1992 were identified through spectral change analysis (band differencing between the two image dates), and these change pixels were reclassified to derive the 1989 land-cover database. The processing was accompanied by an intensive field verification effort carried out in cooperation with CREST and other local cooperators.

Field verification was carried out by two- or three-person teams, each equipped with a portable color laptop computer linked to a global positioning system (GPS). The NMFS Point Adams Field Station runs software that supports the classified data as a raster background with the road network as a vector overlay while simultaneously displaying live GPS coordinates. The GPS is equipped with an external antenna that can be mounted to the top of any vehicle. Personnel can use the field station to efficiently navigate between ground points of interest. Accuracy assessment points were generated with Erdas Imagine software using a stratified random sample. To make the acquisition of field reference data more practical, a 20-pixel buffer area around roads (i.e., 10 pixels on either side of the road), including logging trails, was created. Using this technology in the CREST study area, 600 random sites were visited for the 1992 classification, and 100 random sites of potential change were visited in May 1996 (USDOC 1997). Overall accuracy for the 1992 classification was 90%, and overall accuracy for the change data were 92%. Horizontal error was less than one-half pixel for the 1989 and 1992 products, or between 12 and 15 m (for full metadata, see USDOC 1997). The complete land-cover change detection product is available at no cost from the NOAA Coastal Services Center in a format that is easily incorporated into a GIS.

Both the spatial and spectral resolution of the TM data make forest clearing discernible. Forest clearing radically alters the spectral response of the target area on the ground in both the visible and near-infrared portions of the spectrum, to which the TM sensor is sensitive. The data are in raster format with a ground resolution of 27.5 m. The accuracy figure found for the C-CAP data corresponds to the accuracy figure found in a recent study of forest clear-cuts in the Pacific Northwest that used TM data. Cohen et al. (1998) reported accuracy of TM imagery-classified clear-cuts in excess of 90% using a change-detection algorithm similar to the algorithm described in this study.

Rivers and streams.—Location of streams containing salmon spawning habitat were acquired from the NMFS in Newport, Oregon. These data contain a 1:250,000-scale stream network. The spatial data have been linked to NMFS fisheries salmon data including dam location, river reach files, and location of salmon species habitat. The data were available for all seven subwatershed basins in the study area.

A coverage of hydrography at 1:24,000 scale was obtained for the Trenholm 7.5-min quadrangle in Oregon from the Internet site provided by the Saint Charles County Geographic Information System.[2] These large-scale data depicted more streams than the 1:250,000-scale layer and included greater detail (Figure 2). Data uncertainty for each layer varies with scale. National Map Accuracy Standards are 125 m for the 1:250,000-scale data layer and 12 m for the 1:24,000-scale data layer, and the reported RMSE is 100–130 m and 7–18 m for the 1:250,000- and 1:24,000-scale data layers, respectively (Bolstad and Smith 1995).

Watershed basins.—Seven subwatershed units were used in this study. These units were compiled by the Oregon Department of Water Resources from 1:24,000-scale base maps. The seven subwatershed basins are numbered 2, 3, 4, 16, 21, 25, and 29, and they vary in size from 30,000 to over 80,000 ha (Figure 1). The data also were downloaded from the Internet site provided by the Saint Charles County Geographic Information System.[2] The reported RMSE for these data are 7–18 m (Bolstad and Smith 1995).

Digital Elevation Models.—Digital Elevation Models (DEMs) provide elevation above sea level in raster format. Two base scales for DEMs are currently available: the 7.5-min (30-m) DEM data constructed from 1:24,000-scale topographic maps, and the 1-degree or three-arc-second (90-m) model (1:250,000 scale), both provided by the U.S. Geo-

---

[2] For more information, see http://www.sscgis.state.or.us.

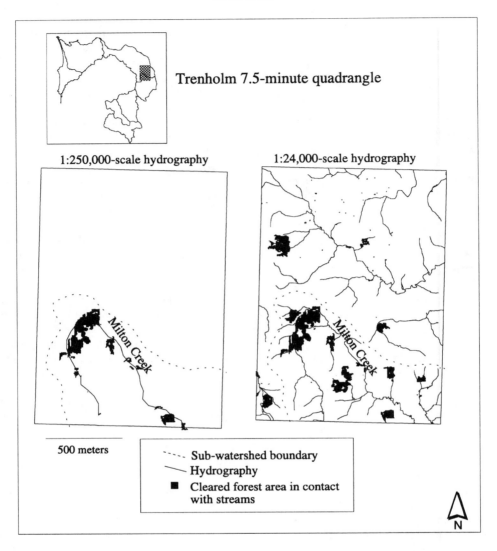

FIGURE 2.—Trenholm 7.5-min quadrangle hydrography with 1:250,000-scale data (left) and with 1:24,000-scale data (right) showing number and size of patches in contact with streams.

logical Survey. Digital Elevation Models of 1:24,000 scale were not available for the entire study area, so the initial slope measurements for the entire area were calculated from the 1-degree data. Four 1:250,000-scale DEMs were used for the landscape-scale analysis: Vancouver-east, Vancouver-west, Hoquiam-east, and Hoquiam-west. These DEMs were downloaded directly from the U.S. Geological Survey Geo-Data Internet site.[3] A 7.5-min DEM for the Trenholm 7.5-min quadrangle was downloaded

[3] For more information, see http://edcwww.cr.usgs.gov/doc/edchome/ndcdb/ndcdb.html.

from the Internet site provided by the Saint Charles County Geographic Information System.[2] Vertical RMSE for the 1:24,000-scale data are 15 m or better, and horizontal RMSE is 3–15 m. Vertical and horizontal RMSE for the 1:250,000-scale DEM is commensurate with the RMSE of the 1:250,000-scale maps, at around 125 m.[3]

The combination of data of different source scales requires consideration of data detail. Specifically, 1:24,000-scale vector data will provide more detail than 1:250,000-scale data. The larger-scale hydrography contains more detailed streams and more higher-order streams. Elevation values provided by DEMs can also vary with source scale, but the relationship is usually linear (Isaacson and Ripple 1990).

Methods

Preprocessing

The vector data sets used were provided by the source agencies in either Arc/INFO coverage format or ArcView shapefile format.[4] The C-CAP data were converted from Erdas Imagine image format to Arc/INFO GRID format without change in spatial resolution or projection. Digital Elevation Model data were converted to Arc/INFO GRID format. All data were examined and analyzed in ArcView 3.0 (ESRI 1998). The seven subwatershed basins each contained streams that had salmon spawning and rearing habitat, and each basin was completely within the extent of the C-CAP coverage. By converting these seven watershed basin boundaries to each of the original projections, the study area was used as a mask to cut out the C-CAP data layer, the DEM data layer, and the stream data before reprojection.

Geographic information system analyses of multiple layers of spatial data require that the features in all layers be registered to a common projection and grid system (Lunetta et al. 1997). For this project, all vector coverages and raster grids were reprojected from native format to Lambert conformal conic format to reduce error (Table 1). Resampling of the raster coverage used the nearest-neighbor method. Error estimates derived for the Lambert projection system indicated a maximum error of 0.053% for the entire state (compared to a maximum error of 0.29% for the Universal Transverse Mercator [UTM] projection system zone 10) and a mean error of 0.017% for the entire state (compared to 0.073% for UTM zone 10) (Snyder 1987).[2] In the northern Oregon study area, error was minimized due to the placement of a second standard parallel through the area at 45°30 N; maximum error as a result of the projection system was 0.03%.

Areas of forest clearing between 1989 and 1992 were defined as areas that showed conversion from forest to grassland or conversion from forest to bare ground. The C-CAP data layer depicting cleared forest was converted from raster to vector, yielding

---

[4] Reference to trade names does not imply endorsement by the National Oceanic and Atmospheric Administration.

an overlay of vector polygons, or patches. This process did not alter areal measurements. Before reprojecting the DEM, the four 1-degree elevation models were joined and clipped to the study area. The 1-degree and the 7.5-min DEMs were reprojected using a nearest-neighbor resampling algorithm. A slope coverage derived from the 1-degree DEM and the 7.5-min DEM using standard GIS techniques yielded percent slope for each pixel (Burrough and McDonnell 1998).

Spatial Data Analysis

The size and slope of cleared forest patches and proximity of cleared patches to streams can greatly exacerbate the deposition of sediment in streams (Chamberlin et al. 1991; Meehan 1991; Desbonnet et al. 1995). Size, slope, and proximity were measured in the GIS as described below. Using the vector layer of cleared forest patches with the layer of subwatershed basins, the following spatial characteristics of cleared forest patch size were measured for each basin: total amount of forest cleared, number of cleared patches, mean size of cleared patches, and largest cleared patch.

The proximity of cleared areas to the streams closest to them was calculated for each basin. First, a centroid for each cleared forest patch was determined, and the distance from the centroid of each cleared forest patch to the closest stream containing essential fish habitat was calculated as a Euclidean distance. The results of the distance calculation were added to the cleared forest patch coverage as an additional attribute, and mean distance from stream for all cleared forest patches was calculated for each basin. Second, cleared forest patches that were immediately in contact with a stream containing EFH were determined by using a spatial query that determined the spatial intersection between the stream coverage and the individual cleared patches. This new layer was used to calculate the number of cleared forest patches in contact with streams, mean sizes of cleared forest patches in contact with streams, and largest cleared forest patches in contact with streams. The DEM data were used to calculate percent slope across the study area to analyze the relationship between forest clearing and slope. The slope layer was resampled (i.e., converted from one spatial resolution to another) to the spatial resolution of the cleared forest layer. Cleared forest patches that were in contact with streams containing EFH were queried for their maximum slope

260   KELLY ET AL.

TABLE 2.—Spatial characteristics of cleared forest patches in subwatershed basins in the lower Columbia River basin calculated by evaluating changes in satellite imagery from 1989 and 1992 using a geographic information system.

Basin	Total forest cleared in basin (ha)	Percent of forest cleared in basin	Number of cleared patches	Mean size of cleared patches (ha)	Maximum size of cleared patches (ha)
2	2,709.0	6.8	1,836	1.3	196.4
3	92.2	0.4	350	0.2	9.8
4	1,945.3	7.9	4,140	0.4	75.0
16	1,529.8	13.8	1,744	0.8	152.5
21	1,069.8	9.4	1,686	0.5	64.7
25	538.8	4.6	457	0.9	76.9
29	609.0	3.5	894	0.6	41.1

value, and the maximum slope values for each cleared forest patch were classified as critical (>25%) or noncritical (<25%). The threshold for determination of critical slope is based on Heidtke and Auer (1993). The additional item of maximum slope underlying each cleared forest patch was added to each cleared forest patch centroid point as an attribute. Mean size and largest size were calculated for cleared forest patches in contact with streams having slopes in excess of 25% grade.

From these results, four critical sites were identified that met the following criteria: largest cleared forest patches in contact with streams, and the largest cleared patches near water on steep slopes (>25% grade). We attempted to examine each of the four target areas with large-scale data, but large-scale stream data and DEM data were available for only one of the four sites. This fourth site along Milton Creek is contained in the Trenholm 7.5-min quadrangle. Number of cleared patches, mean size, maximum size, and total area of cleared forest patches in contact with streams were calculated for both 1:250,000-scale and 1:24,000-scale stream data. Number of cleared patches, mean size, maximum size, and total area of cleared forest patches in contact with streams on a steep grade (>25% grade) were calculated using both the 7.5-min and the 1-degree DEMs.

Results

Forest clearing varied widely by basin, and in the three years covered by the remotely sensed data, a measurable amount of forest cover was removed from several of the watersheds (Table 2). The entire study area experienced a 2% removal rate annually, three times larger than the amount reported by Cohen et al. (1998). Basins were classified into three groups:

heavy forest harvesting (basins 2, 4, 16, and 21); slight harvesting (basin 3); and intermediate forest harvesting (basins 25 and 29). In subwatershed basins 4 and 16, over 1,500 ha of forest cover were cleared in 3 years, and over 2,500 ha were cleared in subwatershed basin 2. Figure 3 shows the pattern of forest clearing throughout the study area. The number of cleared patches was as many as 4,140 in basin 4, and the number of cleared patches demonstrated that basins 2, 4, 16, and 21 were more heavily harvested than the other basins. Mean size of cleared patches varied from 0.2 ha (basin 3) to 1.3 ha (basin 2). Large clear-cuts greater than 100 ha were found in basins 2 and 16, and in basins 4, 21, and 25, clear-cuts greater than 60 ha were found. Subwatershed basin 3, a heavily forested area, remained relatively unchanged during the three-year time period.

The relationship between cleared area and proximity to stream varied by drainage basin. Table 3 lists the change in each basin with respect to cleared forest patch proximity to streams. Forest clearing occurred closer to streams in basins 2, 16, and 25 than in the other basins. More patches were in contact with streams in basins 2 and 16 than in other basins. In basin 16, a total of 231 ha of forest, or nearly 15% of total clearing in basin 16, was cleared in areas that were in contact with streams. In basin 16, more than half of the cleared area in contact with streams was found in one large contiguous patch of cleared forest over 150 ha in size. Basin 2 also had a large contiguous cleared forest patch that drained into a stream containing EFH. In basin 2, the mean size of cleared patches in contact with streams was large (19.3 ha) and indicated the presence of larger-than-average clear-cuts draining into streams. In basin 3, the mean size of cleared forest patches was less than 1 ha, and these patches were further away from streams.

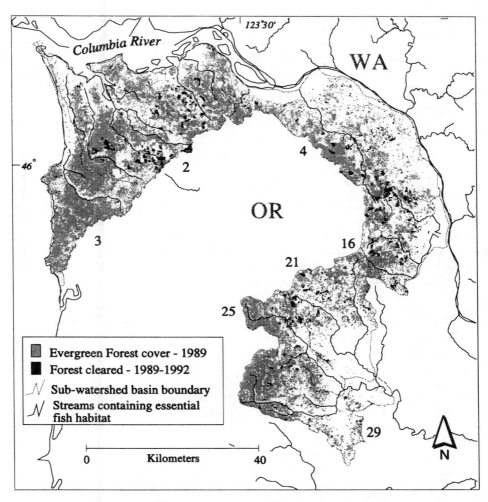

FIGURE 3.—Forest cover and forest clearing in seven subwatershed basins in the lower Columbia River basin, Oregon, between 1989 and 1992. Cleared forest is estimated from Coastal Change Assessment Program (C-CAP) data. Subwatershed basins are numbered.

Consideration of the slope of harvested patches in contact with streams containing EFH is crucial to evaluating potential disturbance. Several of the cleared forest patches in contact with streams were on partially steep slopes. Table 4 lists the size characteristics of cleared patches that contacted streams on steep slopes (>25% grade). Although the amount of forest clearing that contacted streams on steep slopes was less than the overall amount of clearing in contact with streams, three basins mentioned above (2, 4, and 16) deserve mention here. Over 8 ha of cleared forest patches in basins 2 and 16 were in contact with streams containing EFH, and at least some portion of these cleared patches were on steep slopes. The patches listed in Table 4 are small cleared

forest patches (0.13–1.32 ha) found in river valleys with steep walls, but the patches may contribute significantly to downstream effects on habitat because of their steep slopes. Basins 2 and 4 had single cleared patches greater than 1 ha located on partially steep slopes that were in contact with streams.

Four critical areas in basins 2, 4, and 16 contained the largest cleared forest patches in contact with streams and the largest cleared forest patches in contact with streams on partially steep slopes. The locations of all four critical areas in the study area are displayed in Figure 4, and Figure 5 provides a close-up view of the critical areas. Area "a" in Figure 5 shows forest clearing in basin 2 along the Young's and Klaskanine rivers and the south fork of

TABLE 3.—Proximity of cleared patches to streams containing essential fish habitat in seven subwatershed basins of the lower Columbia River basin, 1989–1992.

Basin	Size of cleared area immediately in contact with a stream (ha)	Mean distance from cleared patches to streams (all patches) (m)	Number of cleared patches immediately in contact with a stream	Mean size of cleared patches immediately in contact with a stream (ha)	Largest cleared patch immediately in contact with a stream (ha)
2	173.12	1,609.4	129	19.3	103.3
3	1.72	4,136.3	15	0.8	9.8
4	40.54	2,942.7	70	0.7	15.3
16	231.32	1,392.0	128	2.0	152.5
21	3.18	2,344.2	30	0.2	2.3
25	36.49	1,613.2	24	1.6	23.1
29	14.86	2,938.1	11	1.6	8.6

the Klaskanine Rivers; the largest area of clearing (103 ha) is along Young's River. Area "b" in basin 2 (Figure 5) shows a closer view than in area "a" of the 28.3 ha of clearing along Klaskanine River. Area "c" shows clearing along the Claskanie River in basin 4; this clearing is found on partially steep slopes. Area "d" in basin 16 shows Milton Creek, which includes the largest clear-cut found in the study area (152.5 ha). Area "d" was covered by the Trenholm 7.5-min quadrangle, and finer-scale data were only available for this area (see Figure 2).

Analysis of the Trenholm 7.5-min quadrangle that covers area "d" reveals the changes in measurements that can result from changes in data scale. The 1:24,000-scale stream data and information resulting from the 7.5-min DEM are presented in Table 5 and compared to 1:250,000-scale data and information resulting from the 1-degree DEM. The 1:250,000-scale and 1:24,000-scale hydrography are mapped for the area covered by the Trenholm 7.5-min quadrangle (total area 13,458 ha) in Figure 2. Areas of cleared forest in contact with streams are shown for each scale. The 1:24,000-scale hydrography contains more detailed streams and more higher-order streams. Because of this mapped detail, the 1:24,000-scale hydrography recorded more cleared forest patches intersecting with the streams (69 patches compared to 15) and more total cleared area draining into the streams (461 ha compared to 208 ha) than the 1:250,000-scale hydrography. The mean size of cleared forest patches decreased with the 1:24,000-scale data as smaller patches of cleared forest were found that intersected with streams, although the large (152 ha) patch remained the maximum-sized patch according to both sets of stream data. Despite the lower accuracy of the 1:250,000-scale data, the landscape-scale analysis successfully located the largest cleared forest patch. The slope

information yielded similar results. Although none of the cleared forest patches located using the 1:250,000-scale stream data were on partially steep slopes as depicted by the 1-degree DEM, when the analysis was performed using 1:24,000-scale stream data and the 7.5-min DEM, several cleared patches in contact with streams were identified on partially steep slopes. A total of 331.6 ha of cleared forest land intersecting with the streams in the 7.5-min quadrangle occurred on partially steep slopes. When the 7.5-min DEM was used for slope analysis, the largest cleared patch in the study area (shown in diagram "d" in Figure 5 and in both diagrams in Figure 2) was shown to contain partially steep slopes. This change in slope value was caused by the greater heterogeneity of the 7.5-min DEM data. With 7.5-min DEM data, elevation is captured with more detail, and in areas of steep terrain this can result in greater variance in slope value (Isaacson and Ripple 1990).

Discussion

A synoptic or landscape-scale analysis of forest clearing across seven subwatershed basins revealed differing patterns of forest clearing by basin and successfully targeted areas for larger-scale examination of the effects of forest clearing on essential fish habitat. Areas that showed the most cleared forest exhibited a pattern of clearing that could be detrimental to EFH. The forest clearing pattern shown in subwatershed basins 2, 4, and 16 has the potential to increase soil erosion from upland clearing adjacent to streams, to increase instream soil deposition from bank failures, and to change shading alongside streams. These habitat alterations can be detrimental to the reproduction and survival of salmonids. In basins 2, 4, and 16, in which 7, 8, and 14%, respectively, of forest cover was cleared dur-

TABLE 4.—Size characteristics of cleared patches in contact with streams containing essential fish habitat on steep slopes (>25% grade).

Basin	Total area in contact with streams (ha)	Mean size of cleared forest patch (ha)	Size of largest cleared forest patch (ha)
2	8.10	0.12	1.26
3	1.50	0.14	0.33
4	5.00	0.11	1.32
16	8.60	0.13	0.66
21	3.40	0.15	0.39
25	0.90	0.13	0.13
29	0.90	0.13	0.26

ing the 3 years covered by the study, larger areas were cut and clearing occurred closer to streams and partially on steeper slopes than in the other basins studied. Three streams in particular, Milton Creek (basin 16), Young's River (basin 2), and Claskanie River (basin 4) had large cleared patches along streams, and some of these patches were on partially steep slopes. These areas should be targeted for future research (see below). In basin 16, nearly 20% of logging patches were in contact with streams, and one cleared patch along Milton Creek was over 150 ha in size. This area in the Trenholm 7.5-min quadrangle along Milton Creek was examined with large-scale data, and the results of those examinations strengthened results obtained from the landscape scale. The larger amount of detail in the 1:24,000-scale stream data and the 7.5-min DEM data reveal more cleared forest patches in contact with streams, more cleared forest patches on partially steep slopes, and a larger total area affected. These results provide an initial justification for searching for problem areas at a synoptic or landscape scale, with further research performed at a finer scale. Further fine-scale research includes modeling soil erosion

from cleared areas and linking results with salmon count data. In addition, these results reveal the effect on measurement that often results from the use of multiple-scale data (Cao and Lam 1997).

Quantification of forest-clearing patterns is an important predecessor to determining possible links between land-cover change and downstream effects on structure and function of essential fish habitat and ultimately on salmonid production. This project provides a method for use in salmon restoration research that expands upon habitat modeling by introducing accurate land-cover change data. The project also serves as a precursor to functional analysis and soil-erosion and nonpoint source modeling at the watershed scale. Further, these techniques provide an inexpensive and thorough method to evaluate upland land-use activities and essential fish habitat.

Lessons Learned

Geographic information systems allow the integration of diverse data for overlay analysis, change assessment, and habitat suitability modeling. Landscape-scale analysis of uplands allows comparisons

TABLE 5.—Comparison of proximity measurements and slope measurements between 1:24,000-scale and 1:250,000-scale stream data and the 1:24,000 and 1-degree Digital Elevation Model for the Trenholm 7.5-minute quadrangle.

Data source	Number of cleared forest patches	Number of cleared patches on steep grade (<25%)	Mean size of cleared forest patches (ha)	Maximum size of cleared patch (ha)	Total cleared area draining into streams (ha)
Rivers and Stream data					
1:24,000-scale	69		6.6	152.5	461.1
1:250,000-scale	15		13.8	152.5	208.3
Digital Elevation Models					
7.5-minute DEM (1:24,000 scale)		9	36.8	152.5	331.6
1-degree DEM		0			

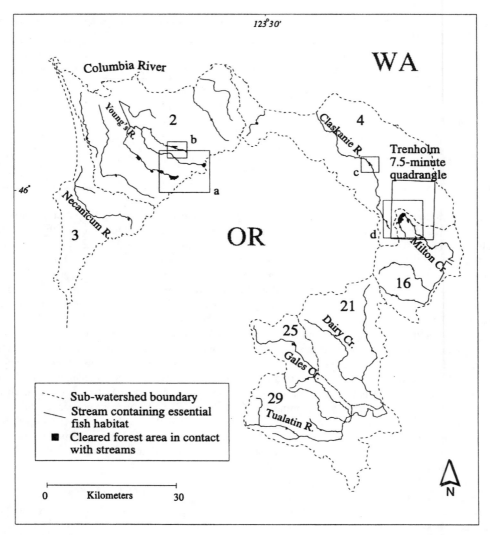

FIGURE 4.—Distribution of patches of cleared forest in seven subwatershed basins in the lower Columbia River basin, Oregon. The locations of four areas depicted in Figure 5 are also shown.

across basins while simultaneously examining many watersheds in various stages of change and allows targeting of areas of concern that require intensive field-based research (Brickner and Ruggiero 1998). This method of landscape-scale analysis should be applied elsewhere.

Continued research is needed to address the problems of integrating geographic data from multiple sources and scales. Although landscape-scale analysis successfully located critical areas with large patches of cleared forest in contact with streams and some patches on partially steep slopes, the accuracy of the small-scale data requires that research with large-scale data should follow to substantiate results.

This procedure was performed for one area in this study because large-scale data were not available for the entire area. Wherever possible in similar studies, multiscale analysis should be performed to confirm landscape-scale results. In addition, the results of large-scale analysis should be verified with field sampling. Data uncertainty introduced in the processing flow, in particular co-registration uncertainty, should be examined in the field before any intensive field-based research. Future analysis will build on this technique to model functional change as a result of changes in land-cover patterns. The method described here forms an important adjunct to salmon habitat studies and links the management of whole

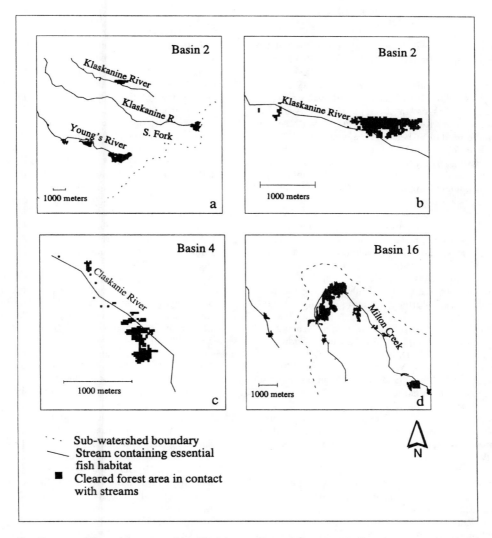

FIGURE 5.—Four specific problem areas identified from seven subwatershed basins in the lower Columbia River basin, Oregon: (a) in subwatershed basin 2, showing areas draining into streams containing essential fish habitat (EFH); (b) in subwatershed basin 2, showing areas that drain steep slopes and flow into streams containing EFH; (c) in subwatershed basin 4, showing areas that drain steep slopes and flow into streams containing EFH; and (d) subwatershed basin 16, showing areas draining into streams containing EFH.

watershed ecosystems with management of anadromous fish. Finally, these techniques should be used to evaluate salmonid essential fish habitat from Washington to California.

Acknowledgments

The authors would like to acknowledge funding support from the National Oceanic and Atmospheric Administration's (NOAA's) Coastal Ocean Program, NOAA's National Marine Fisheries Service, and the Coastal Services Center. Special thanks are extended to Paul Genovese, who compiled the salmon data in geographic information system format, David Colby for help in reviewing the manuscript, and the San Diego Supercomputer Center for use of computing and visualization resources. The authors would also like to thank the thorough and insightful comments of three anonymous reviewers.

References

Baker, B. 1995. Is overfishing or habitat destruction the key culprit in fishery depletion? BioScience 45:751.

Beechie, T., E. Beamer, and L. Wasserman. 1994. Estimating coho salmon rearing habitat and smolt production losses in a large river basin, and implications for habitat restoration. North American Journal of Fisheries Management 14:797–811.

Bolstad, P. V., and J. L. Smith. 1995. Errors in GIS: assessing spatial data accuracy. Pages 301–312 in J. G. Lyon and J. McCarthy, editors. Wetland and environmental applications of GIS. Lewis Publishers, Boca Raton, Florida.

Brickner, O. P., and M. A. Ruggiero. 1998. Toward a national program for monitoring environmental resources. Ecological Applications 8(2):326–329.

Burrough, P. A., and R. A. McDonnell. 1998. Principles of geographic information systems. Oxford University Press, Oxford, UK.

Cao, C., and N. Lam. 1997. Understanding the scale and resolution effect in remote sensing and GIS. Pages 57–72 in D. A. Quattrochi and M. F. Goodchild, editors. Scale in remote sensing and GIS. Lewis Publishers, Boca Raton, Florida.

Chamberlin, T. W., R. D. Harr, and F. H. Everest. 1991. Pages 181–206 in W. R. Meehan, editor. Influences of forest and rangeland management on salmonid fishes and their habitats. American Fisheries Society, Special Publication 19, Bethesda, Maryland.

Chapman, D. W. 1988. Critical review of variables used to define effects of fines in redds of large salmonids. Transactions of the American Fisheries Society 117(1):1–21.

Cohen, W. B., M. Fiorella, J. Gray, E. Helmer, and K. Anderson. 1998. An efficient method for mapping forest clearcuts in the Pacific Northwest using Landsat imagery. Photogrammetric Engineering and Remote Sensing 64(4):293–300.

Congalton, R. G. 1997. Exploring and evaluating the consequences of vector-to-raster and raster-to-vector conversion. Photogrammetric Engineering and Remote Sensing 63(4):425–434.

Davis, F. W., and nine coauthors. 1991. Environmental analysis using integrated GIS and remotely sensed data: some research needs and priorities. Photogrammetric Engineering and Remote Sensing 57(6):689–697.

Desbonnet, A., and six coauthors. 1995. Development of coastal vegetated buffer programs. Coastal Management 23:91–109.

Dobson, J. E., and ten coauthors. 1995. National Oceanic and Atmospheric Administration Coastal Change Analysis Program (C-CAP): guidance for regional implementation. U.S. Department of Commerce, NOAA, Coastwatch Change Analysis Project, Coastal Ocean Program, Silver Spring, Maryland.

ESRI (Environmental Systems Research Institute). 1998. ArcView 3.0 and Arc/INFO 7.0.3.

Gong, P. 1994. Integrated analysis of spatial data from multiple sources: an overview. Canadian Journal of Remote Sensing 20(4):349–359.

Hartman, G. F., and J. C. Scrivener. 1990. Impacts of forestry practices on a coastal stream ecosystem, Carnation Creek, British Columbia. Canadian Bulletin on Fisheries and Aquatic Sciences 223. Department of Fisheries and Oceans, Ottawa.

Heidtke, T. M., and M. T. Auer. 1993. Application of a GIS-based nonpoint source nutrient loading model for assessment of land development scenarios and water quality in Owasco Lake, New York. Water Science Technology 28(5):595–604.

Isaacson, D. L., and W. J. Ripple. 1990. Comparison of 7.5-minute and 1-degree digital elevation models. Photogrammetric Engineering and Remote Sensing 56(11):1523–1527.

Lunetta, R., R. Congalton, L. Fenstermaker, J. Jensen, K. McQuire, and L. Tinney. 1991. Remote sensing and geographic information system data integration: error sources and research issues. Photogrammetric Engineering and Remote Sensing 57(6):677–687.

Lunetta, R., B. L. Cosentino, D. R. Montgomery, E. R. Beamer, and T. J. Beechie. 1997. GIS-based evaluation of salmon habitat in the Pacific Northwest. Photogrammetric Engineering and Remote Sensing 63:1219–1229.

Meehan, W. R. 1991. Introduction and overview. Pages 1–16 in W. R. Meehan, editor. Influences of forest and rangeland management on salmonid fishes and their habitats. American Fisheries Society, Special Publication 19, Bethesda, Maryland.

Meehan, W. R., and T. Bjornn. 1991. Salmonid distributions and life histories. Pages 47–82 in W. R. Meehan, editor. Influences of forest and rangeland management on salmonid fishes and their habitats. American Fisheries Society, Special Publication 19, Bethesda, Maryland.

Moring, J. R. 1982. Decrease in stream gravel permeability after clear-cut logging: an indication of intragravel conditions for developing salmonid eggs and alevins. Hydrobiologia 88:295–298.

Newcombe, C. P., and D. D. MacDonald. 1991. Effects of suspended sediments on aquatic ecosystems. North American Journal of Fisheries Management 11:72–82.

NMFS (National Marine Fisheries Service). 1997. Magnuson-Stevens Act provisions: essential fish habitat: interim final rule and request for comments. Federal Register [Docket 961030300–7238–04; I.D. 120996A]: 66531–66559.

Reid, L. M., and T. Dunne. 1984. Sediment production from forest road surfaces. Water Resources Research 20(11):1753–1761.

Ringler, N. H., and J. D. Hall. 1988. Vertical distribution of sediment and organic debris in coho salmon (*Oncorhynchus kisutch*) redds in three small Oregon streams. Canadian Journal of Fisheries and Aquatic Sciences 45:742–747.

Scrivener, J. C., and M. J. Brownlee. 1982. An analysis of the Carnation Creek gravel quality data 1973 to 1981. Pages 154–173 *in* G. F. Hartman, editor. Proceedings of the Carnation Creek workshop: a ten-year review. Canadian Department of Fisheries and Oceans, Nanaimo, British Columbia.

Snyder, J. P. 1987. Map projections–a working manual. U.S. Government Printing Office, Washington, D.C.

Stow, D. A. 1994. The role of geographic information systems for landscape ecological studies. Pages 11–22 *in* R. Haines-Young, editor. Landscape ecology and GIS. Taylor and Francis, London.

USDOC (U.S. Department of Commerce). 1997. C-CAP–changes in land cover in the Columbia River estuary 1989-1992. USDOC, National Oceanic and Atmospheric Administration, Coastal Services Center (NOAA CSC/1-97/001), Charleston, South Carolina.

Waters, T. F. 1995. Sediment in streams: sources, biological effects, and control. American Fisheries Society, Monograph 7, Bethesda, Maryland.

American Fisheries Society Symposium 22:268–284, 1999
© Copyright by the American Fisheries Society 1999

Addressing Nonfishing Threats to Habitat through Public and Private Partnerships

PAUL A. HEIKKILA

Coos County Oregon State University Extension Service
290 North Central, Coquille, Oregon 97423, USA

Abstract.—The Coquille watershed contains the largest coastal river originating within the Coast Range of Oregon. The Coquille River presently supports over 57 species of fish including coho salmon *Oncorhynchus kisutch*, spring and fall chinook salmon *O. tshawytscha*, resident and sea-run cutthroat trout *O. clarki*, winter steelhead trout *O. mykiss*, and a remnant population of chum salmon *O. keta*. Coho salmon have been listed as threatened under the Endangered Species Act. Many factors including habitat alterations, harvests, hatchery introductions, and ocean conditions have led to the decline of many Coquille River fish stocks. Habitat changes since European settlement began in the mid-1800s include logging and log transport, road building, draining and diking for agriculture, and urbanization, which have all contributed to the decline of fish stocks and water quality within the watershed. The recognition of habitat problems as a key limiting factor for fish production and water quality led to the formation of the Coquille Watershed Association (CWA) in early 1994. The formation of the CWA was another step in a 20-year local effort to address habitat problems through restoration of natural processes. The CWA is organized as a nonprofit corporation and is governed by a 26-member executive council representing landowners and stakeholders within the watershed. The goals of the CWA, which arrives at decisions through consensus, include creating water quality conditions that will meet Clean Water Act standards and enhancing native fish survival and production through public and private partnerships. To reach those goals, the CWA has organized a technical advisory group and developed an Action Plan that address limiting factors and sets priorities for identifying, prioritizing, coordinating, accomplishing, and monitoring restoration projects and educational efforts. To date the CWA has generated over US$2.5 million in public and private funding to implement projects including riparian restoration through fencing and planting, wetland development, the addition of large-channel wood and rock, off-channel livestock watering, and over 40 educational tours.

The early 1990s brought some serious watershed management issues directly to the people who live, work, and recreate on the Coquille watershed and adjacent basins in Coos and Curry Counties of Oregon (Figure 1). Five years of court challenges to the management of the northern spotted owl and other species dependent on old-growth forests reduced logging to a fraction of the 1980s level on federal land that comprised one-third of the watershed. Because of concerns similar to those for the spotted owl, legislators proposed changes to the Oregon Forest Practices law in 1993 to further protect fish and wildlife habitat. For the first time, local ocean commercial and recreational salmon fisheries were closed, and in-river recreational salmon and trout fisheries were severely restricted. In addition, analysis in the early 1990s revealed serious water quality problems on the Coquille both from point and nonpoint sources. Agricultural and urban interests were being challenged to help resolve the problems.

On a positive note, a number of watershed restoration demonstration projects were being conducted on the Coquille and adjacent watersheds with notable success in the early 1990s. Several local ad hoc groups had formed to address issues including changes in the Oregon Forest Practices law, obstacles to improving fish production, and problems with water quality. The 1993 Oregon legislature also recognized growing watershed problems including declining salmon resources and water quality and passed the Watershed Health Program, a demonstration program that allocated US$7 million for watershed restoration projects in northeastern and southwestern Oregon, including in the Coquille watershed. The legislature also established a framework for the formation of local watershed councils (associations). With the issues, leadership, and resources in place, the Coquille Watershed Association (CWA) and similar groups were formed.

This paper describes the need for and the formation and accomplishments of the CWA. Much of the material in this paper is gleaned from the CWA Action Plan, CWA staff members, members of the CWA Executive Council, and CWA crew members, all of whom are acknowledged at the end of the chapter.

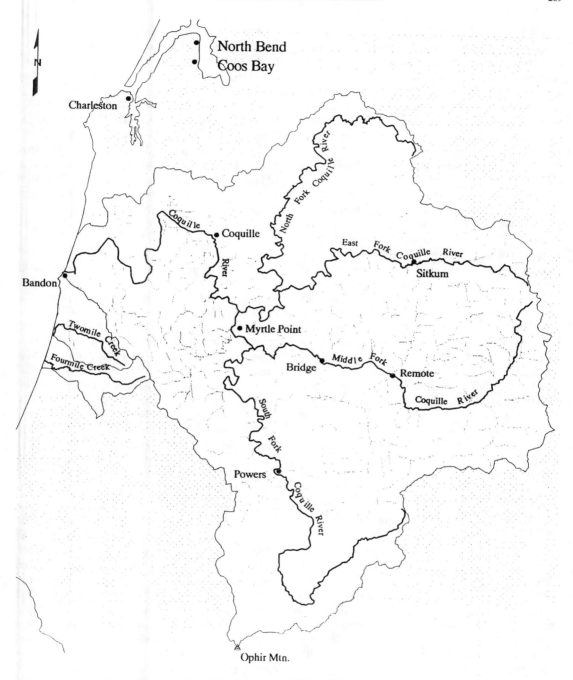

FIGURE 1.—The Coquille watershed and adjoining areas (CWA 1997).

Situation

Pacific Northwest and statewide issues including water quality, loss of anadromous fish, and management of species dependent on old-growth forests have had a major impact on management in the Co- quille River watershed. Recent studies of factors limiting natural production of native anadromous fish in Oregon coastal streams (ODFW 1992; MATG and BLM 1993) have indicated that spawning and rearing habitats within a watershed are moderately to highly limiting. The tidally influenced main-stem Coquille River historically functioned as a rearing area for juvenile fish, but current conditions have severely reduced rearing in this zone (USACE 1972; Benner 1992; ODEQ 1992; ODFW 1992). These limiting factors reflect conditions resulting from long-term natural events and land management practices from post-European settlement to the present, including harvesting of timber, development of cities and associated transportation, and draining and filling of land for agriculture.

In 1993 the Forest Ecosystem Management Team (FEMAT), a group of six scientists appointed by the Clinton Administration, identified six "key watersheds" within the Coquille watershed that became part of the aquatic conservation strategy in the Northwest Forest Plan, which was the product of the FEMAT group. The six key watersheds are on U.S. Forest Service and U.S. Bureau of Land Management lands within the system and are mostly in high-gradient areas of the south and north forks (see Figure 1). Key watersheds serve as a refuge and are areas critical to the maintenance and recovery of potential at-risk stocks of salmonids.

In July 1995 the National Marine Fisheries Service (NMFS) published a proposed rule that identified six evolutionary significant units (ESUs) of coho salmon *Oncorhynchus kisutch*. The NMFS also proposed to list three ESUs as threatened under the federal Endangered Species Act (ESA). Coquille coho fall in the northern Oregon coast ESU, which includes the entire coastal coho population from the mouth of the Columbia River to Cape Blanco, Oregon.

In 1996 the Oregon Department of Environmental Quality (ODEQ) submitted its biannual water quality report to the U.S. Environmental Protection Agency (EPA). The biannual water quality report lists river streams and reaches of streams where parameters do not meet water quality standards under Section 303(d) of the Clean Water Act. Also listed are rivers and streams for which supporting data are needed to make a listing determination. There are 37 total streams or stream segments in the Coquille watershed with current or potential water quality problems.

In February 1997, an updated draft of the Oregon Coastal Salmon Restoration Initiative (which became known as the Oregon Plan) was presented to the Oregon legislature. Over a four-month period, the legislature addressed concerns (including funding) related to the Oregon Plan, made needed changes, and completed a final draft in March 1997.

That draft was submitted to the NMFS for consideration. The Oregon Plan targeted the development of public and private partnerships through watershed associations (councils) as a key tool in improving salmon habitat and water quality.

On April 25, 1997, the NMFS decided not to list the northern Oregon coast coho ESU, which included Coquille coho. The NMFS agreed to a three-year trial of the Oregon Plan. The development and effectiveness of the Coquille Watershed Association and similar groups strongly influenced that decision. The NMFS listed the Oregon coast coho ESU in August 1998 after a ruling by U.S. Magistrate Janice Stewart.

Watershed Description

The 1,059 mi^2 Coquille River watershed is the third largest river system on the Oregon coast, surpassed only by the Umpqua and Rogue rivers. The Coquille is the largest river system that originates in the Coast Range. (The Umpqua and Rogue rivers have their origins in the Cascade Mountains.) The majority of the Coquille watershed lies in Coos County, Oregon, with a small amount in Douglas County. The Coquille's three major tributaries include the north (which in turn includes the east fork), middle, and south forks (Figure 1). These branches converge with the main stem within a few miles of the town of Myrtle Point and flow through a 36-mi-long tidal reach to the Pacific Ocean at Bandon, Oregon (MATG and BLM 1993). (Table 1 lists characteristics of the various forks.)

Although the watershed is large, the Coquille River estuary is one of the smallest in Oregon. The lower bay is long and narrow, measuring about 763 acres. About half of the area consists of tidelands, and the other half consists of permanently submerged eelgrass beds, wetlands, and tidal flats. Over 100 years of diking and filling have reduced or modified many acres of wetlands, tidal creeks, and sloughs, although the tidal-reach areas still continue to be a very important rearing environment for anadromous fishes such as shad, juvenile chinook salmon *Oncorhynchus tshawytscha*, and cutthroat trout *O. clarki*.

From the confluence with the south fork to the ocean, the main stem stretches 36 mi and drains 172 mi^2. It has a very low gradient of about 1 ft/mi. Although the main stem is tidally influenced for 38 mi, river mile 25 marks the observed limit of saltwater intrusion. The main stem almost always annually floods after winter storm events. The south fork of the Co-

TABLE 1.—Length, gradient, and drainage area of the Coquille River and its forks (MATG and BLM 1993).

River section	Length (mi)	Average gradient		Drainage area (mi^2)
		(ft/mi)	%	
Main stream	36.3	1	0.02	172
South fork	62.8	47	0.89	288
Middle fork	40.3	35	0.66	310
North fork	53.3	30	0.57	154
East fork	33.8	70	1.33	135
Total	226.5			1,059

quille River is the longest, with a reach of 62.8 mi and an average gradient of 47 ft/mi. The south fork drains 288 mi^2. The middle fork of the Coquille River is a tributary of the south fork, with the confluence just south of the town of Myrtle Point at river mile 38. It drains an area of 310 mi^2. The north fork of the Coquille River drains 154 mi^2 and joins the main stem again near the town of Myrtle Point, river mile 36. The east fork of the Coquille River is a tributary to the north fork and joins approximately nine miles from the mouth of the north fork. The east fork of the Coquille River has a drainage area of 135 mi^2.

The climate is humid with a strong marine influence and moderate year-round temperatures. Rainfall ranges from a low of 45 in/year in the Camas Valley region, a rain-shadowed region of the Coast Range, to approximately 120 in/year at the headwaters of the south fork. Seventy-five percent of the annual rainfall occurs between November and March, often in heavy storm events. April through October usually produces less than 6 in of rain.

The Coquille watershed drains a geologically complex region of the Klamath and Coast Range Mountains, characterized by a narrow coastal plain and narrow alluvial valleys that extend into the mountainous interior. Elevations range from sea level at Bandon to 4,075 ft at Ophir Mountain on the headwaters of the south fork (Figure 1). The watershed naturally produces sediment because of the interplay of terrain, geology, and rain (ODEQ 1992). The heavy winter rainfall, combined with steep, thinly soiled slopes on unstable bedrock, leaves the drainage highly susceptible to earth flows, debris slides, erosion, and flooding. Fluctuating sea levels and continuing uplifting and infilling of the river channel have deposited marine and alluvial sediment that forms terraces through the lower river drainage. The unconsolidated-to-semiconsolidated deposits that form these terraces are subject to severe stream bank erosion during high winter flows (ODEQ 1992b).

Currently, the population within the watershed is estimated at 16,800 people. The population is concentrated in the valley area, with the majority clustered around the incorporated towns of Bandon, Coquille, Myrtle Point, and Powers. Land uses are predominantly residential, industrial, commercial, and agricultural. Some of the pasturelands extend into the hills above the floodplain, particularly along the south fork. The steep slopes above the valley areas are sparsely populated. Timber production, agriculture, and some mining make up the predominate land uses. Approximately 70% of the watershed is forested. Upper reaches of all four forks and most tidewater streams are in commercial forests. Approximately 40% of the watershed is private industrial forestland, with federal, state, and county lands occupying about 30% of the watershed. The U.S. Bureau of Land Management (BLM) and the U.S. Forest Service (USFS) administer the largest of these holdings. Another 30% of the basin consists of smaller, nonindustrial private holdings (Interrain Pacific 1996). See Table 2 for detailed ownership information.

Fishery Resources and Biology

Although the Coquille watershed ranks high compared to other Oregon coast watersheds for fisheries production and diversity (ODFW 1997), the present populations of some species including coho, chum *Oncorhynchus keta*, spring chinook, and sea-run cutthroat trout are only a small fraction of stock sizes before 1900. The system currently supports at least 57 species of fish including socially important coho, chinook, and chum salmon, plus sea-run and resident cutthroat trout and resident rainbow trout and steelhead *O. mykiss*. The life histories of these species within the Coquille watershed are described in the following sections.

TABLE 2.—Coquille watershed ownership by river section and approximate stream mileage for third-order streams. (BLM = U.S. Bureau of Land Management; USFS = U.S. Forest Service.)

River section	BLM ownership		USFS ownership		Other ownership	
	% of total acres	Stream miles	% of total acres	Stream miles	% of total acres	Stream miles
Main stream	0	0	0	0	100	153
North fork and east fork	44	215	0	0	56	259
Middle fork	22	97	0	0	78	344
South fork	5	7	47	72	48	74
Total		319		72		830

Coho Salmon

Coquille River coho begin their migration into freshwater between October and January, spawning in the upper reaches of the watershed in small-to-medium-sized tributaries from November through February, with peak spawning occurring in late December. During their first summer, the juveniles rear in pools usually associated with wood in the small, cool tributaries of the watershed. After the fall rains begin, many of the juveniles migrate into low-gradient sections of the watershed, wintering in off-channel ponds, pools with large woody debris, side channels, creek-associated wetlands, and beaver ponds. They migrate to the ocean as smolts from March to June.

The Coquille basin has historically supported a large and healthy wild population of coho salmon, but their abundance has declined significantly since 1950, with most of the decreases occurring through the 1950s and 1960s. Harvest rates both in the river and the ocean were historically higher in the 1970s when hatchery stocks were abundant, but in the last 10 years harvest has dropped to incidental levels.

Coho salmon rearing and spawning habitats are not uniform in the Coquille system. The north fork produces a higher portion of habitats than the other forks because of good spawning gravel, and summer and winter rearing habitats are found in both the upper-main-stem north fork and its tributaries. The main-stem east and middle forks hold few suitable areas for coho spawning, but the tributaries, especially in low-gradient portions, are important coho producers. The south fork is a winter steelhead and chinook salmon spawning stream, but some tributaries hold suitable coho habitat.

Coho salmon numbers within the Coquille have fallen dramatically since the turn of the century. Early gill-net records (CWA 1997) indicated peak landings in 1908 of 120,000 coho. A recent survey of spawning grounds (ODFW 1997) indicated that the total number of spawners in the system ranged from 3,000 to 15,000 during the last six years, a dramatic drop from the turn of the century.

Chinook Salmon

Coquille chinook salmon have two life history forms, a fall-run chinook and a spring-run chinook. Chinook salmon have diverse life histories with large variations in time of spawning, age of juvenile entry into the ocean, ocean migration patterns, spawning habitat selections, and age of maturity. Spring chinook populations in the Coquille watershed are estimated at less than 400 fish based on observations by Oregon Department of Fish and Wildlife staff (J. Muck, Oregon Department of Fish and Wildlife, personal communication). Spring chinook enter the river as two-to-five-year-old adults from April to June and then spend the summer holding in deep, cool pools before spawning in September and October. Juvenile spring chinook tend to have an in-river residence of slightly over six to eight months before moving to the sea.

Fall chinook enter the river from July through November, with peak spawning during mid-November. Annual spawning-ground surveys published through the Oregon Department of Fish and Wildlife (ODFW) from 1958 to 1996 indicate that the fall chinook population in the Coquille has expanded since 1950 and appears to be in good condition (Muck, personal communication). Spawning fall chinook in the Coquille are normally four or five years old, but there are also significant numbers of three- and six-year-old fish. Some precocious males return as sexually mature two-year-old "jacks." Fall chinook emerge from the gravel, depending on water temperature, in 50–100 d and begin the migration downriver from the spawning areas toward the estuary. Most of the juveniles reach the tidal area between April and July. While in the estuary, the juveniles grow rapidly and enter the ocean from late August through October, depending on rain events. The south fork, being gravel rich, is the key fork for natural production of Coquille fall chinook. Spawning areas are not thought to be limiting in the south fork. Spawning in the east, north, and middle forks is less abundant and may limit production.

Coastal Cutthroat Trout

Coastal cutthroat trout within the Coquille basin are both anadromous and resident. Sea-run individuals are silvery, and characteristic spotting may be masked when the fish return from saltwater. Cutthroat trout that remain in freshwater are usually darker with distinctive cutthroat slash marks. Oregon sea-run cutthroat rarely exceed 20 in in length. Coastal cutthroat trout exhibit diverse life history patterns that are probably the most complex of any salmonid in Oregon. The following major life history patterns are common within the Coquille watershed:

- Sea-run populations migrate to the ocean or estuary in the spring and feed less than a year before returning to freshwater to winter over. Anadromous cutthroat trout either spawn during the first winter or spring after they return from the ocean or undergo a second ocean migration before maturing and spawning in freshwater.
- Fluvial populations undergo in-river migrations between small spawning tributaries and main-river sections downstream, similar to ocean migration but entirely within the watershed.
- Nonmigratory (i.e., resident coastal cutthroat trout) populations generally occur within the small headwater streams, often above barriers, and apparently exhibit little instream movement. These fish are generally smaller because of poor feeding conditions and become sexually mature at a younger age.

The current status of the cutthroat trout population relative to historic levels is unknown, although on the basis of anecdotal accounts, current numbers are probably lower. Population declines are most likely occurring due to the factors affecting other salmonids within the basin. Between 1975 and 1985,

legal-size hatchery cutthroat trout were planted in all forks, but the discontinuation of these plantings in 1985 has resulted in little recent influence on Coquille River cutthroat populations.

Winter Steelhead Trout

Winter steelhead are common in the Coquille. They normally spend two to three years in freshwater and two to three years in saltwater. The Coquille population is 80% "two salts" (two years in the ocean) and 20% "three salts" (three years in the ocean). Spawning occurs from late December to June in tributaries of all the major forks. Unlike salmon, not all steelhead adults die after spawning. Between 10% and 25% of adults are repeat spawners, and 1% to 3% spawn a third time.

Most Oregon coastal steelhead populations have declined from historic levels. Some of the factors influencing the downturn are loss of habitat, decreased ocean survival since 1985, and hatchery introductions. Alsea River (central Oregon coast) steelhead smolts were routinely released in the Coquille watershed between 1948 and 1990. Beginning in 1990, all hatchery releases of steelhead trout were from Coquille River stocks, with 60% to 70% being "wild × wild" smolts. Hatchery releases were moved to a lower point in the system to minimize the effects of hatchery strays on wild-fish spawning areas, and harvest was restricted to hatchery fish only.

Chum Salmon

The Coquille watershed is on the extreme southern edge of the natural range of chum salmon, and these salmon were probably never abundant within the basin. Chum salmon spawn in lower-gradient tributaries, many of them within the tidal reaches. The juveniles rear for a very short time (one to four weeks) in freshwater and move to the estuary and ocean in the spring.

Rainbow Trout

Resident rainbow trout are probably native to the Coquille watershed in a few isolated locations above secondary barriers (such as falls) on the upper south fork and its tributaries. In the past, legal-size hatchery rainbow trout were released to provide recreational fishing opportunities on all forks of the

Coquille system and adjacent ponds. This practice was discontinued in the Coquille watershed in the mid-1970s because of potential impacts on wild cutthroat trout and winter steelhead.

Overview of Reasons for Wild Population Declines

The decline of the wild population of anadromous salmonids in Oregon, including in the Coquille watershed, is due to a combination of many factors. These factors, which have affected different species to varying degrees, include the degradation of rearing and spawning habitat, the reduction in summer stream flows, passage problems, a decrease in ocean productivity, and excessive fishing. Impacts caused by hatchery programs have also been implicated in most of the declines and in some extinctions of coho salmon populations in the lower Columbia River in Oregon.

Salmon evolved in freshwater ecosystems that were historically characterized by a high degree of structural complexity, including large wood in streams, floodplains, side channels, beaver ponds, wetlands, and, in some cases, lakes. Human activities since the 1850s—including timber harvesting, mining, water withdrawals, livestock grazing, road construction, stream channelization, wetland diking, waste disposal, gravel removal, farming, urbanization, and historic splash-dam logging— have intensively altered most Oregon coastal freshwater ecosystems, including the Coquille watershed. The combination of these factors has left many salmonid populations, especially coho, in a depressed state. Coho, spring chinook, steelhead, and sea-run cutthroat populations within the Coquille watershed have all declined over the last 50 years. Of these populations, coho has received the most attention.

The cumulative impacts of natural and human events on a dynamic watershed such as the Coquille have changed salmon habitat, resulting in a long-term decline in wild salmon populations within the watershed. Oregon coastal watersheds are dynamic systems by nature and are affected annually by drought, freezing, and floods, as well as by long-term trends such as cooling, warming, low rainfall, high rainfall, and high or low oceanic productivity. Compounding the loss of habitat are the already-mentioned human activities. Contemporary salmon habitats in the Coquille are often characterized by a combination of problems:

- Stream channels generally lack complexity, and there is insufficient wood in stream channels.
- Off-channel wetland and slough habitat is isolated and uncommon compared to historic levels.
- Water temperatures are higher in some areas because riparian vegetation has been reduced.
- Channel depth has decreased and width has increased, which has in turn increased water temperatures and sedimentation.
- Summer flows are lower in many areas because of withdrawals for irrigation and animal and domestic use.

History of Habitat Alteration

A limited amount of information is available regarding the condition of the Coquille River during the late 1800s and early 1900s. However, based on the available information, it is apparent that the last 100 years have brought major alterations to the Coquille watershed. Historically, most dramatic habitat changes to the Coquille River were on the tidal reaches and low-gradient sections of the main tributaries. Early settlers were attracted to the lower sections of coastal rivers where natural ports and protection were available. This was especially true of the Coquille watershed. At the beginning of the European settlements in the early 1850s, the Coquille watershed not only provided a navigable harbor but also offered over 40 mi of navigable river. This distance is exceeded in Oregon only by the Columbia River. The Coquille River initially lacked a safe river entrance, but beginning in 1881 the U.S. Army Corps of Engineers dredged the bar and constructed jetties that narrowed, deepened, and stabilized the river mouth. Early steamboat records describe the lower tidal reaches as being up to 300 ft wide for nearly 20 mi and as being navigational for that distance by vessels drafting 14–15 ft of water. Vessels of lesser draft were able to reach another 10 mi or more above the town of Myrtle Point.

At the time of European settlement, the valley's landscape features included vegetation communities associated with annual winter flooding from surface channel overflows and upland subsurface runoff. Original notes from Government Land Office surveys (Benner 1992) of the Coquille Valley between 1857 and 1872 (Benner 1992) give detailed information on historic features. The tidal section of the Coquille River at that time was linked with over 20,500 acres of floodplain, 70% of which were described as marshy and 14,350 acres of which were densely covered in trees, shrubs, sedges, grasses, and salt marsh.

Even before 1900, diking, filling, and draining activities were encouraged and were carried out widely on the lower Coquille River. These alterations were necessary to make the valley habitable and allow agricultural development. By the turn of the century, up to 60% of the native wetlands had been converted to pasture and other farm uses through filling and diking. Beaver dams, which were part of the landscape and created excellent habitat for anadromous fish, were removed. Riparian areas along the alluvial valley streams were cleared for fuel and lumber, causing bank failure, erosion, and sedimentation in many areas of the lower Coquille River. Another major change to the watershed was the removal of large wood, not only from the tidal reaches of the river but throughout the system. Wood removal became common soon after settlement because of navigation problems for commercial boat traffic and net hazards for the commercial gill-net fishery that operated in the tidal reach. By the 1880s, natural navigation channels had begun to widen and shallow, causing navigation problems. The U.S. Army Corps of Engineers started channel maintenance projects but by 1924 had abandoned efforts except for in the lower two miles.

The Port of Coquille River was formed in 1911 to assume responsibility for maintaining the channels above the city of Coquille because at that time the channels were not regularly maintained by the federal government. The port worked intensely to maintain navigable channels up to Myrtle Point between 1915 and 1923. Between the Port of Coquille River and the U.S. Army Corps of Engineers, an average of eight snags per mile per year were removed from the tidal reach below Myrtle Point. The Port of Bandon, which was formed later to maintain the area from Coquille to the river mouth, also periodically dredged and cleared the channel of large wood (Benner 1992).

As recently as the 1970s, the Oregon Department of Fish and Wildlife, federal agencies, and private timber companies removed log jams and other wood structures from many miles of coastal streams, including the Coquille. The belief at that time was that these materials affected the passage of salmonids up and down streams. Although many of the jams did impair fish passage, at some flows eliminating wood structure greatly reduced winter and summer rearing habitat for juveniles.

The upland areas above the floodplains at the time of European settlement were heavily forested with Douglas fir, Port Orford and western red cedar, hemlock, Sitka spruce, and some pine. The heavily forested hills of the Coquille watershed, like many other coastal basins in Oregon, attracted large investments in timber harvesting. Standard logging practices before 1972 included splash dams, downhill logging, storage of logs in streams, roads and railroads built along stream courses, and elimination of hundreds of miles of riparian vegetation along streams.

Before forest road construction, the Coquille forks and their tributaries were the only viable option for logging companies to transport logs downriver to the mills, except for the south fork, where a railroad was built for log transportation. Before 1900, the transport of logs down tributaries could occur only during winter with high flows. A more convenient method of log transport was to augment stream flows by the construction of wooden splash dams. Splash dams spanned the forks and stored water and logs through the fall. The dam boards were pulled during high flows, releasing thousands of logs to float the flows to the mills at tidewater. At least 25 splash dams operated in the Coquille watershed, including eight on the north fork, four on the east fork, and three on the middle fork. Splash dams were also built on tributaries, including Middle, Elk, Big, Sandy, and Cherry Creeks. Two dams each were on Myrtle and Rock Creek, and a single dam was built on Dement Creek, off the south fork (Beckham 1990).

The Port of Coquille River, which was created at about the same time the first major splash dams were being built, worked with log transport companies to improve log transport and navigation by removing riparian trees and brush to open channels, blasting channel boulders, and removing instream snags. These actions, combined with the erosive nature of thousands of large conifer logs floated down the tributaries, had major impacts on the streams. At the same time, the removal of vegetation and instream structures streamlined the transportation of logs. The Port of Coquille River reported, "that on three miles of the east fork it normally took about three days of work to drive 1,000 logs through the segment, but after channel work it took about one and one-half hours for the equal amount logs to pass through" (Benner 1992). River transport and widespread splash damming continued through at least 1946, with the last dams being removed from the middle fork of the Coquille in the 1950s.

Floods and other natural events are an important means to build and maintain the Coquille watershed. Floods form and reform channels and distribute large wood throughout the system. Since European settlement, large floods have been reported in 1861, 1881, 1890, 1964, and 1996. Some of these events have had major impacts, including the 1861 flood that was responsible for relocating the mouth of the river. The storm and persistent rainfall of 1890 created a large landslide on Salmon Creek (a tributary of the south fork) that persisted for several days, building a reservoir behind the debris dam that broke and sent tons of sediment and debris throughout the south fork and lower reaches of the river.

Habitat-Related Limiting Factors

The accumulative effects of over 150 years of human alteration of fish habitat, heavy fishing pressure, and out-of-system hatchery releases have left a number of Coquille anadromous fish stocks at low levels. The last 20-year reduction in ocean productivity has exacerbated the problem. Although natural events may cause large variations in salmonid populations, continued human-induced habitat changes have limited the ability of many stocks to recover (Nickelson et al. 1992).

Key factors limiting anadromous fish production on the Coquille watershed are water quality, including low dissolved oxygen, sedimentation, and erosion; nonpoint-source pollution, including increased chlorophyll production; point-source pollution; and elevated temperature. Also threatening water quality within the basin are major habitat alterations including draining and filling of wetlands, removal of woody debris, channeling, isolation of the floodplain, and lack of riparian vegetation. Twenty-two streams or stream segments of the Coquille River have been identified as not meeting the water quality standards under Section 303(d) of the Clean Water Act for fisheries and other beneficial uses. Many other areas within the system have yet to be analyzed for their condition (ODEQ 1995). Dissolved oxygen in the main stem and lower reaches of the north and south forks may reach low enough concentrations during low flows to be lethal to juvenile salmonids. In the higher-gradient sections of the tributaries, dissolved oxygen has not been found to be a limiting factor.

Increased erosion and evaluated temperatures, coupled with point- and nonpoint-source organic loading from agriculture, urban areas, roads, and sewage treatment plants, all serve as limiting factors. Oil and other toxins are also thought to be problematic within the basin, although compared to larger, more urbanized areas, the Coquille basin contains small amounts of toxic substances. Toxic substances are introduced from a variety of point and nonpoint sources, such as storm-water discharges, spillage, and minor industrial sources.

Erosion and sedimentation are key limiting factors within the Coquille watershed. High sediment loads fill pools and cover spawning gravel, and organic materials reduce intergravel dissolved oxygen. Sediment deposition can create temporary barriers to adult migration during low flows. Extreme turbidity can result in gill abrasion and chronic effects on the fish. The Coquille watershed naturally produces large amounts of sediment because of the interplay of terrain, geology, and rainfall (ODEQ 1992a). The heavy seasonal rains, combined with steep, thinly soiled slopes on unstable bedrock, leave the system susceptible to earth flows, debris slides, erosion, and flash flooding. Elevated turbidity and sediment production is a problem in all forks and can be attributed to soil-disturbing activities such as road building, timber harvesting, forest fires, riparian vegetation removal, and other land activities.

Adequate temperature to support salmonids (52–68°F) is problematic on all forks of the Coquille. Warm waters work in concert with other limiting factors such as dissolved oxygen to compound impacts on fish. Low summer flows (less than 1% of the Coquille watershed annual discharge is between August and September) naturally warm the system above optimum temperatures for salmonids. Human activities that have removed tree cover have increased erosion and shallowed and widened channels. These activities, coupled with summer water withdrawals, make elevated temperatures the main reason why many segments of the Coquille River are listed as water quality limited under the Clean Water Act.

Another limiting factor within the basin is fish passage. During the last 70 years, roads have been constructed on many areas of the Coquille basin, and in the process numerous culverts have been installed for drainage on both annual and intermittent streams. Most of the culverts were installed before adult and juvenile fish passage or other wildlife passage problems were considered. A recent survey of 200 culverts on private and public roads indicated that nearly 50% were incapable of passing fish, especially juveniles, during some flow periods (CWA 1994). Culverts block many miles of small-stream summer and winter rearing habitat for coho, steelhead, and cutthroat.

Tide gates, which are designed to block the flood tide from pastureland and allow drainage during the ebb, can also create habitat problems. Tide gates not only may block fish passage but also may reduce water quality in a variety of ways, including reducing available salt-marsh transition zones and constricting and obstructing flows from flooded wetlands. In these ways, tide gates interrupt historical tidal fluctuation. A tide gate can also present a physical barrier due to either poor maintenance or improper design (although this issue is poorly understood), and water quality often suffers behind tide gates because an artificial head of tide is formed and water behind the closed tide gate has elevated temperatures and low levels of dissolved oxygen (J. Charland, Oregon State University, personal communication). Although small dams and diversions do exist in the watershed, they do not represent a major limiting factor within the system.

Spawning gravel availability within the system may be a limiting factor in some of the forks, including the north and east forks, primarily because of the historic loss of large-channel wood that captured and retained gravel. Without channel structures, gravel is free to move into reaches below the normal spawning areas during high flows. The removal of large woody debris and boulders intrained in the riparian and river systems began soon after the arrival of European settlers. The removal of structural complexity resulted in a significant loss of instream habitat during elevated flows, loss of sediment and gravel deposition areas, and loss of channel diversity, including deepwater pool habitat. Lack of large wood recruitment is also a problem in all forks of the Coquille.

Although the riparian areas of the Coquille watershed have been highly modified, the current Oregon Forest Practices Act requires riparian buffers on private timberlands, and riparian buffers are also heavily used on public timberlands. Many of the historic riparian areas in the low- and midgradient reaches of the Coquille River were removed over 60 years ago, increasing bank width and erosion deposition within the system. Currently, Coos County has an ordinance to provide some protection, including a 50-ft riparian buffer along the agricultural and urban areas of the river.

Another limiting factor for fish production is floodplain connectivity. The main stem of the Coquille River remains connected to its historic floodplain and floods annually, although this connectivity has been affected by diking from roads and agriculture. Many tributary floodplains have been disconnected and no longer function during 5-, 10-, 15-, and 100-year storm events. Much of the connectivity has been lost through the building of roads and bridges and the laying of inadequate culverts. The loss of connectivity to floodplains and wetlands has resulted in accelerated sedimentation, loss of overflow channels, and decreased natural application of upland sediments to wetland areas through floods.

Many parts of this system have been channelized to remove meanders and maximize agricultural production. Dike and drainage ditches employed for flood control typically run parallel to the streams. Flood-control dikes, tide gates, and channel-maintenance practices that promote rapid drainage have decoupled side-channel tributaries in the low-gradient portions of the Coquille River and its tributaries. These changes have resulted in corresponding fish habitat losses and problems, particularly for coho salmon and cutthroat trout attempting to access winter rearing areas.

Organizational Development of the CWA

Growing awareness of the decline in anadromous fish stocks (particularly coho salmon) driven by freshwater habitat alterations and other human actions, plus many water quality problems caused by human alterations and a fear of federal intervention through the ESA and the Clean Water Act, led to the organization of the Coquille Watershed Association (CWA) in February 1994. The formation of the CWA and similar organizations on the Coos watershed and on smaller watersheds in Curry County, Oregon to the south was a major step in a 20-year local effort to address fish habitat and water quality issues by restoring natural watershed processes through public and private partnerships.

During the 1970s, the BLM and the USFS initiated a number of restoration projects on their lands. Many of these early efforts involved trying to replace large woody debris lost through splash damming and other actions. Although many of the projects did not met their intended goals, many did, and 20 years later some of the projects are still furnishing fish habitat in the Coquille and Coos watersheds.

Beginning in 1981, there was a coastwide and later a statewide effort to involve local communities in the restoration of salmon and trout stocks. In 1983 the Oregon legislature formalized the effort through the Oregon Salmon Trout Enhancement Program (STEP). Early efforts by the STEP primarily involved rearing juvenile fish, but a number of projects addressed long-term habitat issues, encouraging strategies such as riparian tree planting on private lands.

Two other key projects were initiated during the late 1980s. One was the Near Coastal Waters Program administered by the Oregon Department of Environmental Quality (ODEQ). This effort, which was funded by EPA, began to analyze and address some of the water quality issues on the tidal reaches of the Coquille watershed. Both point sources such as sewage-treatment plants and nonpoint sources such as agricultural runoff were addressed in this project. The Near Coastal Waters Program also produced a videotape identifying the cooperative public and private actions needed to address water quality problems. The second effort during the late 1980s was the development of a Winter Habitat Project by the Oregon Department of Fish and Wildlife. This program was a cooperative effort to address winter habitat needs for salmon through the creation of off-channel ponds and the addition of large wood through a joint program with the ODFW and private timber operators. Most of the early efforts in this program involved industrial timber operators, but some small woodland owners also were involved.

As a follow-up to both the Near Coastal Waters Program and the Winter Habitat Project, an agency-driven group was organized to build a larger-scale demonstration project that would address limiting factors on a watershed basis. The group, which included the Natural Resource Conservation Service, ODFW, ODEQ, and Oregon State University Extension and Sea Grant, began to work with both large industrial landowners and small agricultural landowners on Palouse Creek, a tributary of Coos Bay. During a two-year period, a number of restoration projects were initiated on Palouse Creek, including fencing and planting on the lower tidal reaches of the creek, adding large wood in appropriate areas on both public and private lands, and adding off-channel rearing areas in natural wetlands and tributaries. This project has been successful and has resulted in a dramatic increase in coho salmon production in Palouse Creek (Muck, personal communication).

Another key action was the development of a local public–private partnership called Bring Back the Natives. This organization provided funding through the USFS, BLM, and private sources to address limiting factors and bring public and private interests together. The group was successful in obtaining funding for projects that included some major restoration efforts on industrial and nonindustrial private forest lands. The partnership has continued to be one of the key funding sources and forums for subsequent development of the Coquille Watershed Association and other groups.

These community-based organizations were not the only forces important to the development of local watershed associations. Several events, including the initial filing to place Oregon coastal coho salmon on the federal endangered species list, the listing of the lower Coquille as a "water quality limited stream" by the ODEQ under the Clean Water Act, and 1993 Oregon legislation entitled the Watershed Health Program, helped to jump-start the development of the CWA. The water quality problems and potential species listings may have been the impetus to form the organization, but the Watershed Health Program was the catalyst. The legislation included $10 million for on-the-ground watershed demonstration projects in southwestern Oregon (which included the Coquille watershed) and northeastern Oregon. An organizational structure was required to manage the legislation's funding, which totaled approximately $3.5 million for each region after administrative costs. The early organizational structure in Coos County, Oregon was the Coos Watershed Coordinating Authority (CWCA). This group, which was appointed by the Coos County Board of Commissioners, was made up of over 80 large and small landowners and others interested in watershed restoration within the county. It was important that the Coos County Board of Commissioners appointed people to the organization, not only because the Watershed Health Program legislation required such appointments, but also because this appointment process demonstrated the political will to do the watershed projects.

It became apparent after three meetings of the CWCA that to effectively initiate watershed restoration, it would be necessary to break the group into three watershed councils encompassing the Coos,

Tenmile, and Coquille watersheds. (The Coquille is the largest of the three major watersheds within Coos County.) Under legislative direction and local interpretation, a watershed council is defined as a "locally organized, voluntary, nonregulatory group established to assess the watershed condition and build a work plan to implement, enhance, and protect the processes within the watershed" (CWA 1997). Watershed councils bring together diverse interests around a common goal of watershed health and offer local residents the opportunity to make decisions that affect their own watersheds. Under these guidelines the Coquille Watershed Association was formed in February 1994 as an Oregon nonprofit corporation. The organization consists of a general membership made up of landowners, stakeholders, agency representatives, and other interested parties. The general membership elects a 26-member (originally 13-member) executive council that governs the organization. The general membership also sets the size and makeup of the executive council with recommendations from the stakeholders, and executive council members serve two-year terms. The membership of the executive council is shown in Table 3.

The executive council operates by consensus. The CWA defines consensus as finding a proposal acceptable enough that all members can support it and no member opposes it. Under the executive council is a five-member board of directors that advises the day-to-day operations of the organization. The CWA's officers consist of a president, vice-president, secretary, treasurer, officer-at-large, and resource advisor. Since its inception the CWA also has hired a watershed coordinator whose job has been to administer the organization, develop and implement projects, perform reporting and monitoring duties, and carry out all other necessary actions.

The CWA has created a mission statement, which consists of a vision statement, goals, and a set of operating objectives. The mission statement states that the CWA is composed of a broad array of participants with interests, livelihoods, or land ownership found in the Coquille watershed. In developing the goals of the CWA mission statement, the CWA executive council also identified areas that are not appropriate for action by the CWA, including:

- factors relating to the directed and incidental harvest of fish by recreational and commercial fisheries;

TABLE 3.—Membership of the Coquille Watershed Association executive council, 1998. (USFS = U.S. Forest Service; BLM = U.S. Bureau of Land Management; PAC = Provincial Advisory Committee; SWCD = Soil and Water Conservation District; ODFW = Oregon Department of Fish and Wildlife; ODEQ = Oregon Department of Environmental Quality; OSU = Oregon State University.)

Membership category (number of members)	Representation
Large landowners	
Federal (2)	USFS—Powers District Ranger
	BLM—Coos Bay District
Private (2)	The Timber Company (formally Georgia Pacific Corporation)
	Menasha Corporation
County	Coos County Forest
Small landowners	
North, east forks	Agriculture and timber landowner
Middle fork	Agriculture and timber landowner
South fork	Agriculture landowner
Middle, lower mainstem	Agriculture landowner
Stakeholders	
Salmon Trout Enhancement Program	Board member
Southwestern Oregon PAC	Board member
Friends of the Coquille	Board member
Livestock	Livestock Association member
Small woodland owners	Board member
Coos SWCD	Elected director
Oregon Farm Bureau	Board member
Ports, cities, other	
Port of Coquille	Elected commissioner
Port of Bandon	Elected commissioner
Bandon area	City council member
Local cities	City councilor
Technical advisory team	ODFW; ODEQ
Coquille Tribe	Tribal chairman
At-large members (2)	Citizens
Resource advisor	OSU extension staff
SW Coos Sub-Watershed Association	Board member

- factors related to the management of hatcheries, including broodstock selection, numbers and locations of releases, and expansion or reduction of hatchery programs;
- large-scale factors that influence overall environmental conditions, such as climatic changes within the northeast Pacific Ocean; and
- predation by birds and marine mammals.

Specifically, the mission statement of the CWA is as follows (CWA 1997).

The Coquille Watershed Association has a vision of the Coquille system in which commercial activities occur in a way that integrates resource values. This includes the following:

- Create water quality conditions that will meet the Clean Water Act standards.
- Enhance native fish survival and production; increase salmonid production within the basin.
- Create understanding and acceptance of the need for sustainable economic activities representing long-term resource conservation.
- Respect and protect private property rights during implementation of projects designed to improve watershed productivity and health. The association will engage in a project only with written permission of the landowner. Any commitment the landowner makes will be clearly defined and will be strictly on a volunteer basis. Adequate language will be added to agreements to assure property owners that no hidden claim to their land will result from implementation of the project.

The goal of the CWA is to provide an organizational framework to coordinate the assessment of the watershed, implement and monitor proven management practices, and test new management practices that are designed to support environmental integrity and economic stability for the communities of the Coquille watershed and adjacent areas. The objectives of the CWA are to

- facilitate communication among affected landowners, citizens, political organizations, associations, and agencies within the Coquille watershed;
- provide a framework to coordinate projects and management practices within the Coquille watershed that will improve its overall health;
- coordinate comprehensive programs for the strategic management of the Coquille watershed;
- provide opportunities to resolve problems and conflicts arising over the management of and management practices within the Coquille watershed;
- provide opportunities for community-based education on the values and functions of the Coquille watershed;
- enhance and restore salmonids within the Coquille basin;

- monitor and evaluate activities accomplished through the CWA; and
- solicit funding and other resources necessary to implement the objectives of the CWA.

The CWA is also advised by a technical advisory committee made up of more than 20 individuals affiliated with public and private organizations who have expertise in a variety of areas such as fisheries, forestry, agriculture, hydrology, silviculture, land-use planning, and political science. The technical advisory committee is a key component that helps the CWA to advise on the technical soundness of projects and the possibility of cooperative projects and funding, particularly with federal and state agencies. The CWA executive council has required that two of its members should be members of the technical advisory committee. A member of the technical advisory committee also serves on the board of directors.

Soon after the CWA was organized, it became apparent that a plan was needed to effectively develop a strategy for addressing the goals and objectives of the CWA and involving private landowners. Several members of the technical advisory committee and the executive council completed the initial Action Plan for the CWA in 1994. This was a working document that allowed for future additions and modifications. The Action Plan was rewritten in 1996 by a steering committee of representatives from the technical advisory committee. Throughout its development the Action Plan was reviewed by the CWA executive council, federal and state agencies, and landowners. Although some minor changes were made, the plan was approved by the executive council. The Action Plan reviews legacy actions within the basin that have affected fish production and water quality. The plan lays out a set of strategies that address the condition of the watershed, limiting factors for fish and water quality, and ways in which the goals and objectives of the CWA might be met. The plan also establishes priorities for action, including a conceptual framework for identifying, prioritizing, coordinating, and accomplishing short-term and long-term restoration activities. Monitoring is an important part of the plan, which includes guidelines for implementation monitoring and project-effectiveness monitoring. With project-effectiveness monitoring, strategies can be modified to better address the limiting factors for fish and water quality.

Accomplishments

Since the initial organization of the CWA, accomplishments have been measured in three areas: (1) the growth and management of the organization, (2) the development and implementation of projects (including funding) that address limiting factors, and (3) the extent of internal and external educational programs. These areas are discussed in the following sections.

Growth

The CWA started with approximately 30 dedicated members representing a diversity of interests. Industrial timber groups, small woodland owners, agricultural landowners, fisheries interests, and representatives of local government, environmental groups, and state and federal agencies were all part of the initial members. The initial group established and elected a 13-member executive council that represented all the interests and elected a 5-member board of directors. The original executive council developed the following set of first-year tasks:

- Develop articles of incorporation and incorporate the CWA as a nonprofit Oregon corporation.
- Develop a set of bylaws that establish the operating structure of the organization. (The bylaws went through both legal and organizational review.)
- Organize an administrative structure to dispense funds for CWA activities. A partnership with the Coos Soil and Water Conservation District (SWCD) was the key to developing an effective administrative structure. The SWCDs, which are governed by an elected board, already had the people and legal protections in place to help the CWA organize projects on private land. A small percentage of funds received by the CWA are dedicated to the Coos SWCD for administrative services.
- Hire a watershed coordinator to develop and initiate projects.
- In cooperation with the technical advisory committee and watershed coordinator, organize and approve CWA Action Plan 1.0, which would develop a strategy to address the CWA's objectives and the limiting factors in the watershed.
- Expand a growing list of partners for cooperative projects.

After four years of existence, the CWA general membership has grown from the original 30 members to over 250 members. The size of the executive council has doubled to 26 members. New executive council positions were recruited and include representatives from small rural communities located on the forks and from stakeholder groups. In four years the CWA has organized and implemented over $2.5 million in projects on mostly private lands and has carried out surveys and monitoring efforts. The number of partners involved in projects has grown from the initial six small landowners, two industrial timber owners, and four state and federal agencies to over 150 small landowners, five industrial timber owners, and over 15 state and federal agencies.

Funding for the CWA has come from a variety of sources. The following are some of the key contributors:

- The Bring Back the Natives (BBN) project, sponsored by the USFS and the BLM.
- The State of Oregon, first through the Watershed Health Program funded by the 1993 legislature and then through the Governor's Watershed Enhancement Board, which was recognized by the 1997 legislature to be the key funding source for watershed councils (statewide funding is $30 million for two years).
- Funds provided by the EPA, which are distributed through the ODEQ, as well as other federal disaster funding due to the reduction of the commercial salmon fishery, which is administered through the National Oceanic and Atmospheric Administration to the Natural Resource Conservation Service and local SWCDs. Disaster funding allowed the CWA to hire displaced salmon fishers to do restoration work. The ODEQ and ODFW also provided direct grants for a variety of projects and in-kind services.
- Bureau of Land Management and USFS grants and joint projects, including contracts with the CWA for a Jobs in the Woods crew (a federally sponsored training program for unemployed timber workers) and large in-kind contributions. Funds from the federal Northwest Economic Adjustment Act, which is designed to help communities adjust to the loss of revenues from the downturn in federal timber harvest, are primarily used to hire restoration crews.

282 HEIKKILA

TABLE 4.—Project screening criteria and relative importance of criteria (CWA 1997; P. Slater, Coquille Watershed Association, personal communication).

Criterion	Critical	High
Landowner desires restoration project(s) on his or her property.	X	
Landowner's stewardship incentives are high (e.g., the landowner can provide in-kind services such as labor, equipment, and materials, or desires to provide long-term maintenance or monitoring).		X
The project addresses limiting factors.	X	
Good opportunities for coordination with private, federal, and state groups to treat or restore subwatersheds are available.		X
The project will focus on high-priority salmonid habitat or water-quality—limited streams.		X
Opportunities exist for cooperative funding.		X
Projects are technically sound with clearly defined goals and objectives and are compatible with watershed-scale processes.	X	
Projects embrace and define a broad spectrum of values, supporting the CWA's educational, cultural, scientific, and economic goals and objectives.		X
Projects promote public awareness and participation and enhance educational opportunities associated with watershed health.		X

- For the Sake of the Salmon, a regional public–private partnership that solicits and distributes federal funding for watershed coordinator positions and other watershed improvement efforts.
- The U.S. Fish and Wildlife Service, which provided matching grants for a number of projects.
- Cash and in-kind services from timber companies, Coos County, and all the landowners involved in projects.

The rapid expansion of the CWA led the organization to rewrite the Action Plan. Version 2.0 was organized by a subcommittee of the executive council and the technical advisory committee. The executive council hired a technical writer to finish the Action Plan. The new Action Plan clearly stated that to improve water quality and fish production, limiting factors should be seriously addressed through restoration projects that target the private landowners who own over 60% of the watershed. To be effective, restoration projects should mimic natural processes; be appropriate for the gradient zone of the river, site specific, and based on watershed analysis; and include a monitoring program.

The CWA Action Plan 2.0 also established initial project screening criteria, which are listed in Table 4. In addition, other screening criteria are applied depending on the project. Once projects make it through the screening process, they are reviewed by the technical advisory committee and executive council. If approved, a landowner agreement is developed, which clearly states the objectives of the

project and the responsibilities of the landowner and the CWA. Major CWA projects from 1994 to 1998 are summarized in Table 5.

Surveys and Monitoring

All CWA projects have monitoring components to track effectiveness and implementation, and these components are designed to ensure that projects are completed according to design guidelines. In addition, all CWA projects have follow-up monitoring procedures to measure project effectiveness against the objectives of the project. Surveys are performed to add to the information base for watershed analysis and to provide preproject baseline evaluation procedures. Monitoring and survey efforts performed by the CWA have included:

- four projects with high school students to monitor fish habitat and water quality;
- a full survey of all riparian projects covering tree survival, vegetation competition, and fence condition;
- pre- and postspawning surveys on eight tributaries;
- full physical habitat surveys on four tributaries; and
- two logging road and landing surveys on project streams.

All surveys and monitoring have been conducted by CWA crew members or temporary help after training, which has been provided by cooperating agen-

TABLE 5.—Major projects of the Coquille Watershed Association (1994 to February 1998) (P. Slater, Coquille Watershed Association, personal communication).

Project	Focus or goal
Over 60 mi of riparian restoration through fencing and planting of over 40,000 native conifers and hardwoods and approximately 150,000 willows	Water quality; erosion and turbidity; temperature (shade); runoff buffers; future source of wood debris for channel structure
Developed six off-channel livestock watering sites	Water quality; erosion and turbidity; nonpoint-source pollution
Installed 157 instream structures consisting of large wood and boulders at 20 different reaches; cooperatively developed three off-channel ponds	Provide interim large woody debris for channel complexity and gravel retention; wetland losses; winter salmon habitat
Replaced or retrofitted nine culverts and unplugged four culverts	Adult and juvenile fish passage
Modifying and managing tide gates for fish passage and restoring low-gradient tributaries to original channels (in progress)	Wetland losses; fish passage

cies. Monitoring and surveying information is normally shared between the CWA and cooperating agencies.

Education

Educating CWA membership, agency representatives, politicians, environmental groups, and the broader community on the issues facing the Coquille watershed has been a priority with the CWA since its beginning. The major educational activities sponsored or cosponsored by the CWA have included the following:

• Ten evening workshops for CWA members and the general public, covering subjects ranging from ocean factors affecting fish survival to landslides.
• The production of two newsletters.
• The coproduction of two videotapes, one in cooperation with the Coos Watershed Association and a second, entitled *The Coquille Project*, with the BBN project. Both tapes were widely distributed throughout Oregon and regionally.
• Over 40 field tours, which are designed to inform people about (1) the cooperative projects carried out by the CWA and others and (2) the strategies that the organization uses. Target au-

diences for tours have included agencies, legislators, environmental groups, timber and agriculture interests, and the membership of the CWA.

Conclusion

Watershed protection and restoration through the CWA is a dynamic, continuing process with solid, membership-developed goals and objectives as a guide. The CWA has been recognized on a number of levels for cooperative, community-based watershed work. The CWA received the Oregon Private Industries Council "Distinguished Performance Award" in 1997 and a nationwide joint award from the USFS and BLM "for exemplary work in cooperative watershed restoration" in 1998. The CWA also is a finalist for the U.S. Department of the Interior's "Caring for the Land Award."

With recognition comes responsibility to help duplicate this effort in other watersheds. The educational and outreach efforts performed by the CWA and other southwestern Oregon watershed associations and councils have been key in (1) convincing legislatures and other policy makers to develop the Oregon Plan for Salmon and Watersheds (or Oregon Plan) and (2) developing an organizational structure that can be adapted to other watersheds. Since the formation of the CWA and the other southwestern Oregon associations, over 80 Oregon watershed councils have formed, most since 1997. Many of the groups were formed to take advantage of the funding available through the Oregon Plan for Salmon and Watersheds, and some of the groups are struggling to find goals and a direction.

For groups such as the CWA that are successfully protecting and restoring fish habitat and water quality, a number of common themes emerge:

1. Before and during the formation of the organization, there was a community-based education effort to inform the watershed community about their issues and problems.
2. The organization of political support on a local level allowed the formation of successful groups.
3. The organizational structure of the successful groups was inclusive with representation from landowners (large and small), diverse stakeholder groups, and state and federal agencies.
4. Preliminary analysis allowed groups to proceed with projects that addressed the defined limiting factors within the watershed.

With commitment, watershed associations can be a key factor to help restore and protect fish habitat and water quality.

Acknowledgments

The author thanks the Coquille Watershed Association's executive council and board for their strong commitment to the goals and objectives of the organization and their make-it-happen attitude. The CWA Action Plan was key in developing an active organization and furnishing the material for this paper. Therefore, the author would especially like to thank Pam Blake of the ODEQ and Jim Nielsen, the first CWA coordinator, for their persistence in developing Action Plan version 1.0.

Action Plan version 2.0 was developed by a subcommittee of the technical advisory committee, with representatives from the ODEQ; ODFW; BLM; Georgia Pacific West, Inc.; the Menasha Corporation; the CWA; the city of Bandon; the Oregon Department of Agriculture; the Port of Coquille River; the USFS; and Gail Grifantini, the technical writer.

Special thanks goes to Kitty Trolard of the Coos County Extension Office and Sandy Ridlington, Managing Editor, Oregon State University Sea Grant Communications for extraordinary help in organizing and editing this chapter.

References

Beckham, D. 1990. Swift flows the river: log driving in Oregon. Arago Books, Lake Oswego, Oregon.

Benner, P. 1992. Historical reconstruction of the Coquille River and surrounding landscape (draft). U.S. Forest Service, Pacific Northwest Forest and Range Experiment Station, Corvallis, Oregon.

CWA (Coquille Watershed Association). 1994. Culvert survey. CWA, Coquille, Oregon.

CWA (Coquille Watershed Association). 1997. Action plan. CWA, Coquille, Oregon.

Interrain Pacific. 1996. Coquille subbasin working atlas. an introduction to available geographic information. Interrain Pacific, Portland, Oregon.

MATG, and BLM (Multi-Agency Task Group, and U.S. Bureau of Land Management). 1993. Coquille River watershed: background and scoping document. U.S. Forest Service, BLM, Oregon Department of Fish and Wildlife, and Oregon Department of Environmental Quality. Portland, Oregon.

Nickelson, T. E., and six coauthors. 1992. Status of anadromous salmonids in Oregon coastal basins. Oregon Department of Fish and Wildlife, Corvallis, Oregon.

ODEQ (Oregon Department of Environmental Quality). 1992a. Oregon's 1992 Water Quality Status Assessment Report (305b). ODEQ, Portland, Oregon.

ODEQ (Oregon Department of Environmental Quality). 1992b. Action Plan for Oregon Coastal Watersheds, Estuary, and Ocean Waters. Near Coastal Waters National. Pilot Project. 1988-1991. ODEQ, Portland, Oregon.

ODEQ (Oregon Department of Environmental Quality). 1995. 1992-1994 Water Quality Standards Review. ODEQ, Standards and Assessment Section, Portland, Oregon.

ODFW (Oregon Department of Fish, and Wildlife). 1992. Coquille Basin Fish Management Plan, Draft. ODFW, Portland, Oregon.

ODFW (Oregon Department of Fish, and Wildlife). 1997. Tenmile-Coos-Coquille District Guide to Restoration Site Section. ODFW, Portland, Oregon.

USACE (U.S. Army Corps of Engineers). 1972. Review report, Coquille River tributaries, Oregon. USACE, Portland, Oregon.

American Fisheries Society Symposium 22:285–298, 1999

Habitat-Based Assessment of Lobster Abundance: A Case Study of an Oil Spill

J. Stanley Cobb and Michael Clancy

Department of Biological Sciences, University of Rhode Island
Kingston, Rhode Island 02881 USA

Richard A. Wahle

Bigelow Laboratory for Ocean Sciences, West Boothbay Harbor, Maine 04575, USA

Abstract.—The American lobster *Homarus americanus* is usually associated with rocky substrate that provides or can be modified into shelter and that may be an essential habitat to early benthic-phase juveniles. The dependence on shelter-providing habitat not only makes possible the definition of essential habitat for lobsters but also permits the assessment of abundance based on the areal extent of habitat. Here, we describe such a habitat-based assessment, performed in response to an oil spill on the coast of Rhode Island, USA. Results from a side-scan sonar survey performed after the spill indicated that the amount of lobster habitat affected by the oil was approximately 9.8 km^2 along nearly 15 km of coastline. Postspill lobster density ranged from 0.24 lobsters m^{-2} in the impact region to 1.63 lobsters m^{-2} in the control region. Qualitative (map contours of lobster density) and quantitative (statistical tests) approaches suggested a significant effect of the spill had been detected by our sampling. An estimate of the total number of lobsters killed was required to scale restoration efforts. We calculated the total number of lobsters in the area by overlaying contours of lobster density on a habitat map generated by side-scan sonar, then multiplying the density of lobsters in each contour interval by the area of appropriate lobster habitat (cobble and boulder) in the contour interval. To calculate loss, we subtracted postspill abundance from prespill abundance. Prespill density was estimated to be 1.76 m^{-2}, which is an adjusted average of airlift samples taken at six Rhode Island sites four months prior to the spill. Calculations of loss based on habitat-specific density estimates were adjusted to reflect undersampling. The loss was estimated to be to be 9.0 ∞ 10^6 lobsters. Variability associated with this loss estimate is large; 95% confidence intervals estimated that between 6.7 ∞ 10^6 and 15.6 ∞ 10^6 lobsters were lost. The calculated loss was very sensitive to changes in prespill density estimates; a change of 0.1 lobsters m^{-2} resulted in a change of 0.75–0.9 ∞ 10^6 lobsters lost. Habitat-based assessment of lobster population size is possible but requires detailed habitat maps and accurate density estimates. Natural variability and sampling limitations give such assessment a wide range of possible values. Nevertheless, the airlift sampling technique, together with side-scan sonar maps of habitat, could provide a powerful tool for estimating the abundance of inshore lobsters.

Habitat availability has long been considered integral for understanding population and community ecology (Elton 1966; Southwood 1977). Availability of physical structures can affect survival for particularly sensitive life stages of crustaceans and produce bottlenecks that limit population size (Wahle and Steneck 1991; Beck 1995). Habitat quality can vary over time and affect overall population size (Herrnkind et al. 1997). Recently, federal agencies have recognized the importance of habitats to the survival of individual species and entire ecosystems (GAO 1994). Examples include particularly sensitive and productive regions such as hardwood forests and wetlands (GAO 1994; Meyer and Swank 1996). Attempts have been made recently to manage ecosystems for the well-being of many organ-

isms by taking a landscape perspective to habitat management (Meyer and Swank 1996). One form of ecosystem management adopted by the National Marine Fisheries Service is the essential fish habitat (EFH) provisions of the 1996 Magnuson-Stevens Fishery Conservation and Management Act, which require the definition of habitat requirements for the entire life cycle of commercially important species (Kurland 1998).

Geographically or physically distinct areas indispensable for survival at some phase in the life history of a species, which is a prerequisite for an area to be designated as an EFH, are threatened by adverse fishing practices, coastal development, and pollution (Langton et al. 1996). Effective management demands knowledge of species-specific habitat requirements. For some species, such knowledge is extensive, but for other species knowledge of species-specific habitat requirements is limited. Definition of essential habitat requires description of the physical environment as well as population-level characteristics such as abundance for each species.

Habitat relationships have been described for all stages of the life cycle of the American lobster *Homarus americanus*, arguably the most important fisheries resource in the northwest Atlantic (Cooper and Uzmann 1980; Lawton and Lavalli 1995). Lobsters, particularly the smaller size classes, are found in shelter-providing habitats. Nearshore cobble substrates appear to be essential postsettlement habitat, providing refuge from predation in many small crevices (Hudon 1987; Wahle and Steneck 1991; Wahle 1992), although small lobsters are occasionally found in habitats as diverse as salt-marsh peat (Able et al. 1988) and estuarine mud (MacKay 1929). Juvenile through adult-phase lobsters are found in more diverse habitats ranging from bedrock to sand and mud, although they most commonly are found where shelters are available or can be constructed. The requirement for shelter decreases with size as the lobster outgrows many of its smaller predators (Wahle 1992; Wahle and Steneck 1992) and habitat requirements become less well-defined (Lawton and Lavalli 1995).

The pollution event we studied was the result of the grounding of a tug and barge loaded with No. 2 fuel oil on the southern Rhode Island, USA, coast in a fierce storm on 19 January 1996. The barge spilled nearly $3.13 \infty 10^6$ liters of oil, contaminating an approximately 13-km stretch of shoreline. Strong wave action at the time of the accident entrained oil and drove it into the water column to depths of at least 10 m (French 1998). The coastal environment adjacent to the accident has sand beaches alternating with rocky headlands, while subtidally large patches of cobble and boulder are interspersed with areas of sand to depths of 12–15 m. The effects of oil contamination were immediately evident from the large quantities of dead lobsters, surf clams, and other invertebrates washed up on the beaches in the area. From a survey of beach strandings, Gibson et al. (1997) estimated that nearly 3 million lobsters washed ashore.

Here we report a habitat-based effort to assess loss to the lobster population. We had two objectives in this paper. Our first objective was to answer the question, was there a statistically significant effect of the oil (beyond what was observed on the beaches) on subtidal lobster density? We answered this question by estimating lobster density in control, impacted, and transitional areas (depending on proximity to the accident) and statistically examining the differences. Our second objective was to answer the question, how many lobsters were in the affected area before and after the accident? We approached this by estimating the amount of lobster habitat in the affected area and lobster density in that habitat, and then multiplied the two quantities to estimate lobster abundance in the affected area. Control and prespill estimates of lobster density were available for comparison; loss was estimated by the difference between pre- and postspill estimates of abundance. This conceptually simple approach provided challenges in sampling and statistical analyses and in deriving absolute density from sample density.

Methods

First, we wished to describe the extent of the area in which lobster mortality occurred and to compare lobster density in areas impacted by oil to unimpacted control locations. Scuba divers sampled sites along the southern Rhode Island coast from points well to the east and west of the area of impact and in the impacted area (Figure 1). We sampled three times: winter (28 February–7 May 1996), summer (9–24 July 1996), and autumn (11–30 September 1996). For the purposes of this paper, which focuses on habitat-based assessment, we concentrate only on the winter survey that we used to estimate loss; the summer and autumn data are used here only to assist in assessing sampling efficiency and are reported elsewhere in detail (Cobb and Clancy 1998). At each site we made airlift and visual estimates of lobster density. In the visual sampling divers swam belt transects. For this paper we do not include belt transect data because they were not habitat-specific and because sample sizes were low. Airlift sampling was performed by a pair of divers using a polyvinylchloride (PVC) pipe, approximately 10 cm in diameter and 2 m long, attached to a scuba tank via a low-pressure hose. The vacuum at the bottom of the tube produced by escaping air lifted animals, silt, sand, and small pebbles to the top of the tube and into a 1-mm mesh bag. Each airlift sample was a 0.5-m^2 quadrat, haphazardly placed in cobble or boulder habitat, and suctioned to a depth of 2–4 cm; all moveable rocks were overturned by one of the

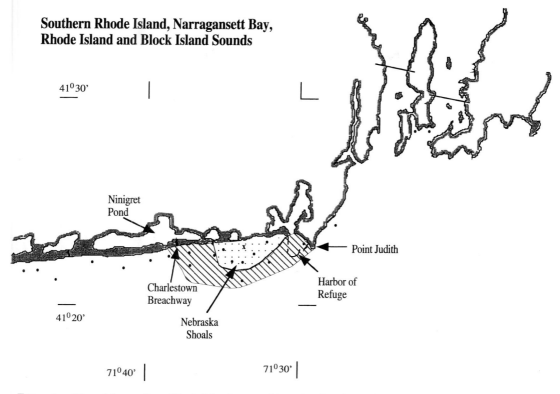

Southern Rhode Island, Narragansett Bay, Rhode Island and Block Island Sounds

41°30'

Ninigret Pond

Point Judith

Charlestown Breachway

Harbor of Refuge

41°20'

Nebraska Shoals

71°40'   71°30'

FIGURE 1.—Map of the southern Rhode Island coast with station locations (dots) and regions defined for statistical purposes shown (impacted = stippled; transition = hatched; control = no shading). Location of the grounding of the oil barge is shown by X. One station (sampled only in winter) was far to the west and is not shown on this map.

divers while the other diver vacuumed carefully. Divers did not note or record lobsters escaping from the quadrat during sampling. At each site the target sample size was 12 quadrats.

Side-scan sonar was used during September 1996 to determine the areal extent of habitat types from near shore to a depth of 15 m from the eastern extent of the Harbor of Refuge to approximately 1 km west of the Charlestown Breachway (see Figures 1 and 2), a total area of about 37.4 km². The boundaries of the side-scan survey were defined relying on results of simulation modeling of the advection of oil (French 1998) and stranding of lobsters on the beaches (Gibson et al. 1997). Little or no oil was predicted to be east of the Harbor of Refuge, and no beached lobsters were found east of Point Judith. The western boundary was more difficult to define because there were very few beach strandings of lobsters west of the Charlestown Breachway (Gibson et al. 1997), but the circulation model predicted low concentrations of oil there. We therefore

used all the side-scan data available to us, continuing approximately 1 km beyond the Charlestown Breachway (Figure 2). The side-scan sonar field work and interpretation were performed by Golder Associates (Redmond, Washington) and supplied to us by Beak Consultants (Kirkland, Washington) in electronic form as an Arc/INFO export file. Four habitat classifications were used: fine sediment, coarse sediment, cobble, and boulder. Visual confirmation of the habitat classification was provided by images from a video "drop camera" that recorded images of bottom type at precisely identified locations. Qualitative review of the videotape confirmed that the visual images coincided with side-scan interpretations. The resolution of the side-scan sonar was sufficient to resolve habitat areas of 10 m ∞ 10 m or larger. Divers reported that patches of cobble smaller than 100 m² existed within sand areas and, conversely, areas of sand smaller than 100 m² were found within cobble habitat. After assigning one habitat classification to each 100-m² cell in the map,

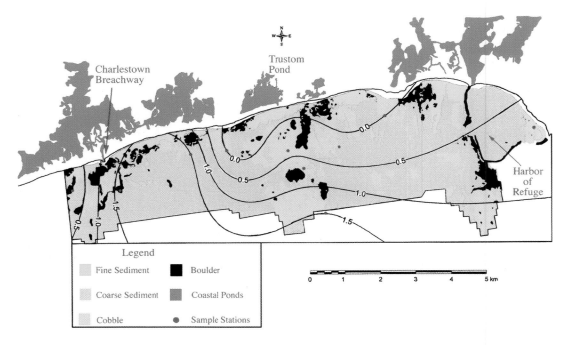

FIGURE 2.—Side-scan sonar image of the benthic environment from Point Judith to west of the Charlestown Breachway, Rhode Island. Four sediment types—fine sediment, coarse sediment, cobble, and boulder—are shown. Cobble and boulder are considered suitable habitat for lobsters. Contours of lobster density estimated from winter 1996 airlift sampling are overlain on the habitat map. The total amount of cobble and boulder habitat (appropriate for lobsters) enclosed in each contour interval is shown in Table 5.

we assumed that patches differing from the chosen habitat category were present and randomly distributed in each cell and hence cancelled each other out.

To test the null hypothesis that oil had no effect on lobster density, we assumed that lobsters would be exposed to the oil along a diminishing gradient from the spill site. Wind and current patterns were likely to have affected this gradient. Accordingly, we classified sites into three regions: (1) impacted (nearest the site of the spill), (2) transition, or (3) unimpacted control (clearly unaffected by oil), based on the distribution of lobsters stranded on the beaches (Gibson et al. 1997) and results of model simulations of the trajectory of subsurface oil (French 1998). The three areas are illustrated in Figure 1; further explanation of the choice of designation can be found in Cobb and Clancy (1998). We tested the null hypothesis of no difference in lobster density among these three regions.

We considered two statistical models for these data, a nested analysis and a random effects analysis. The former model had stations fixed and nested within regions while the latter assumed stations were arrayed randomly within regions. Arguments can be made for either model (Bennington and Thayne 1994). Initially, we planned analysis of variance (ANOVA) tests, but density data did not conform to the assumptions of parametric analysis: data were nonnormally distributed (Kolmogorov–Smirnov tests), and the variances were unequal (Hartley's F_{max} tests). Most samples returned no lobsters, so the frequency distributions of density were dominated by zeros; both the visual and the airlift data appeared to fit a negative binomial distribution. A logarithmic transformation, where we added a constant to each observation, was inappropriate because of the large number of zero observations (J. Heltsche, University of Rhode Island, and M. J. Fogarty, Chesapeake Biological Laboratory, personal communications), so two other data transformations were attempted. Rank transformation and the performance of a random-effects ANOVA returned the same statistical conclusion as the Kruskal–Wallis tests on untransformed data. A Delta transformation (Pennington 1996), followed by a random-effects ANOVA, concluded that significant differences existed between the control and impacted regions, which agreed with our original conclusions. Because data transformations were either inappropriate or yielded the same statistical conclusions as analyses on untransformed data, we chose to present only analyses on raw data. To our knowledge, a fixed-effects analysis is not possible with a Delta transformation.

We performed a series of statistical tests that progressed from most to least liberal. Subsequent tests were conducted only if preceding tests were significant with the experiment-wise error rate set at $\alpha = 0.05$. First, a Kruskal–Wallis test was performed on the data arrayed by station without regard to region. Second, a log-likelihood-ratio test was used to determine whether there was a difference between regions in the number of zero and nonzero samples. Third, a Kruskal–Wallis test compared density among regions, followed by a Dunn's multiple-comparison test in the event of a significant result. Finally, a nested ANOVA, the most restrictive parametric analysis, was performed.

Mean lobster densities were plotted by station location and contoured with Surfer (version 6) using a Radial Bias grid. Contours of lobster density were then overlaid on the habitat map using MapInfo. To estimate the total postspill lobster abundance by habitat type, the area of cobble and boulder habitat within the bounds of each density contour was summed by MapInfo. Lobsters are found in cobble and boulder habitat; it is not likely that many lobsters would be in fine or coarse sand during the winter months. Multiplying the total area by the estimated density of lobsters within each contour, taken as the midpoint in the range of the density contour, gave an estimate of the total number of lobsters in the area defined by that contour.

Results

The geology of Rhode Island varies considerably over its relatively short southern coastline, which faces Rhode Island and Block Island sounds. To the east of Point Judith lie rock cliffs interspersed with small sandy beaches. Below the cliffs, in the nearshore subtidal, there are some outcroppings of bedrock and large, well-defined patches of cobble and boulder fields that grade into cobble and rubble and then sand or silt. West of Point Judith, the coast is characterized by broad sandy beaches interspersed with rocky headlands. The Charlestown and Point Judith moraines, formed from till as glaciers receded, dominate the coastal and subtidal geology of this area (Morang 1978). One large cobble and boulder

field, which is the result of these glacial processes and known as Nebraska Shoals, extends nearly 4 km offshore (see Figure 2); the oil barge grounded just inshore of Nebraska Shoals. A number of smaller headlands are present adjacent to Nebraska Shoals and have nearshore subtidal cobble and boulder patches, with fine sediment nearshore and coarse sediment offshore (Figure 2). These smaller patches of cobble and boulder fields are less well defined, with frequent small patches of sediment lying within them. Further to the west, the subtidal habitat changes considerably as the frequency and areal extent of cobble and boulder fields decrease. Large boulders surrounded by sand sheet are found, but these boulders do not make good lobster habitat, especially for smaller lobsters (J. S. Cobb and M. Clancy, University of Rhode Island, personal observations).

We first attempted to determine whether there had been a statistically detectable effect of the spill on lobster density immediately after the spill occurred. Mean lobster density is shown by station and region in Table 1. Density contours for the impact and transition regions provided by the Surfer program are shown in Figure 2. Note that no confidence intervals are provided on the contours because of

TABLE 1.—Mean lobster density (# per m^{-2}) and standard deviation (SD), by station and region from airlift samples collected in winter 1996. Location of stations and regions are illustrated in Figure 1. (Regions: I = impacted; T = transition; C = control.)

Region	Station number	Number of samples	Mean lobster density and (SD)
I	2	12	0.00
I	3	10	0.40 (0.84)
I	7	12	0.67 (1.30)
I	8	12	0.17 (0.58)
I	10	13	0.00
Mean for I		59	0.24 (0.75)
T	1	12	0.17 (0.58)
T	4	11	1.64 (1.50)
T	5	12	1.50 (2.97)
T	6	12	1.50 (1.93)
T	11	12	0.67 (0.98)
Mean for T		59	1.08 (1.83)
C	12	12	0.33 (0.78)
C	13	11	4.36 (3.20)
C	14	14	1.57 (1.40)
C	22	12	0.50 (1.24)
Mean for C		49	1.63 (2.37)

TABLE 2.—Frequency of zero observations by region from airlift samples taken in winter 1996. Region is the statistical area illustrated in Figure 1 and refers to proximity to the point of impact of the North Cape oil spill.

Region	Zero	Non-zero	% Non-zero
Impacted	53	6	10.2%
Transition	37	22	37.3%
Control	26	23	46.9%

the great amount of variability and few number of stations. In the impact area mean lobster density in the cobble and boulder habitat was 0.24 m^{-2}, while in the transition region density was 1.08 lobsters m^{-2}, and in the control region density was 1.63 m^{-2} (Table 1). A Kruskal–Wallis test on stations indicated a significant difference in lobster density among stations (H = 57.60, P = 0.0001). Comparing regions, the likelihood-ratio test showed significantly more samples with 0 observations in the impacted region than in the control or transition regions (G = 21.05, P = 0.001; Table 2), and the Kruskal–Wallis test on regions also showed a significant effect (H = 19.69, P = 0.0001). A Dunn's multiple-comparison test showed that both control and transition regions were different from the impacted region. However, a nested ANOVA showed no significant difference among regions ($F_{2,11}$ = 2.21, P = 0.15). These results suggested that the spill had a statistically significant effect on lobster density.

Our second question was, how many lobsters were likely to have died as a result of the spill? Our approach to this question was to use side-scan sonar to estimate the amount of suitable lobster habitat (areas containing cobble and boulder). We then multiplied habitat by the contoured, postspill lobster densities to determine the total number of lobsters present in the area immediately after the spill. The calculated number of lobsters was then compared to the expected number of lobsters, developed from prespill density estimates collected in Rhode Island waters the previous year and applied to the same habitat template (Figure 2).

We then estimated prespill lobster density by examining data from three sources: (1) airlift samples taken after the spill at four control sites in February–May 1996, (2) visual quadrat samples taken in 1995 at one of the control sites, and (3) airlift samples taken from other Rhode Island sites (not the impact area) during 1991–1996. The airlift estimates taken at four control sites in winter 1996 consisted of 11–

14 quadrats at three sites east of the spill and one site west of the spill. The means varied from 0.33 (±0.78) lobsters m^{-2} to 4.36 (±3.20) m^{-2}, with an overall mean of 1.63 ± 2.37 lobsters m^{-2} (Table 1). Visual quadrat surveys were conducted in the summer of 1995 using circular 5-m^2 quadrats at Fort Wetherill (station 14), one of the control sites to the east of the impacted area (Clancy and Cobb, unpublished data). Sand, gravel, and rock substrates were sampled (N = 22 in each). Mean lobster density in the rock (cobble, boulder, and bedrock) habitat was 1.4 lobsters m^{-2}. Few lobsters ≤20 mm carapace length (CL) were captured in this survey. The third source of data were airlift samples collected annually at sites in Rhode Island Sound since 1991. Twelve 0.5-m^2 quadrats were sampled at each of several sites in the control region to the east of the spill and at one site in the Harbor of Refuge (station 11 in the transition region). The annual mean lobster density estimates ranged from 1.2 to 3.2 lobsters m^{-2}, with a mean over all years of 1.8 m^{-2} (Incze et al. 1997; Table 3). Samples taken in September 1995, 4 months before the spill occurred, yielded a mean density of 1.7 lobsters m^{-2}.

Thus, previous census data using both airlift and visual sampling methods resulted in means that ranged from 1.2 to 3.2 lobsters m^{-2}. The mean of the postspill control site airlift sampling was 1.6, the mean of 6 years of airlift sampling in control areas was 1.8, and a 1995 visual survey mean at a control station was 1.4 lobsters m^{-2}. Three of the stations in the postspill transition region showed mean densities of 1.5, 1.5, and 1.6 lobsters m^{-2}. We had no estimates of prespill lobster density in the impact region. We chose to use the 1995 airlift estimate, 1.7 lobsters m^{-2}, for the prespill density for several reasons. First, it is the prespill estimate taken

TABLE 3.—Mean lobster density (# per m^{-2}) and standard error (SE) in airlift sampling taken between 1991 and 1996 in Rhode Island Sound (Incze et al. 1997). Twelve samples were taken each year at each site.

Year	Number of sites	Mean lobster density and (SE)
1991	3	3.2 (0.2)
1992	4	1.6 (0.1)
1993	6	1.2 (0.1)
1994	6	2.1 (0.1)
1995	6	1.7 (0.1)
1996	6	1.2 (0.2)
Overall		1.8

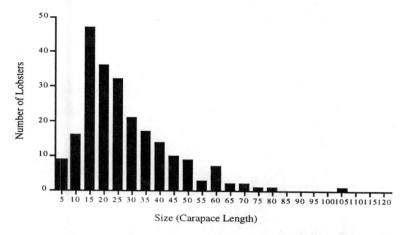

FIGURE 3.—Number of lobsters in each 5-mm size-class in all airlift samples from all sampling periods ($N = 228$).

closest to the time of the accident. Second, it reflects the low level of larval settlement in that year, with only 0.3 lobsters m^{-2} found in the young-of-year (age-0) class. Third, the estimate matches very well the 1995 Fort Wetherill visual estimate of 1.4 lobsters m^{-2}, which, if augmented by the 1995 age-0 density (age-0 lobsters are not well-sampled by the visual method), comes to 1.7 lobsters m^{-2}. The prespill density value is critical to the estimation of loss to the lobster population.

Lobster density estimates from the airlift samples were sufficient for comparison among regions. However, to calculate the actual number of lobsters present, and by inference the total number of lobsters killed, we needed to know whether the density estimates were valid assessments of the true lobster density. Two pieces of evidence suggested they were not. First, efficiency tests ($N = 30$) of the airlift methods, performed in October 1997 for another project, showed that 80% of 2-cm lengths of PVC welding rods (approximately the same length and weight as a newly settled lobster) were returned by the airlift technique. This suggests a 20% undersampling of the smallest size-class using the airlift technique.

Second, the length-frequency distribution of any population in which there is high juvenile mortality should approximate a type-III survivorship curve resulting in a large proportion of the population in the smallest size classes. However, the length-frequency distribution of all lobsters taken in all airlift samples (including summer and autumn) during this study suggests that the technique did not adequately sample the 10–14-mm size-class (Figure 3). Lob-

ster larvae settle in June and July at the size of 4–5 mm CL and grow throughout the rest of the summer until low water temperatures halt further molting. By the end of the first summer, age-0 lobsters in Rhode Island range from 9 to 14 mm CL (James-Pirri 1996). Lobsters grown in captivity at nearby Martha's Vineyard averaged 13.5 mm CL at the end of the first growing season (Hughes and Mattiessen 1962). This suggests that most of the lobsters that settled in the summer of 1995 would have grown through the 5–9-mm size-class and would have been in the 10–14-mm CL size-class at the time of the spill. If recruitment is constant from year to year, the numbers in the 10–14-mm size-class must be at least equal to those in the next-larger size-class; however, they make up only 7% of the observed data in the airlift samples, while the next-larger size-class includes 21% of the total population.

We compared the distribution of density by size returned by the airlift samples with the length-frequency distribution (Figure 4) generated from visual samples taken in winter, summer, and autumn of 1996 in which 20, 1-m^2 quadrats were sampled by divers at each of the winter sites and several others. Judging from this comparison, it appeared that the airlift did not adequately sample larger lobsters. Airlift densities were much higher in the 10- and 15-mm CL size classes, while the visual sampling returned higher densities in size classes greater than 25 mm CL. This undersampling was likely due to the divers not recording or capturing lobsters that escaped the airlift, as has been our practice in other studies (e.g., Wahle and Steneck 1991; Incze et al. 1997).

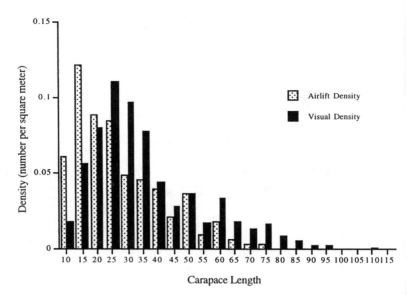

FIGURE 4.—Comparison of the observed densities of lobsters by size-class in all the airlift samples and in the winter, summer, and autumn visual samples (airlift $N = 228$; visual $N = 812$).

It seemed clear that airlift sampling provided data that allowed us to make comparisons of relative density among areas, but estimating absolute abundance required an adjustment for undersampling. We adjusted the prespill and postspill estimates in different ways. The prespill estimate of lobster density was taken from the airlift samples made in 1995. In this case, divers used a combined visual and airlift census technique: divers examined the quadrat prior to airlift sampling, recorded large lobsters, and noted any escapees. For these airlift data it was only necessary to adjust the smallest size-class, which efficiency tests showed was likely to be undersampled by 20%. The age-0 density in 1995 was 0.3 m^{-2}. Thus the prespill density estimate was adjusted upward to 1.76 m^{-2}.

The adjustment for undersampling of the postspill density was more complicated. In brief, we developed a composite distribution of lobster density by size-class that (1) contained no lobsters in the 5–9-mm class, (2) used observed airlift density values for the 15–20-mm and 20–25-mm classes, (3) used observed visual density values for the size classes 25–85 mm, and (4) adjusted the age-0 (10–15-mm) size-class upward by 20% as suggested by the airlift efficiency test. The composite distribution for the size classes 15–85 mm is described by the equation

$$\text{Log}_e\ (\# \text{ m}^{-2}) = -0.041\ (\text{CL}) - 1.352$$
$$r^2 = 0.923$$

The relationship between size and density in all the airlift samples (taken at all three sampling periods) was

$$\text{Log}_e\ (\# \text{ m}^{-2}) = -0.061\ (\text{CL}) - 0.999$$
$$r^2 = 0.913$$

We calculated the difference between the composite and airlift distributions and used the difference as an estimate of undersampling in each size-class between 10 and 85 mm CL (Table 4). The total difference between the composite and airlift distributions was 0.2446 lobsters m^{-2}, which we took to represent the amount of undersampling. The total airlift density summed over all size classes was 0.5866 lobsters m^{-2}. The adjustment for undersampling in the size classes 10–85 mm was 0.2446/0.5866, or 41.7%. Very few lobsters greater than 90 mm CL were found because the minimum legal size is 82.5 mm, and fishing removes a large proportion of the legal-sized animals each year. To adjust for the lobsters in larger size classes ($\geq$90 mm), we examined the beach stranding data of Gibson et al. (1997) and found that 0.12% of 18,297 lobsters were $\geq$90 mm, so we added this percentage to make the total adjustment 41.82%.

Calculations of loss due to the oil spill are shown in Table 5. To estimate the number of lobsters present in the affected area after the oil spill, we calculated the amount of cobble and boulder habitat contained within each lobster density contour interval (Figure 2) and

TABLE 4.—The composite predicted distribution compared with the airlift predicted distribution, with the difference between the two for each size class shown in the right column. (CL = carapace length.)

Lobster size class (mm CL)	Composite distribution predicted # per m^2	Airlift distribution predicted # per m^2	Difference
10–15	0.3334[a]	0.2778[b]	0.0556
15–20	0.1420	0.1475	−0.0055
20–25	0.1163	0.1087	0.0075
25–30	0.0952	0.0801	0.0150
30–35	0.0779	0.0591	0.0189
35–40	0.0638	0.0435	0.0203
40–45	0.0522	0.0321	0.0201
45–50	0.0428	0.0237	0.0191
50–55	0.0350	0.0174	0.0176
55–60	0.0287	0.0129	0.0158
60–65	0.0235	0.0095	0.0140
65–70	0.0192	0.0070	0.0122
70–75	0.0157	0.0051	0.0106
75–80	0.0129	0.0038	0.0091
80–85	0.0105	0.0028	0.0077
85–90	0.0086	0.0021	0.0066
Total difference			0.2446

[a] In the 10–15-mm size class, the predicted value is the observed value (see footnote b) adjusted upward by 20% to account for undersampling.

[b] In the 10–15-mm size class, the observed airlift value is taken as the density of age-0 lobsters in the winter airlift samples from control and transition regions.

multiplied it by the midpoint of the density range described by the contours, that is, if the area was between contours 0.5 and 1.0, the density was taken as 0.75 lobsters m^{-2}. We then adjusted that figure upward to account for undersampling, as explained above. To calculate the expected (prespill) number of lobsters within each contour, we multiplied the adjusted estimate of prespill density of lobsters (1.76 m^{-2}) by the amount of cobble and boulder habitat. The difference between the two numbers, summed over the contour intervals and shown in the lower right corner of the Table 5, is the loss presumed to be due to the oil spill.

Discussion

The American lobster lives in habitat where shelter can be constructed or found. The postsettlement juvenile stages are particularly dependent on shelter-providing habitat, usually characterized by the presence of rocks or boulders, but sometimes peat or cohesive mud (Lawton and Lavalli 1995). Langton et al. (1996) suggested that cobble beds, which are regionally restricted in areal extent, should be considered critical habitat for postsettlement lobsters. Later in life, as lobsters out-

grow some of their predators, the need for shelter as refuge diminishes, and lobsters are found on a wider variety of substrates. Nevertheless, lobsters of all sizes when given the opportunity will occupy shelter and choose it based on their body size (Cobb 1971). Featureless habitat such as sand or mud will support populations of larger lobsters, particularly in summer (Herrick 1909), but at low population densities, sand and mud probably will support less than 10% of those found in rocky habitats (Lawton and Lavalli 1995). Thus shelter-providing habitat, primarily cobble and boulder in inshore waters, should be considered essential for all life stages. Shelter bottlenecks, which impose disproportionate mortality, slower growth, or emigration to new habitats on a specific size-class within an obligate shelter-dwelling stage (Caddy 1986), have been proposed for a number of crustaceans (Steger 1987; Moran and Reaka 1988; Beck 1995, 1997; Butler and Herrnkind 1997). Cobble habitat may be a shelter bottleneck (Wahle and Steneck 1991) for American lobsters in the second or third year of life (Wahle 1992; Wahle and Incze 1997). This identifies a critical period in lobster life history during which cobble is essential and potentially limiting.

TABLE 5.—Habitat area-based calculation of loss of lobsters from the adjusted estimates of pre- and post-spill density of lobsters by contour interval.

Post-spill contour interval (lobsters/m^{-2})	Contour midpoint	Area (m)	Pre-spill abundance (# lobsters)	Post-spill abundance (# lobsters)	Loss (# lobsters)
0	0.00	1,502,331	2,644,103	0	2,644,103
0.0–0.5	0.25	3,105,397	5,465,499	1,100,863	4,364,635
0.5–1.0	0.75	2,915,215	5,130,778	3,100,331	2,030,447
1.0–1.5	1.25	2,252,276	3,964,006	3,992,159	0[a]
Total		9,775,219	17,204,385	8,193,354	9,039,185

[a] The loss estimate for the 1.0–1.5 contour actually was a small negative number, but under the assumption that the oil spill did not actually increase the size of the lobster population, we set the loss in this contour interval to 0; thus some rows and columns do not sum to the same values.

In this paper we report a habitat-based assessment of the impact of a single, pulse-type impact, an oil spill, on a population of lobsters in Rhode Island. Habitat-based assessment of commercially important marine populations has been used when traditional stock assessment methods are difficult to apply, as in the case of the yelloweye rockfish *Sebastes ruberrimus*, which is closely associated with rocky bottom (O'Connell and Carlile 1993). Geostatistical methods (kriging) were applied to intensive trawl survey data on snow crab *Chionoecetes opilio* living on muddy bottoms in the Gulf of St. Lawrence (Moriyasu et al. 1998) to determine stock abundance and predict catches. A situation somewhat analogous to our own was described by Herrnkind et al. (1997) in which a bloom of blue-green algae caused mortality of sponges in Florida Bay. The resulting loss of shelter for juvenile spiny lobsters was predicted to decrease lobster abundance and therefore fishery catch, but this did not occur. The oil spill in Rhode Island affected approximately 9.8 km^2 of cobble and boulder habitat to varying degrees. Our sampling for lobsters within the habitat showed a gradient of increasing postspill lobster density with distance and depth from the point of impact of the barge. Comparison of control, transition, and impacted regions suggested that the oil had a statistically significant impact on lobster density in the winter sampling. Summer and fall sampling showed diminished and no detectable effects, respectively (Cobb and Clancy 1998), suggesting that the spill caused a pulse disturbance (e.g., Underwood 1994) and that the area recovered quickly.

Density contours overlain on a habitat map allowed an estimate (adjusted for undersampling) of nearly 8.2 × 10^6 lobsters present in the cobble and boulder habitat after the spill. The estimated prespill abundance (similarly adjusted) was over 17.2 × 10^6 lobsters. The difference, 9.0 × 10^6, is the number of lobsters of all sizes we infer were lost as a result of the spill. This loss figure depends critically on two values: the estimate of prespill lobster population density and the adjustment made for undersampling. We next present a summary of some of the issues we encountered when attempting to assess total loss.

Data on lobster density are inherently variable. Sample standard deviations typically exceed the mean, and often data sets have a large number of zeros. We used nonparametric distribution-free tests, but these tests were unable to analyze the data with stations nested within regions. However, we believe a nonnested, random-factor analysis is a reasonable alternative, given our method of station and sample location and our goals (Bennington and Thayne 1994). We needed to distribute a spatially limited sampling effort across regions from unimpacted to impacted areas and to sample only cobble and boulder habitat. Stations were chosen within each region using bathymetric charts and the expertise of local fishers to identify suitable substrate. Within the habitat, site locations were haphazardly chosen from a nearly infinite range of possible locations and thus can be considered subsamples of the appropriate habitat. There was no intentional bias in the choice of individual sites, although one transition and two control stations were chosen because we had sampled there previously. Although initial selection was by map coordinate, finer selection was haphazardly determined by where the vessel captain dropped anchor and finally by action of divers who, once on the bottom, were instructed to sample cobble and boulder habitat without regard to the presence or absence of lobsters. Divers occasionally drifted as much as 200 m from the vessel while sampling. Thus, while a nested analysis is an appropriate statistical design, given the goals of our project and the sampling methods, a random-factor nonparametric analysis is a reasonable alternative, although this may raise the question of pseudoreplication (Hurlbert 1984). The consistency among the analyses and the concordance with the qualitative (contouring) analysis suggest that we can have a high degree of confidence in our conclusion: that a statistically significant effect of the oil spill was observed in our data.

The population density of lobsters we measured by airlift sampling, and our choice of prespill density, adjusted for undersampling to 1.76 lobsters m^{-2}, lie well within the range of estimates made in other locations (which were neither tested nor adjusted for undersampling). At eight geographically separate sites in mid-coast Maine, cobble habitat was sampled at the end of the postlarval settlement period by airlift over an 8-year period, yielding annual mean population densities from 3.6 to 4.9 lobsters m^{-2} (Incze et al. 1997). In salt marsh peat on Cape Cod, Able et al. (1988) found an average of 2.1 lobsters m^{-2} using a pumped suction technique. At the Iles de la Madeleine, divers hand-capturing lobsters searched 10-by-4-m corrals (to prevent escapement) set on single habitat types (sand base with stone or boulder) twice in succession; density ranged from 0.75 to 3.80 lobsters m^{-2} (Hudon 1987). Lower densities were found by Bologna and Steneck (1993), who hand-searched kelp habitat and found 1.6 lobsters m^{-2}. However, Bologna and Steneck probably were not sampling lobsters much less than 20–25 mm CL. Bernstein and Campbell (1983) also used hand sampling repeatedly over 3 months to capture lobsters ≥20 mm CL in a 4.5-ha site in which cobble–boulder habitat was interspersed with sand, finding population densities of 0.1 lobsters m^{-2}, which they calculated to equal 4,932 ± 257 lobsters at the site. Hand-capture techniques also were used by Cobb (1971), who found up to 0.35 lobsters m^{-2} in Rhode Island, and by Cooper et al. (1975), who found up to 0.12 lobsters m^{-2} in mid-coast Maine. These earlier surveys took place before the enormous increase in lobster catch of the 1980s and 1990s, which probably reflects an increase in abundance (Fogarty 1995), and the surveys did not capture many lobsters smaller than 20–25 mm CL, at least in part explaining the densities lower than contemporary

studies. In addition, the earlier studies did not use airlift techniques. The results of other recent surveys suggest to us that our adjusted estimate of 1.76 lobsters m^{-2} is a reasonable estimate of the prespill population density.

We found it necessary to correct for undersampling to reflect true population density because two independent estimates suggested the airlift sampler did not sample the entire population with equal efficiency. The rationale for increasing the prespill density of age-0 lobsters by 20% and adjusting postspill density upward by 41.82% is stated in the preceding section. Adjustments to density estimates are not routinely made in ecological studies because relative, rather than absolute, estimates suffice to make comparisons among times, locations, or experimental treatments. In the case of assessing total impact of an environmental insult to a population, however, absolute estimates of the loss are required to scale restoration efforts. The size of the required adjustment surprised us somewhat and suggests that even with quantitative airlift sampling, we may be routinely underestimating the true size of the smallest size classes of the lobster population. Visual, hand-capture techniques certainly undersample the smallest size classes. If absolute abundance estimates are required, tests of sampling efficiency for a given sampling methodology should be standard.

The amount of variability inherent in the final estimates of pre- and postspill abundance should be recognized. We wanted to place confidence intervals around our loss estimate, but no variance estimate was associated with the postspill density contour midpoints or, strictly speaking, with the value chosen to represent prespill density. To estimate an error for the prespill density from the 1995 airlift census, we used $N = 72$, mean = 1.76, and standard deviation = 0.85. For the postspill density estimate, it seemed reasonable to use the standard deviation of all the airlift samples ($N = 167$, mean = 0.95, and standard deviation = 1.82). The coefficient of variation for each estimate was 85.0% and 192.5% for the pre- and postspill estimates, respectively. Using two standard errors on either side of the mean to approximate the 95% confidence interval gave 1.76 ± 0.20 for the prespill and 0.95 ± 0.28 for the postspill estimate. Applying the respective confidence intervals to the loss estimate shows that we are 95% confident that the loss lies between 6.7 × 10^6 and 15.6 × 10^6 lobsters.

In addition to the variance in the estimate of density, there is great sensitivity in the kill estimates to levels of prespill lobster abundance. A change of only 0.1 lobsters per m^{-2} results in a difference of approximately $0.75–0.90 \times 10^6$ lobsters killed. Such great variability emphasizes the need to regard any loss figure chosen for scaling a restoration effort to be a reflection of both the inherent variability of the biological system and sampling error, and thus a "best professional judgement" rather than a precise rendering of the true value.

Our best estimate of the number of lobsters likely to have been killed by the North Cape oil spill, 9.0×10^6, reflects the immediate results of the spill on the entire population, not the loss of legal-sized lobsters or the effects on future catch, both of which will be much smaller. Our estimate compares reasonably well to the results of French (1998), who used a computer simulation model to estimate that between 9.7 and 10.3×10^6 lobsters were killed by the accident, depending on initial conditions. In another study, the number of lobsters stranded on the beaches was estimated to be 2.9×10^6 by Gibson et al. (1997). We would not expect all lobsters killed to be transported to the beaches. It appears that the ratio between stranding and total kill was about 1:3.

Recognizing the link between habitat and population dynamics (e.g., Southwood 1977), the principle of essential fish habitat seeks to preserve habitat deemed indispensable to the survival of commercially important species. Many studies suggest cobble and boulder substrates are essential to the survival of American lobsters (e.g., Cobb 1971; Wahle and Steneck 1992; Langton et al. 1996). We studied the effects of an oil spill on a lobster population to determine the number of lobsters killed and assist in the scaling of restoration efforts. We quantified the essential habitat using side-scan sonar and divers to estimate density in that habitat. We were extremely fortunate to have had a time series of lobster abundance data from nearby areas for comparison. This emphasizes the need for long-term monitoring of commercially important species.

The conceptually simple task of multiplying lobster density by habitat area and subtracting postspill from prespill abundance provided more challenges than expected. Several methodological issues arose during the study that emphasize the importance of determining sampling efficiency and the difficulty of working with highly variable, nonnormal field data. Nevertheless, we were able to estimate the total number of lobsters killed and, just as importantly, to estimate our confidence in that number. As mentioned above, our estimate was remarkably close to the results provided by a simulation model of the oil spill (French 1998) and, as expected, higher than an estimate of strandings of lobsters on adjacent beaches (Gibson et al. 1997).

Acknowledgments

Many people helped with this work and we are grateful to all of them. Beak Consultants coordinated financial support and provided the side-scan sonar data that made the study possible. Gary Mauseth (Beak Consultants) insisted throughout the process that the goal was to find out the truth about the effects of the spill. Deborah French (Applied Science Associates) and the Marine Technical Working Group made many constructive (if not always accepted) suggestions. The Rhode Island Sea Grant program has funded much of our research for 20 years, and in doing so, made this study possible. Lobstermen who helped were Bob Smith, Pete Brodeur, Steve Northup, John Lane, Dick Allen, Rob Braman, and Mike Conroy. Cheryl Gibeault-Milliken coordinated the many divers who worked under often very difficult conditions. For assistance in the laboratory we thank Tim Feehan, Kelly Byron, Elena Martin, Jim Salierno, Charlene Snyder, Rich Sweetman, and Stacey Tighe. Saul Saila and Mark Gibson made very helpful suggestions regarding populations and statistics. Joe Klinger of the URI Coastal Hazards Group provided contouring and mapping. Jim Heltsche, Choudray Hanumara, and Mike Fogarty helped with knotty statistical problems. Greg Challenger, Don Hart, and Gary Mauseth provided very useful critiques of our reports.

References

Able, K., K. L. Heck, M. P. Fahay, and C. T. Roman. 1988. Use of salt-marsh peat reefs by small juvenile lobsters on Cape Cod, Massachusetts. Estuaries 11:83–86.

Beck, M. W. 1995. Size-specific shelter limitation in stone crabs: a test of the demographic bottleneck hypothesis. Ecology 76:968–980.

Beck, M. W. 1997. A test for the generality of the effects of shelter bottlenecks in four stone crab populations. Ecology 78:2487–2503.

Bennington, C. C., and W. V. Thayne. 1994. Use and misuse of mixed model analysis of variance in ecological studies. Ecology 75:717–722.

Bernstein, B. B., and A. Campbell. 1983. Contribution to the development of a methodology for sampling and tagging small juvenile lobsters (*Homarus americanus*). Canadian Manuscript Report of Fisheries and Aquatic Sciences 1741.

Bologna, P. A. X., and R. S. Steneck. 1993. Kelp beds as habitat for American lobster *Homarus americanus*. Marine Ecology Progress Series 100:127–134.

Butler, M. J. IV, and W. F. Herrnkind. 1997. A test of recruitment limitation and the potential for artificial enhancement of spiny lobster (*Panulirus argus*) populations in Florida. Canadian Journal of Fisheries and Aquatic Sciences 54:452–463.

Caddy, J. F. 1986. Modelling stock-recruitment processes in Crustacea: some practical and theoretical perspectives. Canadian Journal of Fisheries and Aquatic Sciences 43:2330–2344.

Cobb, J. S. 1971. The shelter-related behavior of the lobster, *Homarus americanus*. Ecology 52:108–115.

Cobb, J. S., and M. Clancy. 1998. North Cape oil spill: an assessment of impact on lobster populations. University of Rhode Island, Kingston.

Cooper, R. A., R. A. Clifford, and C. D. Newel. 1975. Seasonal abundance of the American lobster, *Homarus americanus*, in the Boothbay region of Maine. Transactions of the American Fisheries Society 104:669–674.

Cooper, R. A., and J. R. Uzmann. 1980. Ecology of juvenile and adult *Homarus americanus*. Pages 97–142 *in* J. S. Cobb and B. F. Phillips, editors. The biology and management of lobsters. Academic Press, New York.

Elton, C. 1966. The pattern of animal communities. Methuen, London.

Fogarty, M. J. 1995. Populations, fisheries and management. Pages 111–138 *in* J. R. Factor, editor. Biology of the lobster *Homarus americanus*. Academic Press, San Diego.

French, D. 1998. Estimate of injuries to marine communities resulting from the North Cape oil spill based on modelling of fates and effects (final draft report). National Oceanic and Atmospheric Administration contract 50-DSNC-7-90032. Science Applications, Inc., Narragansett, Rhode Island.

GAO (Government Accounting Office). 1994. Ecosystem management: additional actions needed to adequately test a promising approach. U.S. GAO RCED-94-111.

Gibson, M. R., T. E. Angell, and N. B. Lazar. 1997. Estimation of lobster mortality following the North Cape oil spill on Block Island Sound. Research Reference Document 97/1. Rhode Island Division of Fish and Wildlife, Providence, Rhode Island.

Herrick, F. H. 1909. Natural history of the American lobster. Bulletin, United States Bureau of Fisheries 29:149–408.

Herrnkind, W. F., M. J. Butler IV, J. H. Hunt, and M. Childress. 1997. Role of physical refugia: implications from a mass sponge die-off in a lobster nursery in Florida. Marine and Freshwater Research 48:759–769.

Hudon, C. 1987. Ecology and growth of postlarval and juvenile lobster, *Homarus americanus*, off Iles de la Madeleine (Quebec). Canadian Journal of Fisheries and Aquatic Sciences 44:1855–1869.

Hughes, J. T., and G. C. Mattiessen. 1962. Observations on the biology of the American lobster, *Homarus americanus*. Limnology and Oceanography 7:414–421.

Hurlbert, S. J. 1984. Pseudoreplication and the design of ecological field experiments. Ecological Monographs 54:187–211.

Incze, L. S., R. A. Wahle, and J. S. Cobb. 1997. Quantitative relationships between postlarval production and benthic recruitment in lobsters, *Homarus americanus*. Marine and Freshwater Research 48:729–743.

James-Pirri, M. J. 1996. Growth and behavior during the settlement periods of the American lobster, *Homarus americanus*. Doctoral dissertation. University of Rhode Island, Kingston.

Kurland, J. M. 1998. Implications of the Essential Fish Habitat provisions of the Magnuson-Stevens Act. Pages 104–106 *in* E. M. Dorsey and J. Pederson, editors. Effects of fishing gear on the sea floor of New England. Conservation Law Foundation, Boston.

Langton, R. W., R. S. Steneck, V. Gotceitas, F. Juanes, and P. Lawton. 1996. The interface between fisheries research and habitat management. North American Journal of Fisheries Management 16:1–7.

Lawton, P., and K. L. Lavalli. 1995. Postlarval, juvenile, adolescent, and adult ecology. Pages 47–88 *in* J. R. Factor, editor. Biology of the lobster *Homarus americanus*. Academic Press, San Diego.

MacKay, D. A. 1929. Larval and post-larval lobsters. American Naturalist 63:160–170.

Meyer, J. L., and W. T. Swank. 1996. Ecosystem management challenges ecologists. Ecological Applications 6(3):738–740.

Moran, D., and M. Reaka. 1988. Bioerosion and availability of shelter for benthic reef organisms. Marine Ecology Progress Series 44:249–263.

Morang, A. 1978. Nearshore sedimentary processes and circulation along the southwestern Rhode Island shoreline based on side-scan sonar surveys. Master's thesis., University of Rhode Island, Kingston.

Moriyasu, M., E. Wade, A. Sinclair, and Y. Chiasson. 1998. Snow crab, *Chionoecetes opilio*, stock assessment in the southwestern Gulf of St. Lawrence by bottom trawl survey. Canadian Special Publication of Fisheries and Aquatic Sciences 125:29–40.

O'Connell, V. M., and D. W. Carlile. 1993. Habitat-specific density of adult yelloweye rockfish, *Sebastes ruberrimus*, in the eastern Gulf of Alaska. Fishery Bulletin 91:304–309.

Pennington, M. 1996. Estimating the mean and variance from highly skewed marine data. Fishery Bulletin 94:498–505.

Southwood, T. R. E. 1977. Habitat, the templet for ecological strategies? Journal of Animal Ecology 46:337–365.

Steger, R. 1987. Effects of refuges and recruitment on gonodactylid stomatopods, a guild of mobile prey. Ecology 68:1520–1533.

Underwood, A. J. 1994. On beyond BACI: sampling designs that might reliably detect environmental disturbances. Ecological Applications 4(1):3–15.

Wahle, R. A. 1992. Substratum constraints on body size and the behavioral scope of shelter use in the American lobster. Journal of Experimental Marine Biology and Ecology 159:59–75.

Wahle, R. A., and L. S. Incze. 1997. Pre- and post-settlement processes in recruitment of the American lobster, *Homarus americanus*. Journal of Experimental Marine Biology, and Ecology 217:179–207.

Wahle, R. A., and R. S. Steneck. 1991. Recruitment habitats and nursery grounds of the American lobster (*Homarus americanus* Milne Edwards): a demographic bottleneck? Marine Ecology Progress Series 69:231–243.

Wahle, R. A., and R. S. Steneck. 1992. Habitat restrictions in early benthic life: experiments on habitat selection and in situ predation with the American lobster. Journal of Experimental Marine Biology and Ecology 157:91–114.

American Fisheries Society Symposium 22:299–321, 1999

Human-Induced Nonfishing Threats to Essential Fish Habitat in the New England Region

Anthony R. Wilbur[1] and Michael W. Pentony

New England Fishery Management Council[2]
5 Broadway, Saugus, Massachusetts 01906, USA

Abstract.—New England aquatic, estuarine, and marine environments are highly variable and present distinct habitat features that support a number of commercial, recreational, and nontarget organisms. The heterogeneous environmental conditions found throughout New England provide important habitat characteristics for the reproduction, development, growth, feeding, and sustainability of fishery resources. Organisms have specific ontogenetic requirements that demonstrate their evolutionary adaptation to particular riverine, inshore, and offshore habitats. Habitat alteration and disturbance occur due to natural processes and human activities. Human-induced chemical, biological, and physical threats to habitat can have direct and indirect effects on local fish and mollusk populations. Increases in coastal development and human-generated pollutants entering the environment are major threats to marine and aquatic habitats and are a result of increasing human population. Human activities and direct habitat alteration (e.g., hydrologic modifications) can disrupt environmental processes and conditions, and pollutants are discharged from a variety of nonpoint and point sources including runoff and industrial discharge, respectively. The sustainability of fishery resources in the New England region depends upon the protection of essential fish habitat. This protection includes identifying and understanding all potential nonfishing threats, point and nonpoint pollutant sources, and anthropogenic activities and impacts.

The New England Fishery Management Council (Council) manages 17 fish species and 1 mollusk species. The varied managed species range from the anadromous, highly migratory Atlantic salmon *Salmo salar* and demersal monkfish *Lophius americanus* (also called goosefish) to the sessile mollusk Atlantic sea scallop *Placopecten magellanicus*, and they inhabit large geographic regions at varying temporal scales. The geographic distribution of these species ranges from hundreds of miles inland within rivers and coastal, estuarine waters to the deepest basins in the Gulf of Maine and the relatively shallow waters on Georges Bank. The diversity of marine habitats in New England that are necessary for the survivorship, reproduction, and growth of the managed species require a great deal of protection. The 1996 amendments to the Magnuson-Stevens Fishery Conservation and Management Act, also known as the Sustainable Fisheries Act, expanded the focus of the Act by emphasizing the importance of habitat protection to healthy fisheries and by strengthening the ability of the Council and National Marine Fisheries Service to protect and conserve the habitat of marine, estuarine, and anadromous finfish, mollusks, and crustaceans.

The Essential Fish Habitat (EFH) Amendment to the Council's fishery management plans is the Council's initial attempt to complement traditional management approaches based on stock assessments with the identification and protection of habitats that support critical fishery populations. The recovery and sustainability of New England's fishery resources will be facilitated through the conservation of habitat, which includes the identification of EFH and the reduction of human-induced nonfishing impacts to EFH. Before human-induced impacts can be reduced, they must be identified and understood. The Council's main goal in identifying nonfishing threats was to promote awareness of the variety of threats, point and nonpoint pollutant sources, and activities that could impact EFH. To achieve this goal, the Council:

1. identified the chemical, biological, and physical nonfishing threats, nonpoint and point pollutant sources, and activities that have the potential to impact EFH quantity, quality, or both;
2. described the short- and long-term impacts of the potential threats to EFH;
3. briefly discussed a few locations within New England that are threatened by nonfishing activities; and

[1] Present address: Commonwealth of Massachusetts, Executive Office of Environmental Affairs, Office of Coastal Zone Management, 100 Cambridge Street, Boston, Massachusetts 02202, USA. E-mail: Tony.Wilbur@state.ma.us
[2] The views presented in this chapter do not necessarily reflect the views of the New England Fishery Management Council.

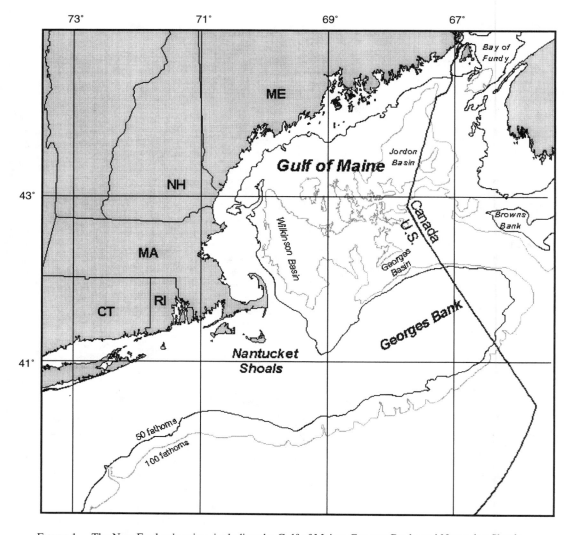

FIGURE 1.—The New England region, including the Gulf of Maine, Georges Bank, and Nantucket Shoals.

4. discussed the cumulative nature of threats impacting EFH.

This chapter presents some of the information
gathered by the Council during the creation of the
EFH Amendment. After a brief description of the
New England region and an overview of the wide
variety of potential threats to habitats in the region,
the chapter describes in detail a variety of potential
chemical, biological, and physical threats to EFH in
New England. The chapter concludes with a brief
discussion of cumulative impacts and the role of fishery management in nonfishing activities.

New England

The New England region, including the Gulf
of Maine, Georges Bank, and Nantucket Shoals (Figure 1), supports populations of commercial, recreational, and nontarget marine organisms and
provides habitat necessary for the sustainability of
these resources. New England aquatic and marine
habitats are characterized by diverse topographic and
oceanographic features, heterogeneous and dynamic
environmental conditions, and high levels of primary
production that supported one of the historically most
productive fishing grounds in the world (Schlee
1973; Valentine et al. 1993; Buchholtz ten Brink et

Riverine regions are freshwater streams, rivers, and streamside wetlands including banks and associated vegetation that may be bordered by other freshwater habitats (e.g., palustrine emergent, scrub--shrub, or forested vegetation) (Cowardin et al. 1979).

Inshore regions are coastal marine and estuarine environments including rocky intertidal areas, exposed beaches, mudflats, salt marshes, sea-grass flats, kelp beds, nearshore rocky bottoms, nearshore soft bottoms, tidal inlets, and other coastal habitats (Moyle and Cech 1988). Important habitat conditions exist in pelagic inshore waters (e.g., the neritic zone).

Offshore regions are open waters, including habitat seaward of the inshore designation. Offshore benthic habitats are characterized by patchy deposits of glacial debris (Schlee 1973; Valentine et al. 1993) and include topographic features such as sand waves, shell aggregates, gravel beds, boulder reefs, deep basins, and submerged canyons that provide nursery requirements for demersal fishes (P. J. Auster, National Undersea Research Center for the North Atlantic and Great Lakes, unpublished data). The pelagic environment (e.g., epipelagic, mesopelagic, and bathypelagic regions) includes notable habitat features such as water mass fronts and boundaries in offshore waters.

A threat is any chemical, biological, or physical stress that may diminish, disrupt, degrade, or eliminate essential fish habitat.

A source is a point of origin of environmental stress or disruption. Nonpoint (e.g., runoff) and point (e.g., industrial discharge) sources are found throughout the New England region.

An impact is any short- or long-term activity or stress that has an effect on or alters the natural function of an environment.

FIGURE 2.—Descriptions of regions and other definitions of terms appearing in this chapter.

al. 1996; Fogarty and Murawski 1998). Several studies have demonstrated the importance of particular environmental features in New England that provide essential habitat conditions for the anadromous, estuarine, and offshore species managed by the Council (e.g., Valentine and Lough 1991; Gotceitas and Brown 1993; Lough and Potter 1993; Short and Burdick 1994; Auster et al. 1995, 1997; Langton et al. 1995; Collie et al. 1997). Species have distinct ontogenetic requirements that demonstrate evolutionary adaptations to particular habitats in riverine, inshore, and offshore regions (see Figure 2 for region characterizations and definitions). These adaptations enhance survivorship and recruitment to the fishery.

The Nature and Variety of Nonfishing Threats

Natural processes and human activities can cause habitat alteration and disturbance. Natural disturbances to habitat can result from phenomena including seasonal droughts; winter freezes; heavy precipitation; and strong winds, waves, currents, and tides associated with major storms (e.g., hurricanes and nor'easters) and worldwide climatic events such as El Niño. Biotic factors, including bioturbation and predation, may also disturb habitat (Auster and Langton 1999, this volume). These natural events may disrupt and alter important biological, chemical, and physical processes and may impact fish and invertebrate populations.

Nonpoint sources
- Municipal runoff (includes sewer overflows and storm-water runoff)
- Agricultural runoff
- Atmospheric deposition
- Wildlife feces (wildlife is defined as animals other than domesticated livestock and pets)
- Industrial shipping
- Recreational boating (includes fishing boats, pleasure cruisers, personal watercraft, etc.)
- Septic systems
- Contaminated groundwater (2°)
- Contaminated sediments (2°)
- Nuisance and toxic algae (2°)

Point sources and other activities
- Industrial discharge (may include pulp and paper mills; tanneries; textile mills; metal fabricating and finishing operations; chemical-, plastic-, rubber-, electronics-, and equipment-manufacturing plants; etc.)
- Power plants (includes nuclear, hydropower, and fossil fuel-burning plants)
- Sewage treatment plants
- Ocean disposal of dredged material
- Aquaculture
- Aquariums
- Biotechnology laboratories
- Silviculture
- Water diversion
- Decaying shoreline structures
- Energy and mineral exploration and transportation (includes mining, pipeline transport, and other byproducts)
- Marine transportation (includes ferry transportation)
- Coastal development
- Port and harbor development
- Erosion control

FIGURE 3.—Activities and sources of threats to essential fish habitat in the New England region (2° = a secondary source of contamination).

Potential threats to habitat from human activities may include direct (e.g., hydrologic modifications); indirect (e.g., loss of prey or reduction of species diversity); site-specific; or habitat-wide impacts and may result in individual, cumulative, or synergistic consequences (Figure 3). Increasing coastal development and pollutants are major threats to marine and aquatic habitats and result from increasing human population. These human-induced threats may disrupt environmental processes and conditions and limit the productivity and sustainability of New England fishery resources in various riverine, inshore, and offshore regions. For example:

- Riverine regions are necessary for substantial portions of the life histories of Atlantic salmon populations, which are severely depleted. New

England rivers have been drastically altered by a variety of human activities, from dam construction and hydropower operations to deforestation, water diversion, and mill pollution.

- Inshore regions provide environmental conditions critical for many fishery resources. Estuaries characterized by extensive eelgrass *Zostera marina* are important habitats for juvenile fish and shellfish such as Atlantic cod *Gadus morhua* and blue mussel *Mytilus edulis*. Inshore habitats have been impacted by centuries of habitat destruction and degradation throughout the United States (NMFS 1994). Coastal development has reduced habitat important to finfish, lobsters, mollusks, and aquatic vegetation. Estimates indicate that half of the United States' original 11.7 million acres of coastal wetlands have been lost since 1780 and continue to be removed at a rate of 20,000 acres per year (NMFS 1994).

- Offshore regions are used for dredged material disposal and are being explored to supply natural resources or to replace resources such as oil, gas, and gravel aggregate that have been eliminated from coastal environments. Heterogeneous offshore habitats are found in deep waters with stable biological communities (e.g., Wilkinson Basin) and in high-energy environments in which conditions are continuously changing (e.g., Northeast Peak of Georges Bank). The variety of bottom habitats in offshore regions appears to provide important conditions for New England fishery resources. For example, cobble and gravel surficial seafloor sediments with emergent epifauna provide optimum conditions for juvenile cod and haddock *Melanogrammus aeglefinus* growth (Valentine and Lough 1991).

Many threats to essential fish habitat are chemical, biological, and physical in nature. These threats and their potential impacts to riverine, inshore, and offshore habitats are described in detail in the following sections. Point and nonpoint sources of the chemical, biological, and physical threats also are listed below.

Chemical Threats

Human activities produce many chemical threats that can impact riverine, inshore, and offshore habitats (Table 1). These chemical threats include oil, heavy metals, acid, chlorine, radioactive waste

TABLE 1.—Potential chemical nonfishing threats to fish habitat in New England prioritized among regions (H = high, M = moderate, L = low, blank = no threat). Threats are not prioritized against one another.

Threat	Riverine	Inshore	Offshore
Oil	M	M	M
Heavy metals	M	M	M
Acid	H	M	
Chlorine	M	M	
Radioactive wastes	L	M	M
Thermal wastes	M	M	
Nutrients	H	H	L
Metabolic and food wastes	M	M	
Pesticides	M	M	L
Herbicides and fungicides	M	M	L
Suspended particles	M	M	L
Greenhouse gases	M	M	M

and other effluents, nutrients, pesticides and herbicides, sediments, greenhouse gases, and ozone loss, all of which are described in the following subsections. Chemical threats do not behave in the exact same manner among geographic regions, and some threats do not impact particular regions at all due to different habitat conditions. The threats can be prioritized by evaluating the potential severity of the impact for each of the regions in which it occurs. In general, inshore and riverine regions, heavily urbanized areas, and waste disposal sites appear to have the highest concentration of chemical threats (Gould et al. 1994). Regardless of the region, however, chemical threats can impact habitat necessary for the sustainability and recovery of New England's fishery resources.

Oil

Oil (characterized as any hydrocarbon [e.g., polycyclic aromatic hydrocarbons or PAHs] or petroleum substances [e.g., gasoline]) may have a major impact on riverine, inshore, and offshore fish habitats because they interfere with biotic communities (see Wilk and Barr 1994 for review). Short-term impacts include interference with the reproduction, development, growth, and behavior of fishes, especially early life history stages (see Gould et al. 1994 for review). Larsen (1992) discussed the potential carcinogenic and mutagenic properties of oil compounds that may impact living resources. Oil spills may cover and degrade coastal habitats and associated benthic communities or may produce a slick on surface waters that disrupts the pelagic community, including pelagic fishes and plankton. Oil slicks on surface waters may be the most serious impact in offshore waters, considering the large volume of water capable of diluting oil as it settles to the seafloor. Habitats in all regions with low physical energy may be the most sensitive to oil pollution because the habitats (e.g., tidal marshes, embayments, seafloor sediments) are slow to repurify.

Oil can disrupt the growth of vegetation in aquatic and estuarine habitats (Lin and Mendelssohn 1996) and can persist in sediments for years after the initial contamination. This persistent quality may cause problems for the physiological and metabolic processes of demersal fishes (Vandermeulen and Mossman 1996). These impacts may eventually disrupt community organization and dynamics in affected regions. Nonpoint sources of oil include municipal and agricultural runoff, industrial shipping, recreational boating, and contaminated sediments. Point sources include power-plant discharge, marine transportation, energy and mineral exploration and transportation, and ocean disposal of contaminated dredged material. Rivers may also transport inland sources of oil to adjacent estuarine and inshore habitats.

Heavy Metals

Metal contaminants (characterized as any toxic heavy metal including arsenic, cadmium, chromium, copper, lead, mercury, etc.) are found in the water column and persist in riverine and coastal sediments in settings from urban centers to uninhabited areas (Larsen 1992; Readman et al. 1993; Buchholtz ten Brink et al. 1996). High levels of metals are found in New England rivers and estuarine sediments due to industrial use of hydropower and past industrial activity since the 19th century (Larsen 1992). As of this writing, there are approximately 200 industrial facilities concentrated around Boston and the industrialized rivers of New Hampshire whose effluent enters the Gulf of Maine (Buchholtz ten Brink et al. 1996). The offshore region is also potentially impacted by the discharge of heavy metals due to activities including marine transportation and dredged material disposal.

Heavy metals may initially inhibit reproduction and development of marine and aquatic organisms, but high concentrations can directly or indirectly kill or contaminate fish and invertebrates. The early life history stages of fish are most susceptible to toxic impacts associated with heavy metals (Gould et al.

1994). Nelson et al. (1991) observed that for winter flounder *Pseudopleuronectes americanus*, embryo abnormalities were most frequent and hatching success was lowest in areas of high contamination in Long Island Sound. The same study found that winter flounder larvae were smallest near a contaminated area in Boston Harbor.

Heavy metal contamination within the water column may promote shifts in phytoplankton species composition, altering planktonic functional groups and community structure. Indigenous primary producers may be replaced by organisms with little worth as a food source to the trophic structure. Shifts in benthic fauna composition appear over a geographic and temporal gradient of contamination. For example, areas of recently disposed dredge material are dominated by a few species of polychaetes that eventually are replaced over time and space by a more diverse group of organisms including mollusks that live deeper in marine sediments (reviewed by Valiela 1995). Later stages of recovery are characterized by relatively complex habitat conditions that may provide important ecological benefits to fish species. Heavy metals may also disrupt endocrine secretions of marine organisms, which in turn may disrupt natural biotic properties (Brodeur et al. 1997).

Although the long-term impacts of heavy metals do not appear to be substantial in marine and aquatic organisms, heavy metals may cascade through trophic levels and accumulate in fish at toxic levels (i.e., bioaccumulation), which can eventually cause health problems in human consumers. For example, fish consumption advisories are frequently in effect in heavily contaminated areas along the Northeast coast, including the Hudson-Raritan Estuary and Boston Harbor (Turgeon and Robertson 1995). Municipal and agricultural runoff, contaminated groundwater and sediments, industrial shipping, recreational boating, and atmospheric deposition are nonpoint sources of heavy metals. Point sources include industrial discharges, power plants, ocean disposal of dredged material, and marine transportation (e.g., hull paints containing butylin compounds to hinder biofouling).

Acid

The influx of acid (i.e., substances with lower pH than ambient conditions) to riverine environments can cause severe habitat degradation and disruption because the freshwater environment does not have the buffering capacity of marine ecosystems. The brackish waters of estuaries are also especially sensitive to acid effluents due to their relatively low buffering capacity (compared to higher-salinity oceanic waters). Acidification can disrupt or prevent reproduction, development, and growth of fish (USFWS 1995). Low pH (<5.0) has been linked to osmoregulation problems (Staurnes et al. 1996); pathological changes in eggs (Peterson et al. 1980; Haines 1981); and reproduction prevention (Watt et al. 1983) in Atlantic salmon. Municipal and agricultural runoff, contaminated groundwater, and atmospheric deposition are nonpoint sources of acid influx, and industrial and sewage treatment plant discharges are point sources of acid entering New England waters.

Chlorine

Chlorine can have acute and sublethal effects on marine and aquatic organisms (Sasikumar et al. 1993; Manning et al. 1996), especially early life history stages (Hose et al. 1989). Chlorine effluent can decrease habitat quality and quantity, leading to the reduction of suitable habitat conditions. Chlorinated compounds (e.g., organochlorides–dioxins, polychlorinated biphenyls [PCBs], etc.), which can harm humans, have been found to accumulate in the tissue of fish such as bluefish *Pomatomus saltatrix* (Eldridge and Meaburn 1992). Compounds containing chlorine are often used to inhibit settlement of biofouling organisms (Sasikumar et al. 1993). Long-term exposure to chlorine may alter natural community structure and dynamics. Chlorine nonpoint sources include septic systems and contaminated groundwater, and point sources include discharges from sewage treatment plants, industrial facilities, and power plants.

Radioactive Waste and Other Effluents

Radioactive wastes, including nuclides generated from metal hydrides (e.g., ^{238}Uranium and ^{226}Radon), may be a threat to riverine, inshore, and offshore environments. Fish may accumulate radioactive isotopes in their tissues, which poses problems for organisms on all trophic levels, including humans (ICES 1991). Long-term exposure to radioactive waste may alter the natural dynamics of habitat conditions and living resources. Potential sources of radioactive waste are sunken vessels and submarines; municipal runoff; atmospheric deposition; industrial and power plant discharges (e.g., nuclear power plants); and contaminated groundwater and sediments (e.g., past dumping locations) (Table 2). As of this writing, three nuclear power plants operate along the New England coast: Millstone (Waterford, Connecticut); Pilgrim (Plymouth, Massachusetts); and Seabrook (Seabrook, New Hampshire). The Maine Yankee nuclear power plant (Wiscassett, Maine) ceased operations in 1997 but may have contributed to habitat degradation while active.

Past, present, and potential sites of offshore disposal of domestic (e.g., sewage) and industrial wastes are potential areas of concern to fishery managers. Barr and Wilk (1994) described dump sites in New England waters and two industrial waste dump sites

TABLE 2.—Past and current industrial and sewage sludge discharge and dump sites (Barr and Wilk 1994).

Site	Materials	Timeframe
Boston Sewage Outfall (located in Massachusetts Bay)	Treated effluent	Started in October 1998
Massachusetts Bay Industrial Waste Site (42°27.7'N, 70°35.0'W), located 19 mi off Boston	Radioactive wastes; toxic and hazardous chemicals; heavy metals	1876–1976
Acid Waste Site, New York Bight (40°16' to 40°20'N, 73°36' to 73°40'W), located off New York City	Acid and alkaline; wastes	Closed in 1988
Deepwater Dump Site 106 (38°45'N, 72°20'W), located 106 mi from New York Harbor	Industrial waste; sewage sludge	Closed in 1991
12-Mile Dump Site, located 12 mi off Sandy Hook, New Jersey	Sewage sludge; heavy metals	1924–1987

in the Mid-Atlantic Bight that may influence New England fishery resources (Table 2). Currently, there are no sewage sludge dump sites in the Gulf of Maine. However, until December 1991, sewage sludge had been discharged into Boston Harbor from the Deer Island and Nut Island wastewater treatment plants for decades. The sewage outfall in Boston Harbor is being replaced by a new discharge pipe that will release treated effluent into Massachusetts Bay. There is concern that the new outfall will contaminate living marine resources around the effluent and in adjacent areas, especially Stellwagen Bank, which contains habitat and other features important to a variety of Council-managed species (Butman 1998; USGS 1998).

Dams, power plants, and industrial facilities produce thermal effluents and plumes that may impact fishery resources. Thermal effluents in inshore and riverine habitats can directly alter the benthic community or kill marine and aquatic organisms (e.g., thermal shock), especially larval and juvenile fish (Gibson 1996). Temperature influences biochemical processes of the environment and the behavior and physiology of marine and aquatic organisms (Blaxter 1969). Long-term thermal discharge may change habitat conditions and associated functional groups. Forestry activities such as clear-cutting and the alteration or removal of riparian habitat can also contribute to above-normal water temperatures in riverine and estuarine habitats.

Nutrients

Aquatic and marine productivity is strongly influenced by nutrients including nitrogen and phosphorus, and nutrient over-enrichment can advance habitat degradation (ASMFC 1992; NOAA 1997a, 1997b). Eutrophication of aquatic and marine habitats is a well-documented impact of nutrient over-enrichment (see O'Reilly 1994 and Wilk and Barr 1994 for reviews). Eutrophic habitats are characterized by low dissolved oxygen levels (anoxia is possible), high turbidity, phytoplankton and filamentous algal blooms, and inhibited denitrification. Severely eutrophic conditions may promote harmful algal blooms (HABs), which reduce submerged aquatic vegetation (SAV) (Short and Burdick 1996; Goldsborough 1997) and have been implicated in fish diseases and kills (see the following "Biological Threats" section) (NSF and NOAA 1998). In particular, eutrophic conditions hinder and degrade

sea grass beds, which provide critical habitat conditions in New England estuaries and serve many ecological functions for fishery resources (Short and Burdick 1994; Stephan and Bigford 1997). Atlantic cod and blue mussels use eelgrass for particular life stages (Gotceitas et al. 1997). Waquoit Bay, Massachusetts is one example of an area that has experienced a dramatic decline in eelgrass cover. Nutrient loading coupled with housing development has led to the demise of eelgrass and the proliferation of algal species (Short and Burdick 1996). Summertime algal blooms in Waquoit Bay have restricted light penetration, oxygen, and juvenile fish movements and stimulated anoxic conditions (Valiela et al. 1992).

An increase in nutrient levels within the open ocean can also markedly affect the productivity of phytoplankton communities (Omori et al. 1994). Increased surface productivity may increase the flux of organic material from the sea surface to the deep-sea benthos (Omori et al. 1994). The stable, deep-sea environment is trophically linked to the surface waters, and an increasing flux of organic matter may have substantial impacts on bottom habitats (Omori et al. 1994). Long-term impacts of persistent eutrophication in marine, estuarine, and freshwater habitats include mass mortality of fishery resources (e.g., Atlantic menhaden *Brevoortia tyrannus* kills have coincided with eutrophic conditions within estuaries along the east coast [Burkholder et al. 1992]) and altered natural community dynamics. Excess nutrients within riverine, coastal, and offshore waters originate from nonpoint sources such as municipal and agricultural runoff, contaminated groundwater and sediments, atmospheric deposition, septic systems, industrial shipping, recreational boating, wildlife feces, and nuisance and toxic algae. Point sources include industrial discharges, aquaculture, aquariums, sewage treatment plants, water diversion, ocean disposal of dredged material, silviculture, and energy and mineral exploration and transportation.

Metabolic and excess organic matter can increase levels of nutrients and pathogens (e.g., fecal coliform bacteria) entering the environment and can contribute to eutrophic conditions and disease transmission. Major sources of metabolic and food wastes are agriculture and aquaculture facilities. Runoff from farmlands includes animal wastes and organic fertilizers. Aquaculture operations may contribute to the organic loading of the water column and

TABLE 3.—Current and proposed aquaculture sites in federal waters off New England. The majority of aquaculture efforts in federal waters have involved mollusks.

Name	Location	Type	Reared organisms
Current			
Seastead Site (formerly Westport)	South of Martha's Vineyard	Bottom	Sea scallops
Sea Scallop Cage Grow-out Project	Off Gloucester, Cape Ann, Massachusetts; Stellwagen Bank; Jeffreys Ledge	Bottom cage	Sea scallops
Proposed			
American-Norwegian Fish Farms, Inc.	Gulf of Maine	Net pens	Atlantic salmon
Woods Hole Oceanographic Institution Blue Mussel Project	Southern New England	Submerged longline	Blue mussels

benthos through feeding practices and the congregation of high densities of organisms (Table 3) (Rosenthal 1994; deFur and Rader 1995; Grant et al. 1995). The additional nutrients and metabolic wastes from aquaculture may disrupt nutrient cycling between the benthos and water column (Kelly 1992) and promote hypernutrification and oxygen depletion (Rosenthal 1994). Aquaculture operations, especially finfish culture within marine and aquatic environments, must properly site facilities to minimize the potential impacts of metabolic wastes and excess organic matter (e.g., feed) entering and accumulating in the environment. Septic systems, wildlife feces, and nuisance or toxic algae are other nonpoint sources of metabolic and excess organic matter, and sewage treatment plants represent another point source of organic waste that can impact habitat conditions.

Pesticides and Herbicides

Pesticides (such as aldrin, chlordane, and endrin) entering riverine, coastal, and offshore habitats may impact marine and aquatic organisms and accumulate in sediments. Pesticides within sediments can be re-released into the water column during substrate disturbance, such as channel dredging. Short-term impacts appear minimal, but the persistence of pesticides in the environment poses long-term problems to fishery resources. Pesticides may bioaccumulate through absorption by sediments and detritus and then ingestion by zooplankton or plankters, which in turn are eaten by fish (ASMFC 1992). For example, winter flounder livers from Boston and

Salem Harbors contain the highest concentrations of dichlorodiphenyl trichlorioethane (DDT) found on the U.S. east coast, and these flounder are ranked first and third, respectively, in the country in terms of total pesticides in fish (Larsen 1992). This accumulation of toxic pesticides may cause health problems in human consumers. Agricultural runoff is a major nonpoint source, but pesticides can also occur at notable levels in residential areas. Water diversion and hydrologic alteration may increase the amount of contaminated runoff reaching aquatic and marine waters. Other sources of pesticides entering New England waters include atmospheric deposition and contaminated groundwater and sediments (nonpoint sources) and aquaculture and ocean disposal of dredged material (point sources) (see Meyers and Hendricks 1982 for review).

Herbicides may alter long-term natural community structure by hindering aquatic plant growth or directly destroying aquatic plants. Hindering or destroying aquatic vegetation can affect fishery resources by limiting important habitat functions, including contaminant filtering. The chemicals used in herbicides also may cause mortality in aquatic insects that contribute to the food base of salmonids in New England rivers (USFWS 1995). Coastal development, hydrologic modification, and water diversion contribute to increased levels of herbicides entering New England habitats. In offshore waters, phytoplankton communities may be impacted by herbicides, resulting in cascading effects through trophic levels. The major nonpoint sources of herbicides are agricultural and municipal runoff, contaminated groundwater, and atmospheric deposition

(Goldsborough 1997). Aquaculture operations (see Table 3) often use herbicides to control environmental conditions and organism health. Herbicides are also frequently used to inhibit algal and seaweed colonization of boat hulls and pipes (Readman et al. 1993).

Sediments

Fish and invertebrate habitats may be impacted by an unnatural influx of suspended particles (Arruda et al. 1983). Lethal and sublethal impacts to organisms may occur with various levels of suspended sediments (Barr 1993). Short-term impacts of increased suspended particles include high turbidity, reduced light penetration, and sedimentation of benthic habitat, which may contribute to the reduction of phytoplankton and the loss of SAV and other benthic structures. Other problems associated with suspended solids include respiration disruption of fishes and invertebrates, disruption of water transport rates in marine organisms, reduction of filtering efficiency of invertebrates, sorption of metals and organic materials, diminished primary production, reduction of egg buoyancy, disruption of ichthyoplankton development, reduction of growth and survival of filter feeders, and decreased foraging efficiency of sight feeders (Messieh et al. 1991; Barr 1993). Toxic metals and organics absorbed by sediments may recur and become more available to marine and aquatic organisms when suspended (e.g., by channel dredging and prop scarring). Resuspension of sediments may supply nutrients to the water column that are needed for primary production; however, increased flux of nutrients into the water column may stimulate phytoplankton production, contribute to increased turbidity, and alter nutrient cycles. Frequent high levels of suspended particles can lead to the loss of habitat for particular species.

Increased particulate matter in the water column and subsequent embedding of matter in the benthos may be stimulated by deforestation and watershed development (USFWS 1995). For example, Atlantic salmon fry and parr find refuge within interstitial spaces provided by gravel and cobble in rivers, and erosion caused by deforestation could contribute to the clogging of these spaces with sediments and subsequently decrease salmon survivorship (USFWS 1995). Suspended particles enter riverine, inshore, and offshore areas from nonpoint sources including municipal and agricultural runoff, industrial shipping, and recreational boating. Point sources include industrial discharge, channel dredging, ocean disposal of dredged material, water diversion, energy and mineral exploration and transportation, erosion control, silviculture, and marine transportation.

Greenhouse Gases

Sea levels have fluctuated throughout the earth's history and have been rising since the end of the Pleistocene era (10,000 years ago). Changes in the rate of sea-level rise result from tectonic and postglacial isostatic adjustments and effects of increased atmospheric temperature (Valiela 1995). There is concern that global warming may be accelerated by the continued release of greenhouse gases due to human activities. Greenhouse gases, including carbon dioxide and methane, are discharged into the atmosphere from the respiration of all living organisms and the burning of fossil fuels and forests. Possible impacts on inshore and riverine habitats from sea-level rise are the loss of wetlands, salinization of freshwater environments (eliminating freshwater supplies), and change in natural marine and aquatic biotic (e.g., species composition) and abiotic (e.g., currents and nutrient availability) properties (see Kelley 1992 for review). For example, a shift in fish composition to cyprinids and percid dominance may be observed with the decline of colder-water species such as salmonids in freshwater environments in conjunction with global warming and subsequent sea-level rise (Lehtonen 1996).

Salt marshes may be unable to accrete fast enough to keep pace with sea-level rise; however, salt marshes appear to be keeping pace with the current rate of sea-level rise along the U.S. northeast coast (Valiela 1995), provided that uplands adjacent to the salt marshes are undeveloped. However, other studies indicate that salt marshes of Maine are not keeping pace with sea-level rise (e.g., Wood et al. 1989). According to Bigford (1991), the severity of the impacts of sea-level rise on natural resources depends on physical obstruction of inland habitat shifts due to natural and human barriers, ability of species to withstand new environmental conditions during periods of erosion-induced transition, and rate of environmental change.

Ozone Loss

The continued loss of ozone, which is associated with the increase of greenhouse gases and the release of ozone-depleting substances (e.g., chloroflourocarbons), will result in higher levels of ultraviolet light reaching the earth's surface, and these higher levels of light may impact marine environments through damage to phytoplankton populations (Hanson 1998). Phytoplankton populations are the base of the trophic web throughout the world's marine environment and may influence fishery resources in New England. The long-term impacts of decreased ozone on higher trophic levels remain unknown (Hanson 1998) but may present environmental problems for habitat and fishery resources.

Biological Threats

New England habitats are impacted by several biological threats, yet the implications of a particular threat may not be the same in all regions (Table 4). For example, nuisance and toxic algae may impact SAV in inshore areas and phytoplankton assemblages in offshore waters. The most evident biological threats include the introduction of nonindigenous and reared species, nuisance or toxic algal blooms, and the spread of disease. These threats are described in the following subsections.

Nonindigenous and Reared Species

The nonindigenous and reared organisms inhabiting New England waters (Rosecchi et al. 1993; USFWS 1995; Witman 1996) have been closely associated with human activities (Pearce 1998). The development of technologically advanced, large vessels may increase the potential for exotic introductions due to the capability of fast travel and subsequent transport of exotic species around the world. The introduction of nonindigenous organisms has altered the biological and physical composition of several freshwater and marine habitats (Omori et al. 1994). The release of exotic and reared species including finfish, shellfish, plants, and parasites to the wild is possibly the largest problem for marine resource managers, ecologists, and aquaculturists (deFur and Rader 1995). Reared and exotic organisms have been released accidentally through aquaculture escapement and ballast water and intentionally through stock enhancement programs (Bedzinger 1994).

Many nonindigenous organisms inhabit New England. Nonnative plants such as the common reed *Phragmites australis* have invaded several New England salt marshes and can potentially degrade coastal habitat by changing natural habitat qualities and functions. The introduction of bryozoan *Membranipora membranacea* has reduced kelp populations, ascidian *Botrylloides diegensis* has competitively displaced native hydroids, nudibranch *Tritonia plebia* has reduced invertebrate prey populations, and macroalgae *Codium fragile* has changed benthic structure (see Witman 1996) along the New England coast. Possibly the best-documented example of a nonindigenous organism is the introduction of farmed Atlantic salmon. The U.S. Fish and Wildlife Service has determined that salmon aquaculture poses a substantial threat to the wild stocks of Atlantic salmon (Conkling and Hayden 1997). Farmed salmon can spawn successfully in the wild (Jonsson et al. 1991; Lura and Saegrov 1991); dominate native salmon spawning habitat (Bedzinger 1994); and limit the success of wild populations. In addition, the introduction of infectious diseases such as infectious salmon anemia, which is released and transmitted through salmon aquaculture facilities, is posing a serious threat to native salmon populations along the coasts of Maine and Canada.

Nonindigenous and reared species can change natural community structures and dynamics by competing with natural stocks, diluting genetic diversity and phenotypic plasticity of organisms, and transmitting or introducing exotic lethal diseases. Exotic organisms enter the environment from industrial shipping, recreational boating, aquaculture, biotechnology, and aquariums. Nonindigenous species of algae accidentally introduced into the environment are another potential problem impacting habitat conditions.

TABLE 4.—Potential biological nonfishing threats to fish habitat in New England prioritized among regions (H = high, M = moderate). Threats are not prioritized against one another.

Threat	Riverine	Inshore	Offshore
Nonindigenous and reared species	M	M	M
Nuisance and toxic algae	M	H	M
Disease	M	M	M

Nuisance or Toxic Algae

Nuisance and toxic algae including harmful algal blooms (HABs) threaten estuarine habitat conditions and functions that are important throughout ontogeny for many marine and estuarine fishes and a variety of living marine resources and have been a nearly annual event in New England coastal waters for several years (White et al. 1993). Riverine and offshore habitats also can be impacted by HABs. An increase in nutrient levels due to human activities can stimulate HABs, which can impact habitats and have toxic effects on organisms and humans (see Milligan and Cosper 1994; O'Reilly 1994; Boesch et al. 1997; Burkholder and Glasgow 1997). Organisms responsible for HABs have naturally occurred in the environment for a long time, so the apparent increase of HABs may simply reflect better detection of natural phenomena (NSF and NOAA 1998). However, the current increased intensity and frequency of HABs compared to recent years appears to indicate more toxic algal species and toxins, more areas affected, more fishery resources impacted, and higher economic losses (Boesch et al. 1997; NSF and NOAA 1998).

Nonindigenous algal species may be introduced to the environment through ballast water of commercial vessels; recreational boating; shellfish transfer (e.g., seeding); dredging; and disposal of contaminated sediments (Boesch et al. 1997), and these nonindigenous species can compound problems caused by native species. Harmful algal blooms can indicate eutrophic conditions; alter, impair, or kill plankton and fish communities; smother indigenous vegetation; and lower dissolved oxygen (NOAA 1997a, 1997b). Certain toxic organisms including *Pfiesteria* spp. are associated with HABs and have caused major outbreaks of disease and fish kills (Burkholder et al. 1992; NCSU 1998). These short-term impacts can eventually change natural habitat processes, reducing long-term viability of fishery resources.

Disease

The spread of disease among organisms is a potential impact to fishery resources and habitat conditions in riverine, inshore, and offshore regions. Pathogens introduced into the environment may contribute to the spread of sublethal or lethal infections that can decrease the health and fitness of fishery resources (Kent et al. 1995). Human activities (e.g.,

nutrient over-enrichment) have been associated with blooms of naturally occurring pathogens (NCSU 1998). Following are examples of pathogens impacting fishery resources and habitat conditions:

- The toxic dinoflagellate *Pfiesteria piscicida* and other species have been implicated as the primary causative agents of many fish kills and disease episodes in mid-Atlantic estuarine and inshore areas (Burkholder et al. 1992; NCSU 1998), and concern has been voiced about the possibility of the organism impacting New England resources (A. R. Wilbur and M. W. Pentony, New England Fishery Management Council, unpublished data).
- Mortality and gill lesions in Atlantic salmon were associated with a bloom of *Skeletonema costatum* and *Thalassiora* spp. (Kent et al. 1995). Salmon are also susceptible to a number of diseases and parasites including the gill maggot *Salmincola salmonea*, freshwater louse *Argulus foliaceus*, leech *Piscicola geometra*, trematodes, cestodes, acanthocephalans, nematodes, sea louse *Lepeophtheirus salmonis*, and sea lamprey *Petromyzon marinus*, as well as numerous bacterial, viral, and fungal diseases (see USFWS 1995).
- Shellfish area closures have resulted from infestation of diseases such as paralytic, amnesic, and neurotoxic shellfish poisoning caused by the pathogens *Alexandrium*, *Pseudo-nitzchia*, and *Gymnodinium breve*, respectively.
- Fecal coliform bacteria have been responsible for many shellfish area closures in New England coastal waters, including Cape Cod estuaries and embayments.

Toxins released by a variety of pathogens move up through the trophic web, affecting zooplankton, fish, birds, marine mammals, and humans (Boesch et al. 1997). Aquaculture projects have contributed to the problem of introducing diseases (e.g., whirling disease caused by *Myxobolus*) to wild stocks through stock-enhancement projects and organism transfers. Other potential sources of pathogens entering the environment include nonpoint sources such as municipal and agricultural runoff, septic systems, wildlife feces, industrial shipping, and recreational boating. Point sources include disposal of dredged material, biotechnology laboratories, aquariums, and sewage treatment (ASMFC 1992).

TABLE 5.—Potential physical nonfishing threats to fish habitat in New England prioritized among regions (H = high, M = moderate, L = low, blank = no threat). Threats are not prioritized against one another.

Threat	Riverine	Inshore	Offshore
Channel dredging	M	H	
Dredged material disposal	L	M	M
Dredging and filling	H	H	
Marina and dock construction	M	H	
Vessel activity	M	H	L
Erosion control			
bulkheads	M	M	
seawalls		M	
jetties		M	
groins		M	
Tidal restriction	M	H	
Deforestation	H	M	
Dam construction and operation	H	M	
Water diversion			
water withdrawal	H	M	
irrigation	M	M	
Mining			
gravel and mineral	M	M	M
oil and gas	L	M	M
peat	L		
Debris	M	M	M
Artificial reefs	L	M	M

Physical Threats

Human activities cause several substantial physical threats to New England EFH (Table 5). Physical threats appear more likely to occur in riverine or inshore waters, but offshore waters are increasingly impacted by several nonfishing physical threats. The Council, in writing its EFH Amendment, found it difficult to determine the magnitude and severity of threats and often concluded that it was impossible to prioritize all physical threats against each other. For example, channel dredging may pose a high threat in inshore waters, a moderate threat in riverine areas, and no threat in offshore regions, but it is difficult to determine whether channel dredging may be more of a threat to a particular region than any other activities. Activities in New England including channel dredging and dredged material disposal, marina and dock construction, vessel activity, shoreline alteration, deforestation, dam construction and operation, water diversion, nonliving resource extraction, debris, and artificial reefs (all discussed in the following subsections) pose potential physical impacts to fish habitat.

Dredging and Disposal

Channel dredging is a frequent long-term maintenance activity associated with coastal development, port and harbor development, and vessel activity (see Barr 1987 for review). Rivers, channels, shoals, ponds, canals, harbors, and bays are occasionally dredged to maintain navigable waterways for safe navigation, economic growth, and social purposes (e.g., recreational boating). Fifty-four federal navigation projects that could require dredging are designated in Massachusetts alone, including river, harbor, and port projects. Increased amounts of marine transportation, increased vessel size, expansion of commercial fleets, and alterations in sedimentation patterns of estuaries due to hydrological modifications have increased the need for channel dredging (Messieh et al. 1991).

The short-term impacts of dredging to biological, chemical, and physical habitat conditions can be substantial. Dredging resuspends sediments and associated contaminants and potentially impacts habitat quality and fishery resources. Changes in tidal prism, depth, water temperature, salinity, water velocity, bottom topography, and sediment type are associated with channel dredging. Benthic features including SAV and cobble substrate can be degraded by direct removal or changes in oceanographic properties. The reconfiguration of sediment type and removal of biogenic structure may decrease the stability of the bottom and increase the ambient turbidity levels (Messieh et al. 1991). A dredged channel can increase the transport of sediment into an embayment and increase siltation rates, altering habitats around the mouth of the channel. Increased siltation can affect spawning, feeding, and recruitment habitat (Messieh et al. 1991). Habitat fragmentation due to channel dredging can hinder the movements of fishery resources. Channel dredging requires continual maintenance, which can eventually change the indigenous habitat and population dynamics of a region.

Disposal of dredged material occurs in inshore and offshore waters at many locations in New England (Table 6) and can impact habitat conditions and biotic communities. Dredged material does not immediately sink and may be transported by internal waves at fronts and boundaries for miles beyond the dump site. Threats such as oil, heavy metals, nutrients, and suspended particles associated with contaminated dredged material can impact habitat conditions at the dump site and in adjacent areas.

TABLE 6.—Major and minor sites of dredged material disposal (adapted from Kurland et al. 1994). Abbreviations are: ME = Maine; MA = Massachusetts; CT = Connecticut.

Site	Description
Major	
Rockland, ME	3.30 mi northeast of Rockland Harbor; used since 1973.
Portland, ME	3.50 mi from Portland Harbor; used since 1973.
Cape Arundal, ME	2.75 mi southeast of Cape Arundal; used since 1985.
Massachusetts Bay, MA	"Foul Area" west of Stellwagen Basin.
Buzzards Bay, MA	1.40 mi from Chappaquoit Point, West Falmouth.
New London, CT	2.00 mi south of harbor; used since 1972.
Cornfield Shoals, CT	6.50 mi southwest of the Connecticut River delta.
Central Long Island Sound	5.00 mi south of New Haven Harbor; used since 1955.
Western Long Island Sound	2.70 mi south of Noroton, CT; used since early 1980s.
Minor	
St. Helena, ME	Outside St. Helena Harbor entrance; last used in 1988.
Frenchman's Bay, ME	Used infrequently.
Saco Bay, ME	Used once in 1989.
Sandy Bay, ME	Used once in 1987.
Sheep Island, ME	Used twice in 1987 and 1988.
Cape Cod Bay, MA	Used since 1995.
Wellfleet, MA	Adjacent to Wellfleet Harbor entrance; last used in 1983.

Primary ports and harbors
- Portland, Maine (ME)
- Boston, Massachusetts (MA)
- Gloucester, MA
- New Bedford, MA
- Providence, Rhode Island (RI)
- Point Judith, RI

Secondary ports and harbors
- Boothbay, ME
- Bucksport, ME
- Eastport, ME
- Ellsworth-Bar Harbor, ME
- Jonesport, ME
- Searsport, ME
- Southwest Harbor, ME
- Stonington, ME
- Ogunquit, ME
- Kennebunkport, ME
- Portsmouth, New Hampshire
- Provincetown, MA
- Chatham, MA
- Wellfleet, MA
- Newport, RI

FIGURE 4.—Major ports and harbors within the New England region (adapted from NOAA 1996).

Disposal of dredged material not only contaminates habitat but also directly disturbs benthic and pelagic communities. Sedimentary composition may be altered, benthic communities are smothered, associated physicochemical conditions are altered, and increased turbidity may hinder pelagic processes (e.g., photosynthesis of algae). In the long term, a frequently used dump site may alter natural habitat conditions and associated functional groups due to the colonization of opportunistic species.

The dredging and filling of wetlands for shoreline, coastal, port, and harbor development removes habitat, alters habitat functions, and may pose one of the more serious threats to riverine and inshore fishery resources. Dredge-and-fill activities reduce wetland functions such as floodwater retention and nutrient uptake and decrease the amount of detrital food available to biotic communities. Hydrologic modifications can impact riverine and inshore habitats by removing or altering natural vegetation and increasing the amount of runoff entering aquatic and marine habitats. For example, the construction of golf courses along the coast changes natural habitat parameters and functions and potentially increases the amount of nutrient-rich runoff entering the environment. In addition to these specific impacts of wetland dredge-and-fill activities, the short- and long-term impacts of wetland dredge-and-fill activities are similar to those of channel dredging.

Marina and Dock Construction

Marina and dock construction is an inevitable consequence of coastal and port development. The New England coast is characterized by many urban centers and associated harbors and ports (Figure 4). Ports and harbors are usually developed in areas that contain important estuarine and riverine habitats such as salt marshes, wetlands, and sea grass-flats. Development may remove or alter important habitat features (Vandermeulen 1996) and impact fishery resources (Levings 1985). The construction of marinas and docks also aggregates contaminants associated with the vessels that use the facilities. In addition to habitat contamination, dock construction can change habitat parameters such as tidal prism, depth, water temperature, salinity, current velocity, and SAV composition, distribution, and abundance. Submerged aquatic vegetation may be removed during construction or shaded by structures after construction, eventually destroying the vegetation. Mooring chains are often associated with marinas and pose a threat to habitat conditions. Mooring chains may uproot SAV or disrupt other benthic features as the chains scour the seafloor during tidal flux. The long-term presence of marinas may contaminate localized areas and change natural habitat qualities and population dynamics in a region. Channel dredging and vessel activity is often directly associated with the development of ports and harbors.

Vessel Activity

Vessel activity, including industrial shipping, recreational boating, and marine transportation, may contribute to the physical degradation of marine and riverine habitats and related fishery resources. Increased vessel activity within coastal waters is directly related to increased coastal urbanization and port and harbor development (Figure 4). Although information on boat-use levels is lacking, increasing numbers of boats have been using coastal waters during the last two decades (N. E. Stolpe, New Jersey Seafood Harvesters' Association, personal communication). For example, Portland, Maine is one of the busiest fishing ports on the east coast and is the third largest east-coast oil port (Larsen 1992). The high level of industrial shipping activity in Portland Harbor may impact habitat conditions and fishery resources.

Recreational boating may be a particular concern because most boating activity occurs in warmer months—the time of greatest biological activity in east-coast estuaries (Stolpe, personal communication). The severity of boating-induced disruption on coastal and riverine habitats may depend on geomorphology (e.g., water depth, width of channel or tidal creek, etc.); current

speed; composition of sediments; vegetation type and extent of cover; and classification of boat traffic in the impacted area (Yousef 1974; Karaki and vanHoften 1975; Barr 1993). Intensified impacts to habitat conditions may occur in heavily used riverine and inshore regions where hundreds of vessel trips per day occur (Barr 1993). Benthic, shoreline, and pelagic habitat may be disturbed or altered by vessel use due to:

- direct disturbance of bottom topography (e.g., prop scarring), which can result in increased turbidity, re-release of nutrients and contaminants, and direct and indirect loss of SAV, nursery, and forage habitat (Yousef 1974; Hilton and Phillips 1982; Barr 1993; Stolpe, personal communication);
- elevated wakes caused by the continual disturbance of water along frequently traveled routes, which can lead to wake erosion and pelagic disturbance causing shore erosion, substrate disturbance, and increased turbidity (Karaki and vanHoften 1975; Barr 1993; Stolpe 1998); and
- propellers or impellers of vessels, which may directly damage or kill ichthyoplankton and other creatures in the upper water column (Stolpe, personal communication; Stolpe 1998).

Barr (1993) and Stolpe (1998) also suggested that noise and direct disturbance of the upper water column, especially within frequently traveled ferry routes, may significantly disturb migration or recruitment patterns, spawning behavior, and egg and larval transport of coastal and offshore organisms.

Shoreline Alteration

Coastal development pressure promotes the construction of structures along coasts to prevent erosion and stabilize shorelines. Bulkheads, seawalls, jetties, and groins (all defined below) are structures designed to slow or stop shoreline erosion in order to protect beaches and personal property. In many cases, erosion rates increase along the coast where erosion-control or shoreline-stabilizing structures are built, especially in locations where the structures prevent or alter longshore transport of sediment and where no alternate source of depositional sediment is available. The following erosion-control structures can alter adjacent coastal and riverine habitat and cause short- and long-term impacts to fishery resources:

- Bulkheads are rigid structures built parallel to the shoreline (Leatherman 1988) of bays and rivers that can alter habitat conditions by changing wave-energy dynamics, removing the land–water interface along the coast, and altering sedimentation patterns.

- Seawalls are similar to bulkheads but are built along the coast facing the open ocean. Seawalls have impacts similar to bulkheads with greater alteration of littoral drift and the associated dispersal patterns of planktonic eggs and larvae.

- Jetties are paired structures constructed perpendicular to the shore at the mouth of a channel, often used to reduce the filling of channels with sediments in order to protect and maintain navigable inlets (Leatherman 1988). Jetties can impact inshore habitats by trapping longshore transport of sediment on the updrift side; eroding beaches on the downdrift side and preventing accretion to replace sediments; changing sedimentation, tidal, and current patterns; and altering the dispersal of eggs and larvae.

- Groins are a series of small jetties constructed perpendicular to the shore that extend from the beach into the surf zone (Leatherman 1988) with impacts similar to but less severe than jetties.

Shoreline development may also include the building of structures such as roads, bridges, and dikes that restrict tidal movements. Tide-restricting structures can hinder important and long-term ecological functions such as the natural flushing of estuarine habitats and freshwater wetlands. Confined inshore waters with restricted water exchange may allow HABs to persist (Boesch et al. 1997) and contribute to the growth of invasive vegetation. Physicochemical properties (e.g., salinity, dissolved oxygen, flow, etc.) may be altered, changing habitat characteristics and functions. Habitat alteration may also hinder migratory, spawning, feeding, and dispersal movements of marine and aquatic resources.

Deforestation

Deforestation is a particular problem to the long-term sustainability of New England's freshwater and anadromous fisheries resources. Silviculture practices have short- and long-term impacts that may adversely affect riverine and inshore habitat (USFWS 1995). Silviculture practices and shoreline development lead to the removal of vegetation, alteration of hydrology, and decrease of watershed water retention. These watershed changes may result in inadequate river flows, increased stream bank and streambed erosion, sedimentation of riparian habitat, and an increase of contaminated runoff. Deforestation alters hydrologic characteristics (e.g., water temperature) and levels of stream discharge (USFWS 1995). Debris, including wood and silt, added to water as a result of forestry activities can smother benthic habitat. These adverse effects of deforestation can spread throughout watersheds and adjacent inshore waters.

Dam Construction and Operation

Dam construction and operation designed for flood control, power generation, navigation, and reservoir formation occur within New England riverine habitat. Dam construction and operation can directly impact riverine resources and indirectly impact estuarine and coastal resources. The construction of dams with either inefficient or nonexistent fishways was the primary agent of the population decline of U.S. Atlantic salmon (USFWS 1995). Historical records link the decline of Atlantic salmon with construction of dams (USFWS 1995 for review). Dams alter water flow and sedimentation patterns; water depth, temperature, and quality; and streambed properties. Salmon migration can be hindered, blocked, or threatened by unnatural conditions created by dams, including passage over spillways, passage through turbines and impoundments, and entrainment and impingement (Ruggles 1980). Fishes are exposed to dissolved gas supersaturation, aggregated contaminants, and high concentrations of predators and diseases in the waters surrounding dams. Dams also limit the flow of fresh water and sediment into estuarine waters, which may consequently reduce wetland coverage.

Operational dams are found throughout New England rivers and watersheds and may be the most thorough example of a nonfishing activity contributing to fish population declines. The Connecticut River watershed historically supported large runs of U.S. Atlantic salmon (USFWS 1995), but the vast number of operational dams on the river (the main stem has 12 operational dams, and its tributaries have

131 additional operational dams [based on CRASC 1997]) has drastically changed habitat conditions and contributed to the decline of salmon populations.

Water Diversion

Freshwater flows are subject to human alteration through water diversion and use and watershed modifications (e.g., deforestation, tidal restrictions, and channelization) (Boesch et al. 1997). Water withdrawal for freshwater drinking supplies, power plant coolant systems, and irrigation is increasing along urban and agricultural coasts, and freshwater supply is becoming limited. Natural events (e.g., droughts); increasing demand for potable water; and inefficient water use contribute to the limited supply of fresh water. Water withdrawal can alter natural current patterns, water temperature, salinity, tidal prisms, and associated biotic communities.

The mass flow of water into a power plant or other reservoirs may entrain and impinge fishes, especially early life history stages. Larval and juvenile demersal fishes and invertebrates are susceptible to entrainment and impingement around intake pipes (ASMFC 1992). Power plants may destroy essential habitat for organisms incapable of settling around an intake pipe, and this habitat loss may impact finfish and shellfish populations. The three active nuclear power plants in Connecticut, Massachusetts, and New Hampshire require large amounts of water to operate and may be a threat to habitat surrounding influent and effluent pipes. Water diversion may add another source of mortality to early life history stages of fish and impact recruitment and year-class strength (Travnichek et al. 1993). Water withdrawal and diversion along with hydrologic changes have been related to increases in some HABs (Boesch et al. 1997).

Nonliving Resource Extraction

Demand for high-quality sand and gravel aggregate, as well as oil exploration, is increasing, and offshore habitats are seen as a potential source of these resources (Messieh et al. 1991). Toxic operational chemicals (e.g., drilling muds); accidental discharge of wastes; removal of benthic flora and fauna; changes in substrate character; increased coastal wave action and erosion; and suspension of sediments make up some of the mining-related threats to inshore and offshore habitats (Scarrat 1987;

ICES 1991; Messieh et al. 1991). These potential impacts also pose problems in habitats surrounding mines. Structures built within habitats to assist in mining and transporting materials, including wells and pipelines, contribute to potential habitat impacts. For example, a proposal from the North Atlantic Pipeline Partners to construct a natural gas pipeline along the Gulf of Maine seafloor from Country Harbor, Nova Scotia to Seabrook, New Hampshire is in the initial stages (S. Snow-Cotter, Massachusetts Coastal Zone Management, personal communication). In a review by Pearce (1994), the effects of mining were listed as (1) destruction of existing benthic biotic community, (2) resuspension of sediments with impacts on fishes, (3) changes in bottom topography and sediment composition, and (4) consequences related to the transport of sediment from the site by currents.

Gravel, mineral, oil, and peat extraction may occur in New England habitats that are essential for fishery resources, and operational and accidental discharges are an environmental concern (Messieh et al. 1991). Gravel aggregates are abundant throughout the Gulf of Maine and are a potential source for mining (Messieh et al. 1991). As of this writing there are no active oil operations in the New England region, but Georges Bank is being explored as a possible source for development, especially in Canadian waters. Oil drilling in Canadian waters can have direct impacts on New England's fishery resources and habitat, ranging from the destruction of habitat to water pollution. Oil drilling has physical impacts to the benthos that are similar to those of gravel mining, but more risk is associated with oil spills and blowouts (Wilk and Barr 1994). Deposits of peat are common in the watersheds of eastern Maine (USFWS 1995). Peat mining can remove riverine habitat and vegetation and release contaminants including peat fiber and arsenic residues and other toxic chemicals.

Debris

Whether it is floating on the surface, suspended in the water column, covering the benthos, or littering the shoreline, debris can impact essential habitat (see Coe and Rogers 1997). Debris is usually defined as manmade solid objects introduced into the environment (Hoagland and Kite-Powell 1997). Benthic communities can be smothered or shaded by debris, which results in alteration of the benthic community. Marine organisms may ingest pellets or plastic fragments or become entangled in rope or plastic strings, which may eventually kill the organisms. Natural environmental processes can be disrupted by debris discharged into riverine, inshore, and offshore habitats.

Hoagland and Kite-Powell (1997) reviewed the types, sources, and fates of marine debris in the Gulf of Maine. Plastics account for nearly half of the marine debris found in Maine, New Hampshire, and Massachusetts, and metals, glass, paper, and cigarette butts also constitute a substantial proportion of marine debris in the three states. Major nonpoint sources of nonfishing-related debris entering riverine and marine environments include industrial shipping, recreational boating, municipal runoff, and decaying shoreline structures. Solid waste disposal, landfills, offshore mineral exploration, and industrial discharges are potential point sources of debris (USEPA 1994).

Artificial Reefs

Artificial reefs can be an effective tool in fishery development with proper management (McGurrin et al. 1989; ASMFC 1993). Properly constructed artificial reefs can enhance bottom habitat and provide high-quality fishing grounds to the benefit of anglers and coastal communities (Stone 1982). The location and composition of artificial reefs in inshore and offshore waters should be assessed thoroughly to determine the most effective methods to enhance fish and shellfish populations. Improperly placed artificial reefs may change natural habitat conditions and community structure by attracting unnatural species assemblages. Inappropriate reef material (e.g., combustion and incineration ash and tires) may decompose and release toxic substances into the surrounding area, and reefs may become dislodged from the bottom and disrupt benthic structure.

Cumulative Impacts

Natural, uncontrolled environments are rarely impacted by isolated threats. A number of the above-mentioned threats can combine or act simultaneously to change or degrade habitat. Cumulative impacts are the combined outcome of numerous actions and stresses that alone may have relatively minor impacts but may add up to severe habitat degradation or loss (Vestal et al.

1995). For example, the alteration of habitat through loss of wetlands, degradation of water quality due to nonpoint and point sources of pollution, and changes in water chemistry from water-diversion operations can lead to substantial losses of habitat both spatially and temporally on a broad scale.

Fishing and nonfishing activities influence habitat condition and function. Depending on the characteristics of habitat, including spatial and temporal variations and physical, biological, and chemical properties, a suite of potential activities and threats, both human and natural, can impact habitat differently. The dispersant nature of contaminants and the variability in the distribution and migration of finfish and shellfish populations throughout ontogeny warrant detailed investigations of cumulative impacts of not only nonfishing threats but also fishing impacts that directly and indirectly affect EFH and the sustainability of New England fisheries. Programs to assess and mitigate cumulative impacts in coastal regions are beginning to be developed and are needed for thorough management decisions regarding nonfishing threats in New England (Vestal et al. 1995).

The Role of Fishery Management in Nonfishing Activities

The activities and effects described in this chapter represent substantial risks to the sustainability of New England's fishery resources. Fishery management agencies and organizations, however, do not have direct authority or jurisdiction to regulate these activities. The Magnuson-Stevens Fishery Conservation and Management Act requires federal agencies (such as the U.S. Army Corps of Engineers and the U.S. Environmental Protection Agency) to consult with the National Marine Fisheries Service regarding any of their actions authorized, funded, or undertaken, or proposed to be authorized, funded, or undertaken, that may adversely affect essential fish habitat. This consultation process includes a review of the activity and requires the action agency to address mitigation. State agencies responsible for regulating nonfishing activities are under no obligation to consult with NMFS or the Councils regarding any activity that may threaten essential fish habitat. It falls, then, to the fishery management agencies and organizations to establish working relationships with nonfishing-related state and federal agencies, as well as nonfishing industries, and to ensure that impacts to essential fish habitat are considered in the decision-making process.

Acknowledgments

This chapter reflects a portion of the essential fish habitat amendment to the New England Fishery Management Council's fishery management plans. The Council's EFH Technical Team, Advisors, and Committee members contributed many useful content and editorial comments on an early draft of this document. Special thanks are extended to several members of the EFH Technical Team, Advisors, and Committee including Peter Auster, Brad Barr, Robert Buchsbaum, Jeremy Collie, Jeff Cross, Laura Ernst, Jon Kurland, Arnie Howe, Rich Langton, John Nelson, Joe Pelczarski, Chris Powell, Steve Rideout, Dianne Stephan, and Valerie Whalon. Three anonymous reviewers are greatly appreciated for several editorial and content comments that strengthened the chapter.

References

Arruda, J. A., G. R. Marzolf, and R. T. Faulk. 1983. The role of suspended sediments in the nutrition of zooplankton in turbid reservoirs Ecology 64(5):1225–1235.

ASMFC (Atlantic States Marine Fisheries Commission). 1992. Fishery management plan for inshore stocks of winter flounder. Fisheries Management Report No. 21. ASMFC, Washington, D.C.

ASMFC (Atlantic States Marine Fisheries Commission). 1993. Resolution II: in opposition to the use of combustion/incineration ash for artificial reef construction. Resolutions adopted by the Atlantic States Marine Fisheries Commission: 52nd annual Meeting. ASMFC, Washington, D.C.

Auster, P. J., and R. W. Langton. 1999. The effects of fishing on fish habitat. Pages 150–187 in L. R. Benaka, editor. Fish habitat: essential fish habitat and rehabilitation. American Fisheries Society, Symposium 22, Bethesda, Maryland.

Auster, P. J., R. J. Malatesta, and C. L. S. Donaldson. 1997. Distributional responses to small-scale habitat variability by early juvenile silver hake, Merluccius bilinearis. Environmental Biology of Fishes 50:195–200.

Auster, P. J., R. J. Malatesta, and S. C. LaRosa. 1995. Patterns of microhabitat utilization by mobile megafauna on the southern New England (USA) continental shelf and slope. Marine Ecology Progress Series 127:77–85.

Barr, B. W. 1987. Dredging handbook: A primer for dredging in the coastal zone of Massachusetts. Massachusetts Coastal Zone Management, Boston.

Barr, B. W. 1993. Environmental impacts of small boat navigation: vessel/sediment interactions and management implications. Page 1756 in O. T. Magoon, W. S. Wilson, H. Converse, and L. T. Hobin, editors. Proceeding of the coastal zone 1993 conference. American Society of Civil Engineers, New York.

Barr, B. W., and S. J. Wilk. 1994. Sewage sludge and industrial waste dumping. Pages 41–43 in R. W. Langton, J. B. Pearce, and J. A. Gibson, editors. Selected living resources, habitat conditions, and human perturbations of the Gulf of Maine. National Oceanic and Atmospheric Administration Technical Memorandum NMFS-NE-106, Woods Hole, Massachusetts.

Bedzinger, V. 1994. Salmon aquaculture: is there an impact on the wild stock? Aquaculture Magazine 20(5):38–42.

Bigford, T. E. 1991. Sea-level rise, nearshore fisheries, and the fishing industry. Coastal Management 19:412–437.

Blaxter, J. H. S. 1969. Development: eggs and larvae. Pages 178–241 in W. S. Hoar and D. J. Randall, editors. Fish physiology, volume 3. Academic Press, New York.

Boesch, D. F., D. M. Anderson, R. A. Horner, S. E. Shumway, P. A. Tester, and T. E. Whitledge. 1997. Harmful algal blooms in coastal waters: options for prevention, control and mitigation. National Oceanic and Atmospheric Administration Coastal Ocean Program Decision Analysis Series No. 10. NOAA Coastal Ocean Office, Silver Spring, Maryland.

Brodeur, J. C., G. Sherwood, J. B. Rasmussen, and A. Hontela. 1997. Impaired cortisol secretion in yellow perch (Perca flavescens) from lakes contaminated by heavy metals: in vivo and in vitro assessment. Canadian Journal of Fisheries and Aquatic Sciences 54:2752–2758.

Buchholtz ten Brink, M. R., F. T. Manheim, and M. H. Bothner. 1996. Contaminants in the Gulf of Maine: what's there and should we worry? Pages 91–116 in D. Dow and E. Braasch, editors. The health of the Gulf of Maine ecosystem: cumulative impacts of multiple stressors. Regional Association for Research on the Gulf of Maine Report 96–1. Dartmouth College, Hanover, New Hampshire.

Burkholder, J. M., and H. B. Glasgow, Jr. 1997. Pfiesteria piscicida and other Pfiesteria-like dinoflagellates: behavior, impacts, and environmental controls. Limnology and Oceanography 45:1052–1075.

Burkholder, J. M., E. J. Noga, C. H. Hobbs, and H. B. Glasgow Jr. 1992. New 'phantom' flagellate is the causative agent of major estuarine fish kills. Nature (London) 358:407–410.

Butman, B. 1998. Contaminant transport in Massachusetts Bay. U.S. Department of the Interior, U.S. Geological Survey, USGS fact sheet. http://marine.usgs.gov/fact-sheets/mass/mass-bay.html, 19 November 1998.

Coe, J. M., and D. B. Rogers, editors. 1997. Marine debris: sources, impacts, and solutions. Springer-Verlag, New York City.

Collie, J. S., G. A. Escanero, and P. C. Valentine. 1997. Effects of bottom fishing on the benthic megafauna of Georges Bank. Marine Ecology Progress Series 155:159–172.

Conkling, P., and A. Hayden. 1997. New England aquaculture: a case study of Maine. Pages 153–166 in R. Goldburg and T. Triplett, editors. Murky waters: environmental effects of aquaculture in the United States. Environmental Defense Fund, Washington, D.C.

Cowardin, L. M., V. Carter, F. C. Golet, and E. T. LaRoe. 1979. Classification of wetlands and deepwater habitats of the United States. U.S. Fish and Wildlife Service, FWS/OBS-79/31, Washington, D.C.

CRASC (Connecticut River Atlantic Salmon Commission). 1997. Strategic plan for the restoration of Atlantic salmon to the Connecticut River. U.S. Fish and Wildlife Service, Sunderland, Massachusetts.

deFur, P. L., and D. N. Rader. 1995. Aquaculture in estuaries: feast or famine? Estuaries 18(1A):2–9.

Eldridge, P. J., and G. M. Meaburn. 1992. Potential impact of PCB's on bluefish, Pomatomus saltatrix, management. Marine Fisheries Review 54(4):19–24.

Fogarty, M. J., and S. A. Murawski. 1998. Large-scale disturbance and the structure of marine systems: fishery impacts on Georges Bank. Ecological Applications 8(1)Supplement:S6–S22.

Gibson, M. R. 1996. Comparison of trends in the finfish assemblage of Mt. Hope Bay and Narragansett Bay in relation to operations at the New England Power Brayton Point Station. A report to the Brayton Point Technical Advisory Committee. Rhode Island Division Fish and Wildlife Research Reference Document 95/1. RIDFW, Wickford, Rhode Island.

Goldsborough, W. J. 1997. Human impacts on SAV–a Chesapeake Bay case study. Pages 36–39 in C. D. Stephan and T. E. Bigford, editors. Atlantic coastal submerged aquatic vegetation: a review of its ecological role, anthropogenic impacts, state regulation, and value to Atlantic coastal fisheries. Atlantic States Marine Fisheries Commission Habitat Management Series #1. ASMFC, Washington, D.C.

Gotceitas, V., and J. A. Brown. 1993. Substrate selection by juvenile Atlantic cod (Gadus morhua): effects of predation risk. Oecologia 93:31–37.

Gotceitas, V., S. Fraser, and J. A. Brown. 1997. Use of eelgrass beds (Zostera marina) by juvenile Atlantic cod (Gadus morhua). Canadian Journal of Fisheries and Aquatic Sciences 54:1306–1319.

Gould, E., P. E. Clark, and F. P. Thurberg. 1994. Pollutant effects on demersal fishes. Pages 30–40 in R. W. Langton, J. B. Pearce, and J. A. Gibson, editors. Selected living resources, habitat conditions, and human perturbations of the Gulf of Maine. National Oceanic and Atmospheric Administration Technical Memorandum NMFS-NE-106, Woods Hole, Massachusetts.

Grant, J., A. Hatcher, D. B. Scott, P. Pocklington, C. T. Schafer, and G. V. Winters. 1995. A multidisciplinary approach to evaluating impacts of shellfish aquaculture on benthic communities. Estuaries 18(1A):124–144.

Haines, T. A. 1981. Acid precipitation and its consequences for aquatic ecosystems: a review. Transactions of the American Fisheries Society 110:669–707.

Hanson, A. K. 1998. Global ozone depletion: effects of ultraviolet light on marine plankton. Maritimes 40(1):8–9.

Hilton, J., and G. L. Phillips. 1982. The effect of boat activity on turbidity in a shallow broadland river. Journal of Applied Ecology 19:143–150.

Hoagland, P., and H. L. Kite-Powell. 1997. Characterization and mitigation of marine debris in the Gulf of Maine. A report prepared for the U.S. Gulf of Maine Association. GM 97-13, Halifax, Nova Scotia.

Hose, J. E., D. D. Fiore, H. S. Parker, and T. Sciarrotta. 1989. Toxicity of chlorine dioxide to early life stages of marine organisms. Bulletin of Environmental Contamination and Toxicology 42:315–319.

ICES (International Council for the Exploration of the Sea). 1991. Report of the study group on ecosystem effects of fishing activities. Lowestoft, 11-15 Mar. 1991. ICES C.M. 1991/G:7 Session Y.

Jonsson, B., N. Jonsson, and L. P. Hansen. 1991. Differences in life history and migratory behavior between wild and hatchery-reared Atlantic salmon in nature. Aquaculture 98:69–78.

Karaki, S., and J vanHoften. 1975. Resuspension of bed material and wave effects on the Illinois and upper Mississippi Rivers caused by boat traffic. Contract number LMSSD 75-881. U.S. Army Engineer District, St. Louis.

Kelley, J. T. 1992. Sea-level change and coastal erosion in the western Gulf of Maine. Pages 27–44 in D. W. Townsend and P. F. Larsen, editors. The Gulf of Maine. National Oceanic and Atmospheric Administration Coastal Ocean Program Regional Synthesis Series No. 1. Washington, D.C.

Kelly, L. A. 1992. Dissolved reactive phosphorus release from sediments beneath a freshwater cage aquaculture development in West Scotland. Hydrobiolgia 235/236:569–572.

Kent, M. L., N. C. Whyte, and C. LaTrace. 1995. Gill lesions and mortality in seawater pen-reared Atlantic salmon Salmo salar associated with a dense bloom of Skeletonema costatum and Thalassiosira species. Diseases of Aquatic Organisms 22:77–81.

Kurland, J. M., F. M. Ludwig, S. W. Gorski, and C. Mantazaris. 1994. Dredging and dredged-material disposal. Pages 44–47 in R. W. Langton, J. B. Pearce, and J. A. Gibson, editors. Selected living resources, habitat conditions, and human perturbations of the Gulf of Maine. National Oceanic and Atmospheric Administration Technical Memorandum NMFS-NE-106, Woods Hole, Massachusetts.

Langton, R. W., P. J. Auster, and D. C. Schneider. 1995. A spatial and temporal perspective on research and management of groundfish in the northwest Atlantic. Reviews in Fisheries Science 3:210–229.

Larsen, P. F. 1992. An overview of the environmental quality of the Gulf of Maine. Pages 71–95 in D. W. Townsend and P. F. Larsen, editors. The Gulf of

Maine. National Oceanic and Atmospheric Administration Coastal Ocean Program Regional Synthesis Series No. 1. Washington, D.C.

Leatherman, S. P. 1988. Barrier island handbook, 3rd edition. Coastal Publications Series, College Park, Maryland.

Lehtonen, H. 1996. Potential effects of global warming on northern European freshwater fish and fisheries. Fisheries Management and Ecology 3:59–71.

Levings, C. D. 1985. Juvenile salmonid used of habitats altered by a coal port in the Fraser River Estuary, British Columbia. Marine Pollution Bulletin 16(6):248–254.

Lin, Q., and I. A. Mendelssohn. 1996. A comparative investigation of the effects of south Louisiana crude oil on the vegetation of fresh, brackish, and salt marshes. Marine Pollution Bulletin 2:202–209.

Lough, R. G., and D. C. Potter. 1993. Vertical distribution patterns and diel migrations of larval and juvenile haddock *Melanogrammus aeglefinus* and Atlantic cod *Gadus morhua* on Georges Bank. Fisheries Bulletin 91:281–303.

Lura, H., and H. Saegrov. 1991. Documentation of successful spawning of escaped farmed female Atlantic salmon, *Salmo salar*, in Norwegian rivers. Aquaculture 98:151–159.

Manning, T. M., S. P. Wilson, and J. C. Chapman. 1996. Toxicity of chlorine and other chlorinated compounds to some Australian aquatic organisms. Bulletin of Environmental Contamination and Toxicology 56:971–976.

McGurrin, J. M., R. B. Stone, and R. J. Sousa. 1989. Profiling United States artificial reef development. Bulletin of Marine Science 44(2):1004–1013.

Messieh, S. N., T. W. Rowell, D. L. Peer, and P. J. Cranford. 1991. The effects of trawling, dredging and ocean dumping on the eastern Canadian continental shelf seabed. Continental Shelf Research 11:1237–1263.

Meyers, T. R., and J. D. Hendricks. 1982. A summary of tissue lesions in aquatic animals induced by controlled exposures to environmental contaminants, chemotherapeutic agents, and potential carcinogens. Marine Fisheries Review 44(12):1–17.

Milligan, K. L. D., and E. M. Cosper. 1994. Isolation of virus capable of lysing the brown tide microalga, *Aureococcus anophagefferens*. Science 266:805–807.

Moyle, P. B., and J. J. Cech, Jr. 1988. Fishes: an introduction to ichthyology–2nd edition. Prentice-Hall, Englewood Cliffs, New Jersey.

NCSU (North Carolina State University Aquatic Botany Laboratory). 1998. *Pfiesteria piscicida* homepage. http://www2.ncsu.edu/unity/lockers/project/aquatic_botany/pfiest.html, 19 November 1998.

Nelson, D. A., and nine coauthors. 1991. Comparative reproductive success of winter flounder in Long Island Sound: a three-year study (biology, biochemistry, and chemistry). Estuaries 14(3):318–331.

NMFS (National Marine Fisheries Service). 1994. Habitat protection activity report 1991-1993. National Oceanic and Atmospheric Administration, Silver Spring, Maryland.

NOAA (National Oceanic, and Atmospheric Administration). 1996. An appraisal of social and cultural aspects of the multispecies groundfish fishery in New England and the Mid-Atlantic regions. A report by Aguirre International submitted to NOAA. NOAA, Silver Spring, Maryland.

NOAA (National Oceanic, and Atmospheric Administration). 1997a. NOAA's estuarine eutrophication survey. volume 2: Mid-Atlantic region. NOAA Office of Ocean Resources Conservation and Assessment, Silver Spring, Maryland.

NOAA (National Oceanic, and Atmospheric Administration). 1997b. NOAA's estuarine eutrophication survey. volume 3: North Atlantic region. NOAA Office of Ocean Resources Conservation and Assessment, Silver Spring, Maryland.

NSF (National Science Foundation) and NOAA (National Oceanic, and Atmospheric Administration). 1998. The harmful algae page. http://habserv1.whoi.edu/hab/, 19 November 1998.

Omori, M., S. VanDerSpoel, and C. P. Norman. 1994. Impact of human activities on pelagic biogeography. Progress in Oceanography 34:211–219.

O'Reilly, J. E. 1994. Nutrient loading and eutrophication. Pages 25–29 *in* R. W. Langton, J. B. Pearce, and J. A. Gibson, editors. Selected living resources, habitat conditions, and human perturbations of the Gulf of Maine. National Oceanic and Atmospheric Administration Technical Memorandum NMFS-NE-106, Woods Hole, Massachusetts.

Pearce, J. B. 1994. Mining of seabed aggregates. Pages 48–50 *in* R. W. Langton, J. B. Pearce, and J. A. Gibson, editors. Selected living resources, habitat conditions, and human perturbations of the Gulf of Maine. National Oceanic and Atmospheric Administration Technical Memorandum NMFS-NE-106, Woods Hole, Massachusetts.

Pearce, J. B. 1998. An agenda for the AFS Continuing Education Program. Fisheries 23(4):31.

Peterson, R. H., P. G. Daye, and J. L. Metcalfe. 1980. Inhibition of Atlantic salmon (*Salmo salar*) hatching at low pH. Canadian Journal of Fisheries and Aquatic Sciences 37:770–774.

Readman, J. W., L. L. W. Kwong, D. Grondin, J. Bartocci, J.-P. Villeneuve, L. D. Mee. 1993. Coastal water contamination from triazine herbicide used in antifouling paints. Environmental Science & Technology 27:1940–1942.

Rosecchi, E., A. J. Crivelli, and G. Catsadorakis. 1993. The establishment and impact of *Pseudorabora parva*, an exotic fish species introduced into Lake Mikri Prespa (north-western Greece). Aquatic Conservation: Marine and Freshwater Ecosystems 3:223–231.

Rosenthal, H. 1994. Aquaculture and the environment. World Aquaculture 25(2):4–11.

Ruggles, C. P. 1980. A review of the downstream migration of Atlantic salmon. Canadian Technical Report of Fisheries and Aquatic Sciences 9852.

Sasikumar, N., J. Azariah, and K. V. K. Nair. 1993. Sublethal response of barnacles to chlorine: an experimental study for power plant biofouling control. Marine Behaviour and Physiology 24:55–66.

Scarrat, D. J. 1987. Fisheries interests and ocean mining. Marine Mining 6:141–147.

Schlee, J. 1973. Atlantic continental shelf and slope of the United States–sediment texture of the northeastern part. U.S. Geological Survey Professional Paper 529-L, Woods Hole, Massachusetts.

Short, F., and D. Burdick. 1994. Research and management needs to assess the extent and functional value of eelgrass habitats in the Gulf of Maine. Pages 100–101 in D. Stevenson and E. Braasch, editors. Gulf of Maine habitats: workshop proceedings. Regional Association for Research on the Gulf of Maine Report 94–2. Dartmouth College, Hanover, New Hampshire.

Short, F. T., and D. M. Burdick. 1996. Quantifying eelgrass habitat loss in relation to housing development and nitrogen loading in Waquoit Bay, Massachusetts. Estuaries 19:730–739.

Staurnes, M., L. P. Hansen, K. Fugelli, and O. Haraldstad. 1996. Short-term exposure to acid water impairs osmoregulation, seawater tolerance, and subsequent marine survival of smolts of Atlantic salmon (*Salmo salar* L.). Canadian Journal of Fisheries and Aquatic Sciences 53:1695–1704.

Stephan, C. D., and T. E. Bigford, editors. 1997. Atlantic coastal submerged aquatic vegetation: a review of its ecological role, anthropogenic impacts, state regulation and value to Atlantic coastal fisheries. ASMFC Habitat Management Series #1, Washington, D.C.

Stolpe, N. E. 1998. Boating generated turbulence. Pages 22–24 in R. E. Crawford, N. E. Stolpe, and M. J. Moore, editors. The environmental impacts of boating: proceedings of a workshop held at the Woods Hole Oceanographic Institution, Woods Hole, Massachusetts USA, Dec. 7 to 9, 1994. WHOI Technical Report WHOI-98–03. Woods Hole, Massachusetts.

Stone, R. B. 1982. Artificial reefs: toward a new era in fisheries enhancement? Marine Fisheries Review 44(6–7):2–3.

Travnichek, V. H., A. V. Zale, and W. L. Fisher. 1993. Entrainment of ichthyoplankton by a warmwater hydroelectric facility. Transactions of the American Fisheries Society 122:709–716.

Turgeon, D., and A. Robertson. 1995. Contaminants in coastal fish and mollusks. Pages 408–412 in E. T. LaRoe, G. S. Farris, C. E. Puckett, P. D. Doran, and M. J. Mac, editors. Our living resources: a report to the nation on the distribution, abundance, and health of U.S. plants, animals, and ecosystems. U.S. Department of the Interior, National Biological Service, Washington, D.C.

USEPA (U.S. Environmental Protection Agency). 1994. Status and efforts to control aquatic debris. EPA-842-K94-002. USEPA Office of Water, Washington, D.C.

USFWS (U.S. Fish and Wildlife Service). 1995. Status review for anadromous Atlantic salmon in the United States. USFWS, National Oceanic and Atmospheric Administration, and National Marine Fisheries Service, Hadley, Massachusetts.

USGS (United States Geological Survey). 1998. Predicting the impact of relocating Boston's sewage outfall: effluent dilution simulation in Massachusetts Bay. USGS fact sheet 185–97, U.S. Department of the Interior, USGS. http://marine.usgs.gov/fact-sheets/fs185–97/, 19 November 1998.

Valentine, P. C., and R. G. Lough. 1991. The influence of geological and oceanographic environmental factors on the abundance and distribution of fisheries resources of the northeastern United States continental shelf. The seafloor environment and the fishery of eastern Georges Bank. Open-File Report 91-439. U.S. Geological Survey, Woods Hole, Massachusetts.

Valentine, P. C., E. W. Strom, R. G. Lough, and C. L. Brown. 1993. Maps showing the sedimentary environment of eastern Georges Bank. U.S. Geological Survey Miscellaneous Investigation Series, Map I-2279-B, scale 1:250,000. USGS, Woods Hole, Massachusetts.

Valiela, I. 1995. Marine ecological processes, 2nd edition. Springer-Verlag, New York City.

Valiela, I., K., and eleven coauthors. 1992. Couplings of watersheds and coastal waters: Sources and consequences of nutrient enrichment in Waquoit Bay, Massachusetts. Estuaries 18:443–457.

Vandermeulen, J. H. 1996. Environmental trends of ports and harbours: implications for planning and management. Maritime Policy and Management 23(1):55–66.

Vandermeulen, J. H., and D. Mossman. 1996. Sources of variability in seasonal hepatic microsomal oxygenase activity in winter flounder (*Pleuronectes americanus*) from a coal tar contaminated estuary. Canadian Journal of Fisheries and Aquatic Sciences 53:1741–1753.

Vestal, B., A. Rieser, M. Ludwig, J. Kurland, C. Collins, and J. Ortiz. 1995. Methodologies and mechanisms for management of cumulative coastal environmental impacts. part I–synthesis, with annotated bibliography; part II–development and application of a cumulative impacts assessment protocol. National Oceanic and Atmospheric Administration Coastal Ocean Program Decision Analysis Series No. 6. NOAA Coastal Ocean Office, Silver Spring, Maryland.

Watt, W. D., C. D. Scott, and W. J. White. 1983. Evidence of acidification of some Nova Scotia rivers and its impact on Atlantic salmon. Canadian Journal of Fisheries and Aquatic Sciences 40:462–473.

White, A. W., J. Nassif, S. E. Shumway, and D. K. Wittaker. 1993. Recent occurrence of paralytic shellfish toxins in offshore shellfish in the northeaster United States. Pages 435–438 *in* T. J. Smayda and Y. Shimizu, editors. Toxic phytoplankton blooms in the sea. Elsevier, New York City.

Wilk, S. J., and B. W. Barr. 1994. Multiple-use issues in estuarine and coastal habitat loss. Pages 51–52 *in* R. W. Langton, J. B. Pearce, and J. A. Gibson, editors. Selected living resources, habitat conditions, and human perturbations of the Gulf of Maine. National Oceanic and Atmospheric Administration Technical Memorandum NMFS-NE-106, Woods Hole, Massachusetts.

Witman, J. D. 1996. Dynamics of Gulf of Maine benthic communities. Pages 51–70 *in* D. Dow and E. Braasch, editors. The health of the Gulf of Maine ecosystem: cumulative impacts of multiple stressors. Regional Association for Research on the Gulf of Maine Report 96–1. Dartmouth College, Hanover, New Hampshire.

Wood, M., J. T. Kelley, and D. F. Belknap. 1989. Patterns of sediment accumulation in the tidal marshes of Maine. Estuaries 12:237–246.

Yousef, U. A. 1974. Assessing effects on water quality by boating activity. Environment Protection Technology Series EPA-670/2-74-072. U.S. Environmental Protection Agency, National Environmental Research Center, Cincinnati, Ohio.

American Fisheries Society Symposium 22:323, 1999

Part Five:
Fish Habitat Rehabilitation and Socioeconomic
Issues—Focus on the Great Lakes

CARLOS FETTEROLF

National Sea Grant Review Panel
8200 Pine Cross, Ann Arbor, Michigan 48103, USA

The concept of essential fish habitat (EFH) introduced through the 1996 reauthorization of the Magnuson-Stevens Fishery Conservation and Management Act (also called the Sustainable Fisheries Act) has the potential to energize the sleeping giant within fishery management programs. The Sustainable Fisheries Act unfortunately applies only to the National Marine Fisheries Service and regional fishery management councils and not to the Great Lakes. However, the overwhelming recognition by Congress that habitat management is essential if we are to have healthy fish stocks will infuse the thinking of fishery and water managers in the eight Great Lakes states, the Province of Ontario, the six Great Lakes Sea Grant College Programs, and several federal agencies. The EFH policy focuses thinking on habitat and is destined to be the fisheries buzz phrase of the decade in marine systems as we work to define, refine, and fully understand EFH. Essential fish habitat is not glamorous (yet), but the excitement will begin when research dollars start to flow and some court cases make the headlines.

The effects of the EFH policy will carry over into freshwater systems and will put new life into the evolving thrusts of Great Lakes resource management agencies. This carryover will facilitate the Canada–U.S. Great Lakes Fishery Commission's movement toward integrated lamprey and fisheries management on a fish community basis supported by habitat rehabilitation, as well as the International Joint Commission's movement toward development and implementation of comprehensive management plans to restore beneficial uses, including fish and wildlife habitat.

The chapter by John Hartig and John Kelso traces the increase in importance of habitat considerations in Great Lakes management, identifies key factors necessary for scientifically defensible, ecosystem-based management, and provides examples of successful efforts to rehabilitate and conserve habitats using an ecosystem approach.

Contrary to the ecosystem approach and highlighting the theme of opportunism found in the chapter by Hartig and Kelso, the next chapter by David Kelch et al. describes the immediate reaction of fish and fishermen to an artificial reef construction project. Working with the Ohio Department of Natural Resources and the U.S. Army Corps of Engineers, the project successfully used donated materials to improve nearshore sportfishing opportunity and to increase on-site fishing pressure and catch. Whether this project was beneficial to the fish community of Lake Erie remains unknown, but construction of fish-concentrating devices remains popular.

Leroy Hushak et al. examine the immediate socioeconomic impact of one of the reefs described in Kelch et al. Using questionnaires, Hushak et al. discovered that the total value of the reef to Lorain County, Ohio anglers using the reef in 1992 was US$276,000 compared with total construction costs of less than $100,000. It is easy to see why taking advantage of opportunities offered by the availability of donated materials for reef construction is popular with agencies and citizen groups.

Finally, returning to the concept that habitat quality, quantity, and suitability determine production from a given aquatic area, Charles Minns et al. go through a detailed procedure to determine how much of what habitat is essential. The procedure includes performing habitat assessment through remote sensing, integrating thermal regimes with habitat elements, estimating suitability of habitat for life stages and species of fish, and creating population, biomass, and production models for comparison with available records.

In summary, this section of the book contains four chapters dealing with habitat modifications and suitability: two chapters describing long-term ecosystem approaches to management, and two chapters describing successes with short-term habitat "tweaking." Who is to say that there is anything wrong with being opportunistic and achieving rapid success? And who is to say that long-term ecosystem approaches to management are not worthy of enthusiasm and admiration?

American Fisheries Society Symposium 22:324–334, 1999

Fish Habitat Rehabilitation and Conservation in the Great Lakes: Moving from Opportunism to Scientifically Defensible Management

JOHN H. HARTIG

International Joint Commission
100 Ouellette Avenue, 8th Floor Windsor, Ontario N9A 6T3 Canada

JOHN R. M. KELSO

Department of Fisheries and Oceans
Great Lakes Laboratory for Fisheries and Aquatic Sciences
1 Canal Drive, Sault Ste. Marie, Ontario P6A 6W4 Canada

Abstract.—The Canada–U.S. Great Lakes Water Quality Agreement (GLWQA) is an evolving instrument for ecosystem-based management. Its initial emphasis in 1972 was on controlling phosphorus inputs. In 1978, the GLWQA focused on control and management of persistent toxic substances and the use of an ecosystem approach in management and research. The 1987 Protocol to the GLWQA adopted new annexes that focused on sources and pathways of persistent toxic substances and on development and implementation of comprehensive management plans to restore beneficial uses, including fish and wildlife habitat. Canada and the United States have achieved a number of Great Lakes successes. Examples of successes include: reversing cultural eutrophication in the lower Great Lakes and maintaining the oligotrophic-mesotrophic state of the upper Great Lakes as a result of phosphorus control programs, and achieving US$2–4 billion in economic return to the Great Lakes region annually as a result of fish stocking, restrictions on harvests, and sea lamprey control. As such successes have been achieved and cooperative management efforts have evolved to address ecosystem integrity and sustainability, the relative importance of habitat as a Great Lakes issue has increased. Current major challenges to further ecosystem-based management of habitat include: ensuring that all levels of government adopt strong habitat conservation and rehabilitation policy statements; recruiting and retaining trained habitat personnel to ensure that local and regional actions are consistent with such policies; sustaining creative ecosystem-based processes in light of government cutbacks; addressing the need for fish habitat assessment and analysis via effective institutional arrangements; agreeing on a core set of indicators and allocating required resources to sustain monitoring programs; and exchanging information about successful experiences with modifying habitat to support fish stocks and communicating broadly both ecological and economic benefits.

The International Joint Commission (IJC) has been active in Great Lakes water management issues for approximately 90 years. Under the terms of the 1909 Boundary Waters Treaty, the IJC receives "references" or requests for international studies by governments of the United States and Canada. Those international studies provide the basis for recommendations to the two countries to resolve problems. However, the recommendations are not binding.

The success of the IJC process can be attributed to using an ecosystem approach (i.e., accounting for the interrelationships among land, air, water, and all living things, including humans, and involving all stakeholder groups in comprehensive management) in problem solving. This problem-solving approach by design facilitates common fact-finding and learning by experts from both countries serving in their personal and professional capacities. The process provides a means of obtaining agreed-upon

and trusted physical, chemical, biological, and socioeconomic data. Such trusted data, together with an inclusive public participation process, enable citizens of both countries to have greater confidence in decisions on solutions to problems affecting shared resources.

One of the most notable successes of the IJC process has been the binational phosphorus management program. This program, funded at more than US$9 billion and designed to control phosphorus inputs, reversed cultural eutrophication in the lower Great Lakes and has maintained the oligotrophic-mesotrophic state of the upper Great Lakes (IJC 1985). Concurrent with these efforts, Canada and the United States (working in cooperation with the Great Lakes Fishery Commission) stocked fish, restricted harvests, and managed sea lamprey in the Great Lakes, thus creating a sportfishing industry valued at $2–4 billion annually (Talhelm 1988). As Great

Lakes programs achieved success in phosphorus management efforts and restored or created fisheries, and as cooperative management efforts evolved to address ecosystem integrity and sustainability, the relative importance of habitat as a Great Lakes issue increased. This chapter traces the increase in importance of habitat as a consideration in Great Lakes management; identifies factors necessary for scientifically defensible, ecosystem-based management; and provides examples of efforts to rehabilitate and conserve habitats using an ecosystem approach. Further, this chapter was written during the 25th anniversary of the signing of the 1972 Great Lakes Water Quality Agreement (GLWQA) in the spirit of looking back to review progress and looking forward to address future challenges.

The Evolution of the Great Lakes Water Quality Agreement

The need for Canada–United States cooperation in resolving water pollution problems was first recognized at the turn of the 20th century as a result of typhoid fever and cholera epidemics along Great Lakes connecting channels like the Detroit and Niagara Rivers. These epidemics resulted in the United States and Canada signing the 1909 Boundary Waters Treaty. The Boundary Waters Treaty established the IJC to cooperatively resolve water and air pollution, water level, and other disputes between the two countries. In response to widespread concern about cultural eutrophication of Lake Erie and other Great Lakes waters, the first Great Lakes Water Quality Agreement was signed by the United States and Canada in 1972. The 1972 GLWQA gave the IJC responsibility to review and assess progress under the GLWQA and provided the focus for a coordinated effort to control cultural eutrophication by reducing phosphorus inputs to the Great Lakes (United States and Canada 1972).

In 1978, the GLWQA was revised and expanded in recognition of the need to understand and effectively address the effects of toxic substances on Great Lakes biota (United States and Canada 1978). An ecosystem approach formed the basis of the 1978 GLWQA. The GLWQA was again revised in 1987 to include annexes to address atmospheric deposition of toxic substances, contaminated sediment, nonpoint source pollution, and remedial action plans (RAPs) and lakewide management plans (LaMPs) (United States and Canada 1987). Remedial action

plans use an ecosystem approach to identify the responsibility and time frame for implementing remedial and preventive actions necessary to restore impaired uses in 42 degraded areas (called Areas of Concern) of the Great Lakes. Lakewide management plans use an ecosystem approach to identify the responsibility and time frame for implementing remedial and preventive actions necessary to reduce loadings of critical pollutants in order to restore impaired uses in the open waters of each Great Lake.

Each revision to the GLWQA has been the result of new knowledge and increased concern for restoring and maintaining the integrity of the Great Lakes. As a result, the GLWQA is an evolving instrument for ecosystem-based management (NRC and the Royal Society of Canada 1985).

Growing Emphasis on Habitat Rehabilitation and Conservation

The evolution of the Canada–United States Great Lakes Water Quality Agreement toward ecosystem-based management and the GLWQA's recognition of and emphasis on habitat occurred within two decades (Table 1). This evolution of the GLWQA as an ecosystem-based management tool demonstrates the increase in importance of habitat as a Great Lakes issue. Increased importance of habitat as a Great Lakes issue is further manifested by the more than 50% increase from 1989 to 1997 in the number of RAP teams (i.e., multistakeholder groups charged with developing and implementing RAPs to restore impaired uses in Areas of Concern) that acknowledged loss of habitat as a serious problem (Figure 1).

Another important indicator of growing emphasis on habitat rehabilitation and conservation has been the State of the Lakes Ecosystem Conferences sponsored by the United States and Canada. Environment Canada and the U.S. Environmental Protection Agency (1995, 1997) reported increased recognition that the condition of the Great Lakes basin ecosystem was being determined by three major factors: (1) habitat loss and degradation, (2) pollution, and (3) exotic species, all of which are driven by human activities. Increased recognition of the importance of habitat loss and degradation was further supported by the work of Richter et al. (1997) on threats to imperiled freshwater fauna. Based on a survey of anthropogenic stressors on freshwater fauna, Richter et al. (1997) identified the five leading stressors implicated in causing historic declines of species as (1) hydrologic regime alteration, (2)

TABLE 1.—The evolution of the Canada–U.S. Great Lakes Water Quality Agreement (GLWQA) as a tool for ecosystem-based management and the GLWQA's recognition of and emphasis on habitat; RAPs = remedial action plans; LaMPs = lakewide management plans.

Version of GLWQA	Primary focus	Recognition of and emphasis on habitat
1972	Phosphorus control and management	None or limited
1978	Control and management of persistent toxic substances; use of an ecosystem approach	Implicit recognition of habitat through the goal of restoring physical, chemical, and biological integrity
1987	Prevention and remediation of persistent toxic substance problems; development and implementation of RAPs for Areas of Concern and LaMPs	Explicit recognition of habitat, i.e., loss of fish and wildlife habitat was identified as 1 of 14 use impairments to be restored through RAPs and LaMPs

streambed sediment load changes (including siltation), (3) habitat destruction, (4) channel or shoreline changes in morphology or bed structure, and (5) changes in nutrient loads. In addition, direct removal of or damage to habitat was implicated as a threat for nearly 60% of species undergoing historic declines and nearly 50% undergoing current declines.

Moving toward Scientifically Defensible Management

Today, governmental programs focus on restoring ecosystem integrity and achieving sustainability. For example, the GLWQA calls for the restoration and maintenance of the physical, chemical, and biological integrity of the waters of the Great Lakes basin ecosystem (United States and Canada 1987). In this context, integrity is generally accepted to mean the ability of an ecosystem to maintain its structure and function when confronted with change (Karr and Dudley 1981). Ecosystems that cannot maintain their structure and function following perturbation are said to have lost their integrity.

Fishery management agencies throughout the Great Lakes basin ecosystem support the GLWQA goal to restore and maintain the physical, chemical, and biological integrity of the waters of the Great Lakes basin ecosystem (Eshenroder et al. 1995). Indeed, both fishery and water quality management agencies have similar goals of restoring degraded fish communities and habitat in the effort to achieve ecosystem integrity (Hartig et al. 1996).

To date, much effort in the Great Lakes has gone into defining fish community objectives (i.e., lake-specific objectives for the structure and function of the fish community) and identifying management actions to achieve those fish community objectives (Eshenroder et al. 1995). However, environmental issues and other issues like habitat that have the po-

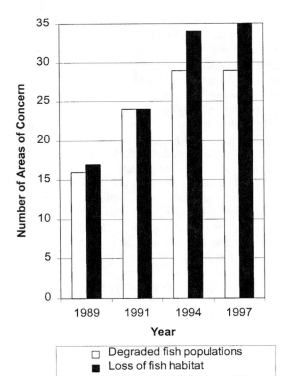

FIGURE 1.—Number of Great Lakes Areas of Concern characterized by degradation of fish populations and loss of fish habitat from 1989 to 1997. (Each Area of Concern has established a remedial action plan team.)

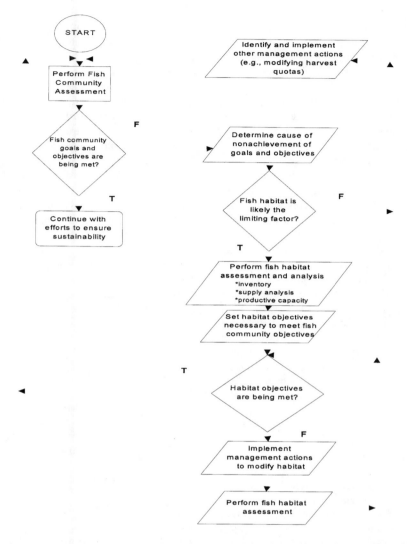

FIGURE 2.—A generalized decision-making framework designed to manage habitats needed to support fish stocks.

tential to prevent achievement of fish community objectives are yet to be addressed. In addition, as of this writing, much of the Great Lakes fishery management effort has gone into managing fish yield or harvest.

In general, habitat management in the Great Lakes has been opportunistic (Hartig et al. 1996). In a management context, one might say that habitat has no home. No management agency is given clear authority for habitat management, and responsibility for habitat is shared among numerous federal, state, provincial, and local agencies. A major challenge in the Great Lakes is to develop the institutional capacity to manage habitats needed to sup-

port fish stocks (Koonce et al. 1996). In this context, institutional capacity building can be accomplished by a combination of (Hartig et al. 1995):

- human elements and strategies (e.g., empowerment, long-term vision- and mission-driven management, shared decision making);
- tools and techniques (e.g., habitat inventory techniques, habitat supply analyses, habitat rehabilitation and enhancement methods); and
- management support systems (e.g., ecosystem performance measures, geographic information systems, decision support systems) to restore and maintain both human and nonhuman uses.

Both the GLWQA and the Strategic Plan for Management of Great Lakes Fisheries (GLFC 1994) advocate an ecosystem approach for planning, management, and research. Just as there is a need to develop the institutional capacity to manage habitats to support fish stocks, there is a need to develop the institutional capacity to implement an ecosystem approach in management.

Managing habitats that support fish stocks in a manner that is consistent with the use of an ecosystem approach will require recognition that some managers have a limited understanding of the relationship between habitat and fish community structure and function. Figure 2 presents one management framework to help understand and manage habitats to support fish stocks. Great Lakes managers are currently establishing fish community goals and objectives. If these goals and objectives are not being met, managers must determine the cause. If habitat is likely a limiting factor, managers need to undertake an assessment and analysis of fish habitat. Much greater effort will have to be placed on understanding habitat requirements for achievement of fish community objectives to accomplish scientifically defensible, ecosystem-based management. Scientific understanding of the interrelationships between fish community structure and function and habitat must provide a sound basis for ecosystem-based management actions.

Baird (1996) has shown that lack of scientific understanding and institutional problems are major impediments to scientifically defensible management of coastal habitats. This is also true in the Great Lakes. Current challenges include securing adequate scientific knowledge bases required by management and ensuring institutional arrangements that make effective use of scientific knowledge. In ecosystem-based management, the process of generating and applying scientific knowledge must be undertaken in an adaptive manner (i.e., assess, set priorities, and take action in an iterative fashion) (Figure 2). Shifting from managing fish stocks to managing habitats to support fish stocks in a scientifically defensible fashion will be a formidable task. Indeed, Baird (1996) recognized this enormous challenge, particularly in an environment of limited investment in research and management infrastructure.

There is an obvious need to identify, quantify, and understand essential habitats as a prerequisite to successful fishery management. There are three critical elements of fish habitat assessment and analysis: (1) habitat inventory, (2) habitat supply

analysis, and (3) determination of potential productive capacity of these habitats (Figure 3). Each element must be fully addressed to determine any habitat intervention to achieve fish community objectives. Today, many fishery managers continue to focus most of their habitat resources on inventories. However, moving forward with scientifically defensible management requires addressing all three elements of fish habitat assessment and analysis identified in Figure 3.

Minns et al. (1996) demonstrated the effective use in management of a simple model of the effects of life stage habitat supply limits on a northern pike *Esox lucius* population in Hamilton Harbour (western Lake Ontario). This modeling approach assumes that habitat supply for life stages can be estimated and that the key population processes in each life stage are controlled by a saturation function of habitat supply. As of this writing, Minns is applying this approach to Lake Erie (see Minns et al. 1999, this

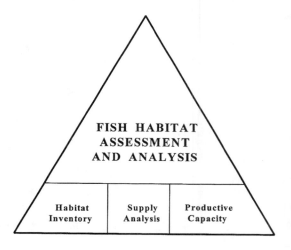

FIGURE 3.—A simple, conceptual depiction of the essential elements of fish habitat assessment and analysis. (**Habitat inventory:** a physical, chemical, and biological description of the place where a fish or fish community lives, usually collected in a systematic and comprehensive fashion; **supply analysis:** a systematic evaluation of the supply of habitat required to support different life stages of fishes [analysis of life stage habitat supply limits on fish populations]; **productive capacity:** the maximum predicted capability of habitats to produce healthy fish that are safe for human consumption or to support or produce aquatic organisms upon which fish depend [in practice, this definition is translated into a set of site-specific, measurable ecosystem attributes that can help management agencies make predictions about and monitor effects of habitat modifications].)

volume). Jones et al. (1996) demonstrated the effective use of a framework that applies the concept of productive capacity using a systematic methodology for organizing knowledge of linkages between habitat modification and ecological effects. This framework focuses on rigorous assessment of possible effects of habitat modification in an effort to advance beyond piecemeal habitat management and to effectively practice adaptive habitat management.

Considerable emphasis is now being placed on the use of sound science in management of the Great Lakes basin ecosystem (USEPA 1998). Therefore, there must be a strong coupling between research and management. How to ensure the acquisition and effective use of scientific knowledge by regulatory and resource management agencies remains a major challenge. Key issues that should be addressed— by international organizations like the GLFC and IJC and professional societies like the American Fisheries Society and International Association for Great Lakes Research—to help move forward consistent with scientifically defensible, ecosystem-based management include:

• demonstrating effective use of ecosystem approaches to set priorities and make trade-offs for habitat modification and conservation;
• treating habitat modification projects as experiments (see the Cootes Paradise Marsh rehabilitation project in Table 2);
• ensuring priority is given to adequate research and assessment;
• communicating simple, conceptual thinking about habitat for management agencies (Figures 2 and 3);
• sharing management experiences that use quantitative target setting (Hartig et al. 1997);
• pooling data on effectiveness of habitat modification projects (noting both economic and ecological benefits); and
• placing further emphasis on synthesizing and communicating knowledge and transferring technologies.

Examples of Successful Habitat Rehabilitation and Conservation

Habitat is defined as the physical, chemical, and biological factors that integrate to support a particular species or assemblage. As noted earlier, the binational Great Lakes phosphorus management program, initiated in the early 1970s, is a good example of a basinwide management initiative to reverse cultural eutrophication in the lower Great Lakes and maintain the oligotrophic-mesotrophic status of the upper Great Lakes. This phosphorus management program addressed the chemical factors limiting trophic status and the fishery. As improvements in the Great Lakes have occurred as a result of the phosphorus management program, the relative importance of physical factors limiting fish productivity has increased. It is recognized that biological (e.g., exotic species) and chemical factors (e.g., contaminated sediment in localized areas of the Great Lakes) continue to limit the fishery. However, more management emphasis is now being placed on modification of physical habitat.

One good example of a promising ecosystem-based management program that is achieving some success, and has the potential to achieve much greater success, is the Great Lakes remedial action plan program. Remedial action plans are addressing physical as well as chemical and biological factors limiting fisheries in Great Lakes Areas of Concern. However, it must be noted that RAPs are only addressing a small portion of the Great Lakes, and not all of the RAPs are adequately addressing habitat.

The RAP program is a multistakeholder effort to restore beneficial uses in 42 Great Lakes Areas of Concern. Remedial action plans are developed and implemented using locally designed ecosystem approaches (see Table 2). Many Areas of Concern are defined by watershed boundaries (e.g., Rochester Embayment, New York; Hamilton Harbour, Ontario; Rouge River, Michigan). Further, these RAPs include innovative institutional arrangements to help build the capacity to restore uses (Hartig and Law 1994). Although it can be argued whether these institutional arrangements are sufficient to adequately manage habitats to support fish stocks in a scientifically defensible fashion, the arrangements offer unique opportunities to recouple science and management to rehabilitate and conserve habitats to help achieve fishery objectives.

One RAP that is leading by example is the Hamilton Harbour RAP. Hamilton Harbour is on western Lake Ontario. Remedial action plan development was initiated in 1985 with the formation of a 43-member Hamilton Harbour Stakeholder Group. This group was the institutional structure established to foster cooperation and public participation and to implement an ecosystem approach to restore uses. Following a recommendation of the Stakeholder

TABLE 2.—Selected examples of habitat rehabilitation and conservation projects in the Great Lakes basin ecosystem.

Category	Project and location	Project description	Results	Reference
Wetland rehabilitation or preservation	Cootes Paradise Marsh rehabilitation project (Hamilton Harbour, Ontario)	Construction of carp barrier and fishway, reestablishment of emergent and submergent vegetation, and enhancement of pike spawning habitat	Monitoring in 1997 showed regeneration of both emergent and submergent vegetation; prevention of 90% of the carp from entering the marsh (reducing total fish biomass); an increase in the total number of fish (showing that the marsh is being used as a nursery); and an increase in the number of fish using the open water of the marsh (due to increased submergent vegetation).	Hall (1997)
Shoreline and streambank stabilization	Urban streambank stabilization in urban parks along Waukegan River (Waukegan, Illinois)	Construction of "lunkers" and "A-jacks" at three major bank erosion sites to stabilize shoreline, enhance habitat, and increase public access	Monitoring has documented a 300% increase in smallmouth bass fry survival and a 50% increase in largemouth bass residence.	Illinois State Water Survey (1994)
Channel modification	Canal rehabilitation in an island park (Belle Isle) in the Detroit River (Detroit, Michigan)	Dredging canals, improving circulation, and rehabilitating habitats to enhance the fishery and increase recreational use	Preliminary results have documented increased emergent wetland and deepwater habitats, increased flow, reduced roughfish populations, and increased gamefish populations.	Denison et al. (1998)
Rehabilitation of spawning habitat	Improvement of walleye spawning habitat in the Fox River (Wisconsin)	Increasing desirable substrate adjacent to good-quality, highly-used spawning area	In 1991, the first fall after spawning occurred on the new substrate, the relative abundance of fall fingerling walleye was 100–1,000 times greater than any other year-class measured. The average annual recruitment of fall fingerlings for the 1991–1993 period (post-project implementation) was 200–300 times greater than the 1987–1990 average (pre-project).	Lychwick (1995)

TABLE 2.—(Continued.)

Category	Project and location	Project description	Results	Reference
Reestablishment of native species	Restoration of native fish stocks in the Nipigon River (Ontario)	Restoration of walleye population by augmenting remnant stock (over 12,000 walleye stocked), reopening migratory routes, and rehabilitating degraded habitats	Preliminary results from monitoring conducted after stocking have documented low-level recruitment of walleye.	K. Cullis, Lake Superior Programs Office, personal communication
Incidental habitat enhancement	Submerged breakwater reef modification in Burns Harbor (Portage, Indiana)	Construction of submerged reefs to reduce wave energy damage and enhance spawning habitat for lake trout	Lake trout spawning first documented in 1993. Seven submerged barrier reefs constructed between 1995 and 1997. Over 6,300 eggs collected in 1996, of which 834 were collected on new reefs and 5,508 were collected on new cobble. Catch per unit effort varied from 0.05 to 15.40 eggs per trap per day, compared with catches of 0.02–2.30 noted on Stony Island Reef, a natural spawning area in eastern Lake Ontario. Twelve fry caught in 1996 and 31 in 1997 on one reef; 8 fry caught on the new cobble in 1997. Catch per unit effort was 0.01–0.10 fry per trap per day, compared with 0.04(in 1996) on Stony Island Reef.	Marsden (1994)

Group, a Bay Area Implementation Team made up of key implementing agencies and a Bay Area Restoration Council (which provides public oversight and is incorporated by law to acquire donations) were established to ensure RAP implementation.

From the outset, the Hamilton Harbour RAP had strong multistakeholder cooperation and strong linkages between management and research. Water quality and fishery researchers and managers worked through the RAP process to establish water-use goals, including one for the fishery stating "that water quality and fish habitat should be improved to permit an edible, naturally reproducing fishery for warmwater species, and that water and habitat conditions in Hamilton Harbour should not limit natural reproduction and the edibility of coldwater species" (HHSG 1991). This water-use goal was then translated into scientifically defensible targets for a stable and desirable fish community in littoral habitats (200–250 kg/ha total fish biomass in littoral habitats, 20–25% native piscivore biomass, 80–90% native species, 40–60 kg/ha piscivores in littoral habitats, 70–100 kg/ha specialists, and 30–90 kg/ha generalists) (HHRAPWT 1992). Criteria used to establish these targets included emphasis on fish communities in the littoral zone; attainment of a balanced, stable, and self-sustaining community; consideration of healthy habitats and the ecosystem; consistency with GLWQA use impairments (United States and Canada 1987); and emphasis on quantifiable parameters.

The Hamilton Harbour RAP is now in the implementation phase. One major effort to achieve the fishery targets is a 5-year, $19 million project designed to test and demonstrate rehabilitation techniques. This project will rehabilitate the 250 ha marsh in Cootes Paradise (located at the upper end of Hamilton Harbour), enhance the pike-spawning marsh in Grindstone Creek, improve the littoral habitat in the harbor, rehabilitate the littoral fish community, and provide nesting and loafing sites for colonial waterbirds. Restructuring the fish community will be accomplished by the combined efforts of carp control, habitat improvement, and introductions of top predators. The project has a large public-participation component. Construction of fishing piers, boardwalks, wildlife-viewing platforms, and an information center will enhance opportunities for access and education. More than 29 partners contributed to this project.

The Hamilton Harbour RAP is a good example of a multistakeholder, ecosystem-based process to achieve site-specific goals and objectives. Rodgers (1992) noted that this RAP benefited from considerable seed money, numerous dedicated individuals representing diverse science interests who moved the RAP forward, and proximity to a research facility (the Canada Center for Inland Waters). Further, this RAP is a good example of adaptive management. Preliminary results are promising (see Cootes Paradise Marsh rehabilitation project in Table 2). However, as is the case in all RAPs, rehabilitation is a long-term endeavor.

Conclusion

To move beyond opportunistic, piecemeal habitat management and achieve ecosystem-based management of habitats to support fish stocks will require substantial changes in how management agencies, research institutions, and other stakeholder groups work together. This will require getting beyond the rhetoric of partnerships and improving or creating new institutional arrangements to ensure scientifically defensible habitat decisions.

Holling and Meefe (1995) argued that governments have traditionally implemented top-down, command-and-control programs that attempt to reduce variation through regulation and control. The purpose of these programs is to eliminate extreme behavior to promote conformity to a specific set of standards, which to some degree is certainly desirable in civilized society. However, bureaucracies deeply entrenched in rigid rules often do not adapt well to new challenges because the current system discourages innovation and behavioral variation. An ultimate pathology emerges when regulatory and resource management agencies, through initial success with command-and-control programs, lose sight of their original purposes, eliminate research and monitoring, and focus on efficiency of control (Holling and Meefe 1995).

Governments need to shift their emphasis from control to responsiveness. To achieve responsiveness, governments must use management processes that generate learning and meaning, which are key criteria of responsive management actions (Westley 1995). The discontinuity between knowledge and action and the role played by institutional structures present an important challenge for those wishing to make management of ecosystems truly adaptive. It is clear that for adaptive, ecosystem-based management to succeed, organizations must find sense-making processes that simultaneously open the organization to new stimuli and provide strong action generation (Westley 1995).

If government organizations, particularly large bureaucratic ones, wish to increase responsiveness and adaptability, they must harness the instinctive learning of the front lines instead of actively inhibiting instinctive learning (Westley 1995). Monitoring, assessment, and research (e.g., fish habitat assessment and analysis; Figure 3) must be seen as a priority to ensure cooperative learning. There must be a strong relationship among management, research, and monitoring via cooperative learning. In addition, viewing management actions as experiments will promote learning and provide opportunities to practice and make errors. As Ohio and Ontario have learned through their RAP programs (Hartig et al. 1998), successful RAP processes:

- are innovative and achieve cooperative learning;
- have a strong relationship among management, research, and monitoring (i.e., knowledge from assessment, monitoring, and research provides the foundation for management action);
- treat management actions as experiments that test policy hypotheses;
- achieve broad-based public outreach and understanding; and
- develop strong partnerships to build the capacity to restore uses.

Although progress in ecosystem-based management is occurring, progress is not proceeding as rapidly as hoped because the problems are complex, government resources are generally declining, and many management agencies resist the shift from control to responsiveness. Current, major challenges for the Great Lakes include:

- sustaining creative ecosystem-based processes like RAPs in light of state, provincial, and federal budget cutbacks;
- addressing the need for fish habitat assessment and analysis (see Figure 3) via effective institutional arrangements among management, research, and monitoring entities;
- reaching agreement on a core set of ecosystem indicators (e.g., fishery, habitat) and allocating required resources to sustain monitoring programs; and
- exchanging successful experiences with modifying habitat to support fish stocks and communicating broadly both ecological and economic benefits of habitat rehabilitation and conservation.

One cannot emphasize enough the importance of adoption of strong habitat conservation and rehabilitation policy statements by all levels of government, including local governments in their "master plans" and "official plans." The Great Lakes Fishery Commission has developed a draft Binational Habitat Policy and Action Plan (www.glfc.org/habitat.html) that provides a strategic approach to habitat conservation and rehabilitation. Equally important is the recruitment and retention of trained habitat personnel to ensure that local and regional actions are consistent with such habitat policies. The current shortage of trained habitat personnel remains a critical management challenge in stemming the continuing trend of habitat loss and degradation in the Great Lakes basin ecosystem.

References

Baird, R. C. 1996. Toward new paradigms in coastal resource management: linkages and institutional effectiveness. Estuaries 19(2a):320–335.

Denison, D., G. Crawford, C. Silveri, and R. Hautau. 1998. Rehabilitation of Belle Isle lakes and canals. Pages 6–9 in L. A. Tulen, J. H. Hartig, D. M. Dolan, and J. H. H. Ciborowski, editors. Rehabilitating and conserving Detroit River habitats. Great Lakes Institute for Environmental Research Occasional Publication 1, Windsor, Ontario.

Environment Canada and U.S. Environmental Protection Agency. 1995. State of the Lakes. Burlington, Ontario and Chicago.

Environment Canada and U.S. Environmental Protection Agency. 1997. State of the Lakes. Burlington, Ontario and Chicago.

Eshenroder, R. L., M. E. Holey, T. K. Gorenflo, and R. D. Clark, Jr. 1995. Fish-community objectives for Lake Michigan. Great Lakes Fishery Commission Special Publication 95-3, Ann Arbor, Michigan.

GLFC (Great Lakes Fishery Commission). 1994. A joint strategic plan for management of Great Lakes fisheries. GLFC, Ann Arbor, Michigan.

Hall, J. D. 1997. Cootes Paradise Marsh: mid-summer checkup. Fish and Wildlife Habitat Rehabilitation Newsletter (Great Lakes 2000 Cleanup Fund) 3(2):1–3, Burlington, Ontario.

Hartig, J. H., and six coauthors. 1997. Quantifying targets for rehabilitating degraded areas of the Great Lakes. Environmental Management 21(5):713–723.

Hartig, J. H., J. R. M. Kelso, and C. Wooley. 1996. Are habitat rehabilitation initiatives uncoupled from aquatic resource management objectives in the Great Lakes? Canadian Journal of Fisheries and Aquatic Sciences 53(Supplement 1):424–431.

Hartig, J. H., and N. L. Law. 1994. Institutional frameworks to direct the development and implementation of Great Lakes remedial action plans. Environmental Management 18:855–864.

Hartig, J. H., and five coauthors. 1995. Capacity-building for restoring degraded areas in the Great Lakes. International Journal of Sustainable Development and World Ecology 2:1–10, Pearl River, New York.

Hartig, J. H., M. A. Zarull, T. M. Heidtke, and H. Shah. 1998. Implementing ecosystem-based management: lessons from the Great Lakes. Journal of Environmental Planning and Management 41(1):45–75, Oxfordshire, UK.

HHRAPWT (Hamilton Harbour Remedial Action Plan Writing Team). 1992. Remedial action plan for Hamilton Harbour. Goals, options, and recommendations, volume 2, main report, stage II RAP. HHRAPWT, Burlington, Ontario.

HHSG (Hamilton Harbour Stakeholder Group). 1991. The remedial action plan for Hamilton Harbour. HHSG, Burlington, Ontario.

Holling, C. S., and G. K. Meefe. 1995. Command and control and the pathology of natural resource management. Conservation Biology 10:328–337.

IJC (International Joint Commission). 1985. Report on Great Lakes water quality. Great Lakes Water Quality Board, Windsor, Ontario.

Illinois State Water Survey. 1994. Waukegan River restoration in urban parks. Land and Water 38(5):33–36.

Jones, M. L., and six coauthors. 1996. Assessing ecological effects of habitat change: moving beyond productive capacity. Canadian Journal of Fisheries and Aquatic Sciences 53(Supplement 1):446–457.

Karr, J. R., and D. R. Dudley. 1981. Ecological perspective on water quality goals. Environmental Management 5:55–68.

Koonce, J. F., and eight coauthors. 1996. A commentary on the role of institutional arrangements in the protection and restoration of habitat in the Great Lakes. Canadian Journal of Fisheries and Aquatic Sciences 53(Supplement 1):458–465.

Lychwick, T. 1995. Fox River walleye habitat improvement. Pages 272–281 *in* J. R. M. Kelso and J. H. Hartig, editors. Methods of modifying habitat to benefit the Great Lakes ecosystem. CISTI (Canada Institute for Scientific and Technical Information) Occasional Paper 1. National Research Council of Canada, Ottawa, Ontario.

Marsden, J. E. 1994. Spawning by stocked lake trout on shallow, inshore reefs in south-western Lake Michigan. Journal of Great Lakes Research 20:377–384.

Minns, C. K., S. E. Doka, C. N. Bakelaar, P. C. E. Brunette, and W. M. Schertzer. 1999. Identifying habitats essential for pike *Esox lucius L.* in the Long Point region of Lake Erie: a suitable supply approach. Pages 363–382 *in* L. R. Benaka, editor. Fish habitat: essential fish habitat and rehabilitation. American Fisheries Society, Symposium 22, Bethesda, Maryland.

Minns, C. K., R. G. Randall, J. E. Moore, and V. W Cairns. 1996. A model simulating the impact of habitat supply limits on northern pike, *Esox lucius*, in Hamilton Harbour, Lake Ontario. Canadian Journal of Fisheries and Aquatic Sciences 53(Supplement 1):20–34.

NRC (National Research Council), and the Royal Society of Canada. 1985. The Great Lakes Water Quality Agreement: an evolving instrument for ecosystem management. National Academy Press, Washington, D.C.

Richter, B. D., D. P. Braun, M. A. Mendelson, and L. L. Master. 1997. Threats to imperiled freshwater fauna. Conservation Biology 11:1081–1093.

Rodgers, G. K. 1992. Hamilton Harbour remedial action planning. Pages 59–72 *in* J. H. Hartig and M. A. Zarull, editors. Under RAPs: toward grassroots ecological democracy in the Great Lakes basin. University of Michigan Press, Ann Arbor.

Talhelm, D. R. 1988. Economics of Great Lakes fisheries: a 1985 assessment. Great Lakes Fishery Commission, Ann Arbor, Michigan.

United States and Canada. 1972. Great Lakes Water Quality Agreement. International Joint Commission, Windsor, Ontario.

United States and Canada. 1978. Great Lakes Water Quality Agreement. International Joint Commission, Windsor, Ontario.

United States and Canada. 1987. Protocol to the 1978 Great Lakes Water Quality Agreement. International Joint Commission, Windsor, Ontario.

USEPA (U. S. Environmental Protection Agency). 1998. Agenda for action. EPA-905-K-98-002, Chicago.

Westley, F. 1995. Governing design: the management of social systems and ecosystems management. Pages 391–427 *in* L. H. Gunderson, C. S. Holling, and S. S. Light, editors. Barriers and bridges to the renewal of ecosystems and institutions. Columbia University Press, New York.

American Fisheries Society Symposium 22:335–347, 1999

Artificial Reefs in Lake Erie:
Biological Impacts of Habitat Alteration

DAVID O. KELCH, FRED L. SNYDER, AND JEFFREY M. REUTTER

Ohio Sea Grant College Program, Ohio State University
1314 Kinnear Road, Columbus, Ohio 43212, USA

Abstract.—From 1984 to 1989, artificial reefs were constructed at two locations in central Lake Erie by Ohio State University's Sea Grant College Program. The goals of the construction projects were to improve sportfishing opportunity in nearshore waters, evaluate the effectiveness of reefs as fish-concentration devices, and eventually assist other coastal communities in developing artificial reef programs. From 1992 to 1995, we conducted evaluations to assess the effectiveness of these artificial reefs as sport fish attractors and to establish their value in sport fishery enhancement projects. Underwater VHS video was used by scuba divers to identify and enumerate fish at both artificial reef sites and at adjacent nonreef control sites. Observation dives were done monthly, weather permitting, from May through October each year. *T*-tests were used to determine seasonal differences in fish abundance between the reef and control sites. At both sites, total seasonal numbers of fish were significantly higher (20–50 times more) at the reef site than the control site ($p = 0.05$). Smallmouth bass *Micropterus dolomieu* were the dominant species at both reef sites, comprising over 80% of the observations during most months. Total seasonal numbers of smallmouth bass were also higher during spring and fall than in midsummer, suggesting seasonal patterns and preferences for artificial structure. We conclude that, when properly planned and located, artificial reefs would provide beneficial fish habitat along most of Lake Erie's nearshore zone and may have application Great Lakes-wide.

Lake Erie is well known for its sportfishing. The shallow western basin (average depth 8 m) with its numerous islands, shoals, and natural reefs, provides excellent angling opportunities, and the Port Clinton–Sandusky area has been rated among the top 10 sportfishing locations in the world. The central basin (average depth approximately 30 m) is also a productive sport fishery, yet it lacks the islands and natural reefs around which many fish congregate. Most of the angling effort in the central basin is concentrated far offshore. The bottom of the central basin is relatively flat and featureless.

In 1982, the newly formed North Central Ohio Sea Grant Advisory Committee reviewed a variety of strategies to enhance tourism and local economies by improving angling opportunities in the central basin of Lake Erie. Artificial reefs were discussed as a strategy that could permanently increase habitat diversity and provide permanent habitats that would concentrate fish and improve angler success rates (Prince et al. 1977; Myatt 1981). Ohio Sea Grant began the Lake Erie Artificial Reef Program in mid-1982 with assistance from the Ohio Department of Natural Resources and the U.S. Army Corps of Engineers.

An extensive body of literature evaluating artificial reef materials, design, and construction has been produced in recent years and is reviewed by Seaman and Sprague (1991). Although the beginning of this project predated many of these papers, construction methods and materials used in this project generally are in agreement with currently accepted guidelines for reef construction and monitoring (Gannon 1990; Bohnsack et al. 1991).

Initial tests for the program began in a small way with a project we refer to as our experimental project. Approximately 3,000 metric tons of broken sandstone material was placed offshore of Lakewood, Ohio in 12.2 m of water. This rubble was placed with a large, 6-compartment dump scow, creating 12 small, 1-to-2-m-high piles of material that were not connected to each other at their bases. These reefs were extremely difficult for anglers to locate. A two-year investigation on these reefs during 1985–1986 (Gerber 1987) and further literature review (Matthews 1981; D'Itri 1985) suggested the structures needed to be larger in profile, connected at the bases, on firmer bottom substrate, and in shallower water.

This paper discusses and evaluates artificial reef development efforts initiated in 1986 using the results from the above experimental study. We refer to these post-1986 projects as demonstration projects because studies like these are needed to determine whether artificial reefs are indeed a useful tool for habitat and sportfishing enhancement in Lake Erie.

Location (Potential artificial reef sites)   Site #1   Site #2   Site #3
Identify each site using land-based
  information and location data

Global positioning system coordinates:
  -each potential site: latitude and longitude

↓ Description of site criteria considerations ↓

Criteria: Determined for each potential site
1. Distance from safe harbor (nautical miles)
2. Availability of boater access sites
3. Commercial navigation conflicts
4. Recreational use conflicts
5. Water depths (feet and meters)
6. Months in which reef may be below thermocline
7. Necessary permits from regulatory agencies:
              - U. S. Army Corps of Engineers
              - U.S. Coast Guard
              - Shipping associations
              - Ohio Division of Wildlife
              - U.S. Environmental Protection Agency
 8. Waves and currents
 9. Ice scour effects
10. Shoreline property ownership onshore from reef site: potential conflicts
11. Reef goals and objectives:
              - recreational benefits
              - habitat benefits
              - biological benefits
              - economic development
12. Target users: anglers, scuba divers, researchers
13. Target species: walleye, yellow perch, smallmouth bass, others
14. Angler and diver use by season: potential conflicts
15. Bottom substrate type and contours
              -current geological maps available
              - fathometer paper graph recordings
              - substrate measurement:
                      - Matthew's hand method (diver)
                      - Penetrometer method (diver)
                      - other unique bottom features
16. Water quality concerns
17. Present use of potential site
18. Possible historic or ecological impacts
19. Potential impacts from exotic species
20. Aquatic macrophyte attachment and growth
21. Reef shape and size
22. Distance from water intakes and discharges
23. Sediment plumes
24. Possible erosion deposition effects
25. Marine contractor secured?
26. Who pays for marine contractor?
27. Concrete or rock rubble secured?
28. Waterfront storage location for rubble?
29. Other sponsor or funding organizations
30. Other considerations and concerns

FIGURE 1.—Simple decision matrix for artificial reef development in Lake Erie (criteria not listed in order of priority).

FIGURE 2.—Approximate locations of Lorain and Lakewood artificial reefs and control sites with respect to Lake Erie and the Ohio shoreline.

Site Selection Criteria, Program Development, and Construction Methods

Reefs can serve many purposes; however, some controversy exists regarding the question of whether artificial reefs increase regional fish production or simply serve to aggregate existing fishes (Grossman et al. 1997; Lindberg 1997). The goals for these demonstration projects were to concentrate fish, enhance angler success, and stimulate the local economies. Although it is quite likely that some successful spawning is occurring on these reefs, due to the reefs' small sizes it is doubtful that this spawning will have a significant positive impact on populations in the central basin.

In siting reefs, it is important to consider a number of variables that may impact the physical structure, user groups, and the biological integrity of the reefs (Figure 1). The artificial reef sites chosen for these projects were located within 1.2 km of shore at Lorain and Lakewood, Ohio (Figure 2), and were selected using the decision matrix presented in Figure 1.

From 1983 through 1989, funding was solicited from private and public sources to support the project; over US$180,000 were contributed. Major contributors included the Cuyahoga County Commissioners, the Polish Fishermen's Club of Lorain, and the Ohio Division of Wildlife. Funding was also secured from sportfishing tournaments, donations from local angler organizations and conservation clubs, collections at marinas and tackle shops, corporate donations, and private donations. Permits in the name of the Ohio Department of Natural Resources, Division of Wildlife, were obtained from

FIGURE 3.—Materials used for construction of artificial reefs at Lorain and Lakewood; reefs consisted of clean concrete, rock, and brick rubble. (Photo courtesy of D. O. Kelch, Ohio Sea Grant.)

FIGURE 4.—Flattop barge and front-end loader used at the Lorain and Lakewood artificial reef sites to better control placement of reef materials. (Photo courtesy of D. O. Kelch, Ohio Sea Grant.)

the U.S. Army Corps of Engineers for both reef locations. Sites to store donated reef material on land before construction were donated by the Ford Motor Company and Ontario Stone Company for the Lakewood reef and by the Lorain Pellet Terminal (LTV Steel Company) for the Lorain reef.

Materials used to construct Lake Erie's artificial reefs consisted of clean rock, concrete, and brick rubble (Figure 3). These materials were chosen to resemble naturally occurring reef material and topography, a concept later validated by Bohnsack et al. (1997). Materials were donated by a number of public entities, private businesses, and private citizens. In total, over

10,900 metric tons of rubble were donated, ranging in size from bricks to large concrete slabs measuring 2.0 m by 3.0 m by 0.4 m. All materials were inspected by the U.S. Army Corps of Engineers before placement in Lake Erie to ensure that quality standards were met.

Knowledge gained from the experimental reef project and research during 1984–1986 was used to modify the methods of artificial reef placement during 1986–1989. The first phase of the demonstration project began in 1986 with the placement of over 1,814 metric tons of reef material at Lorain. The reef site is located 1.6 km west of Lorain Harbor and 1.2 km offshore, in 8.5 m of water.

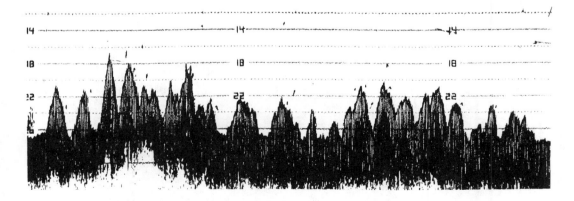

<<<<<<<<<<Approximate distance 457 meters>>>>>>>>>

FIGURE 5.—Original paper graph fathometer profile of the Lorain artificial reef, June 1990. (Lowrance Electronics model X-15 paper graph recorder; measurements in feet.)

TABLE 1.—List of common and scientific names of fishes (according to Robins et al. 1991) appearing in this study.

Family	Common name	Scientific name
Catostomidae	White sucker	*Catostomus commersoni*
	Shorthead redhorse	*Moxostoma macrolepidotum*
Centrarchidae	Rock bass	*Ambloplites rupestris*
	Smallmouth bass	*Micropterus dolomieu*
Clupeidae	Alewife	*Alosa pseudoharengus*
Cyprinidae	Goldfish	*Carassius auratus*
	Carp	*Cyprinus carpio*
Gobiidae	Round goby	*Neogobius melanostomus*
Ictaluridae	Channel catfish	*Ictalurus punctatus*
Percichthyidae	White perch	*Morone americana*
	White bass	*Morone chrysops*
Percidae	Yellow perch	*Perca flavescens*
	Logperch	*Percina caprodes*
	Walleye	*Stizostedion vitreum*
Sciaenidae	Freshwater drum	*Aplodinotus grunniens*

Materials were placed using a flattop barge rather than the dump scow that had been used for the first project. Concrete rubble was loaded onto the barge and towed to the reef location. The barge was secured into position using vertical spud bars, and the material was pushed off with a front-end loader (Figure 4). Marker buoys were placed on each side of the barge to ensure accurate placement of the rubble. The heights of the piles of reef material were determined using a bottom sonar graph recorder. This construction strategy proved far superior to the dump scow used previously and allowed us to create a reef with piles that were not only contiguous but also of desired height.

During 1987, the demonstration project at the Lakewood site began. The same basic methods used at Lorain in 1986 were employed, although the barge was

larger and a crane was used in addition to a front-end loader. The crane was used to place material in the gaps between piles made by the front-end loader, thus making it easier to create a contiguous set of piles or mounds. Over 3,446 metric tons of concrete and rock rubble were placed at the Lakewood location, creating an artificial reef over 243 m in length. The reef site is located 3.7 km west of Cleveland Harbor and 3.7 km east of Rocky River, 0.8 km offshore in 8.5 m of water. This nearshore reef location is approximately 0.8 km south of the 1984 experimental reef site.

During 1988 and 1989, over 5,635 additional metric tons of material were added to the Lorain location, creating a second artificial reef at this site. The first reef, known as the Polish Fishermen's Club Reef, is approximately 457 m in length. The second reef, called The Mountain, is approximately 243 m in length and is located parallel to and 91 m north of the first reef. The additional construction at Lorain was possible due to reduced marine contracting costs. This completed the construction phase of the demonstration project.

Both the Lorain and Lakewood artificial reefs are parallel to shore in 8.5 m of water (Figure 2). From above, the reefs appear to be in a snaking, sawtooth arrangement. The reef material is in contiguous mounds connected at the bases, allowing fish to move along the entire length of the reefs. The mounds vary in height from approximately 2–4 m (Figure 5).

Anecdotal Information from Anglers

Within two weeks after the first materials were placed in 1986, the authors began to receive reports from anglers of catches of yellow perch *Perca flavescens* and smallmouth bass *Micropterus dolomieu* from the artificial reef at

TABLE 2.—Total numbers of taxa and fish observed in 1992 at the Lorain artificial reef and Lorain control sites using mobile and stationary cameras. (Totals are less and greater than 100% due to rounding.)

Species	Artificial reef number	Control site number	Artificial reef % of total	Control site % of total
Smallmouth bass	1,057	16	93.62	29.10
Yellow perch	17		1.51	
Logperch	17		1.51	
Walleye	6	2	0.53	3.64
Freshwater drum	5	28	0.44	50.91
Rock bass	4		0.35	
Unidentified	23	9	2.03	16.36
Total	1,129	55	99.99	100.01

Lorain. Similar reports were received shortly after the Lakewood reef was constructed in 1987. Reports of catches of numerous smallmouth bass, yellow perch, walleye *Stizostedion vitreum*, rock bass *Ambloplites rupestris*, freshwater drum *Aplodinotus grunniens*, white bass *Morone chrysops*, white perch *Morone americana*, and channel catfish *Ictalurus punctatus* have continued to come in from both sites. In addition, since 1996, anglers have frequently caught and submitted specimens of the round goby *Neogobius melanostomus*, documenting the westward expansion of this nonindigenous species from the waters offshore of Fairport Harbor, Ohio, where it originally was reported (Charlebois et al. 1997). Fish species pursued and caught by local anglers vary by season. (Table 1 lists common and scientific names of all fishes cited in this study.)

The artificial reefs have attracted more than just fish and anglers. When the artificial reefs were planned in 1982, zebra mussels had not yet invaded Lake Erie. Discovered in Lake Erie's western basin in 1988 (Snyder et al. 1990), the mussels rapidly spread throughout the lake. By 1991, zebra mussels had covered an estimated 75–80% of the artificial reef substrate at both reef locations. With greater water clarity induced by zebra mussel filtration, scuba divers found the artificial reefs to be good places to visit. For divers, the reefs provide an abundance of fish life to observe and photograph, a great location to search for lost anchors and fishing lures, and a marked, shallow-water area close to ports. Furthermore, few angler–diver use conflicts have been reported.

Biological Assessment Methods

Fish population assessments were done during 1992 and 1993 at the Lorain artificial reef and during 1994 and 1995 at the Lakewood artificial reef. Water clarity due to reductions in phosphorous loading and filtration by zebra mussels made possible the use of underwater VHS video to identify and enumerate fish on the artificial reefs and adjacent, nonreef control sites.

Professional scuba divers from Underwater, Inc., based in Elyria, Ohio, were contracted to perform the monthly underwater VHS video assessment. The divers were expert underwater photographers and were instructed in research procedures by the first author, who also accompanied them on many dives. The camera used for the project was a Sony CCD-V99 high resolution,

8-mm video camcorder, housed in an Aqua-Video underwater housing that provided full external control features.

Data collection occurred on the 15th day of each month, ± a 5-d window of opportunity, from May through October. Weather and water clarity conditions dictated when the dive was made within the 10-d period. Adverse conditions prevented some data collection. All dives were conducted between the hours of 10:00 a.m. and 2:00 p.m. Data were collected during 1992–1993 at the 457-m Lorain artificial reef and during 1994–1995 at the 243-m Lakewood artificial reef. Control sites, located 1,800 m from each artificial reef, also were assessed to provide nonreef comparisons. Each control site was located in the same depth of water and had the same bottom composition as the artificial reef site but possessed no features higher in profile than 0.3 m. For each dive, the research vessel was secured to a permanent marker buoy, which was located in the center of the artificial reef system.

During the 1992–1993 study of the Lorain artificial reef, two underwater video assessment strategies were employed: (1) a stationary video camera assessment with the camera mounted on a tripod in the same location each month, and (2) a mobile assessment with the diver swimming with the camera along a predetermined and repeatable route. The stationary camera technique was used to identify and enumerate any fish species that might avoid divers. After the camera was placed on the tripod, the divers returned to the vessel, and the camera recorded for one hour before being retrieved.

Immediately following the stationary assessment, the divers swam with the underwater camera along a 91-m transect on the south (or nearshore) side of the artificial reef. The divers then crossed over the top of the reef and swam back to the starting point on the open-lake (or north) side of the artificial reef. The entire dive took approximately 30 min, and throughout the dive the divers maintained their relative position along the sides of the reef approximately 2–3 m from the top. The diver operating the camcorder panned the camera slowly from left to right, and also up and down, at a 30° angle. This permitted us to record fish slightly above and to the sides of the camera. Immediately following the reef dive, the divers moved to the control site, where the same assessment procedures were performed.

A review of the data from the 1992 and 1993 assessments at the Lorain site showed that the stationary camera observations were of little value—no fish spe-

TABLE 3. —Total numbers of taxa and fish observed in 1993 at the Lorain artificial reef and Lorain control sites using mobile and stationary cameras. (Totals are greater and less than 100% due to rounding.)

Species	Artificial reef number	Control site number	Artificial reef % of total	Control site % of total
Smallmouth bass	1,366	112	94.60	58.64
Logperch	16		1.11	
Rock bass	9		0.62	
Shorthead redhorse	9		0.62	
Alewife	6		0.42	
Yellow perch	5		0.35	
Freshwater drum	5	60	0.35	31.41
Carp		4		2.09
White sucker	3		0.21	
Walleye	2	3	0.14	1.57
White perch	1		0.07	
Unknown	22	12	1.52	6.28
Total	1,444	191	100.01	99.99

cies were observed that had not also been observed by the mobile camera. Consequently, the stationary camera technique was not used during our 1994 and 1995 assessments at the Lakewood artificial reef site.

Results

Lorain Artificial Reef, 1992 and 1993

One of our initial concerns with our observation technique was whether the underwater VHS camcorder could provide images of fish clear and

sharp enough to allow identification to the species level and thus result in quantitative data suitable for statistical analysis. A review of the 1992 and 1993 data (Tables 2 and 3) showed that this was not a problem as we were able to identify 97–98% of all fish observed each year to the species level (D. O. Kelch and F. L. Snyder, unpublished data). Differences in mean numbers of fish observed on the reefs versus the control sites were subjected to the Student's t-test (Mendenhall and Ott 1972), which determines significant differences among small-sample means.

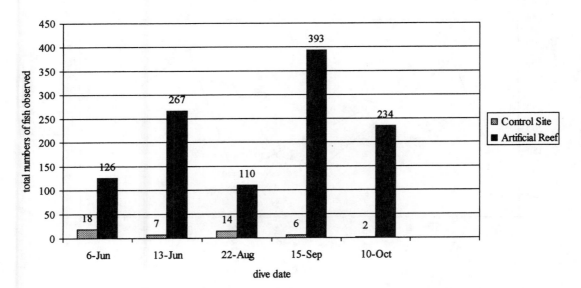

FIGURE 6.—Total numbers of fish observed in 1992 at the Lorain artificial reef and control sites using mobile and stationary cameras.

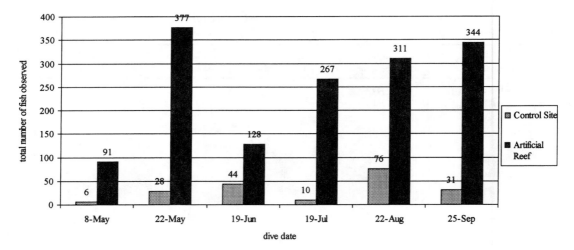

FIGURE 7.—Total numbers of fish observed in 1993 at the Lorain artificial reef and control sites using mobile and stationary cameras.

A summary of the data from 1992 showed more total fish observed at the reef than at the control site (Figure 6). Smallmouth bass was the most abundant species observed at the reef site (1,057 individuals or 93.6% of all fish observed), while freshwater drum were the most numerous at the control site (28 individuals or 50.9% of all fish observed) (Table 2). Furthermore, in 1992 the reef site attracted significantly more fish when all species were combined (1,129) than the control site (55) (a = 0.01). We also evaluated the ability of the reef to concentrate smallmouth bass. Numbers of other fish species were too low for statistical analysis. Results indicated the reef held significantly more smallmouth bass than the control site (a = 0.01).

The 1993 data summary (Figure 7) revealed similar results to the 1992 observations. Smallmouth bass were again the most abundant species at the artificial reef site, comprising 1,366 individuals or 94.6% of all fish observed (Table 3). Numbers at the control site also were dominated by smallmouth bass (112 individuals or 58.6% of all fish observed), with freshwater drum second in abundance (60 individuals or 31.4% of the total) (Table 3). Again in

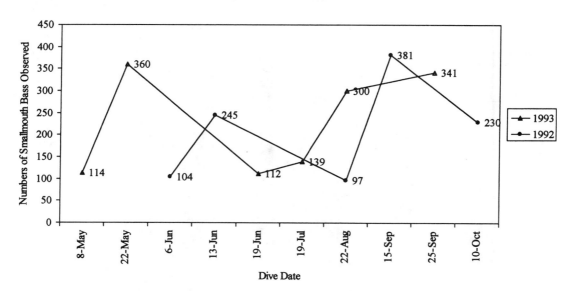

FIGURE 8.—Seasonal trends in smallmouth bass, 1992 and 1993, at the Lorain artificial reef using mobile and stationary cameras.

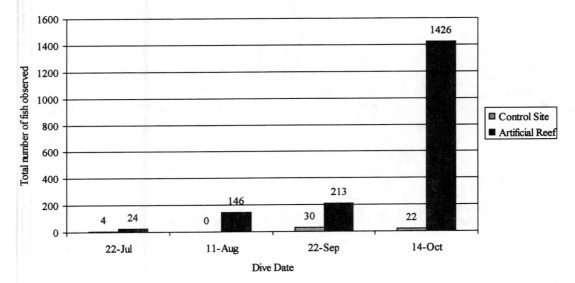

FIGURE 9.—Total numbers of fish observed in 1994 at the Lakewood artificial reef and control sites using mobile camera only.

1993, the reef site attracted significantly more fish (1,444) than the control site (191) (a = 0.05) and significantly more smallmouth bass (a = 0.05). Total numbers of smallmouth bass also were observed to be higher during the spring and fall months, especially in 1993, suggesting possible seasonal preferences (Figure 8). Anecdotal angler data reported to the authors also support this observation of seasonal preferences.

Lakewood Artificial Reef, 1994 and 1995

The same assessment techniques and methods used at Lorain were employed during 1994 and 1995 at the Lakewood reef site, except, as previously discussed, the stationary camera was not used. Observations from Lakewood during both 1994 (Figure 9) and 1995 (Figure 10) showed considerably more fish at the reef than the control site. A summary of the data from 1994 revealed that smallmouth bass

TABLE 4.—Total numbers of taxa and fish observed in 1994 at the Lakewood artificial reef and Lakewood control sites using mobile camera only. (Totals are greater than 100% due to rounding.)

Species	Artificial reef number	Control site number	Artificial reef % of total	Control site % of total
Smallmouth bass	1,477	51	81.65	91.11
Rock bass	205		11.33	
Walleye	53		2.92	
Freshwater drum	22	4	1.22	7.14
Catostomidae sp.	12		0.67	
Carp	7	1	0.39	1.79
Shorthead redhorse	6		0.33	
Yellow perch	4		0.22	
Goldfish	2		0.11	
Percidae sp.	1		0.06	
Unknown	20		1.11	
Total	1,809	56	100.01	100.04

TABLE 5.—Total numbers of taxa and fish observed in 1995 at the Lakewood artificial reef and Lakewood control sites using mobile camera only.

Species	Artificial reef number	Control site number	Artificial reef % of total	Control site % of total
Rock bass	282		30.45	
Smallmouth bass	278	14	30.02	56.00
Logperch	178		19.22	
Yellow perch	95	1	10.26	4.00
Freshwater drum	35	5	3.78	20.00
Walleye	25	1	2.70	4.00
Carp	14		1.51	
Shorthead redhorse	2		0.22	
Catostomidae sp.	6		0.65	
Channel catfish	1		0.11	
Round goby		1		4.00
Unknown	10	3	1.08	12.00
Total	926	25	100.00	100.00

was the most abundant species observed at the reef site (1,477 individuals or 81.6% of all fish observed), followed by rock bass (205 individuals or 11.3% of all fish observed) and walleye (53 individuals or 2.9% of all fish observed) (Table 4). Smallmouth bass was also the most abundant species observed at the control site during 1994 (51 individuals or 91% of all fish observed) (Table 4).

Although many more fish were observed on the reef in 1994 (1,809 total, 1,477 smallmouth bass) than at the control site (56 total fish, 51 smallmouth bass), the differences were not statistically significant due to small sample size and wide variability, induced by a seasonal peak of smallmouth bass during autumn (Figure 9). The empirical differences, however are quite clear.

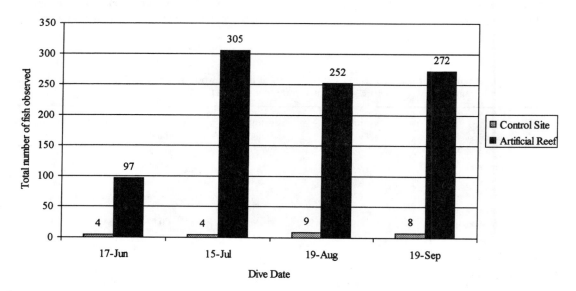

FIGURE 10.—Total numbers of fish observed in 1995 at the Lakewood artificial reef and control sites using mobile camera only.

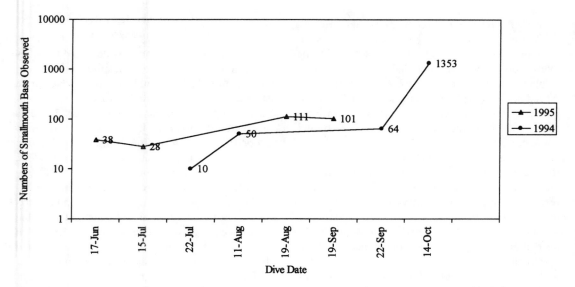

FIGURE 11.—Seasonal trends in smallmouth bass, 1994 and 1995, at the Lakewood artificial reef using mobile camera only.

A summary of the data collected during 1995 showed that rock bass was the most abundant species (282 individuals or 30% of all fish observed) on the artificial reef, followed closely by smallmouth bass (278 individuals or 30% of all fish observed, Table 5). At the control site, smallmouth bass was again the most abundant species (14 fish or 56% of all fish observed) (Table 5). In 1995, the total number of fish observed at the reef (926) and the total number of smallmouth bass (278) were both significantly greater ($a = 0.05$) than the corresponding numbers from the control site (25 total fish and 14 smallmouth bass) (Table 5).

Seasonal preference by smallmouth bass for the Lakewood artificial reef during 1994 and 1995 (Figure 11) are similar to preference observed at Lorain during 1992 and 1993 (Figure 8)—more abundant during the late spring and fall. However, the absence of Lakewood data from May during both years, in June during 1994, and in October during 1995 (Figures 9 and 10) due to boat breakdown and weather and visibility conditions makes this comparison difficult. Despite this lack of video data, anecdotal data from Lakewood artificial reef anglers tend to support the suggestion that the preference exhibited by smallmouth bass toward the Lakewood reef is similar to the preference exhibited by smallmouth bass toward the Lorain reef.

Discussion

During 1992 and 1993, the Lorain artificial reef concentrated fish in numbers, depending upon the observation period, 20–60 times greater than the nonreef control site. Observations at Lakewood from 1994 and 1995 indicated that total fish numbers observed on the artificial reef were 32–37 times greater than those observed at the control site. These artificial reefs also concentrated smallmouth bass, depending upon the observation period, from 12 to 66 times more than the control site at Lorain, and from 20 to 29 times more than the control site at Lakewood. Furthermore, these differences were statistically significant for three of four years (1992, 1993, and 1995) and empirically significant for all four years, for both smallmouth bass and total fish. These results clearly demonstrate that artificial reefs constructed of clean concrete and rock rubble and placed in the nearshore waters of the central basin of Lake Erie are effective fish aggregators, particularly for smallmouth bass.

Recent literature has examined concerns that artificial reefs may serve primarily as fish attractors while contributing little to overall fish production (Lindberg 1997; Bortone 1998). In some cases this attraction could result in local overharvest of sport fish. These artificial reefs were developed as fish concentration devices for sport angler use and were not intended to provide spawning habitat that would measurably increase fish production. Lake Erie fish stock overviews published by the Ohio Department of Natural Resources, Division of Wildlife (ODNR 1998) portray popular sport fish species as being stable or increasing and not subject to overharvest. Anecdotal angler reports indicate that a variety of fish species are being caught on and around the artificial reefs, including walleye, yellow perch, and white bass.

An economic evaluation by Glenn et al. (1994) revealed that during 1992, the most sought-after and kept species by anglers fishing the Lorain artificial reef was walleye, followed by yellow perch and then by smallmouth bass. Our data, however, contained few observations of walleye or yellow perch and instead clearly showed a preponderance of smallmouth bass and rock bass using the reefs (Tables 2, 3, 4, and 5). This supports observations by Bohnsack et al. (1991) that centrarchids respond particularly well to artificial reef structures. Annual Lake Erie smallmouth bass harvest statistics show a steady increase both in harvest and angler effort directed at smallmouth since 1985. Creel survey data suggest that 8 of 10 smallmouth bass caught are released by Lake Erie anglers (ODNR 1998), which can reduce the impact of fishing effort.

Data collection using underwater video to enumerate and identify fish to the species level proved to be an effective technique in Lake Erie. Ten years ago, before the invasion of zebra mussels and further reductions in phosphorus loading (which lowered plankton density), poor visibility would have made this technique impossible. The use of underwater video for research offers many advantages. In this study we were pleased with our ability to gather accurate data without harming specimens or damaging the habitat, as well as our ability to store the results in a format that allows other scientists, managers, and the general public to see the raw observations recorded on each dive.

A limitation of this study is that all data were collected between 10:00 a.m. and 2:00 p.m. to take advantage of maximum light availability and improve the quality of the video results. Therefore, it is possible that crepuscular and nocturnal species are underrepresented in our results.

The Lorain reef is very popular with anglers and has been an economic success, generating annual economic benefits 2.7 times the cost of developing the reef (Glenn et al. 1994). (For more details of the reef's economic benefits, see Hushak et al. 1999, this volume.)

The Future of Artificial Reefs in Lake Erie and the Great Lakes

This assessment effort was designed to determine whether artificial reefs constructed in the central basin of Lake Erie could attract and concentrate fish in a manner that would improve the sport fishery in this portion of the lake. The artificial reefs constructed at Lorain and Lakewood have proven to be popular with recreational anglers and scuba divers. The reefs aggregate both fish and anglers, and research has shown the reefs' value.

Although we consider these reefs to be remarkable successes, we continue to recommend caution when considering artificial reef construction in the Great Lakes as we do not believe every reef will be as successful. In designing this program, we selected what we considered to be the best location for artificial reef construction in the Great Lakes—the central basin of Lake Erie—a basin with high production potential but little natural relief. Within that basin, we selected some of the most suitable locations by applying all of the site selection criteria from Figure 1. Recognizing that this was a demonstration and a test, we selected only the best materials for use in reef construction (Gannon 1990). These materials were designed to remain in the lake based on the knowledge that any reef program would be significantly harmed if reef materials were washed up onto local beaches.

We make the above points because anyone constructing reefs in the future will certainly be contacted, as we were, by individuals with unsuitable materials (e.g., old tires, wooden structures, boats, cars, etc.) that are not as permanent as the material used in these projects. We believe that properly constructed artificial reefs can be "environmental endowments," that is, they are paid for when constructed but produce benefits for the environment and local community well into the future. However, this certainly will not be the case if reefs are poorly placed or if inferior materials are used.

During February 1996, the city of Cleveland and the National Football League announced their plans to build a new football stadium. Ohio Sea Grant urged the city to consider using rubble from the old stadium to build artificial reefs offshore of Cleveland. Many months of investigation and feasibility studies followed. During October and November 1997, the city of Cleveland constructed three artificial reefs from the old stadium rubble, with a total length in excess of 355 m, in 9.7 m of water. The Ohio State University Sea Grant College Program has been charged with the biological assessment of these new reefs and will begin research efforts during 1998.

References

Bohnsack, J. A., A. M. Ecklund, and A. M. Szmant. 1997. Artificial reef research: is there more than the attraction–production issue? Fisheries 22(4):14–16.

Bohnsack, J. D., D. L. Johnson, and R. F. Ambrose. 1991. Ecology of artificial habitats and fishes. Pages 61–107 in W. Seaman Jr. and L. M. Sprague, editors. Artificial habitats for marine and freshwater fishes. Academic Press, San Diego.

Bortone, S. A. 1998. Resolving the attraction-production dilemma in artificial reef research: some yays and nays. Fisheries 23(3):6–10.

Charlebois, P. M., J. E. Marsden, R. G. Goettel, R. K. Wolfe, D. J. Jude, and S. Rudnika. 1997. The round goby, Neogobius melanostomus (Pallas), a review of European and North American literature. Illinois-Indiana Sea Grant Program and Illinois Natural History Survey. INHS Special Publication 20, Champaign, Illinois.

D'Itri, F. M., editor. 1985. Artificial reefs: marine and freshwater applications. Lewis Publishers, Chelsea, Michigan.

Gannon, J. E. 1990. International position statement and evaluation guidelines for artificial reefs in the Great Lakes. Great Lakes Fishery Commission Special Publication 90-2, Ann Arbor, Michigan.

Gerber, J. M. 1987. Fish use of artificial reefs in the central basin of Lake Erie. Master's thesis. The Ohio State University, Columbus.

Glenn, S. J., D. O. Kelch, and L. J. Hushak. 1994. Economic evaluation of the Lorain County artificial reef in 1992: an overview. Ohio Sea Grant Technical Summary OHSU-TS-022, The Ohio State University, Columbus.

Grossman G. D., G. P. Jones, and W. J. Seaman, Jr. 1997. Do artificial reefs increase fish production? A review of existing data. Fisheries 22(4):17–23.

Hushak, L. J., D. O. Kelch, and S. J. Glenn. 1999. The economic value of the Lorain County, Ohio, artificial reef. Pages 348–362 in L. R. Benaka, editor. Fish habitat: essential fish habitat and rehabilitation. American Fisheries Society, Symposium 22, Bethesda, Maryland.

Lindberg, W. J. 1997. Can science resolve the attraction-production issue? Fisheries 22(4):10–13.

Matthews, H. 1981. Artificial reef site selection and evaluation. Pages 50–54 in D. Y. Aska, editor. Artificial reefs: conference proceedings. Florida Sea Grant Report 41, University of Florida, Gainesville.

Mendenhall, W., and L. Ott. 1972. Understanding statistics. Duxbury Press, Belmont, California.

Myatt, D. O. 1981. Planning considerations for reef construction. Pages 41–49 in D. Y. Aska, editor. Artificial reefs: conference proceedings. Florida Sea Grant Report 41, University of Florida, Gainesville.

ODNR (Ohio Department of Natural Resources). 1998. Ohio's Lake Erie fisheries. Federal Aid in Sport Fish Restoration Project F-69-P. ODNR, Columbus.

Prince, E. D., O. E. Maughan, and P. Brouda. 1977. How to build a freshwater artificial reef. Virginia Sea Grant Report VIP-SG-77-02, Virginia Polytechnic Institute and State University, Blacksburg.

Robins, R. C., and six coauthors. 1991. Common and scientific names of fishes from the United States and Canada, 5th edition. American Fisheries Society, Special Publication 20, Bethesda, Maryland.

Seaman, W. Jr., and L. M. Sprague. 1991. Artificial habitats for marine and freshwater fishes. Academic Press, San Diego, California.

Snyder, F. L., M. B. Hilgendorf, and D. W. Garton. 1990. Zebra mussels in North America: the invasion and its implications. Ohio Sea Grant College Program Fact Sheet OHSU-FS-045 (revised 1997), The Ohio State University, Columbus.

American Fisheries Society Symposium 22:348–362, 1999

The Economic Value of the Lorain County, Ohio, Artificial Reef

LEROY J. HUSHAK, DAVID O. KELCH, AND SOPHIA J. GLENN

Ohio Sea Grant College Program
1314 Kinnear Road, Columbus, Ohio 43212, USA

Abstract.—Ohio constructed two artificial reefs beginning in 1986 in Lorain and Cuyahoga counties. The reefs were a demonstration project to evaluate the effects of reefs on fishing satisfaction and the feasibility of reef construction in other areas. Evaluation of the effects of reefs on recreational activity was viewed as essential for further reef development in Ohio and other Great Lakes states. A two-pronged research effort was undertaken: an underwater video investigation and a travel cost study. The travel cost study estimated the economic value derived from use of the Lorain County reef by sport anglers and divers. The results of this research were critical in supporting construction of a large artificial reef off the coast in Cleveland (Cuyahoga County) using rubble from the old Cleveland Stadium. From April to October 1992, 850 individuals who were willing to participate were contacted at Lorain County marinas and launch ramps. In early February 1993, these individuals were mailed questionnaires, with a second questionnaire mailed to nonrespondents in late February. Fifty-five percent responded. We estimated three alternative single-equation travel cost models. The most conservative estimate of consumer surplus (economic value) showed that the typical angler who used the reef in 1991 made nearly 10 more fishing trips during 1992 than the typical angler who did not use the reef in 1991, that is, nearly 26 trips in 1992 compared to 16 trips in 1992 by those who did not use the reef in 1991. The most conservative estimate of consumer surplus also showed that anglers who used the reef before 1992 valued total angling activity at US$302 more for the year 1992 than anglers who did not use the reef before 1992. When aggregated across all Lorain County anglers using the reef during 1991, the total value of the reef was $276,000 in 1992 compared to total construction costs of less than $100,000. Thus, the consumer surplus generated by the reef in one year exceeded construction costs by a wide margin.

Before 1984, the Lake Erie walleye *Stizostedion vitreum* fishery was primarily a western basin fishery. Between 1984 and 1992, there was a significant increase in walleye catch rates in the central basin relative to catch rates between 1975 and 1983 (Anonymous 1993). The increased catch rates in the central basin resulted from the eastward migration of walleye from the western basin during the early 1980s due to a growing walleye population. Between 1980 and 1983, the average catch rate (fish catch per angler-hour) for the central basin was 0.14, and this rate increased to 0.36 between 1984 and 1992. Between 1980 and 1983, western-basin catch rate averaged 0.41 and increased to 0.50 between 1984 and 1992.

The increased catch rates in the central basin greatly improved the opportunity for a central basin walleye fishery. However, because the central basin of Lake Erie is deeper than the western basin, and because the walleye are located further offshore, access to the fish was more difficult. The location of an artificial reef in the central basin became an attractive opportunity. Placing an artificial habitat in the central basin could help develop and increase the

recreational economy of central basin communities by making walleye and other fish species more accessible to a larger number of anglers.

Two artificial reefs were constructed beginning in 1986 in Lorain and Cuyahoga counties, Ohio (Kelch et al. 1999, this volume). The reefs were a demonstration project undertaken by Ohio Sea Grant in 1982 to evaluate the effects of reefs on fishing satisfaction and the feasibility of reef construction in other areas. Evaluation of the effects of reefs on recreational activity was viewed as essential for further Great Lakes reef development in Ohio and other Great Lakes states. A two-pronged research effort was undertaken: an underwater video investigation (Kelch et al. 1999) and a travel cost study reported in this chapter. The results of this research were critical in supporting construction of a large artificial reef off the coast in Cleveland (Cuyahoga County) using rubble from the old Cleveland Stadium.

The general objective of the travel cost study was to estimate the economic value derived from use of the Lorain County reef by sport anglers and divers. To accomplish this general objective, several specific objectives were required. The first objective was to estimate an economic model from which economic value could be estimated. We chose the travel cost demand approach, which estimates economic value based on observed behavior, in contrast to the contingent value approach, which asks respondents to answer hypothetical questions about how they value a resource in a given setting. A second objective was to specify a reef effect in the travel cost demand function to test whether people using the reef achieved greater value from angling or diving than people not using the reef. The third objective was to estimate the economic value of the reef from the reef effect. To proceed to estimation of economic value, several hypotheses were tested: (1) the regression model should explain a significant amount of the variance in angling behavior, and (2) each of the estimated coefficients of the regression equation should have the expected sign. The details of the statistical tests are discussed later in this chapter.

Database

From April to October 1992, 850 individuals who were willing to participate in the survey were contacted at Lorain County marinas and launch ramps. In early February 1993, these individuals were mailed questionnaires, with a second questionnaire mailed to nonrespondents in late February. A random prize drawing was held among respondents to increase the response rate. The response rate was a very respectable 55%, or 468 respondents. However, in many cases in this study the number reporting (N) is far less because respondents did not answer all questions affirmatively.

All of the respondents were contacted in Lorain County, and 52% of the respondents lived in this county. The second largest group of respondents, 23%, came from adjacent Cuyahoga County. The respondents' ages ranged from 23 to 82 years with an average age of 51. The average household size was 2.7 persons. In terms of marital status, 79% of the respondents were married, 10% were single, 9% were divorced, and 2% were widowed. About 98% of the respondents were male.

About 41% of the respondents had an education above the high school level. About 17% of the respondents had annual gross incomes below US$20,000, and 64% of the respondents had incomes between $20,000 and $60,000 per year. Full-time jobs were held by 60% of the respondents, and 32% were retired. The remaining 8% were unemployed, employed on a part-time basis, or seasonally employed.

Because respondents were contacted at a Lorain County site, all respondents made at least one recreational trip to U.S. sites at Lake Erie during 1992. An average of 28 trips per person per year were taken, with an average of 1.5 d per trip. In addition to one or more visits to Lorain County sites, 74% of respondents visited western Lake Erie (Ottawa or Erie counties), and 42% of respondents visited Cuyahoga County sites. Of all survey respondents, 93% stated that they had visited U.S. recreational sites at Lake Erie during 1991. The average number of trips reported for 1991 was 25, and the average trip length was 1.5 d per visit. Approximately 90% of the respondents indicated they would visit U.S. Lake Erie recreation sites during 1993 and that they expected to make an average of 28 trips.

Nearly 82% of the respondents owned a boat, and 43% of these boat owners used their boats in bodies of water other than Lake Erie. Boat owners used their boats on average 37 times during 1992. Respondents used their boats 78% of the time for fishing, followed by 17% for pleasure boating. The remaining 5% was divided among water-skiing, diving, and business-related boating.

Lorain County Trips

During 1992 respondents made an average of 20 trips to Lorain County with an average trip duration of 1.4 d. The average distance traveled was 35 mi. Because 52% of the respondents were from Lorain County, most of them were located near one of the recreational sites in Lorain County. Over 75% of the respondents reported recreational trips to Lorain County during 1991. An average of 22 trips were made with a trip duration of approximately 2 d. About 75% of the respondents expected to make approximately 25 trips to Lorain County during 1993.

The typical group contained three people, and 52% of these groups stayed overnight. The average party of three staying 1.4 d spent an average of $252 per trip, of which 29% was spent at home before the trip and 71% was spent on-site during the trip. The largest expenditures were gas and oil for boats (22%); fishing equipment, that is, gear and bait (16%); and boating supplies and repairs (15%).

Of the individuals who reported their recreational trips to Lorain County during 1992, 94% reported fishing or scuba diving (Table 1). For example, 388 respondents reported an average of 19.7 fishing trips to Lorain County during 1992, while 367 reported that their trip duration averaged

TABLE 1.—Number of scuba diving and fishing trips per individual and trip duration in days for Lorain County, 1992, as reported by survey respondents.

	Number of trips		Trip duration (days)	
Activity	Mean	Number of respondents	Mean	Number of respondents
Fishing	19.69	388	1.47	367
Scuba diving	10.20	15	1.42	12
Fishing and scuba diving	10.09	11	1.33	9

1.5 d. Nearly 92% of anglers looked for particular species when fishing such as smallmouth bass *Micropterus dolomieu* or walleye. The average fishing day was about 6.5 h, where 237 respondents reported catching and keeping an average of 17.7 yellow perch *Perca flavescens* per day, while 323 anglers caught and kept 2.9 walleye per day.

Artificial Reef Trips

The existence of the artificial reef was acknowledged by 87% of the respondents who made recreational trips to Lorain County in 1992, and 64% of respondents stated that they went fishing or scuba diving on the artificial reef during 1992. About 35% of respondents indicated that they went fishing or scuba diving at the reef before 1992. The respondents indicated that they liked utilizing the reef because it was close to shore, because the catch was good, and because it was a marked area. Over two-thirds of respondents traveling less than 40 mi to their Lorain County recreation site used the artificial reef while less than one-half of respondents traveling 40 or more miles used the reef. Table 2 shows the number of respondents, the number of recreational trips made, and the hours spent per day at the reef. For example, 246 respondents reported an average of 7.1 fishing trips to the reef during 1992, while 236 respondents reported spending 5.9 h of their average fishing day at the reef.

When fishing on the reef, 74% of the respondents reporting (245) indicated that they fished for a particular species. Many respondents reported targeting more than one species. More anglers reported targeting walleye (203 respondents) than smallmouth bass (97 respondents) or yellow perch (126 respondents). Nearly 82% of the 203 respondents targeting walleye fished for the species on the reef during the summer; 102 of those respondents reported keeping 2.1 walleye, and 37 respondents reported releasing 1.9 walleye per angler-day while fishing the reef.

Of those respondents who reported harvesting walleye in Lorain County during 1992, about 30% reported harvesting walleye from the reef, while 17% of respondents releasing walleye released fish caught on the reef. The harvest and release rates for yellow perch were similar at 27% and 21%, respectively. About 34% of anglers who harvested smallmouth bass from Lorain County harvested fish from the reef, while 42% of those releasing smallmouth bass released bass caught on the reef.

Of the 323 anglers who reported catching and keeping an average of 2.9 walleye per angler-day on 20 trips in Lorain County, 102 anglers reported keeping 2.1 walleye per angler-day on 7.1 trips to the reef. If we assume similar group size and trip duration, the reef accounts for about 8% of walleye harvest and about 8% of the catch and release by anglers who fish from Lorain County sites. For yellow perch, both reef-associated catches are less than

TABLE 2.—Number of scuba diving and fishing trips to the reef per individual and number of hours spent at the reef per day for the Lorain County artificial reef area, 1992, as reported by survey respondents.

	Number of trips to reef		Hours spent at reef per day	
Activity	Mean	Number of respondents	Mean	Number of respondents
Fishing	7.1	246	5.9	236
Scuba diving	4.0	8	5.3	6
Fishing and scuba diving	7.0	3	8.0	3

5% of the total, while the reef accounts for 13% of smallmouth bass harvest and 30% of smallmouth bass catch and release (Glenn et al. 1994).

Methodology

In this study, the travel cost or proxy demand approach was used to estimate the economic value of the Lorain County artificial reef in contrast to the contingent value approach. The travel cost demand approach and the contingent value approach are the two major alternatives to estimating the economic value of environmental resources. Either approach can be used to evaluate artificial reefs. Several nontechnical publications are available to the noneconomist that discuss these approaches and other components of economic valuation (AFS 1992, 1993; Southwick Associates 1993; Lipton et al. 1995). These publications also provide references to other economic valuation studies.

This study is a direct application of the travel cost demand function methodology to estimate the economic value of the Lorain County artificial reef. The travel cost demand function is a proxy of the demand function that is core to economic theory. The basic concept of the demand function is the existence of a negative relationship between the price of a commodity and the number of units of the commodity that will be purchased by a consumer during any period of time. This relationship is illustrated in Figure 1 for the price of trips and the number of recreational or fishing trips that will be taken. For example, an individual may be willing to pay $2.00 for one loaf of bread each week, but only $1.00 for the second loaf, and only $0.50 for a third loaf. Other variables such as income and the prices of substitute products (for example, crackers instead of bread) are necessary to complete the specification of the demand function. These basic concepts are described in more detail in any "principals of economics" textbook (e.g., Tietenberg 1996).

The demand function similarly applies for fishing trips. An angler might be willing to pay $500 for one fishing trip per year to a unique angling site, but only $200 for the second trip, $75 for a third trip, and so forth. The amount the angler is willing to pay is also likely to depend on the income of the angler and the availability of other angling sites, some of which may be nearby but less unique. The difference between buying a loaf of bread and taking a fishing trip is that a consumer can walk into a grocery store and buy a loaf of bread, but a con-

sumer must assemble the elements of a fishing trip by purchasing travel to and from the site, taking the time to travel to and from the site, purchasing bait and tackle, and so forth, none of which constitute a fishing trip but are components of such a trip. The estimation of a price from these components is what makes the travel cost demand function a proxy function rather than a direct demand function. In the travel cost model, the proxy for price is usually composed of the costs of traveling to and from the site; costs incurred on-site during the trip usually are not included in the travel cost price. The basic elements of the travel cost demand function and its application in environmental valuation are discussed in Hushak et al. (1988), AFS (1992), AFS (1993), Southwick Associates (1993), Lipton et al. (1995), and Tietenberg (1996).

In this study, three single-equation travel cost models are used to estimate (1) the relationship between the number of trips taken during 1992 and the price or cost of making the trip, (2) an angler income threshold variable, and (3) angler knowledge

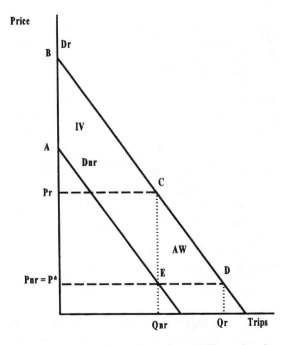

FIGURE 1.—Travel cost demand model illustrating the shift between those who do not use the artificial reef (curve Dnr) and those who do use the reef (curve Dr), and illustrating consumer surplus of reef users compared to nonusers (area ABDE) decomposed into trips common to both groups [(Qnr) = Increased Value (IV)] and added trips [(Qr - Qnr) = Additional Welfare (AW)].

of the artificial reef measured by whether the angler had fished the reef before 1992 (Jeng 1990; Glenn 1995). The three models are:

- the basic travel cost model,
- a modification of the model to incorporate human time costs by McConnell and Strand (MS) (1981), and
- an alternative to MS for incorporation of human time costs developed by Bockstael, Strand, and Hanemann (BSH) (1987).

Because these are straightforward applications of travel cost models, we do not develop travel cost theory in detail here but refer readers to discussions in the nontechnical publications cited earlier. The two points on which we place emphasis are (1) the specification of the reef effect variable, which is hypothesized to shift the travel cost demand function to the right from line AE to BD in Figure 1, and (2) the use of a household income threshold variable instead of a standard household income variable because our estimated coefficients of the standard household income variable were negative, as they are in many other studies, even though the coefficients were expected to be positive.

The travel cost model (TCM) is:

$$\text{Trips} = a + b\text{Price} + c\text{Income} + d_i Z + e \tag{1}$$

where Price is the sum of travel cost and entrance fees, Income is household income, Z represents other variables, and e is the error term. In this model the proxy variable for price is the monetary travel cost (MTC) of getting to and from the recreational site; human time costs (opportunity costs) are not considered.

Becker's theory of household production framework is used to bring human time costs into recreational demand models of McConnell and Strand (1981) and Bockstael et al. (1987). The MS and BSH models are two special cases where the household production framework is applied to recreational studies. In the MS model the price variable is composed of travel costs and a fraction of human time costs. The MS methodology estimates the opportunity cost of time as some proportion (k) of the wage rate. The MS model is written as:

$$\text{Trips} = a + b(\text{Price} + k\text{AV}) + c\text{Income} + d_i Z + e \tag{2}$$

$$\text{Trips} = a + b_1\text{Price} + b_2\text{AV} + c\text{Income} + d_i Z + e \tag{2a}$$

$$k = b_2/b_1 \tag{2b}$$

where Price is the monetary travel cost, A is the hours of travel time per recreational trip, V is wage rate, Income and Z are as defined as above in the TCM, and e is the error term. The opportunity cost of time k is defined as the a ratio of the AV and Price parameters (equation 2b). In this model, it is extremely difficult to distinguish between Income and AV because V is a primary determinant of Income.

The BSH model (Bockstael et al. 1987) includes time costs conditional on the recreator's labor market situation. Empirical observations in the model are separated into groups based on flexible versus fixed work schedules. There are multiple solutions to this model: two corner solutions that we combine as one and an interior solution. Figure 2 graphically illustrates these different subsets in terms of work versus leisure time. At point A are people who have fixed work schedules (corner solution 1), and at point B are people who are unemployed and retired (corner solution 2). In both cases, the individual cannot substitute between work and recreation. The line segment AC represents those with flexible work schedules or those who are self-employed (interior solution). It is assumed that there can be a substitution between work and recreational time. The recreator at the interior solution is assumed to have a variable work schedule, to be a part-time worker, or to hold a second job where work hours can be adjusted and substituted with leisure. If leisure hours are increased, work time and income are reduced. The BSH model results in equation (1) for the corner solution and the MS equation (2) with k = 1 for the interior solution.

Reef as a Site Quality Variable

The key variable in estimating the economic value of the reef is the variable used to measure the shift in the travel cost demand function due to the reef. The questionnaire used in this study presented several options for variables. The best choice, in our judgment, was whether the respondent used (fished or dove) the reef before 1992. (About 34% of respondents fell into this category.)

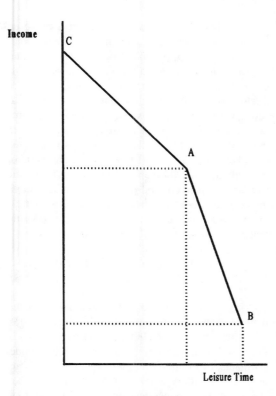

FIGURE 2.—Illustration of corner and interior solutions and implied time constraints for the Bockstael, Strand, and Hanemann model where C and A are alternative corner solutions where work time and leisure time cannot be substituted and the segment AB is the income–leisure substitution rate for the interior solution.

The two primary alternatives to this variable were (1) whether the respondent used the reef during 1992 (about 60% of respondents), an option that is contemporaneous with the dependent variable trips and would require a simultaneous equations estimator, and (2) whether the respondent knew about the reef in 1992 (about 87%). Use of the reef before 1992 is determined before trips during 1992 and can be used as a predetermined explanatory variable in a single-equation estimator, but reef use in 1992 cannot be used in that manner. Because 34% of respondents used the reef before 1992, this variable provides better separation than alternative 2, wherein 87% knew of the reef in 1992. Our alternative hypothesis is that the coefficient of reef use before 1992 is positive where the null hypothesis is that the coefficient is less than or equal to zero.

Income Threshold

In preliminary estimates it was found that the income variable possessed an unexpected negative sign with an often highly significant t-ratio, that is, the estimates contradicted the alternative hypothesis that the income coefficient is positive. This result led us to hypothesize that there may be some type of threshold income level that gives different slopes of demand curves for low-income versus high-income people. We implement threshold income by creating a dummy or dichotomous variable equal to 1 if income exceeds the threshold level and 0 if income is less than or equal to the threshold level. We expect high-income individuals to take fewer and longer trips and low-income individuals to take more-frequent, shorter trips.

We decided to test this hypothesis because the higher-income group generally travels a longer distance, is surrounded by alternate sites, and generally is not limited to any site by income. The high-income group will choose a site based on cost and amenities, not on proximity, that is, low cost. The higher-income people will have more money to spend on their excursions and therefore will take longer trips, but higher-income people may take fewer trips because their work time is valued at a relatively higher rate relative to leisure as compared to lower-income people. However, these higher-income recreators are selected from a larger population with more substitutes or alternatives, and the number making at least one trip is expected to be very flexible. Therefore, although higher-income people making at least one trip are not expected to be highly flexible ("inelastic" in demand theory terminology) in the number of trips taken, the number of higher-income people who make at least one trip is expected to be very flexible (highly elastic). This, in turn, causes the censored or truncated model estimates for the high-income group to result in a relatively elastic demand function in contrast to that of the low-income group, who are primarily local respondents.

Consumer Surplus

Economic value of or willingness to pay (WTP) for recreation is estimated from travel cost models by calculating the Marshallian consumer surplus (CS) (Willig 1976). Willingness to pay is the total value of recreational trips less the cost of those trips to the recreator. In travel cost models, this value is calculated from the truncated maximum likelihood (truncated regression) estimates of the demand equations and the mean values of each of the variables in the sample. Willig (1976) justified the use of CS estimates as a measure of WTP. He established a process for estimating the upper and lower bounds on the percentage error in approximating compensating and equivalent variations with CS. Willig showed that the use of CS to estimate the willingness to pay of an individual is usually a good approximation.

Given a linear demand equation and an estimated mean price we can estimate the area under the curve and above the mean price (p) as consumer surplus. When the demand curve of reef users (BD) is superimposed on the curve of nonreef users (AE) in Figure 1, the difference in CS between reef users and nonusers is the additional benefit or economic value of the reef to those who used the reef before 1992 (area ABDE in Figure 1). In this study the CS is the estimated net benefit of the artificial reef to the average or typical user of the reef calculated from the respective estimated travel cost demand equations.

We decompose the economic value of the reef in Figure 1 (ABDE) into two components IV and AW, where IV is the marginal value of the recreation site to reef users for common trips (the number of trips taken by nonreef users) and AW is the additional welfare obtained by reef users because they make more trips to the recreation site. In Figure 1, the area ABCE is the IV value, and area CDE is the AW value.

The aggregate CS estimates were found by taking the Lorain County estimated angler hours in 1992 and converting them into number of anglers using the average angler hours in 1992 calculated from our sample respondents. The number of Lorain County anglers was multiplied by the percent of reef users to obtain the number of reef users. This in turn was multiplied by CS per angler year to estimate aggregate CS.

Estimation

Truncated maximum likelihood is used to estimate the demand equations (Maddala 1983). A truncated sample occurs when only a portion of the population is sampled, in this case only recreators who used Lorain County to initiate water-based recreation trips. When the full population is sampled, but some do not use the good (that is, are not anglers or divers), the data set is called a censored sample. The accuracy with which the maximum-likelihood function approximates the observed data and its parameters is called a measure of goodness-of-fit. In the case of censored and truncated maximum likelihood, the likelihood-ratio test is used to measure goodness-of-fit. This test serves the same purpose as R^2 in the case of least-squares regression. In the goodness-of-fit test, the value of the maximized log-likelihood function (LOG[L]) and the value of the null log-likelihood function (LOG[L_0])—the value of a log-likelihood function when it is maximized with respect only to the mean (number of trips in this case)—are formed into a log-likelihood ratio that has a chi-squared distribution defined as:

$$X^2 \text{ STAT} = -2[\text{LOG}(L_0) - \text{LOG}(L)]$$

(3)

This statistic is compared to the chi-squared test statistic to determine the significance of the estimates.

The variables used in the models are defined in Figure 3. Before discussing the alternative model estimates, it is important to note that all models are near the boundary between maximum likelihood convergence and nonconvergence. In maximum likelihood, the estimation procedure seeks to find the set of parameters that maximize the value of the likelihood function. When a function fails to converge, it means that there is not a unique set of parameters that generates a maximum; rather, several combinations of parameter values generate approximately the same value of the likelihood function. For example, no version of the McConnell and Strand model for the total sample converged, although the model did converge for some subgroups. In other cases, the addition or deletion of a variable from one of the equations presented below led to an equation that failed to converge. Although all equations discussed below converged and have statistically significant likelihood ratios and coefficients, it is important to recognize that the parameter estimates may not be as tightly bounded as the standard errors imply.

The number of usable observations (N) varies with the variables used in the equations because of incomplete data from respondents. There were 468 total respondents. However, about 25% of responses were not usable because of incomplete data. In models where income is not used, we have 356 usable responses, and in models where income is used either as a direct variable or in calculating the human time cost of travel, we have about 330 usable responses.

Interior observations = Individuals who have flexible work schedules; those who are employed part-time, seasonally, or full-time and have flexible work hours and days or hold a second job.

Corner observations = Individuals who have nonflexible work schedules; those who are retired, unemployed, or otherwise do not meet the criteria of individuals who are in the interior group.

TRIPS = Number of trips made to Lorain County recreation sites during 1992.

MTC = (2* distance * 0.27)/group size = monetary travel cost per person, where 2 converts one-way distance to round-trip distance, and 0.27 is estimated car depreciation and maintenance expenses per mile, which includes oil, gas, and estimated gas mileage.

TRAVTIME = (2 * distance)/55 = round-trip travel time, which is the round-trip distance divided by the approximate speed of 55 miles per hour.

INCOME = Midpoint of the total annual gross income before tax by income class for the respondent's household. This includes labor earnings of the respondent and all other income-earning members, plus earnings from businesses and investments, income from retirement, family public assistance, and any other source.

V = Income/2,000, where V represents the average hourly family income as defined above divided by 2,000 hours.

AV = TRAVTIME * V, which is the variable from which the opportunity cost of time is estimated, as described by McConnell and Strand (1981).

B1 = MTC + AV, which is the opportunity cost of travel for an individual who has satisfied the criteria of the interior observations above.

$REEF_{-1}$ = 0 if the respondent did not fish or scuba dive the reef prior to 1992 and = 1 if the respondent did fish or scuba dive the reef prior to 1992.

TVINC (threshold income variable) = 0 when income is less than $40,000 and = 1 when income is more than $40,000.

TV = MTC * TVINC

N = Number of usable observations.

FIGURE 3.—Definitions of variables and groups used in the empirical models.

Simple Travel Cost Model Estimates

The results for the TCM are shown in Table 3. All equations have significant X^2 statistics at the 0.01 level. Estimate (3.1) is the TCM excluding the income variable. It is expected that the number of trips is negatively associated with the cost of the trip and that use of the reef before 1992 ($REEF_{-1}$) is positively associated with the number of trips taken (see Figure 3 for variable definitions). The MTC and $REEF_{-1}$ variable parameters have their expected signs and are both significant. The reef coefficient of 9.74 means that respondents who used the reef before 1992 took on average 9.7 more recreational trips to Lorain County sites during 1992 than those who did not use the reef before 1992.

Estimate (3.2) is in the form of the TCM equation (1). The income variable does not possess the expected positive sign, but it is also significant at 0.001. This unexpected parameter value also reduces

the significance of the MTC and $REEF_{-1}$ variables. This result led us to the income threshold specification, discussed below.

Graphically, estimate (3.1) is represented in Figure 1. The demand curve Dr (or BD) corresponds to individuals who used the artificial reef before 1992 ($REEF_{-1}$ = 1), while curve Dnr (or AE) corresponds to individuals who did not use the reef before 1992 ($REEF_{-1}$ = 0). In this case, Dr is 9.74 trips greater than Dnr at each price. At the truncated mean of MTC = P* = $2.52, individuals with $REEF_{-1}$ = 0 made a predicted 15.98 trips (Qnr), while reef users made 25.72 trips (15.98 + 9.74 = Qr).

Bockstael, Strand, and Hanemann Model Estimates

The BSH model separates recreators into those who can substitute leisure for work (the interior group) and those who cannot substitute lei-

TABLE 3.—Simple travel cost model (TCM) estimates.

| Variable or statistic | Coefficient (t-value) | |
	3.1	3.2
Intercept	17.14	22.63
	(8.04)	(3.48)
MTC	−0.46	−0.56
	(−5.97)	(−4.89)
REEF$_{-1}$	9.74	13.77
	(3.16)	(2.27)
Income[a]		−0.73E−03
		(−3.64)
Sigma	21.62	31.26
	(22.44)	(13.07)
LOG(L)	−1498.35	−1352.29
LOG(L$_0$)	−1606.34	−1492.79
χ^2 STAT[b]	215.98	281.00
N	356	330

[a] The E notation represents exponents.

[b] At P = 0.01, χ^2 = 9.21 for 2 df and 11.34 for 3 df.

sure for work (the corner group). This separation leads to separate interior and corner equations in Table 4. The truncated maximum likelihood method was used to estimate these model parameters. The log-likelihood ratio tests for both equations are significant at 0.01.

The coefficient of the income variable was negative in all cases, and the variable was excluded. The likelihood function of the interior equation did not converge when income was excluded. Interior estimate (4.1), which is an MS model specification as in equation (2a), was substituted. The difference is the use of MTC and AV instead of B1, where B1 = MTC + AV (see Figure 3). We can analyze this equation as if we were using B1. In this equation the REEF$_{-1}$ and AV coefficient estimates are significant at 0.005, while the MTC coefficient is not statistically significant. The coefficient of REEF$_{-1}$ suggests that interior group respondents (i.e., those who can substitute work and recreation time) who used the reef before 1992 made an additional 22.37 trips in Lorain County during 1992 compared to interior group respondents who did not use the reef.

The likelihood function of corner estimate (4.2) produced an MTC coefficient estimate that possessed the correct sign and was significant at 0.001. The lagged reef (REEF$_{-1}$) parameter estimate was not significant. This equation is the TCM equation (1) with only corner observations used in the estimat-

ing equation. The coefficient of REEF$_{-1}$ suggests that respondents who used the reef before 1992 only took 3 additional trips compared to respondents in this group who did not use the reef before 1992.

Alternative Income Threshold Models

The TCM and BSH model estimates for the alternative threshold specification are shown in Table 5, where the income threshold level is $40,000. In total, 6 threshold levels were tested ranging from $10,000 to $60,000 at $10,000 increments, and $40,000 achieved the most statistically significant equations. All equations in Table 5 have significant log-likelihood ratios at the 0.01 level.

In the TCM model (5.1), the MTC and lagged reef variables both possess the expected signs and are both significant at the 0.001 level. The MTC variable has a negative coefficient similar to estimate (3.1). The demand-shift variable TVINC suggests that higher-income respondents take 7.5 more trips than lower-income respondents. The coefficient is significant at 0.10. The TV variable (TVINC * MTC) can be positive or negative, but if it is positive, the variable must be of smaller magnitude than MTC to preserve the negative slope of the demand curve. The TV variable is negative and significant at 0.20. The two coefficients jointly suggest that higher-income respondents take more trips but that trips are sensitive to price or travel cost changes.

TABLE 4.—Bockstael et al. (BSH) model estimates.

| | Coefficient (t-value) | |
| | Interior | Corner |
Variable or statistic	4.1	4.2
Intercept	22.08	17.51
	(3.64)	(8.44)
MTC	−0.78	−0.40
	(−0.73)	(−5.99)
AV	−0.49	
	(−3.07)	
REEF$_{-1}$	22.37	3.26
	(2.99)	(1.03)
Sigma	26.99	18.34
	(11.63)	(18.18)
LOG(L)	−430.38	−999.28
LOG(L$_0$)	−484.46	−1063.05
χ^2 STAT[a]	108.16	127.54
N	101	246

[a] [Same as FN [b], Table 3]

The corner estimate of the BSH model (estimate [5.2]) is similar to estimate (4.2) where the coefficients of MTC and REEF$_{-1}$ are of the same magnitude in both equations. In addition, TVINC and TV are only marginally significant, but the coefficients are sufficiently large that they are likely to make a difference in consumer surplus estimates.

The interior estimate (5.3) converged with B1, and it was not necessary to resort to MTC and AV as in estimate (4.1). The coefficient of B1 is negative and significant at 0.001. The REEF$_{-1}$ coefficient is similar in magnitude to estimate (4.1) and is significant at 0.005. The TV and TVINC coefficients both have small t-ratios. In addition, when the slope-shifting TV coefficient (1.66) is added to the B1 coefficient (-0.68) to calculate the price coefficient, the slope of the equation becomes positive (-0.68 + 1.66 = 0.98) for the high-income group. Given the small t-ratios for the two threshold variables and the inconsistent coefficient of TV, we accept the null hypothesis that there is no threshold income effect for the interior group and use estimate (4.1) in the consumer surplus estimation. Our hypothesis that the slope of the demand curve for the high-income individuals (TV = 1) would be larger and therefore flatter than for low-income individuals (TV = 0) is supported in estimate (5.2) but not (5.3).

In Figure 4 the line segment IS represents the TCM demand curve (5.1) for low-income individuals who used the reef before 1992 (TV = 0 and REEF$_{-1}$ = 1), and GN represents the demand curve for high-income individuals who used the reef before 1992 (TV = 1 and REEF$_{-1}$ = 1). The slope of the high-income group (slope = -1.52) is smaller than the slope of the low-income group (slope = -0.4). The line segments JP and FO are the low- and high-income demand curves for those who did not use the reef before 1992.

Consumer Surplus Estimates

Four CS estimates are made from the selected models for comparison purposes. The models are:

1. the basic TCM (estimate 3.1),
2. the BSH model (estimate 4.1 and 4.2),
3. the threshold TCM (estimate 5.1), and
4. the BSH threshold model (estimate 5.2 and 4.1).

TABLE 5.—Alternate income threshold model estimates.

	Coefficient (t-value)		
	TCM	BSH	
		Corner	Interior
Variable or statistic	5.1	5.2	5.3
Intercept	16.36	16.88	23.5
	(6.38)	(7.10)	(3.10)
MTC	−0.47	−0.40	
	(−5.80)	(−5.88)	
B1			−0.68
			(−3.11)
TVINC	7.50	6.00	−1.49
	(1.72)	(1.26)	(−0.16)
TV	−1.05	−0.93	1.66
	(−1.63)	(−1.26)	(0.77)
REEF$_{-1}$	10.35	3.73	21.31
	(3.16)	(1.15)	(2.91)
Sigma	22.09	18.18	26.24
	(21.52)	(17.48)	(11.60)
LOG(L)	−1,386.81	−925.48	−428.47
LOG(L$_0$)	−1,492.79	−987.13	−484.46
χ^2 STAT [a]	211.96	123.30	111.98
N	330	229	101

[a] At P = 0.01, χ^2 = 13.28 for 4 df.

The CS, which approximates the net benefits or economic value of the artificial reef to consumers who used the reef before 1992 as compared to those who did not, is calculated as the area between the demand curves of those who did and did not use the reef before 1992 and the area above the truncated mean price (MTC), area ABDE in Figure 1. These CS estimates are based on recreational demand model estimates, the number of estimated trips, and the truncated mean price (MTC).

Table 6 contains the CS estimate for TCM estimate (3.1). This estimate is $441.43 per average respondent who used the reef before 1992. More specifically, this is the net benefit of the artificial reef to the average or typical user of the reef before 1992. Figure 1 graphically shows this amount as area ABDE, which is the difference in the CS estimates for individuals who used the reef before 1992, area P*BD,

$$CS_r = 1/2 [25.72 * (58.43–2.52)] = \$719.00 \qquad (4)$$

and individuals who did not use the reef before 1992 (area P*AE).

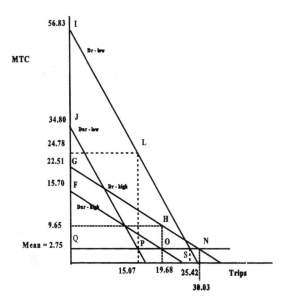

FIGURE 4.—Graphical depiction of the threshold travel cost model with reef use, where line segments JP and IS represent low-income respondents who did not and did (respectively) use the artificial reef before 1992, and where line segments FO and GN represent high-income respondents who did not and did (respectively) use the artificial reef before 1992. The graphical depiction also includes the solution to the statistically estimated equation (6.1) in Table 5 and the implied consumer surplus estimates.

$$CS_{nr} = 1/2 [15.98 * (37.26–2.52)] = \$277.57 \quad (5)$$

These estimates used the truncated mean of 2.52, which is estimated by solving the equation for MTC given the estimated means of the other variables.

$$trips = 17.14 - 0.46 \text{ MTC} + 9.74 \text{ REEF}_{-1} \quad (6)$$
$$19.29 = 17.14 - 0.46 \text{ MTC} + 9.74(0.34)$$
$$\text{MTC} = \$2.52$$

This CS estimate represents the additional value of the Lorain County artificial reef obtained by the average individual who used the reef before 1992 as compared to the average individual who did not use the reef before 1992.

For the first 15.98 trips, the marginal value of the reef is estimated as $21.17 per trip (Table 6), which is the difference in price between reef users (point C) and those who do not use the reef (point E). The increased value (IV) of Lorain County recreation due to use of

the reef by reef users is $338.29 per respondent (15.98 * $21.17). The additional welfare (AW) to reef users is $103.10 (1/2 [(25.72-15.98) * 21.17]). In this equation reef users made 9.74 more trips to the recreation site than nonreef users. These additional trips generated an additional $103.10 in CS, which is added to the $338.29 CS estimate to obtain $441.43.

The BSH model has two equations (Table 6). In the corner estimate (4.2) the truncated mean price is $2.69, and the marginal value of the reef at 16.43 trips is $8.15 ($P_r - P_{nr} = 51.92 - 43.77 = \$8.15$). The IV value in this equation is $133.90 (IV = 8.15 * 16.43), and the AW value of the reef is $13.24; AW = 1/2 [(51.92-43.77) * (19.68-16.43)].

We calculate the CS for the MS interior model (4.1), which approximates the BSH equation. The truncated mean price $8.47 is calculated by solving for the combined price. The marginal value of the reef at 15.47 trips is $29.97 ($P_r - P_{nr} = 58.27 - 28.30$); the CS is $813.74. The IV and AW values are calculated as for the TCM.

TABLE 6.—Basic travel cost model (TCM) and Bockstael (BSH) model consumer surplus (CS) estimates. All estimates in US$ per average respondent per year. Component sums (IV + AW) may not equal the total CS because of rounding.

Model (equation)	CS	Increased value (IV)	Additional welfare (AW)
Basic TCM (3.1) (N = 356)			
Total CS per angler year	$441.43	$338.29	$103.10
CS per trip		$21.17	$10.58
Marginal trips		15.98	25.72
BSH models			
Corner model (4.2) (N = 246)			
Total CS per angler year	$146.93	$133.90	$13.24
CS per trip		$8.15	$4.07
Marginal trip		16.43	19.68
Interior model (4.1) (N = 101)			
Total CS per angler tear	$813.74	$463.63	$350.20
CS per trip		$29.97	$14.98
Marginal trip		15.47	38.84
Weighted CS per angler year	$341.01		

A weighted average of the BSH corner and interior CS components is used to obtain an average BSH model CS estimate. The number of observations in each group are added to obtain a total number of observations, and the percentage of corner and interior observations is obtained. These percentages are multiplied by their CS estimates and added to obtain a weighted average BSH CS estimate of $341.01 (Table 6).

Our second set of CS estimates are derived from the income threshold model for the TCM (estimate [5.1]) and the BSH income threshold model consisting of the corner threshold estimate (5.2) and the MS interior estimate (4.1); the income threshold effect for the interior group was not statistically significant. These estimates contain distinct CS estimates for the average high- and low-income respondents who used the reef before 1992.

Table 7 displays the CS estimates for the threshold TCM. The truncated mean price is $2.75 for estimate (5.1). The CS estimate of the low-income group of estimate (5.1) is $445.86, and $169.28 is the CS estimate for the high-income group. Figure 4 graphically represents these CS estimates as the area JISP for the low-income group and the area FGNO for the high-income group. The low-income CS value was obtained by calculating the difference in the CS estimates of individuals in the low-income group who used the reef before 1992 (area QIS = $687.36) and the CS estimates of individuals in the low-income group who did not use the reef before 1992 (area QJP = $241.50). The high-income CS estimate was obtained by calculating the difference in CS of the high-income individuals who used the reef before 1992 (area QGN = $296.70) and high-income individuals who did not use the reef before 1992 (area QFO = $127.42).

The marginal value of Lorain County recreation due to the reef for the low-income group is $22.03. The increased value of the reef (IV) for the low-income group is $331.99, and the additional welfare of the reef (AV) is $114.00. These values are represented in Figure 4 as the areas JILP and PLS, respectively. For the high-income group the marginal value is $6.80, the IV is $134.02, and the AV is $35.24. The high-income IV and AW values are represented in Figure 4 as the areas FGHO and OHN, respectively. The total weighted CS estimate for this threshold TCM is obtained in the same manner as the weighted CS estimate of the BSH model.

The CS for the BSH threshold model, estimates 5.2 and 4.1, is shown in Table 8. The corner subgroup truncated mean price is $5.26. The low-income group has a marginal value of $9.32 for the first 14.78 trips. Using the same formula equations that were used for estimate (5.1), we obtain the low-income CS value of $155.15, which is the difference between the CS estimates of those who use (CS = $428.14) and do not use (CS = $272.99) the reef. We also calculated the low-income IV and AV values of $137.75 and $17.38, respectively.

The high-income group of estimate (6.2) has a marginal value of $2.80 and a CS estimate of $49.72. This group has an IV estimate of $44.46 and an AV estimate of $5.22. A corner weighted average CS estimate of $76.42 is estimated for the high- and low-income groups of estimate (5.2). This weighted average is obtained using the relative corner subgroup sizes as weights. Then we multiply the percentage weights by their CS estimates. These two products give us the corner weighted average CS. Finally, the threshold BSH weighted average CS is obtained as the weighted average of the corner and interior CS estimates ($302.08).

Aggregate Consumer Surplus and Economic Values

Thus far we have provided CS estimates in dollars per average angler per year for 1992. Because we used the truncated average price for those who

TABLE 7.—Threshold travel cost model (TCM) consumer surplus (CS) estimates. All estimates in US$ per average respondent per year. Component sums (IV + AW) may not equal the total CS because of rounding.

Model (equation)	CS	Increased value (IV)	Additional welfare (AW)
Threshold TCM (5.1)			
(N = 330)			
Low-income group			
CS per angler year			
(TV = 0)(N = 228)	$445.86	$331.99	$114.00
CS per trip		$22.03	$11.01
Marginal trip		15.07	25.42
High-income group CS			
per angler year			
(TV = 1)(N = 102)	$169.22	$134.02	$35.24
CS per trip		$6.80	$3.40
Marginal trip		19.68	30.03
Weighted average CS			
per angler year	$360.10		

took trips, in contrast to a price for a population (holders of fishing licenses, for example), our CS estimates are applicable to users only. We aggregated these estimates for the total number of anglers from Lorain County sites in 1992. Based on our survey, about 34% (N = 356) of the respondents used the Lorain County artificial reef before 1992 (REEF$_{-1}$). During 1992, 459,901 angler hours in Lorain County were estimated from the Ohio creel survey (T. Bader, Fairport Harbor Fisheries Station, personal communication). From this number we calculated the number of anglers who fished in Lorain County during 1992. Multiplying the average number of trips per year (19.29) by days per trip (1.34) and hours per day (6.62) yields 171.11 angler hours per year (Table 9). Dividing the total angler hours for 1992 (459,901) by the average angler hours per year gives us the number of anglers for 1992 (2,687 in Table 9). The number of reef users is 34% of anglers, or 914 users. Multiplying the number of reef users per year by the estimated average

CS per angler year gives us the aggregate CS estimates presented in Table 10, which range from $403,370 to $276,035 per year.

Discussion

In our database, the average reef user based on REEF$_{-1}$ made approximately 10 more trips to Lorain County recreation sites than those who did not use the reef. This result confirms our hypothesis that individuals' demand for recreation differs between reef users and nonreef users. The increase of trips by the reef users demonstrates that there is an increase in demand for recreation by those who use the reef, and therefore there is a positive impact on Lorain County recreation.

The four estimated models that were chosen for our CS estimates were also used to determine which model best estimated Lorain County recreational demand. Within each model, assumptions were made about the recreators. In the BSH model we hypothesized that there is a difference in demand and benefits between individuals with flexible and fixed work schedules. This hypothesis has been confirmed through tests of our demand estimates 4.1, 4.2, 5.2, and 5.3, and through the implied differences of our CS estimates across the models.

We found that individuals valued recreation differently among different income groups. The TCM income threshold model incorporated this hypothesis. The BSH income threshold model also incorporated this hypothesis along with the hypotheses about work flexibility. These hypotheses were also tested and found to affect recreators' demand. In both models, threshold income and work status are factors in determining CS. Excluding these variables, as in the basic TCM, for example, results in a mis-specified equation and biased results. The best CS estimate, in

TABLE 8.—Bockstael et al. (BSH) threshold model consumer surplus (CS) estimates. All estimates in US$ per average respondent per year. Component sums (IV + AW) may not equal the total CS because of rounding.

Model (equation)	CS	Increased value (IV)	Additional welfare (AW)
Threshold BSH corner (5.2) (N = 229)			
Low-income group CS per angler year			
(TV = 0) (N = 58)	$155.15	$137.75	$17.38
CS per trip		$9.32	$4.66
Marginal trip		14.78	18.51
High-income group CS per angler year			
(TV = 1)(N = 171)	$49.72	$44.46	$5.22
CS per trip		$2.80	$1.40
Marginal trip		15.88	19.61
Corner weighted average CS per angler year	$76.42		
Interior BSH (4.1)(N = 101)			
CS per angler year	$813.74	$463.63	$350.20
CS per trip		$29.97	$14.98
Marginal trip		15.47	38.84
Threshold BSH Weighted average CS per angler year	$302.08		

TABLE 9.—Data used in aggregate CS calculations.

Variable	Value
N	356
Trips per year	19.29
Days per trip	1.34
Hours per day	6.62
Average angler hours per angler year	171.11
Number of anglers per 1992	2,687.59
Reef users per 1992	914

TABLE 10.—Aggregate consumer surplus (CS) estimates (US$ per year). (REEF$_{-1}$ was set to 34% reef use.)

Model	CS
Basic TCM	$403,369.90
BSH weighted average	$311,608.12
Threshold TCM	$329,052.18
BSH threshold weighted average	$276,034.66

our judgment, is the BSH threshold model ($302.08). This model takes into consideration the demand preferences of the different income and work groups. The least appropriate CS estimate is the basic TCM ($441.43) because it does not consider any grouping.

The estimated aggregate consumer surplus to reef users for the year 1992 varies with the model specification from a high of $403,370 for the basic TCM to a low of $276,035 for the BSH threshold model. This annual benefit compares to a total construction cost of about $100,000.

One issue of concern is how much of the CS is actually attributable to the reef. In our analysis we assumed that the total amount of these CS estimates is attributable to the reef based on our definition of reef users. This assumption is valid if both reef users and nonusers have the same preference for the Lorain County recreation site. If not, we cannot determine how much of this total to attribute to the reef. For example, it may be that reef users also happen to have a stronger preference for use of Lorain County recreation sites and as a result have a higher consumer surplus than individuals not using the reef. If this is the case, then these CS estimates are too large. We conclude that the artificial reef does play a major role in increasing recreation in Lorain County and that the use of data grouping has proven to be an important element in determining individuals' demand for recreation and value of the artificial reef.

Conclusion

What are the management implications of this study for the construction of additional reefs? In the context of benefit–cost analysis, the benefits of the reef must exceed the costs for the reef to be a beneficial investment. Benefits include not only the angling and diving benefits, but any other benefits that might accrue to fish habitat. Costs include not only construction costs but also other costs that can be attributed to the reef such as increased costs of navi-

gation if large vessels must be diverted around the reef. The consumer surplus estimates generated by this study are one component of a benefit–cost study.

For example, the BSH threshold model estimate of consumer surplus for 1992 is $276,035 per year. If it is judged that 1992 is a typical year, and all of the consumer surplus can be attributed to reef users, that is, the reef users are typical of all Lorain County recreators on Lake Erie, then this estimate can be discounted over the expected life of the reef to obtain the net present value of the benefit stream to reef users. For example, if the Lorain County artificial reef is expected to last 20 years, and the discount rate (interest rate) is 5%, the net present value of $276,035 for 20 years at 5% is about $3.4 million (the present value of annuity factor is 12.46, where $1 for 20 years has a net present value of $12.46). This value would be combined with other benefits, the cost of construction, and other costs to determine the net benefits of the reef. In the case of the Lorain County reef, construction costs were about $100,000, so unless there are other large hidden costs, the reef has been a good investment for Lorain County anglers and divers.

Acknowledgments

This work is a result of research sponsored in part by the Ohio Sea Grant College Program, project R/ME-6 under grant NA90AA-D-SG496 of the National Sea Grant College Program, National Oceanic and Atmospheric Administration, in the U.S. Department of Commerce. This research was also partly sponsored by the State of Ohio. We thank the anonymous reviewers of this paper for their helpful comments.

References

AFS (American Fisheries Society). 1992. Investigation and valuation of fish kills. American Fisheries Society, Special Publication 24, Bethesda, Maryland.

AFS (American Fisheries Society). 1993. Sourcebook for investigation and valuation of fish kills. American Fisheries Society, Special Publication 24 (Supplement), Bethesda, Maryland.

Anonymous. 1993. Status and trend highlights Ohio's Lake Erie fish and fisheries. Ohio Department of Natural Resources Division of Wildlife, Columbus.

Bockstael, N. E., I. E. Strand, and W. M. Hanemann. 1987. Time and the recreational demand model. American Journal of Agricultural Economics 69(2): 293–302.

Glenn, S. J. 1995. Travel cost estimates of the economic value of the Lorain County, Ohio, artificial reef. Master's thesis. The Ohio State University, Columbus.

Glenn, S. J., D. O. Kelch, and L. J. Hushak. 1994. Economic evaluation of the Lorain County artificial reef in 1992: an overview. Ohio Sea Grant College Program, Technical Summary OHSU-TS-022, The Ohio State University, Columbus.

Hushak, L. J., J. M. Winslow, and N. Dutta. 1988. Economic value of Great Lakes sportfishing: the case of private-boat fishing in Ohio's Lake Erie. Transactions of the American Fisheries Society 117:363–373.

Jeng, H. Y. 1990. Endogenization of trip duration and costs in recreation demand models. Doctoral dissertation. The Ohio State University, Columbus.

Kelch, D. O., F. L. Snyder, and J. M. Reutter. 1999. Artificial reefs in Lake Erie: biological impacts of habitat alteration. Pages 335–347 in L. R. Benaka, editor. Fish habitat: essential fish habitat and rehabilitation. American Fisheries Society, Symposium 22, Bethesda, Maryland.

Lipton, D. W., K. Wellman, I. C. Sheifer, and R. F. Weiher. 1995. Economic valuation of natural resources–a handbook for coastal resource policymakers. NOAA (National Oceanic and Atmospheric Administration) Coastal Ocean Program Decision Analysis Series 5, NOAA Coastal Ocean Office, Silver Spring, Maryland.

Maddala, G. S. 1983. Limited-dependent and qualitative variables in econometrics. Cambridge University Press, New York.

McConnell, K. E., and I. E. Strand. 1981. Measuring the cost of time in recreation demand analysis: an application to sport fishing. American Journal of Agricultural Economics 63:153–156.

Southwick Associates. 1993. Handbook of sources and applications of fisheries social science information. American Fisheries Society, Socioeconomics Section, Bethesda, Maryland.

Tietenberg, T. 1996. Environmental and natural resource economics, 4th edition. HarperCollins, New York.

Willig, R. D. 1976. Consumer's surplus without apology. American Economic Review 66:589–597.

American Fisheries Society Symposium 22:363–382, 1999
© Copyright by the American Fisheries Society 1999

Identifying Habitats Essential for Pike *Esox lucius L.* in the Long Point Region of Lake Erie: A Suitable Supply Approach

CHARLES K. MINNS AND SUSAN E. DOKA

Fisheries and Oceans Canada, Great Lakes Laboratory for Fisheries
and Aquatic Sciences, Bayfield Institute
Post Office Box 5050, 867 Lakeshore Road, Burlington, Ontario L7R 4A6 Canada

CAROLYN N. BAKELAAR

Cartographics, Post Office Box 757, Waterdown, Ontario L0R 2H0 Canada

PETER C. E. BRUNETTE

Baytech Environmental, Post Office Box 71074, Burlington, Ontario L7T 4J8 Canada

WILLIAM M. SCHERTZER

Environment Canada, National Water Research Institute, Canada Centre for Inland Waters,
Post Office Box 5050, 867 Lakeshore Road, Burlington, Ontario L7R 4A6 Canada

Abstract.—The quality and quantity of habitats determine ecosystem productivity. Hence, they determine the potential fish productivity that sustains the fish harvests extractable from freshwaters and seas. Efforts to conserve and protect fish habitats are frustrated by key unanswered questions: which habitat types and how much must be protected to ensure natural self-sustaining fish stocks? Minns and Bakelaar presented a prototype method for assessing suitable habitat supply for fish stocks in Lake Erie, an analysis that can be used to address conservation issues. Here, the method is refined and extended, taking the assessment of habitat supply for pike *Esox lucius* in the Long Point region of Lake Erie as a case study. As with the previous study, much emphasis is placed on "learning by doing." Because available inventories of habitat features are coarse and incomplete, improved guidelines for estimating habitat supply are expected from these prototype studies. The habitat supply method previously presented by Minns and Bakelaar is elaborated in three ways here: (1) the basic physical habitat assessment is derived from a remote-sensing inventory database; (2) methods of quantifying the thermal regime and integrating it with other habitat elements are examined; (3) habitat supply estimates are used in a pike population model, and pike biomass and production are simulated for the Long Point region of Lake Erie and then compared with available records. The roles of error and uncertainty are examined for all elements in the estimation and application of suitable habitat supply values. There is potential for supply measurement and analysis to guide fish habitat management.

In all efforts to conserve and manage the earth's biological resources, habitat is emerging as a key issue. Habitat is the living space, with associated structures and functions, needed by organisms to complete their life cycle and maintain a population. This is true for fish, humans, and all other biota. Without appropriate supplies of suitable habitat, efforts to support natural, self-sustaining populations and communities are doomed to failure. Often when species have declined to levels that justify a rare, endangered, or threatened status, the habitat needed to support viable populations is no longer available or habitable. Bringing species back from near extinction is very difficult, but the greater challenge is to develop habitat conservation and management plans long before habitat degradation and declining population trends point inevitably to extinction.

In marine and freshwater ecosystems, fish stocks and fisheries are facing growing threats. Habitat management is becoming a major instrument for fisheries restoration and conservation. Many fish species, mostly in freshwaters, are considered to be at risk (Bruton 1995), and habitat loss, exotic species introductions, and overexploitation are the most cited causes in order of importance (Thomas 1994). Many of the world's fisheries are close to, or beyond, the sustaining capacity of the ecosystems that support them (Brown and Kane 1994). Human encroachments on fish habitats largely continue unabated (Hannah et al. 1994), although the concept of aquatic reserves (e.g., marine protected areas, which are analogous to terrestrial parks and reserves) is gaining increased attention (Lauck et al. 1998). Because knowledge and understanding of the factors and processes linking fish to habitat are limited, it is difficult to identify the habitat types and locations needing the greatest protection. The scientific understanding needed to identify habitats that are "critical," "limiting," and "essential" is in the early stages of development.

Some fish biologists are willing to speak with confidence when asked to identify critical or essential habitats, but often the scientific evidence needed to back that confidence is absent (Minns et al. 1996a). In species that pass through several life stages with discrete or incompletely overlapping habitat requirements, the potential for several productivity "bottlenecks" exists (Shuter 1990; Minns et al. 1996b). The concept of source and sink habitats is similar to this hypothesis but is derived from a landscape perspective (Pulliam and Danielson 1991). The supply of habitat suitable for each life stage may vary through time, changing the position of the bottleneck and affecting population productivity and structure. This can complicate the interpretation of stock–recruitment relationships because optimal stock size and harvest may be determined by different life stage bottlenecks at different times and places (Moussali and Hilborn 1986).

Practitioners of habitat management routinely identify spawning habitat as limiting without any clear, direct evidence and without a balanced assessment of habitat constraints at other life stages. The aggregations often seen during spawning may create a false impression of habitat limitation. The spatial living requirements of fish and other organisms are strongly size dependent (Minns 1995); thus an egg occupies far less space than an adult foraging for food. In contrast, scientific literature often indicates that the early larval stage in fish is the main bottleneck, but often without explicit reference to the role of habitat limitation. Although the science for assessing the dynamics of fish populations is well developed, the science for assessing the role of habitat is still in its infancy.

To examine the linkages between habitat supply and the productivity and dynamics of fish populations in particular ecosystems, three main components are necessary: (1) the size and structure of the fish populations, (2) the extent and quality of fish habitats (habitat supply), and (3) an understanding of the functions linking population-rate processes with habitat features. The first and third components have received considerable attention in the development of population ecology in

general and of fish population ecology in particular. The second element, until comparatively recently, has been confined largely to the realm of natural history or has been treated implicitly in element three. Typically, studies of fish habitat associations have demonstrated the relative use or occupancy of different habitat by fishes without regard to the absolute and relative supplies of different habitat types. Developments in remote sensing and geographic information system (GIS) technologies are allowing progress on this spatially oriented component and applying this component to whole systems (see Meaden and Kapetsky 1991 and Meaden and Chi 1996 for an overview). The transition from site-specific studies to whole ecosystem measures of habitat poses many challenges.

The primary purpose of this study is to further contribute to the development of methods for measuring the supply and quality of fish habitats in large aquatic ecosystems, building on previous work reported by Minns and Bakelaar (in press) on Lake Erie. That study expanded on early efforts directed at the question of how to assess habitat quality and supply on larger scales (Minns et al. 1993b; MacLeod et al. 1995). The secondary purposes here are: (1) to examine how habitat supply mapping can provide a foundation for habitat conservation and management, (2) to illustrate how habitat supply measures can be used in conjunction with supply-driven population models to assess fish productivity, and (3) to consider how various measurement and process uncertainties may influence the robustness of the derived inferences.

The present study is focused on Long Point Bay on the north shore of Lake Erie. The availability of a detailed remote sensing inventory conducted in 1995 provided an opportunity to further develop the habitat supply inventory methodology for an area that has considerable lake-wide fishery significance. The decision to focus on pike *Esox lucius* was influenced by the availability of a population model driven by habitat supply (Minns et al. 1996b). This study is not intended to be an exhaustive treatment of the construction of a habitat supply analysis for a single area but rather is intended to provide an example of the challenges posed, and the potential offered, in the joining of fish population studies and habitat sciences. To date, the approach has been applied using existing information wherever possible, with a guiding principle of "learning by doing." The considerable cost of conducting a directed habitat inventory of systems that are as large or larger than Long Point and Lake Erie dictates that assumptions and methodology should be thoroughly explored and tested first.

Materials and Methods

Study Area

Long Point is a large sand spit on the north shore of Lake Erie that extends out into the eastern basin of the lake, close to the lake's deepest point (Figure 1). Long Point Bay consists of Inner Bay, which is shallow and dominated by emergent and submergent vegetation cover, and an outer bay, which is deeper, vegetated along the fringes, and sheltered by the sand spit. Commercial fisheries developed in the mid-19th century in Long Point Bay with recreational fishing gaining prominence later as summer cottages were acquired and the local population prospered. In the 1970s, major industrial development occurred on the north shore of the outer bay, including a steel mill,

an oil refinery, and a coal-fired electricity-generating station. (See Neff 1981 and other articles on the Long Point Bay area in a special issue of the Journal of Great Lakes Research, Issue 7(2), 1981.)

Whillans (1979) described the long-term changes in the fisheries of Inner Bay. The fishes exploited include esocids, percids, coregonines, and centrarchids. Whillans showed that in the Inner Bay fishery the contribution by weight of pike to the commercial fishery declined from 5 to 30% of the harvest in the mid-19th century to insignificant levels in the 20th century. From the 1950s to the 1970s, the contribution by numbers of pike to sport catches ranged from 1 to 4%. Whillans attributed changes in pike abundance to over-exploitation and declining habitat quality. Baldwin et al. (1979) reported commercial fish catches for all the Great Lakes for the period 1867–1977 and detailed pike catches in Canadian waters of Lake Erie for the same period. Pike catches peaked between 1899 and 1914, when annual harvest ranged from 375,000–1,330,000 kg/yr. Catches rose sharply the decade before that 15-

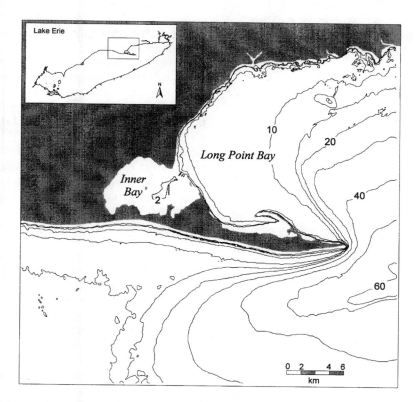

FIGURE 1.—The shoreline and bathymetry of the Long Point Bay area and an inset showing its location on the north shore of Lake Erie.

year period and fell sharply in the decade after. As of 1977 (and since), commercial catches had not recovered to 1899–1914 levels. Catch levels in 1977 were less than 5% of peak values. Much of the Lake Erie pike harvests came from the Long Point area.

From the 1950s to present, Long Point Bay supported large sport and commercial fisheries, with sportfishing in the Bay accounting for a large proportion of angling in the Canadian waters of Lake Erie (L. Sztramko, Ontario Ministry of Natural Resources, personal communication). Sportfishing consisted of a large summer boat fishery and a small winter ice fishery. The summer angling fishery was concentrated in Inner Bay and was dominated, in order of catches, by smallmouth bass *Micropterus dolomieu*, largemouth bass *M. salmoides*, rock bass *Ambloplites rupestris*, and yellow perch *Perca flavescens*. The winter ice fishery catches were overwhelmingly dominated by yellow perch. Commercial seine and hoop net fisheries operated in Inner Bay. Their catches were dominated by bullheads (Ictaluridae), mixed panfish *Lepomis* spp., and crappies *Pomoxis* spp. Pike represented a small proportion of both sport and commercial harvests and amounted to more than 13,000 kg/yr, with almost a quarter of harvests coming from the sport fishery

TABLE 1.—Estimated annual harvest of pike *Esox lucius* in Long Point Bay, Lake Erie.[a]

Fishery and component	Number	Weight (kg)
Sport		
Mean summer boat fishery 1959–1997 (39 yrs)	1,329	
Mean winter ice fishery 1960–1980 (9 yrs)	67	
Mean spring spear fishery 1973–1977 (5 yrs)	2,267	
Subtotal	3,663	3,663[b]
Commercial		
Spring and fall seine fishery 1986–1994 (9 yrs)		2,161
Spring and fall hoop net fishery 1986–1994 (9 yrs)		7,685
Subtotal		9,846
Total		13,509

[a] L. Sztramko, Lake Erie Fisheries Assessment Unit, Ontario Ministry of Natural Resources, personal communication (summarized from information supplied). Years listed indicate number of years of data collected for each particular time span.
[b] Assumed weight per fish of 1 kg.

(Table 1). Because of sustained overexploitation and habitat degradation (Whillans 1979), this harvest lies well below the ecosystem's potential.

Habitat Inventory

Throughout this study spatial data were assembled, analyzed, and displayed using ArcInfo v.7.1.2 and ArcView v.3.0a GIS software (Environmental Systems Research Institute Inc., Redlands, CA 92373 USA).

Geographic boundary of study.—Assembly and analysis of information were confined to the rectangular area bounded by the UTM coordinates (Zone 17): Lower Left 4 690 464.38N, 533 425.98E and Upper Right 4 739 818.54N, 585 744.14E.

Nearshore habitat.—On 27 July 1995, an aerial remote-sensing survey was conducted in the Long Point Bay area to test the usefulness of Compact Airborne Spectrographic Imager (CASI) surveys in the classification and inventory of nearshore fish habitat on the Great Lakes. The study area for the CASI survey included Long Point Peninsula; the majority of Big Creek Marsh, Inner Bay, and Turkey Point; the north shore to Nanticoke, Ontario; and the area approximately 5 km offshore into Long Point Bay. Geomatics International Inc. (1997) prepared an extensive report of the data collection methodologies, verification, and conclusions. Field data were collected by Fisheries and Oceans Canada, Canadian Wildlife Service (CWS), and Ontario Ministry of Natural Resources staff at 74 sites on the day of the aerial survey. Ground-truthing information for emergent vegetation was provided by CWS. The study developed methodologies for assessing submergent vegetation density and discriminating dominant submergent and emergent vegetation species or species assemblages. According to the Geomatics International report, differentiating transitional areas where submergent vegetation became emergent and where submergent vegetation became substrate was difficult using the spectral data. Therefore, definition of some boundaries involved subjective decision making by the GIS analyst.

For the purpose of the Long Point study, substrate, submergent vegetation, and emergent vegetation thematic layers derived from the CASI survey were used to delimit the boundary between wetland and nearshore areas and offshore areas (Table 2). Undifferentiated (deep water) (classes 7 and 12) in the CASI nearshore inventory was joined with areas deeper than 5 m in the bathymetry layer to delineate an offshore zone.

TABLE 2.—Summary of Compact Airborne Spectrographic Imager (CASI) thematic layers and class assignments along with commentary and interpretation notes for the Long Point, Lake Erie survey.

Thematic layer	CASI class	Description	Notes
	0	Not classified	
Substrate	1	Muck (organic material)	
	2	Transition from muck to sand	
	3	Sand	Edited through visual interpretation.
	4	Gravel and rubble	
	5	Rock shelf and boulders	
	6	Submergent vegetation (near surface and dense)	Sand, silt, muck.
	7	Undifferentiated (deep water)	Covered in offshore depth and substrate mapping.
Submergent vegetation density	8	No submergent vegetation	
	9	Less than 30% submergent vegetation	Mix of sand, silt, muck, vegetation. Influenced by substrate composition.
	10	30–70% submergent vegetation	
	11	70–100% submergent vegetation	<0.5m deep.
	12	Undifferentiated (deep water)	
Submergent vegetation species	13	Undifferentiated (deep water)	
	14	Sparse, undifferentiated, or no submergent vegetation (shallow water)	Species differentiation accuracy uncertain.
	15	Dominantly *Cladophora*	
	16	Undifferentiated submergent vegetation	
	17	Dominantly *Myriophyllum* spp. (Milfoil)	Second in abundance to *Chara* in Inner Bay. Deeper water.
	18	Dominantly *Chara vulgaris* (musk grass)	Largest portion of submergent plants in Inner Bay. Shallow water (correlated with depth), sandy bottoms.
Wetlands and land use	19	Narrow-leaved emergents and undifferentiated submergents	
	20	Dominantly floating vegetation and undifferentiated submergents	
	21	Other emergents	Complexes of flat and wet emergents with taller, denser, and possibly drier emergents.
	22	Cattails (*Typha* spp.)	Includes cattail interspersed with water and solid cattail.
	23	*Phragmites*	May conflict with drier emergents and treed areas.
	24	Meadow grasses and sedge	
	25	Trees and shrubs	
	26	Sand and sparse vegetation	
	27	Cultural land use	Includes roads, urban structures, marinas, and recreational area.
	28	Agricultural land use	
	29	Grass, pasture, and hay land use	Not naturally occurring.
	99	Tire reef	

Three layers from the CASI imagery were used to compile the data required to compute habitat suitability values: substrate (CASI classes 1–6), submergent vegetation density (CASI classes 8–11), and emergent vegetation (CASI classes 19–23). The species identification theme was not used in this study. Areas determined to represent dry land were not part of the fish habitat analysis. An examination of unique combinations of classes from the three thematic layers showed that the wetland and dry land classes (CASI classes 19–99) overlapped very little with the submergent vegetation and substrate layers. There was some overlap between the latter two layers because CASI class 6 represents submergent vegetation in the substrate thematic layer. The CASI thematic classes were reassigned substrate and vegetation cover compositions corresponding to the categories used in the Defensible Methods model (Table

TABLE 3.—Assignments of percent substrate and vegetation cover composition linking Compact Airborne Spectrographic Imager (CASI) layer classes to the fish habitat classification used in Defensible Methods (Minns et al. 1995).

Thematic layer	CASI class	Composition (assigned percentage)
Substrate	1	Sand (34), silt (33), clay (33) [a]
	2	Sand (70), silt (15), clay (15)
	3	Sand (90), silt (5), clay (5)
	4	Cobble (33), rubble (33), gravel (34)
	5	Bedrock (40), boulder (40), hardpan clay (20)
	6	Sand (80), silt (10), clay (10) [b]
Vegetation cover	8	No cover (100), submergent (0), emergents (0)
	9	No cover (85), submergent (15), emergents (0)
	10	No cover (50), submergent (50), emergents (0)
	11	No cover (15), submergent (85), emergents (0)
	19	No cover (10), submergent (45), emergents (45)
	20	No cover (10), submergent (50), emergents (40)
	21	No cover (10), submergent (0), emergents (90)
	22	No cover (10), submergent (0), emergents (90)
	23	No cover (0), submergent (0), emergents (100)
Other	24–99	Land

[a] Class 1 substrate used for Class 19–23 vegetation cover where substrate was previously not classified.
[b] Class 6 substrate composition used for Class 8–11 cover where substrate was not classified.

3; Minns et al. 1995). Defensible Methods is a quantitative system for assessing change in habitats using a combination of physical habitat evaluation and fish habitat suitability models. (It is discussed in more detail under the "Physical Habitat Suitability Modeling" section.)

Bathymetry.—Digital depth contour lines were obtained from the U.S. Department of Commerce, National Oceanic and Atmospheric Administration (NOAA). The contour lines represented compiled hydrographic data from Canadian and U.S. sources (Canadian Hydrographic Service [CHS], NOAA National Geophysical Data Center, and NOAA Great Lakes Environmental Research Laboratory). The original data were collected at various scales (Long Point surveys were ± 1:10,000); the whole lake bathymetry was generalized to 1:350,000. These arcs were edited to obtain closed-depth contour polygons. The editing process included closing, cleaning, building, and labeling the arcs and resultant polygons.

Water levels for the CHS survey were corrected to International Great Lakes Datum (IGLD) 1955: 173.3 m above sea level. The water level for July 1995 (the time of the CASI inventory) was 174.4 m and considered to be a high water level month (Source: chswww.bur.dfo.ca/danp/Erie_mean.txt). The bathymetric contours were used to assign depth layer categories (0–1, 1–2, 2–5, 5–10, and > 10 m) in the habitat suitability analysis.

Shoreline definition.—Setting a shoreline boundary for habitat assessments has been and continues to be a major problem in this type of study. Habitat inventories tend to treat shoreline as a static system property although there are wind-induced, seasonal, and temporal changes and regulated changes in water levels. In addition, different thematic habitat inventories may be obtained at different times and at different water levels. The bathymetric data included a shoreline derived from land-based mapping corrected to low water levels. Further correction was required for the high water levels at the time that the nearshore inventory was conducted. To reconcile this discrepancy, the 0-m depth contour in the bathymetry layer was reassigned to 1 m. The land-use categories (CASI classes 24–29) were combined along with unclassified polygons (CASI class 0) from each of the three thematic layers and designated as dry land. The "wet" areas between the new 1-m depth contour (the previous low water, 0-m contour) and the dry land boundary were assigned to the 0–1 m contour area in the bathymetry layer.

Obviously, changes in water level will affect the area of wetland and dry land, especially in the Long Point area where much of the land ranges in elevation from 174 to 180 m (Ontario Basic Mapping chart 10 17 5600 47100). Because the CASI survey was conducted when water levels were above normal, the supply of nearshore habitat is overestimated here.

Offshore habitat.—Rukavina (1976) and Thomas et al. (1976) reported on nearshore and offshore surveys of Lake Erie bottom substrates conducted in the 1970s. More than 1,700 sites were sampled across the lake. The nearshore zone was surveyed more intensely than the offshore zone. The substrate composition data were extrapolated by converting point data to areas using a proximity analysis called Thiessen or Voronoi polygonization. The approach to habitat classification in this portion of the study area was described in detail by Minns and Bakelaar (in press). Each polygon area was assumed to have the percent substrate composition attributed to the associated point observation. Substrate classes included bedrock, boulder, cobble, rubble, gravel, sand, silt, clay, and hardpan clay.

In the offshore zone, vegetation cover was assumed to be zero, although some vegetation in the nearshore zone extended into deeper waters. The substrate polygons and depth contour polygons were overlaid to produce new polygons with associated depth range, substrate composition, and cover values. The measured areas and attributes for each polygon were used to estimate habitat suitability values for pike. The suitabilities were then appended as polygon attributes in the GIS, allowing nearshore and offshore coverages to be combined in suitability maps.

Temperature information.—Temperature data were collected from two sources, the Lake Erie Biomonitoring (LEB) program conducted by Fisheries and Oceans Canada (DFO) and the NOAA Coastwatch Active Archive System (NCAAS). The LEB program was conducted from 1993 to 1994 at three stations within the study area and at biweekly (1993) and weekly (1994) intervals from May until November. Temperature profiles at each station, which ranged in depth from 6 m to 38 m, were determined using a Hydrolab data logger (Dahl et al. 1995; Graham et al. 1996). The original data were collected at irregular depth intervals; however, the maximum interval was 0.5 m. For each sampling date, temperatures were interpolated between the original intervals to 0.2-m intervals. Then, using ice cover information and maps for the winter months (Canadian Ice Service, 373 Sussex Drive, E-3, Ottawa, Ontario K1A 0H3), the profiles were integrated to obtain daily temperature profiles for 1993–1994 at the three sites. Although several models for thermal structure exist for Lake Erie (Lam and Schertzer 1987; Schertzer 1987; Schertzer et al. 1987; Schertzer and Sawchuk 1990), the Long Point area is unique thermodynamically when compared to the remainder of Lake Erie due to different current patterns and mean depths. Therefore, an empirical approach was deemed more appropriate than applying a basin-wide model to predict thermal structure.

The NCAAS database provides access to satellite files from which sea surface temperature imagery for the lower Great Lakes can be extracted. The

original satellite image is a 312-by-312 pixel grid with an image resolution of approximately 1.4 km^2 per pixel and a user-defined temperature resolution per pixel color value (color values range from 0 to 250; temperature resolution is 0.16°C). The original satellite image was delimited to a 32-by-32 pixel grid, or raster image, of the Long Point study area. Remote sensing imagery was available on a sporadic basis, and several satellite maps were discarded due to cloud cover over the study area. To date, the 10 May 1993 image has been processed from the original color values to the final thermal suitability maps. The process included using successive bathymetric layers to delimit the land–water boundary at particular depths and then using the profile information to generate rules and equations for determining the temperature in each successive layer. Because only bottom temperature is relevant to egg survival, the temperature at maximum depth for each pixel in the grid was extracted from the temperature-depth layers, and a complete bottom temperature layer was compiled. The mismatch of thermal and physical (bathymetry, substrate, and vegetation) mapping dates was not considered important for the purposes of this methodological study.

Physical Habitat Suitability Modeling

Minns et al. (1995) developed an empirical model for site-specific assessment of fish habitat suitability based on an aggregate measure of habitat preference and use by all the members of a fish assemblage. The tool, called Defensible Methods, was developed for nearshore projects such as breakwalls, docks, and marinas. The Defensible Methods tool has been further developed as software for eventual use by habitat managers in assessing site-specific activities, and the tool's current state of development is outlined in Minns and Nairn (unpublished data). Minns et al. (unpublished data) have used this tool as part of a littoral fish habitat management plan for Severn Sound on Georgian Bay, Lake Huron. The habitat preferences of Great Lakes fishes were compiled from available literature by Lane et al. (1996a, 1996b, 1996c) using a nil–low–medium–high rating scheme; the ratings are assumed to correspond to suitabilities of 0.0, 0.33, 0.67, and 1.00. In this study the data compiled for pike life stages (Table 4) were used in the analysis of habitat suitability. Suitabilities for combinations of depth intervals, substrate types, and vegetation cover type are cross-multiplied, and then the resulting matrix is rescaled

TABLE 4.—Relative suitability ratings by habitat feature and category for three life stages of pike from Lane et al. 1996a,1996b,1996c. (Ratings were combined multiplicatively across depth, substrate, and vegetation cover and then rescaled between 0 and 1 where high = 1.00, medium = 0.67, low = 0.33, and blank space = 0.)

Feature category	Spawning	Nursery	Adult
Depth (m)			
0–1	High	High	High
1–2	High	High	High
2–5		High	High
5–10			High
10+			
Substrate			
Bedrock			
Boulder			
Cobble			
Rubble	Low		
Gravel	Low		Low
Sand	High		High
Silt	High	High	High
Clay			
Hardpan clay			
Vegetation cover			
None			
Emergent	High		High
Submergent		High	High

TABLE 5.—Summary of percent habitat areas by Defensible Methods (Minns et al. 1995) categories for depth, substrate, and vegetation cover in the nearshore, offshore, and combined zones in Long Point Bay, Lake Erie. (Calculated by summing patch area multiplied by the percentage of substrate or vegetation assigned.)

Feature category	Nearshore	Offshore	Combined
Depth (m)			
0–1	30.75	0.01	3.13
1–2	28.07	0.13	2.97
2–5	34.81	1.58	4.96
5–10	6.28	14.57	13.72
10+	0.09	83.70	75.22
Substrate			
Bedrock	1.07	1.57	1.52
Boulder	1.07	0.12	0.22
Cobble	1.25	1.62	1.59
Rubble	1.25	2.00	1.92
Gravel	1.29	3.35	3.15
Sand	60.93	40.49	42.56
Silt	16.30	25.88	24.90
Clay	16.30	20.81	20.35
Hardpan clay	0.53	4.16	3.79
Vegetation cover			
None	33.97	100.00	93.30
Emergent	14.95	0.00	1.52
Submergent	51.07	0.00	5.18
Area (km²)	200.23	1,772.35	1,972.58

by setting the highest value equal to one. Separate, relative suitability matrices were computed for pike by life stage: spawning, nursery (age-0), and adult.

In Long Point Bay, the nearshore and offshore habitat inventories were organized to generate habitat areas where all polygons have the same combinations of habitat features. These features corresponded with the categories used for habitat preference in Defensible Methods (Table 5). Unique combinations of depth, substrate, and vegetation cover classes were identified and used to obtain suitability values. Where vectors of proportions by category were used to describe a habitat feature (e.g., substrate composition), the suitability value was a sum of the individual suitabilities weighted by the proportion of each category. The suitability values were attached as polygon attributes in the GIS database, allowing suitability maps to be compiled and weighted suitable areas to be estimated. Total weighted suitable area (WSA) is the sum across all habitat patches of the product of suitability and area of each patch or polygon. Cumulative suitability curves were generated by ranking the suitabilities of habitat areas and plotting the cumulative area and weighted suitable areas. These curves can aide in determining cutoffs between low and high suitability areas.

Predicting Pike Abundance and Production using Habitat Supply Estimates

Minns et al. (1996b) described a simple model linking the dynamics of a pike population to estimates of the habitat supply suitable for (1) spawning, (2) rearing young-of-the-year, and (3) juveniles plus adults. The model is age-structured with both sexes represented. Separate habitat supply values are required for spawning–egg hatch, age-0, and juvenile–adult (age 1+) modules with density-dependent mechanisms affecting hatching success, age-0 growth and mortality, and age 1+ growth, respectively. Weighted suitable area was used as the habitat supply measure to predict pike population size and productivity for Long Point Bay, assuming the population is restricted to the area covered by the habitat inventory.

Modeling Thermal Habitat Suitability

The three-dimensional (3-D) and seasonal nature of a lake's temperature regime presents a serious challenge. Previous efforts to formulate fish habitat suitability maps have been developed using a two-dimensional (2-D) perspective that may lose some information about thermal structure. Different approaches to address this problem are presented here. For practical reasons, habitat will inevitably be managed by area, and ways must be sought to capture essential attributes of the thermal regime in the form of 2-D maps of habitat suitability. Some 3-D visualization of thermal structures will aid interpretation. Therefore, three different ways of analyzing and visualizing data within a GIS could be attempted (Figure 2). First, a 2-D representation of suitable isotherm depth can be depicted for particular life stages of pike. Second, 2-D stacked, depth layers can display changes in habitat suitability by depth strata. Third, a 3-D representation of the entire study area can display "spheres" of suitable habitat areas. (This method is not attempted for the current analysis.) Each method will have pros and cons but ultimately must be translated for use in fisheries management at the 2-D surface of the lake.

Most thermal habitat assessments revolve around the early work by Magnuson et al. (1979) that defined a fundamental thermal niche as "a range of temperature around a species' final preferendum [preferred temperature] which defines the optimum conditions for activity and metabolism." Christie and Regier (1988) showed that seasonal integrals of suitable thermal bottom area and volume were correlated with average fish species yields, including pike. Casselman and Lewis (1996) also found that mean July and August temperatures, as well as December mean values, were correlated with year-class strength. Based on thermal optima for pike spawning and growth obtained from several sources (Christie and Regier 1988; Raat 1988; Casselman

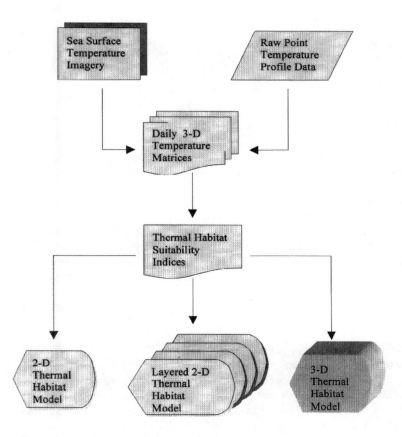

FIGURE 2.—A schema showing the general approach for thermal data processing and habitat suitability analysis.

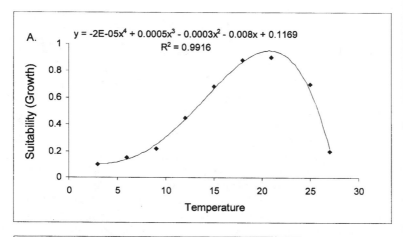

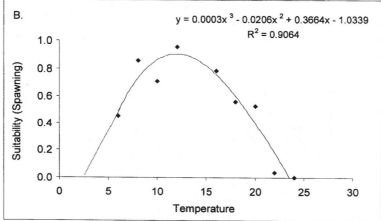

FIGURE 3.—Graphs showing thermal habitat suitability indices for (A) juvenile pike growth and (B) pike egg survival derived from optimal temperature curves (based on Christie and Regier 1988; Raat 1988).

and Lewis 1996), temperature suitability curves were derived for two stages of pike: juvenile growth and egg survival (Figure 3). Thus, temperature values were converted to thermal habitat suitability measures using these curves.

Results

Habitat Supply Analysis

An approximate breakdown of habitat supply can be obtained by summing the product of area and percentages for unique combinations of the habitat features used in the suitability model (Table 5). Approximately 90% of the study area (1,973 km²) has a depth greater than 5 m; this represents most of the offshore zone. In the nearshore zone, the area is evenly distributed across the 0–1, 1–2, and 2–5 m depth ranges. The dominant substrate element is sand, with silt and clay as sub-dominant elements. Hard substrates like bedrock, boulder, and cobble are rare. Vegetation covers two-thirds of the nearshore zone. Of the total nearshore area, 51% is submergent and 15% is emergent vegetation.

Pike Habitat Suitability and Predicted Population Biomass and Yield

Habitat suitabilities were computed for pike life stages. Plots showing cumulative percentages of total area versus suitability indicate whether high-quality habitat is common or rare (Figure 4A).

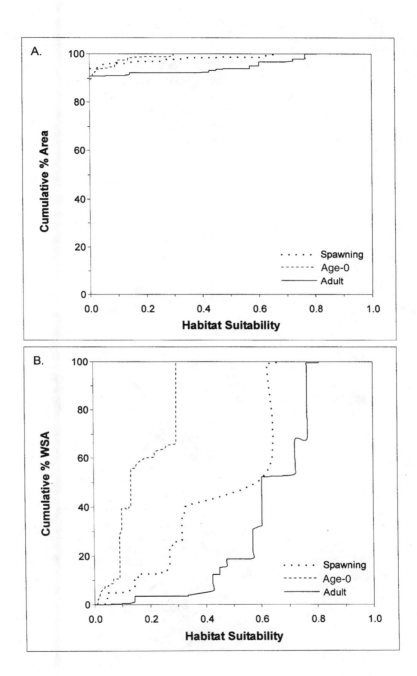

FIGURE 4.—Plots of cumulative percentage of (A) total area and (B) total weighted suitable area (WSA) over increasing suitability for three life stages of pike.

Asymptotically shaped curves indicate that little of the habitat has high suitability, pointing to possible shortages or limitations, and exponentially shaped curves show that high suitability habitat is abundant. The cumulative WSA curves indicate a relative shortage of young-of-the-year pike or suitable nursery habitat (Figure 4B). Using the 50th percentile in the cumulative weighted suitable areas as a cutoff between high and low suitability, the maps show highly suitable habitat is concentrated in the nearshore zone, especially in Inner Bay. The suitability maps indi-

cate that highly suitable pike habitat at different life stages do not overlap but are visually contiguous (Figure 5). In the total study area of 1,973 km^2, WSA values for spawning, age-0, and adult pike were estimated to be 32.9, 18.3, and 98.9 km^2, respectively, with the corresponding maximum suitabilities being 0.67, 0.30, 0.81. The total area and the pike WSA values computed for Long Point Bay were applied as inputs in the pike population simulation model. Despite the low estimate of pike habitat, the population model predicted a biomass of 0.64 kg/ha

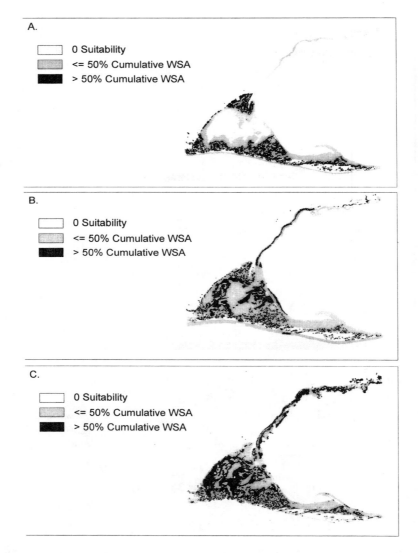

FIGURE 5.—Habitat suitability maps based on Defensible Methods' (Minns et al. 1995) ratings of physical habitat features for three life stages of pike: (A) spawning, (B) young-of-the-year or nursery, and (C) adult. (>50% cumulative weighted suitable area [WSA] = high suitability).

across the whole area. Assuming that sustainable harvest is 50% of unexploited biomass (Beddington and Basson 1993), an expected yield of 63,123 kg/yr was predicted. This is nearly five times the observed value of 13,509 kg/yr estimated from harvest records (Table 1).

Thermal Habitat Suitability

On 10 May 1993, the predicted thermal structure of Long Point Bay became isothermic at 15 m (Figure 6). The temperature ranged from 18°C in the shallows to pockets of cold water at 4°C that were isothermal vertically near the deepest point in the outer bay. The thermocline occurred between 5 and 8 m depending on the maximum depth and surface temperature at that position. At this particular time of year, the relationship between temperature and growth is nearly linear because the inflection point for the growth suitability curves is slightly above 20°C and most of the temperatures fall below this point. Thermal suitabilities for growth are greatest in the 0–4 m depth layers throughout Inner Bay where suitabilities range from 0.6 to 0.7 (Figure 7). Any volume of water below the thermocline is less suitable for pike growth.

The bottom temperature map of the Long Point area reflects the bathymetry (Figure 8A). Warmer waters were predicted for Inner Bay and the shallower shelf region of the outer bay. If eggs were developing on this date, pike would have a greater chance of survival in a band along the edge of the outer bay (Figure 8B). The least suitable areas ranged from a few extremely warm points along the shoreline where temperatures reached about 20°C and in the deeper, colder areas.

Discussion

The habitat suitability maps show where habitat with potentially high utility is located, which in turn can aid in habitat management decisions and aquatic reserve design. In this case, the maximum age-0 suitability is unexpectedly low for an area considered prime habitat for pike, especially because the habitat supply estimates are based on high water levels; suitable areas would be lower given average water levels. The 0–1 m depth layer accounted for 30% of the area in the nearshore zone (Table 5). Furthermore, the addition of thermal habitat to the analysis would reduce the WSA values, lowering the predicted sustainable harvest. To date, implementa-

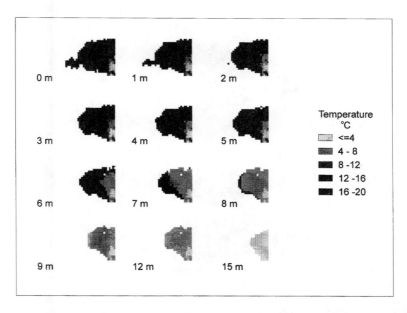

FIGURE 6.—Raster representation of the predicted water temperature at successive depth layers in the open water of Long Point Bay, Lake Erie on 10 May 1993.

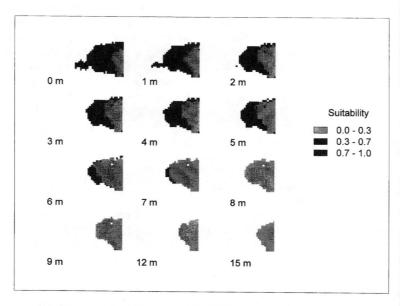

FIGURE 7.—Raster representation of the thermal suitability (0–1) for juvenile pike growth at successive depth layers of Long Point Bay, Lake Erie on 10 May 1993.

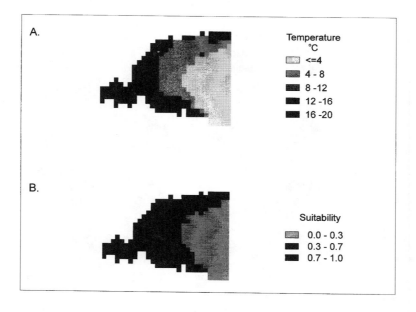

FIGURE 8.—Raster representation of (A) the predicted bottom water temperature and (B) the corresponding thermal suitabilities (0–1) for pike egg survival in Long Point Bay, Lake Erie on 10 May 1993.

tion of these schemas for mapping thermal habitat suitability is incomplete. The first steps in the procedure (Figure 2) require assembly, manipulation, and analysis of immense amounts of data. Cross-linking surface temperatures on a coarse grid with vertical profiles at point locations is complicated by combinations of positional and measurement uncertainties. As is shown, the 2-D perspective taken on physical habitat currently prevents an effective representation of pelagic habitat use. The attempt to generate thermal suitability maps has stimulated method development but, for the present, the data management and manipulation significantly increases the effort required. It is clear that a 3-D approach to mapping physical habitat can be used to make the integration of physical and thermal mapping more realistic, but new means of reducing the resulting products to 2-D will still be necessary for practical habitat management purposes.

The results presented here illustrate both the challenge and the potential of habitat supply analysis. After any discussion of the significance of particular results and before any inferences about their use, the potential errors and the constraints and limitations of the results must be clearly elucidated.

Sources of Uncertainty and Error and their Implications

In his book on GIS, Burrough (1986) devoted 33 of 193 pages to the subject of "data quality, errors, and natural variation." In contrast, most research reports involving habitat mapping and evaluation with GIS ignore the uncertainties. Minns and Bakelaar (in press) neglected a discussion of error and uncertainty and concentrated on establishing methodology. There are many steps in the assembly and manipulation of habitat information and the calculation of supply information for population and community simulation models. These steps make it difficult to assess the impact of compounding various uncertainties or to calculate the cumulative uncertainty for the final suitability or productivity measures. Currently it is not feasible to conduct even a first-order analysis of error. Here we offer a preliminary appraisal of the various uncertainties, an identification of some issues needing further attention, and an evaluation of the significance of uncertainties. Four main sources of error are present:

1. mapping—quantification and classification of basic map elements;
2. suitability—assignment of habitat suitabilities and quantification of supply estimates;
3. productivity—functional forms and parameterization of density-dependent mechanisms determining productivity and response to exploitation and other stresses; and
4. temporal—changes in the distribution and character of habitat features over time.

These sources overlap and interact and may contain within them many forms of uncertainty.

Mapping.—The main components of error in mapping are the position of points, lines, and polygons, as well as the shape and the misclassification of spatial features (Bolstad and Smith 1995). Within defined regional and global frames of reference, position can be measured with precision and accuracy that vary from 100 m to a few cm (typical root mean-square errors range from 2 to 25 m; Bolstad and Smith 1995). The georegistration of satellite images could produce much higher error (Quinn and Kojis 1994). Thus on the day of a survey, the position and shape of the shoreline can be very well known, but satellite information may not be as accurate. Similarly, elevation above and below the water line can be determined to within a few centimeters depending on the technology used. Wide application of global positioning systems is creating the means of overcoming these problems.

Once the raw imagery has been georeferenced, pixels have to be classified. The pixels in the CASI images were assigned to substrate, vegetation, and wetland and land use categories based on ground-truthing information. The classification process can discriminate different habitat features within an image. Pixels are classified based on matching the spectral responses of different habitat types. Increasing the number of ground-truthing sites would reduce misclassification errors by capturing the variability of spectral responses for a specific habitat feature. In this study, the pixels in the satellite images were assigned temperature values based on reflectance. The error in assigning temperature values to a pixel in the Advanced Very High Resolution Radiometer (AVHRR) satellite data are reported as ± 1°C.

Often map themes are derived from point observation using interpolation and extrapolation methods. Most of the interpolations in this study were done independently. The model for creating an offshore substrate layer did not take into account the spatial and temporal variation in wind and wave stresses that might shape moveable substrate distributions.

Satellite images encompass an area that is much larger than the current study area. Therefore, the resolution in such a relatively small area like Long Point Bay is coarse (1.4 km^2 per pixel). Compared to the resolution of the original temperature profiles (maximum distance between temperature readings was 0.5 m), there was a mismatch between horizontal and vertical accuracy. The satellite imagery, when georeferenced to known points in the Long Point region, had a horizontal positional accuracy of approximately ± 0.4 km. Unfortunately, this type of error is inherent in such coarse resolution imagery and can be outweighed by the relatively good spatial coverage of surface temperature that can be gleaned from satellites when compared to conventional point sampling. The temperature point data available for the Long Point region were essential to determining error in position or remotely sensed values. However, more data points would be an asset, especially for interpolating and extrapolating the existing data to calculate 3-D matrices. Currently the shape of the temperature profiles in relation to the maximum depth of each site was used to generate successive depth layers. With the compilation of more temperature data for the modeled study period, a more accurate representation of this nearshore area can be established.

Suitability.—There are many potential errors associated with the estimation of habitat suitabilities. They include designation of category associations within habitat types (e.g., a species may be associated with silty sand rather than sand and silt); assignment of ratings to habitat categories based on limited, fragmentary observations; and the treatment of habitat types as orthogonal for computational purposes (a mathematically simple but untested approach). Although fish assemblage suitability indices may correspond with overall fish species richness and abundance, individual suitability indices may generate a somewhat arbitrary bounding of suitable habitat with sharp edges between categories rather than gradual transitions. However, the integrated supply estimates may bear little resemblance to the facts if models such as Defensible Methods (Minns et al. 1995) are applied beyond the context for which they were developed. The suitability model for pike generates few combinations of habitat categories with nonzero suitability values.

The linkages between population rate processes and habitat features may be process-specific, whereas this approach treats linkages uniformly by life stage. The pike suitability model takes no account of potential differences in vegetation cover preference due to vegetation composition and of gradual changes in habitat use as age-0 pike grow in their first summer (Casselman and Lewis 1996). In addition, winter habitat use is ignored for juveniles and adults. The range of suitability values obtained for age-0 pike is much lower than expected from the background literature on age-0 pike habitat requirements and the conditions occurring in Long Point. The suitability model should be compared with that used by Minns et al. (1996b) in Hamilton Harbour. Potentially, a more detailed suitability model could be derived from information compiled by Casselman and Lewis (1996) and Raat (1988) and compared with the other models. Of course, the limitations of the coarse inventory categories would remain.

The thermal habitat suitability indices also have error. By interpolating and extrapolating point temperatures to daily time intervals, some variability between sampling dates is lost. That loss, coupled with the fact that fish are mobile between patches, may introduce some unknowns into the determination of thermally suitable habitat areas or volumes.

Lastly, the error inherent in collapsing detailed, spatially explicit information into 2-D representations may result in Type I or II errors where areas that are not as suitable, or more suitable, may be lumped together. Spatially explicit depth values are lost altogether or combined with temperature indices that may not be intuitively clear. A layered 2-D model does offer more spatially explicit information and can provide a clearer picture of the whole habitat. However, the implementation of depth structure into an area that is managed two-dimensionally from the water surface is difficult to resolve.

Productivity.—The potential errors in productivity estimates arise in part as a consequence of the uncertainties in habitat supply and suitability estimates and in part from the inherent uncertainties in the production model's formulation and parameterization. Minns et al. (1996b) pointed out the population model's limitations in detail, highlighting the difficulties involved both in measuring rate parameters and in associating them with habitat limitations. The age-0 submodel was the most grounded in field measurements and observations, and the spawning submodel was the least grounded.

Temporal.—As seen with the assembly of bathymetric and shoreline information, changing water levels both seasonally and across years affect the depth at each location and the position of the shoreline. Topographic uncertainty can be contained within a GIS but requires a much better integration of land- and water-based digital elevation information with horizontal and vertical resolutions of centimeters rather than meters. Such precision may be achievable on a local scale but is unlikely to be easily achieved for large systems like Lake Erie and beyond.

Vegetation is not a fixed habitat feature. Seasonal growth and senescence occur, as do secular advance and retreat patterns. Capturing this uncertainty poses an even greater challenge. Persistence of vegetation at specific locations; seasonal variation in vegetation cover; and changes in substrate composition, both gradual (persistent patterns of erosion, transport, and deposition) and sudden (storm-induced), are difficult to capture in a system of representation that is largely static.

The annual, seasonal, and spatial variation in thermal stratification in a lake poses many difficulties. Although most habitat attributes are represented in 2-D maps, and habitat management activities are framed in a 2-D context, temperature presents us with a 3-D variable. Capturing a representation of the changing 3-D patterns involves considerable extrapolation and interpolation of limited observations. Given the transience of water movements due to wind and currents, interpolation among sampling dates is approximate at best. At present, we also have limited experience with the formulation and testing of thermal suitability indices, whether in 2- or 3-D formats. The main dilemma lies in the potential difference between thermal preferences and optimality curves.

Across the four main sources of error, the relative magnitude of error could be relatively categorized as follows: low–medium in mapping error, medium–high in temporal error depending on the habitat feature, and high in suitability and productivity estimate error. The comparative difficulties of assembling the habitat supply components and measuring and containing their uncertainties appear to have similar relative ratings.

Constraints and Limitations

There will probably always be a forced trade-off between two aspects of habitat suitability modeling. On the one hand is the ability to discern patterns of suitability and their linkages with the functional dynamics determining fish productivity.

Alternately, there is the ability to map and inventory habitat features on spatial and temporal scales large enough to encompass the fish stocks being exploited and managed. The previous section on error and uncertainty highlighted the many possible sources of error and the difficulties faced when trying to reduce the uncertainty. The categories used when mapping habitat features over large areas will be coarser than those derivable in site-specific studies when connections between fish and habitat metrics are quantified. Directed studies of suitability and productivity will tend to produce fine-scaled classifications, while spatial and temporal inventories of habitat will tend to remain coarse-scaled due to limitations of technology and cost. Misclassification errors may result in critical habitats not being protected. More effort may need to be directed toward developing ways to nest fine-scale classifications within coarse-scale classifications with minimal classification error, although there needs to be more examination of the implications of fine versus coarse classification schemes.

Mapping of habitat features with important temporal aspects such as temperature and vegetation cover is more difficult than mapping features that are essentially static. Interpolation and extrapolation of limited point data will continue to constrain both temporal and spatial mapping. It may be that hydrodynamic and thermal simulation modeling can be effectively used to derive thermal and current maps with superior properties to point extrapolations.

Validation presents a severe challenge when modeling on the large spatial and temporal scales required for fishery resources. Specific predictions can be compared with observations, but it is difficult to test the validity of classification schemes or the appropriateness of functional habitat-rate process linkages. Large-scale experiments are needed to provide rigorous, integrated tests. The global impact of humans on suitable habitat is a large, unplanned experiment without appropriate controls. Combinations of retrospective analysis and improved assessment of cumulative change in the future in a range of large ecosystems should provide the appropriate scale of testing needed, notwithstanding the difficulties involved in assembling time-series estimates of habitat supply.

Inferences on Essential Habitats

The methods used here to derive supply estimates for suitable habitat can be used to guide habitat managers when trying to conserve and protect "essential" habitat. Suitability maps can be used in the siting of conservation reserves and protected areas. However, the criteria used are still vague and largely nonquantitative despite the immense investments in quantification of both habitat features and fish populations. The suitability-assessment approach assumes equivalence between large areas of low suitability and small areas of high suitability. The results obtained in this study for pike indicate that age-0 habitat is limiting, although the low range of suitabilities was unexpected in Long Point and is potentially misleading. Therefore, tests of the equivalence assumption are needed, but are difficult to accomplish. Cumulative area and weighted suitable area curves (Figure 4) can provide a useful guide, although it is unclear where the suitability and habitat extent limits should be placed if population thresholds are established for conservation purposes.

Future Developments

Whole lake database.—This study and that by Minns and Bakelaar (in press) have revealed the difficulties to be overcome in the development of habitat inventory databases that cover whole ecosystems. These studies also indicate that assembly of such databases is achievable albeit with immense amounts of data assembly, management, and manipulation. These studies have been the building blocks for a larger study aimed at the whole of Lake Erie. Fish stocks in Lake Erie spread across the basins of the lake and ignore political boundaries. The fisheries are jointly managed by four states and one province. Area planning of habitat conservation and restoration must occur on the same scale to be effective.

Methodology.—The integration of 2-D physical and 3-D (space and time) thermal suitability mapping needs to be advanced. The requirement for contiguity of habitats among adjacent life stages needs to be considered, and methods of quantification need to be developed using the supply maps. Incorporation of contiguity may also entail incorporation of temporal patterns of fish movement. The Defensible Methods software needs to be extended from 2-D to 3-D allowing depth, thermal, and other profile variables such as light to be more fully expressed in the evaluation of suitability. More field and experimental work on the development of suitability models is required.

Population simulation modeling.—The Great Lakes Fishery Commission's Board of Technical Experts is supporting research aimed at developing population models with explicit links to habitat supply measures for a series of commercially important species. The species represent a range of life history characteristics, and Lake Erie is the intended testing ground for these models. Without these sorts of models, the criteria for identifying critical, limiting, and essential habitats will remain unresolved.

Thermal suitability modeling.—Currently the thermal suitability analysis is uncoupled from the pike population modeling process. Initially the analysis would be separate because the approach is slightly different from the categorical approach presented for the physical habitat variables. However, the assumption for any future analysis would be that thermal suitabilities would be calculated for the entire area for all the pike life stages and overlayed with the other niche parameters for survival and reproduction based on habitat supply. Initially this will be a 2-D approach; then cumulative weighted suitable areas could be calculated for an expanding suite of multidimensional niche variables.

Potential

Once a habitat supply inventory for any whole ecosystem is available, a wide range of applications will be enabled. Those applications will include population-based modeling (PBM; Minns et al. 1996b) and individual-based modeling (IBM; Tyler and Rose 1994); integrated production estimates for fishery management; and area habitat management plans. If the supply inventory is assembled in a GIS database, spatially explicit IBM models of population processes and populations will be made possible. NerkaSim (Rand et al. 1997) is such a system developed for modeling Pacific salmon species in the dynamic ocean environment of the northeast Pacific Ocean. The use of supply data for PBM modeling has been demonstrated by Minns et al. (1996b) for pike in Hamilton Harbour where population simulations using past, present, and potential habitat conditions following restoration showed how much had been lost and how much might be restored. Supply data can be used empirically to examine the relationships between observed fish distribution and catch patterns and the presence of various habitat features. The inventory can be used to stratify fishery assessment data before estimating abundance and potential harvests. The resulting analyses can be used to guide the spatial allocation of effort. Area habitat management planning can provide a context for limiting the cumulative impacts of development activities and for the design of reserves and protected areas (Lauck et al. 1998). As IBM and PBM models are refined, identification of critical, limiting, or essential habitat areas will be improved. Once habitats important for fish productivity are better known, restoration and conservation activities will be better directed.

Acknowledgments

The authors thank Ron Buliung, School of Geography and Geology, McMaster University, for assistance with GIS aspects of "mapping" thermal habitat. Ora Johansson and Donna Graham, DFO-GLLFAS in Burlington, are thanked for allowing access to temperature profile data from Lake Erie Biomonitoring stations in the Long Point area. Roberta Stanton-Gray, Geomatics International Inc., is thanked for her technical advice on the CASI survey.

References

Baldwin, N. S., R. W. Saalfeld, M. A. Ross, and H. J. Beuttner. 1979. Commercial fish production in the Great Lakes, 1867-1977. Great Lakes Fishery Commission Technical Report 3.

Beddington, J. R., and M. Basson. 1993. The limits to exploitation on land and sea. Philosophical Transactions of the Royal Society of London. Series B Biological Science. 343:87–92.

Bolstad, P. V., and J. L. Smith. 1995. Errors in GIS: assessing spatial data accuracy. Chapter 20 in J. G. Lyon and J. McCarthy, editors. Wetland and environmental applications of GIS. Lewis, Boca Raton, Florida.

Brown, L. R., and H. Kane. 1994. Full house: reassessing the earth's population carrying capacity. W.W. Norton & Co., New York.

Bruton, M. N. 1995. Have fishes had their chips? The dilemma of threatened fishes. Environmental Biology of Fishes 43:1–27.

Burrough, P. A. 1986. Principles of geographical information systems for land resources assessment. Oxford University Press, Oxford, UK.

Casselman, J. M., and C. A. Lewis. 1996. Habitat requirements of northern pike (*Esox lucius*). Canadian Journal of Fisheries and Aquatic Sciences 53(Supplement 1):161–174.

Christie, G. C., and H. A. Regier. 1988. Measures of optimal thermal habitat and their relationship to yields of four commercial fish species. Canadian Journal of Fisheries and Aquatic Sciences 45(2):301–314.

Dahl, J. A., D. M. Graham, R. Dermott, O. E. Johannsson, E. S. Millard, and D. D. Myles. 1995. Lake Erie 1993 western, west central and eastern basins: change in trophic status and assessment of the abundance, bio-

mass, and production of the lower trophic levels. Canadian Technical Report of Fisheries and Aquatic Sciences, No. 2070.

Geomatics International Inc. 1997. Discrimination of substrate, submerged vegetation density and species assemblages and wetland species assemblages using airborne remotely sensed imagery, Long Point, Lake Erie, Ontario. Final Report. Burlington, Canada.

Graham, D. M., J. A. Dahl, E. S. Millard, O. E. Johannsson, and L. L. White. 1996. Assessment of abundance, biomass and production of the lower trophic levels in the eastern basin of Lake Erie, 1994. Canadian Technical Report of Fisheries Aquatic Sciences, No. 2110.

Hannah, L., D. Lohse, C. Hutchinson, J. L. Carr, and A. Lankerani. 1994. A preliminary inventory of human disturbance of world ecosystems. Ambio 23:246–250.

Lam, D. C. L., and W. M. Schertzer. 1987. Lake Erie thermocline model results: comparison with 1967–1982 data and relation to anoxic occurrences. Journal of Great Lakes Research 13(4):757–769.

Lane, J. A., C. B. Portt, and C. K. Minns. 1996a. Nursery habitat characteristics of Great Lakes fishes. Canadian Manuscript Report of Fisheries and Aquatic Sciences 2338.

Lane, J. A., C. B. Portt, and C. K. Minns, C. K. 1996b. Adult habitat characteristics of Great Lakes fishes. Canadian Manuscript Report of Fisheries and Aquatic Sciences 2358.

Lane, J. A., C. B. Portt, and C. K. Minns. 1996c. Spawning habitat characteristics of Great Lakes fishes. Canadian Manuscript Report of Fisheries and Aquatic Sciences 2368.

Lauck, T., C. W. Clark, M. Mangel, and G. R. Munro. 1998. Implementing the precautionary principle in fisheries management through marine reserves. Ecological Applications 8 Supplement:S72–S78.

MacLeod, W. D., C. K. Minns, A. Mathers, and S. Mee. 1995. An evaluation of biotic indices and habitat suitability scores for classifying littoral habitats. Canadian Manuscript Report of Fisheries and Aquatic Sciences 2334.

Magnuson, J. J., L. B. Crowder, and P. A. Medvick. 1979. Temperature as an ecological resource. American Zoologist 19:331–343.

Meaden, G. J., and T. D. Chi. 1996. Geographical information systems: applications to marine fisheries. United Nations Food and Agriculture Organization, FAO Fisheries Technical Paper 356.

Meaden, G. J., and J. M. Kapetsky. 1991. Geographical information systems and remote sensing in inland fisheries and aquaculture. United Nations Food and Agriculture Organization, FAO Fisheries Technical Paper 318.

Minns, C. K. 1995. Allometry of home range size in lake and river fishes. Canadian Journal of Fisheries and Aquatic Sciences 52:1499–1508.

Minns, C. K., and C. N. Bakelaar. In press. A method for quantifying the supply of suitable habitat for fish stocks in Lake Erie. Aquatic Ecosystem Health and Management.

Minns, C. K., V. W. Cairns, R. G. Randall, and J. E. Moore. 1993. UET: a tool for fish habitat management? Pages 236–245 *in* J. Kozlowski and G. Hill, editors. Towards planning for sustainable development. Avebury, Aldershot, England.

Minns, C. K., J. R. M. Kelso, and R. G. Randall. 1996a. Detecting the response of fish to habitat alterations in freshwater ecosystems. Canadian Journal of Fisheries and Aquatic Sciences 53(Supplement 1):403–414.

Minns, C. K., J. D. Meisner, J. E. Moore, L. A. Greig, and R. G. Randall. 1995. Defensible Methods for pre- and post-development assessment of fish habitat in the Great Lakes. I. A prototype methodology for headlands and offshore structures. Canadian Manuscript Report of Fisheries and Aquatic Sciences 2328.

Minns, C. K., R. G. Randall, J. E. Moore, and V. W. Cairns. 1996b. A model simulating the impact of habitat supply limits on northern pike, *Esox lucius*, in Hamilton Harbour, Lake Ontario. Canadian Journal of Fisheries and Aquatic Sciences 53(Supplement 1):20–34.

Moussali, E., and R. Hilborn. 1986. Optimal stock size and harvest rate in multistage life history models. Canadian Journal of Fisheries and Aquatic Sciences 43:135–141.

Neff, D. N. 1981. Introduction (to a special issue on the Long Point Bay Study). Journal of Great Lakes Research 7:77–80.

Pulliam, H. R., and B. J. Danielson. 1991. Source, sinks, and habitat selection: a landscape perspective on population dynamics. American Naturalist 137:S50–S66.

Quinn, N., and B. L. Kojis. 1994. Monitoring sea water temperatures adjacent to shallow benthic communities in the Caribbean Sea: a comparison of AVHRR satellite records and in situ subsurface observations. Marine Technical Society Journal 28(2):10–18.

Raat, A. J. P. 1988. Synopsis of biological data on the northern pike, *Esox lucius* Linnaeus, 1758. FAO Fisheries Synopsis 30 Review 2.

Rand, P. S., J. P. Scandol, and E. E. Walter. 1997. NerkaSim: a research and educational tool to simulate the marine life history of Pacific salmon in a dynamic environment. Fisheries 22(10):6–13.

Rukavina, N. A. 1976. Nearshore sediments of Lakes Ontario and Erie. Geoscience Canada 3:185–190.

Schertzer, W. M. 1987. Heat balance and heat storage estimates for Lake Erie, 1967 to 1982. Journal of Great Lakes Research 13(4):454–467.

Schertzer, W. M., and A. M. Sawchuk. 1990. Thermal structure of the lower Great Lakes in a warm year: implications for the occurrence of hypolimnion anoxia. Transactions of the American Fisheries Society 119(2):195–209.

Schertzer, W. M., J. H. Saylor, F. M. Boyce, D. G. Robertson, and F. Rosa. 1987. Seasonal thermal cycle of Lake Erie. Journal of Great Lakes Research 13(4):468–486.

Shuter, B. J. 1990. Population-level indicators of stress. Pages 145-166 *in* S. M. Adams, editor. Biological indicators of stress in fish. American Fisheries Society, Symposium 8, Bethesda, Maryland.

Thomas, C. D. 1994. Extinction, colonization, and metapopulations: environmental tracking by rare species. Conservation Biology 8:373–378.

Thomas, R. L., J-M. Jaquet, A. L. W. Kemp, and C. F. M. Lewis. 1976. Surficial sediments of Lake Erie. Journal of the Fisheries Research Board of Canada 33:385–403.

Tyler, J. A., and K. A. Rose. 1994. Individual variability and spatial heterogeneity in fish population models. Review of Fisheries Biology 4:91–123.

Whillans, T. H. 1979. Historic transformations of fish communities in three Great Lakes bays. Journal of Great Lakes Research 5:195–215.

American Fisheries Society Symposium 22:383, 1999

Part Six:
Fish Habitat Rehabilitation and Socioeconomic Issues

SCOTT A. HOLT

Marine Science Institute, The University of Texas at Austin
750 Channel View Drive, Port Aransas, Texas 78373-5015, USA

Identification and preservation of critical habitat for fishes is an important component of the federal essential fish habitat policy. Another important component of the overall picture is restoration or creation of habitat. The following four chapters explore issues associated with habitat restoration and enhancement. Habitat restoration projects are becoming a typical part of wetland management programs in both coastal and inland environments. The studies described here show how restoration projects can take advantage of comprehensive basic ecological studies of fishes to maximize the quality of the new habitat.

Two of these studies, by Michele Dionne et al. and Mark Minton, deal with restoration of coastal marshes in the New England area, where relatively little is known about the fish production value of salt marshes compared with other East Coast and Gulf of Mexico marshes. It is clear from both of these studies that the physical aspects of restoration, especially marsh elevation relative to tide height and the ratio of marsh area relative to open water, play important roles in restoration success. Both studies also address persistent questions about the functional capacity of created and restored marshes compared with natural marshes. The chapter by William Herrnkind et al. reviews a long-term study of spiny lobsters in the Florida Keys. This study shows how identification (through long-term research) of critical bottlenecks in the life history of a species may allow effective habitat remediation or enhancement actions that save research time and money. The final chapter by Loren Coen et al. explores the role of oyster reefs as essential fish habitat for both successful settlement of new oysters and for a variety of finfish species. This oyster reef research program has demonstrated the complexities associated with restoring living reefs to produce habitat for associated fishes.

Overall, these studies suggest directions for further research needed to identify habitat characteristics critical to successful fish habitat rehabilitation projects. Habitat rehabilitation will continue to be an important component of management efforts to maintain sustainable fisheries and marine biodiversity.

American Fisheries Society Symposium 22:384–404, 1999

Fish Utilization of Restored, Created, and Reference Salt-Marsh Habitat in the Gulf of Maine

Michele Dionne

Wells National Estuarine Research Reserve
342 Laudholm Farm Road, Wells, Maine 04090, USA

Frederick T. Short and David M. Burdick

Department of Natural Resources
Jackson Estuarine Laboratory, University of New Hampshire
85 Adams Point Road, Durham, New Hampshire 03824-3427, USA

Abstract.—In the Gulf of Maine region, projects to restore or create salt-marsh habitat to replace salt-marsh functions and values reduced or lost to tidal restriction are increasing. We assess fish utilization of marsh restoration and creation projects along the central Gulf of Maine coastline by addressing three questions: (1) how do fish assemblages in manipulated and reference marshes compare, (2) how do differences between manipulated and reference marshes change over time, and (3) how do fishes respond to different types of restoration? Fish utilization of restored and created marshes in New Hampshire and Maine (two created and four tidally restored marshes) is compared to adjacent reference marshes. The comparison of manipulated marshes with local reference marshes provides an internal standard for the monitoring of each restoration project, making it possible (1) to follow changes over time while accounting for natural variation and (2) to make valid comparisons about the magnitude and direction of changes between independent restoration projects. Our study provides the first density estimates for fish utilization of vegetated salt-marsh habitat in the Gulf of Maine. The highest fish densities from this study just overlap with the lowest fish densities reported from more southerly marshes. Overall, fish were distributed similarly among manipulated and reference marshes, and fish distribution did not change with time. Trends in the data suggest that fish utilize elevated marshes restored by dug channels to a lesser degree than impounded marshes restored by culverts. It appears that fish will readily visit restored and created marshes in assemblages similar to those found in reference marshes over the short term (one to five years post-restoration) but are subject to the influence of differences in tidal regime, access to marsh habitat, and vegetation density. In the large majority of cases, hydrologic restoration of tidally restricted marshes will improve a much larger area of fish habitat per unit cost than creation of new marsh and will not be subject to many of the constraints that limit the function of created marshes. The primary consideration in tidal restoration projects is not necessarily the cost of construction but the social, economic, and political issues that must be addressed. Often, tidally restricted marshes are in highly developed coastal areas where many individual property owners may perceive the increased tidal flow as a threat, even when flood hazard studies show that no such threat exists. In spite of this caution, thousands of hectares of coastal fish habitat can be improved through a concerted program to restore the hydrology of tidally restricted marshes in the Gulf of Maine.

The coastline of the Gulf of Maine is characterized in large part by existing or former salt marsh. High marsh, dominated by *Spartina patens*, typically fills large areas behind barrier beaches or in protected drowned valleys both within the Bay of Fundy region and from the Kennebec River in Maine to Provincetown, Massachusetts, while low marsh, dominated by *Spartina alterniflora*, forms a vegetated fringe along the shores of larger rivers and bays throughout the Gulf (Nixon 1982). Recent estimates of the areal coverage of salt marsh throughout the Gulf are 171 km² (Jacobson et al. 1987; Gordon and Cranford 1994), in spite of vast losses of this vulnerable ecosystem since colonial times that range from 84% in the Bay of Fundy (Gordon and Cranford 1994) to 25–50% in Massachusetts,

New Hampshire, and Maine (Cook et al. 1993). Given the important place of salt marshes the coastal landscape, it is surprising how little we know of the role of salt-marsh ecosystems in supporting the fish community of the Gulf of Maine. The occurrence of fishes has been studied in a small number of salt-marsh in estuaries (Lamborghini 1982; Roman 1987; Murphy 1991; Ayvazian et al. 1992; Doering et al. 1995; Lazzari et al. 1996; Cartwright 1997), and fish diets and food webs have been investigated in fewer marshes still (Lamborghini 1982; Cartwright 1997; Deegan and Garritt 1997). The use of salt marshes as nurseries by postlarval and juvenile marine fishes and the value of salt marshes as feeding grounds by adult marine fishes are poorly understood for the Gulf of Maine (Acadian coastal province, using classification of Cowardin et al. 1979) compared to the Viriginian (Smith et al. 1984; Rountree and Able 1992a, 1992b; Rountree and Able 1993; Szedlmayer and Able 1996); Carolinian (Shenker and Dean 1979; Weinstein 1979; Bozeman and Dean 1980; Weinstein and Walters 1981; Rogers et al. 1984; Hettler 1989; Kneib 1993; Kneib and Wagner 1994; Miltner et al. 1995; Irlandi and Crawford 1997); and Louisianan coasts (Boesch and Turner 1984; Felley 1987; Deegan et al. 1990; Deegan 1993; Peterson and Turner 1994; Minello and Webb 1997). Current understanding of the value of salt-marsh estuaries as fish habitat (derived from studies of marshes to the south of the Gulf of Maine) is comprehensively reviewed by Day et al. (1989), Rozas (1995), and Kneib (1997a).

Tidal restrictions such as those created by dikes, roads, railroads, and other marsh crossings present a large potential impact to the fish production value of salt-marsh habitat in the Gulf of Maine. A recent survey of New Hampshire coastal marshes determined that 25% of the total marsh area was being impacted by reduced tidal flow due to human-made structures (USDASCS 1994). Most tidal restrictions have been in place for decades and have been maintained with little thought to their impact on marsh ecosystems. These restrictions can reduce or eliminate the access of estuarine and marine fish to estuarine salt-marsh habitat and over time can lead to major changes in marsh geomorphology and vegetation (Roman et al. 1984; Rozsa 1988; Sinicrope et al. 1990; Frenkel and Morlan 1991; Rozsa 1995; Buchsbaum et al. 1997; Burdick et al. 1997; Chadwick 1997; Portnoy and Valiela 1997; Weinstein et al. 1997; Orson et al. 1998). The abnormal patterns of draining and flooding created by tidal restriction can lead to subsidence of salt-marsh soils, loss of *Spartina patens* high marsh, expansion or invasion of the salt-marsh cattail *Typha angustifolia*, and invasion by *Phragmites australis* or purple loosestrife *Lythrum salicaria*.

There is growing interest in restoring Gulf of Maine salt marshes that have been degraded by tidal restrictions (Reiner 1989; Cook et al. 1993; Dionne 1994; USDASCS 1994; Bryan et al. 1997; Dionne et al. 1998). Salt-marsh creation is already used as an approach to mitigate functions and values lost when areas of marsh are disturbed or destroyed by development or other human activities (Reiner 1989; Bosworth and Short 1993). Restoration refers to activities that aim to enhance degraded sites within naturally occurring systems or habitats; creation refers to activities

designed to establish habitats de novo at a site where no such habitat exists naturally (Reiner 1989; Kusler and Kentula 1990; Sinicrope et al. 1990; Matthews and Minello 1994; Burdick et al. 1997; Weinstein et al. 1997). In this study, we assess the utilization by fishes of restored and newly created salt marshes along the central Gulf of Maine coastline by asking (1) how does the fish assemblage of the manipulated marsh compare with that of an appropriate reference marsh, (2) how does the difference between the fish assemblage of the manipulated marsh and the reference marsh change over time, and (3) how do fishes respond to different types of marsh restoration? We are interested in these questions specifically as they apply to vegetated marsh as opposed to intertidal or subtidal creeks or open estuarine waters.

Methods

Study Sites

The restored, created, and reference marshes in this study were along the New Hampshire and southern Maine coast (Figure 1, Table 1). For each restored or created marsh we selected an adjacent undisturbed area of natural marsh to serve as a reference (Figure 1) so that each manipulated marsh had a paired reference marsh. At each study site, manipulated and reference marshes were sampled simultaneously so that they were flooded by the same tide and, insofar as possible, at similar points during the cycle of tidal inundation. The one exception to this procedure was at the Submarine (SUB) site (Figure 1E) in 1997, where the reference marsh at Inner Cutts Cove (ICC) was separated from the manipulated site by a roadway and was sampled 24 h after sampling of the SUB created marsh. In each year, fish sampling occurred in the early and late growing season (June–July and August–October, respectively). Percentage of plant cover, water table, soil salinities, soil organic carbon, and fish abundances were measured at treatment and reference marshes at each site.

Two of the four tidal restoration sites were in Stratham, along the southwest shore of New Hampshire's Great Bay. The Sandy Point (SDPT) marsh fringes the open waters of Great Bay and lies within the Great Bay National Estuarine Research Reserve (Figure 1F, Table 1). The marshes fringing Great Bay tend to be dominated by *Spartina alterniflora* low marsh with bands of *Spartina pat-*

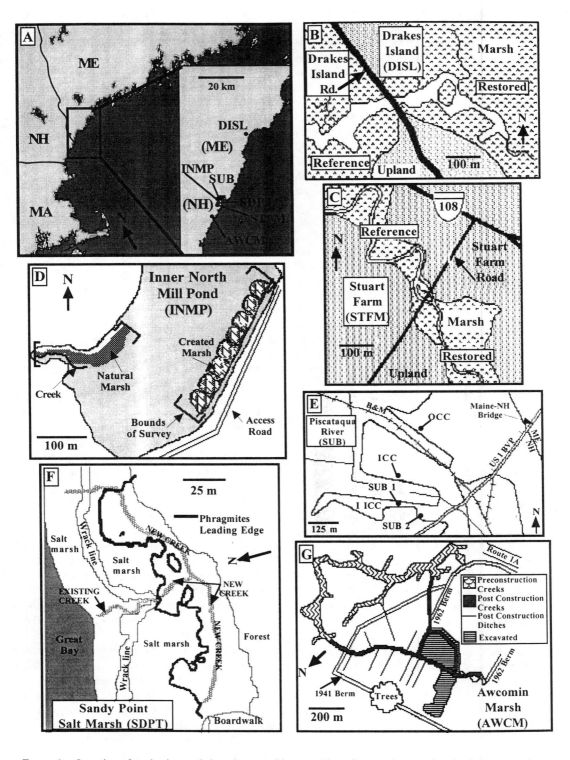

FIGURE 1.—Location of study sites and size, shape, and juxtaposition of restored, created, and reference marshes.

TABLE 1.—Overview of marsh restoration and creation study sites. Sample size (n) refers to the total number of fish samples collected at each reference and each treatment marsh during the entire study (e.g., n = 4 indicates four samples at the reference marsh and four samples at the treatment marsh).

Site	Location	History	Treatment	Monitoring
INMP	Inner North Mill Pond, Portsmouth, New Hampshire (NH); 0.4 ha	Railroad and industrial waste dump; mitigation for port expansion	Planted *Spartina alterniflora* in 1992 and 1993	1993, 1997; n = 4
SUB	Inner Inner Cutts Cove, Submarine Site, Portsmouth, NH; 0.1 ha	Ledge shoreline; mitigation for port expansion	Planted *Spartina alterniflora* in 1994 and 1996	1997; n = 4
AWCM	Awcomin Marsh, Rye, NH; 6.0 ha	Dredge spoil berm (20 cm layer) with *Phragmites* invasion	Dug channels to restore tidal flow and drainage in 1992	1993, 1995, 1996; n = 6
SDPT	Sandy Point, Great Bay, Stratham, NH; 1.5 ha	*Phragmites* berm (10 cm to 20 cm)	Dug channels to restore tidal flow and drainage in 1994	1995, 1996; n = 4
STFM	Stuart Farm Marsh, Squamscott River, Great Bay, Stratham, NH; 4.5 ha	Marsh impounded by flap gate since 1970; marsh surface subsided (15 cm to 30 cm)	Replacement of flap gate with large culvert in 1993	1993, 1995, 1996; n = 7
DISL	Drakes Island Marsh, Webhannet River, Wells, Maine; 16.0–20.0 ha	Marsh impounded for 100 years, most recently by a flap gate; marsh surface subsided (0.6 m to 0.9 m)	Loss of flap gate in 1988	1995, 1996; n = 4

ens and *Scirpus robustus* high marsh. The tidal connection to the landward half of this marsh was impaired by a berm of unknown origin 10–20 cm high. The restriction was associated with a stand of *Phragmites* that had invaded the site. In 1994, channels were dug in the berm to improve tidal exchange. The second Stratham restoration site, Stuart Farm Marsh (STFM), lies within a *Spartina patens*-dominated riverine marsh (technically a fluvial minor salt marsh as described in Kelley et al. 1988) near the mouth of the Squamscott River as it flows into Great Bay (Figure 1C, Table 1). This marsh is upstream of the access road to Stuart Farm and had been deprived of tidal exchange since the 1970s when a bridge was replaced by a narrow culvert and flap gate. Tidal flow was restored by the replacement of the limiting structures by a much larger (2.1 m diameter) arched culvert in October 1993. Measurements of marsh surface elevations in the area deprived of tidal exchange averaged 33 cm lower on average than elevations in the unimpounded reference marsh downstream of the access road, indicating marsh soil subsidence.

The two remaining tidal restoration projects in this study were behind Gulf of Maine barrier beaches. One site was in the Awcomin Marsh (AWCM) in Rye, New Hampshire (Figure 1G, Table 1). This marsh had been used as a disposal site for dredge material from Rye Harbor, resulting in a 20 cm increase of surface elevation of the marsh within a higher berm. In 1992, intertidal creeks were dug to improve tidal flow as a strategy to halt the invasion of *Phragmites*. The channels followed the path of original creeks that had been filled with dredge material. The new creeks were shallower (0.5–1.0 m) than the natural tidal channels into which they drained (2.0 m). The second back-barrier tidal-marsh restoration site was in the Drakes Island Marsh (DISL) of the Webhannet River estuary in Wells, Maine, within the boundaries of the Wells National Estuarine Research Reserve (Figure 1B, Table 1). This site has a long history of impoundment for use as pasture (since circa 1848), first by a dike and then by a road with a box culvert and water control structure from the 1920s to the 1950s. The existing culvert under the road was installed in the 1950s and fitted with a flap gate to prevent tidal flow into Drakes Island Marsh. In the winter or spring of 1988, the flap gate fell off, and tidal flow was partially restored through the existing narrow pipe (0.9 m minimum diameter). The mean elevation of the impounded marsh surface was 73 cm lower than the marsh downstream of the culvert. The tidal restoration sites were of two types: (1) those restricted by berms (SDPT and AWCM) and (2) those restricted by culverts (DISL and STFM).

The two created marshes were established as mitigation for the expansion of the New Hampshire Port Authority ship docking facilities on the Piscataqua River in Portsmouth. Degraded shoreline and debris were excavated, and fine-grained sediment was imported to the sites and contoured to appropriate elevations. One marsh, Inner North Mill Pond (INMP), was in an urban tidal basin (Figure 1D, Table 1). The other created marsh was planted in two discrete areas (SUB 1 and SUB 2 in Figure 1E) near a decommissioned submarine used as a museum in a tidal backwater of the Piscataqua River known as Inner Inner Cutts Cove, downstream of Inner North Mill Pond (see also Table 1). All created marshes were planted with the low-marsh dominant *Spartina alterniflora*. The INMP marsh was planted in 1992 and 1993, and the SUB marsh was planted in 1994 and 1995.

Field Sampling

In this study, we adapted fyke nets (Figure 2) to collect fishes, using a known area of marsh, as the fishes left the marsh as water ebbed during evening spring tides. Nekton assemblages were assessed with fyke nets set to sample evening ebb spring tides. In general, a given manipulated marsh and its corresponding reference marsh were within the same water body and sampled on the same tide. We would have been unable to appropriately compare restored, created, and reference marshes without adjusting for the area of vegetated marsh sampled. Flume weirs (Kneib 1991), drop samplers (Zimmerman et al. 1984), and other enclosure sampling methods are used specifically to estimate nekton densities in vegetated marsh habitats (Kneib 1997a; Rozas and Minello 1997). In this study, shallow flooding, low nekton densities, and a need for nondestructive, removable gear led us to a low-cost alternative to enclosure sampling. Most methods of estuary and salt-marsh nekton sampling (trawls nets, throw nets, seines, flume nets, weirs, pit traps, minnow traps) are not dimension-adjusted in practice (Varnell and Havens 1995), that is, the contents of the sample is not related to the dimensions of the habitat from which it is sampled. Therefore, these data do not provide fish abundance estimates per unit of area sampled (i.e., density), although it is possible to estimate densities with some of these methods. Trawling, seining, and throw-net techniques are not effective in emergent vegetation.

The nylon mesh nets used in this study were constructed of a series of four compartments held open by square frames or fykes, with 15-m wings attached to the first and largest (1.2-by-1.2-m frame) fyke opening. After the first compartment, each compartment contained an internal net funnel connected to the previous fyke frame, with the smaller end of the funnel

FIGURE 2.—Photograph of fyke net in place before sampling an evening high tide. (See "Methods" section for explanation of the sampling process.)

emptying into the center of the compartment. This design compelled fish to swim into the cod end of the net with little chance of escape. The wings and the first three compartments were made of 1.27-cm bar mesh, with the final cod end made of 0.63-cm bar mesh. At low tide, nets were set at the lower edge of the marsh with wings at 45°, fykes upright, and cod end and wings anchored. The wing top line was buoyed and set so that nekton could enter the marsh area by the side or tied down until high tide. At high tide, we staked the flooded area of marsh that would be fished by the net to calculate the area fished. The catch was placed into buckets of water once the tide had receded below the level of the first compartment. All fish and crustaceans were counted and identified to species, and total biomass of each species was measured. Up to 30 individuals of each fish species were measured for total length, sampled haphazardly from the bucket with an aquarium net. For crustaceans, we measured the maximum carapace width for green crab *Carcinus maenus* only.

For most years at most sites, fish were sampled once in the early salt-marsh growing season (June or early July) and once in the late growing season (late August through October), providing the minimum replication for the purposes of statistical analyses. The small sample size was dictated by the very limited funding available to monitor marsh restoration success. In 1993, nekton were sampled on two dates in the fall only at the AWCM, STFM, and INMP sites after restoration and creation efforts at these sites were completed. A total of 3,275 fish were collected from 62 samples during the course of the study, excluding 2,017 of 2,018 fish from a school of Atlantic herring *Clupea harengus* captured at Outer Cutts Cove (an additional reference site associated with the SUB site [Figure 1E]). These fish were removed from the data for analysis because their extremely high density represented an outlier. The area of marsh sampled ranged from 8.7 to 870.0 m², with a mean of 317.0 m². A total of 1.89 ha of vegetated marsh was sampled during the course of the study.

Analyses

Comparisons between treatment (restoration and creation) sites and reference sites for fish density, total length, and species number were made using two-way analysis of variance (ANOVA) ($p < 0.05$) to test the effects of treatment (i.e., restoration or creation) and year (change over time). The same approach was used to test for spatial and temporal variation among three reference sites within the same tidal reach of the Piscataqua River (Figures 1D and 1E). Fish density data were transformed (ln, sine or

square root) as needed to reduce heterogeneity of variance. Data transformations did not change the incidence of statistical outcomes; therefore, all results are presented in original (i.e., not transformed) values. Crustacean data were not analyzed for this report.

Results

We collected 15 fish and 4 crustacean species from the 13 marsh areas sampled (Table 2). Seven species of fishes were marsh residents, four were diadromous, three were transients, and one was an "accidental" freshwater visitor. Comparison of pooled presence–absence data within treatment (restored and created) marshes with such data in reference marshes found nine species in common, four unique species in the treatment marshes (*Apeltes quadracus, Lepomis* sp., *Morone americana, Alosa sapidissima*), and two unique species in the Outer Cutts Cove (OCC) (Figure 1E) reference site (*Clupea harengus, Morone saxatilis*). The number of species ranged from two to eight in the marsh areas sampled. *Fundulus heteroclitus* occurred in all marshes whereas *Menidia menidia* occurred in 71% of the reference and 67% of the treatment marshes. *Anguilla rostrata* were taken in all reference marshes and in 67% of manipulated marshes. *Pseudopleuronectes americanus*,[1] *Gasterosteus aculeatus*, *Pungitius pungitius*, *Fundulus majalis*, and *Microgadus tomcod* were seen less frequently in both treatment and reference marshes (each species was present in 15–43% of reference marshes and 17% of treatment marshes). *Apeltes quadracus, Alosa sapidissima*, and *Morone americana* were only in treatment marshes, with *A. quadracus* at two of the six sites (33% occurrence) and the latter species at only one of the six sites (17% occurrence). The largest differences in the number of species between treatment and reference marshes were found at the STFM (culvert) site, where more species were found in the restored marsh, and at the SDPT (berm) site, where more species were found in the reference marsh (Table 2).

The marsh surface species assemblage identified in this study represents 29% of the species known to occur in marsh-dominated estuaries in the Gulf of Maine (Table 3). Fish life history habits were derived from the classification by McHugh as de-

---

[1] Cooper and Chapleau (1998) have revised the scientific name of winter flounder to *Pseudopleuronectes americanus*.

TABLE 2.—Fish species occurrences at all study sites. The column headings Created, Culvert, and Berm refer to types of restoration or creation projects. Data are pooled across all samples (n = 35 for reference sites; n = 27 for restoration or creation sites). O = reference marsh, X = restored or created marsh. See Table 1 for full spellings of site names.

Scientific name (common name)	Life history [a]	Created			Culvert		Berm	
		INMP	SUB	OCC [b]	DISL	STFM	AWCM	SDPT
Fish								
Fundulus heteroclitus (mummichog)	r	O X	O X	O	O X	O X	O X	O X
Menidia menidia (Atlantic silverside)	r	O X			O X	O X	O X	O
Pungitius pungitius (ninespine stickleback)	r					X	O	
Anguilla rostrata (American eel)	r or m (c)	O X	O X	O	O	O X	O	O X
Fundulus majalis (striped killifish)	r					O		O X
Gasterosteus aculeatus (threespine stickleback)	r				O X			O
Gasterosteus wheatlandi (blackspotted stickleback)	r				O X			O
Pseudopleuronectes americanus (winter flounder)	t			O		X		
Microgadus tomcod (Atlantic tomcod)	t	O	O X	O				
Morone saxatilis (striped bass)	m (a)			O				
Clupea harengus (Atlantic herring)	t			O				
Apeltes quadracus (fourspine stickleback)	r				X	X		
Lepomis sp. (sunfish sp.)	f					X		
Morone americana (white perch)	m (a)					X		
Alosa sapidissima (American shad)	m (a)	X						
Total (15 species)		4 4	3 3	6	5 5	4 8	4 2	6 3
Crustaceans								
Palaemonetes sp. (shore shrimp)		X	O X	O		O X	O X	O X
Crangon septemspinosa (sevenspine bay shrimp)					O X	O X	O X	O X
Carcinus maenas (green crab)		O X	O X	O	O X	O X	O X	O X
Homarus americanus (American lobster)			O					
Total (4 species)		1 2	3 2	2	2 2	3 3	3 3	3 3

[a] r = marsh resident, f = freshwater, m = migratory, c = catadromous, a = anadromous, and t = marine transient.
[b] OCC is an additional reference site (see Figure 1E).

scribed in Ayvazian et al. (1992). Here we use a simplified version, collapsing the seven categories to three: resident, migratory, and transient. Estuarine residents are species that spawn and spend a significant part of their life in the estuary. Migratory fish are those with an anadromous or catadromous life

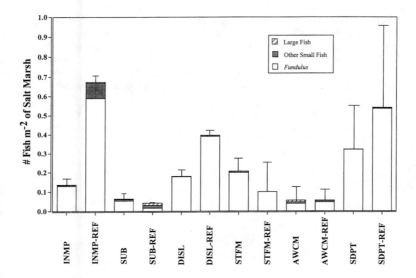

FIGURE 3.—Mean total fish density at all paired treatment (restored and created) and reference (REF) study sites, showing contribution of *Fundulus*, other small fish, and large fish to total. Vertical bars = 1 standard error of the mean for total density. See Table 1 for full spellings of site names.

history. Transient life history classifications for this study include the "spawner" (marine species that spawn in estuaries), "nursery" (marine species that spawn in ocean waters but use the estuary as a nursery), and "marine" (marine fish that visit the estuary as adults) classifications.

Mean total fish density ranged from $0.04/m^{-2}$ for the SUB reference marsh to $0.67/m^{-2}$ for the INMP reference marsh (Figure 3). *Fundulus* comprised from 39 to 99% of mean fish density at each marsh, followed by other small fish (0–31%) and large fish (0–29%; see below for large and small

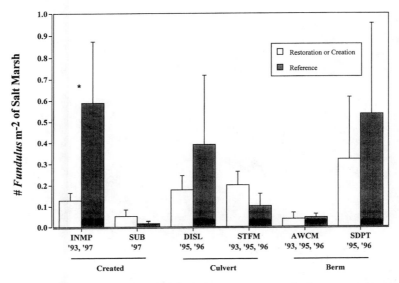

FIGURE 4.—Comparison of mean density of *Fundulus* between treatment and reference marshes at each study site, by two-way ANOVA. Treatment, year, and treatment by year were all significant ($p < 0.05$) for Inner North Mill Pond (INMP). There were no other significant main effects or interactions. Vertical bars = 1 standard error of the mean. The asterisk indicates the significant comparison. See Table 1 for full spellings of site names.

TABLE 3.—Fish species known to occur in Gulf of Maine salt-marsh estuaries. With the exception of the present study, all data are from unvegetated intertidal and subtidal creeks and channels. The Herring River study was located in Massachusetts, and the other studies were located in Maine, with the exception of the present study, which includes sites in New Hampshire and Maine. (For the second Little River and Webhannet River studies, data from vegetated marsh were not included due to paucity of species; these species also occurred in the present study's creek data. The Little and Webhannet rivers occur within the Wells National Estuarine Research Reserve, with Wells Harbor located at the mouth of the Webhannet River.)

Scientific name (common name)	Life history [a]	Present study	Herring River [b]	Little River [c]	Little River [d]	Wells Harbor [e]	Webhannet River [f]	Georgetown Little River [g]	Kennebec Point [h]	Bass Harbor [i]
Alosa aestivalis (blueback herring)	m(a)		X	X		X		X	X	
Alosa mediocris (hickory shad)	m(a)		X							
Alosa pseudoharengus (alewife)	m(a)		X	X		X		X	X	
Alosa sapidissima (American shad)	m(a)	X		X						
Brevoortia tyrannus (Atlantic menhaden)	t		X	X						X
Clupea harengus (Atlantic herring)	t	X		X		X		X	X	X
Ammodytes americanus (American sand lance)	t			X				X	X	
Anguilla rostrata (American eel)	m(c)	X	X	X	X	X		X		X
Apeltes quadracus (fourspine stickleback)	r	X	X	X	X	X	X	X	X	X
Gasterosteus aculeatus (threespine stickleback)	r	X		X	X	X	X	X	X	X
Gasterosteus wheatlandi (blackspotted stickleback)	r	X		X	X	X	X	X	X	X
Pungitius pungitius (ninespine stickleback)	r	X		X	X	X	X	X	X	X
Cyclopterus lumpus (lumpfish)	t			X				X	X	
Liparis atlanticus (seasnail)	t			X						
Decapterus macarellus (mackerel scad)	t								X	
Fundulus heteroclitus (mummichog)	r	X	X	X	X	X	X	X	X	X
Fundulus majalis (striped killifish)	r	X	X						X	
Gadus morhua (Atlantic cod)	t								X	
Microgadus tomcod (Atlantic tomcod)	t	X		X	X	X		X	X	
Pollachius virens (pollock)	t							X	X	X
Urophycis chuss (red hake)	t								X	
Urophycis tenuis (white hake)	t			X		X		X	X	

TABLE 3.—(continued.)

Scientific name (common name)	Life history [a]	Present study	Herring River [b]	Little River [c]	Little River [d]	Wells Harbor [e]	Webhannet River [f]	Georgetown Little River [g]	Kennebec Point [h]	Bass Harbor [i]
Pholis gunnellus (rock gunnel)	t			X				X		
Menidia beryllina (inland silverside)	r					X				
Menidia menidia (Atlantic silverside)	r	X	X	X	X	X	X	X	X	X
Menidia peninsulae (tidewater silverside)	r		X							
Morone americana (white perch)	t	X	X						X	
Morone saxatilis (striped bass)	t	X		X					X	
Mugil cephalus (striped mullet)	t			X						
Hemitriperus americanus (sea raven)	t								X	
Myoxocephalus aeneus (grubby)	t			X						
Myoxocephalus octodecimspinosus (longhorn sculpin)	t			X					X	
Myoxocephalus scorpius (shorthorn sculpin)	t							X	X	
Cryptacanthodes maculatus (wrymouth)	r							X		
Osmerus mordax (rainbow smelt)	m(a)			X		X		X	X	
Peprilus tricanthus (butterfish)	t			X						
Petromyzon marinus (sea lamprey)	m(a)			X						
Pleuronectes ferrugineus (yellowtail flounder)	t									X
Pseudopleuronectes americanus (winter flounder)	t		X	X	X			X	X	
Scopthalmus aquosus (windowpane flounder)	t			X						
Pomatomus saltatrix (bluefish)	t		X	X					X	
Salmo salar (Atlantic salmon)	m(a)			X						
Salmo trutta (brown trout)	m(a)			X						
Salvelinus fontinalis (brook trout)	m(a)			X						X
Scomber scombrus (Atlantic mackerel)	t		X	X						
Sphyraena borealis (northern sennet)	t			X						

394 DIONNE ET AL.

TABLE 3.—(continued.)

Scientific name (common name)	Life history [a]	Present study	Herring River [b]	Little River [c]	Little River [d]	Wells Harbor [e]	Webhannet River [f]	Georgetown Little River [g]	Kennebec Point [h]	Bass Harbor [i]
Syngnathus fuscus (northern pipefish)	t		X	X			X	X	X	X
Tautogolabrus adspersus (cunner)	t			X	X					
Total (48 species)		14	15	35	10	15	6	21	27	13

[a] r = marsh resident, m = migratory, c = catadromous, a = anadromous, and t = marine transient.
[b] See Roman 1987.
[c] M. Dionne, Wells National Estuarine Research Reserve, unpublished data.
[d] See Murphy 1991.
[e] See Ayvazian et al. 1992.
[f] See Murphy 1991.
[g] See Lamborghini 1982.
[h] See Lazzari et al. 1996.
[i] See Doering et al. 1995.

fish designation). Estimates of standing crop were obtained from fish density estimates (Figure 3) and area of the site (Table 1). The two created marshes supported mean standing crops of 544 fish (INMP) and 80 fish (SUB). The two berm marshes supported populations of 2,760 (AWCM) and 4,830 (SDPT) fish, and the two culvert marshes provided habitat for 9,900 (STFM) and 28,800–36,000 (DISL) fish.

Comparisons of fish occurrence between treatment and reference marshes at the six study sites revealed few significant differences in density, total length, or species number. Mean *Fundulus* density was significantly higher at the INMP reference site than at the INMP creation site (Figure 4) due to the great difference between creation sites and their reference sites in the first year after planting. Four years

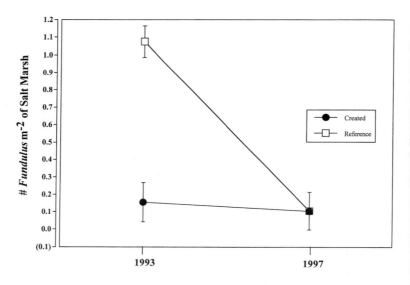

FIGURE 5.—Interaction of density and year effects for the created and reference marshes at Inner North Mill Pond. Data were analyzed as in Figure 4. Treatment, year, and treatment by year were all significant ($p < 0.05$). Vertical bars = 1 standard error of the mean.

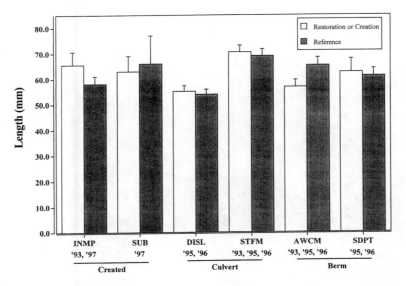

FIGURE 6.—Comparison of mean *Fundulus* total length between treatment and reference marshes at each study site. Vertical bars = 1 standard error of the mean. See Table 1 for full spellings of site names.

later, there was no difference between these marshes (Figure 5) as fish density in the reference marsh was lower in 1997 than in 1993. The total length (TL) of *Fundulus* in the fyke nets ranged from 30 to 130 mm TL, and the means were remarkably similar between treatment and reference marshes at every site (Figure 6), ranging from 53.9 to 70.5 mm. The occurrence and direction of significant statistical outcomes ($p < 0.05$) of analyses for density and total length of all small fishes (*Fundulus* plus other small fish) were the same as the analyses of density and total length for *Fundulus* alone.

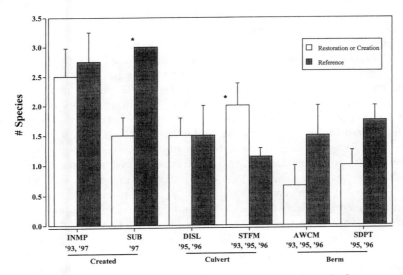

FIGURE 7.—Comparison of mean number of species of fishes between treatment and reference marshes at each study site. Data were analyzed as in Figure 4, except for SUB, where one-way ANOVA was used because the site was sampled in a single year (1997). There were significant differences ($p < 0.05$) in species number between the restored and created marshes at the STFM and SUB sites and their respective reference sites. There were no other significant main effects or interactions. Vertical bars = 1 standard error of the mean. Asterisks indicate significant comparisons. See Table 1 for full spellings of site names.

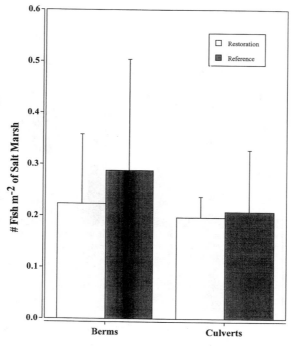

FIGURE 8.—Mean density of small fish (*Fundulus* plus other species) at culvert and berm sites (n = 10). Data were analyzed as in Figure 4. There was no significant effect of treatment or year for either culvert or berm restoration sites. Vertical bars = 1 standard error of the mean.

Mean number of fish species per sample was significantly greater at the STFM restored marsh than at the reference marsh and significantly greater at the SUB reference site at Inner Cutts Cove (ICC, Figure 1E) than for the SUB created marsh (SUB 1 and SUB 2 in IICC, Figure 1E) at Inner Inner Cutts Cove (Figure 7). There were no other significant differences for number of species between treatment marshes and their respective reference marshes. There was a trend toward fewer species in restored berm marshes (compared to reference marshes), whereas species numbers in the restored culvert marshes were the same as or greater than the numbers in the reference marshes.

When data were pooled within berm sites and culvert sites, there were no significant differences in small-fish density between restoration and reference marshes or between marsh types (Figure 8). The mean density was essentially the same for restored culvert marshes and reference culvert marshes ($0.20/m^{-2}$ and $0.21/m^{-2}$, respectively). The mean fish density was lower for the restored berm marshes than reference berm marshes ($0.223/m^{-2}$ and $0.288/m^{-2}$, respectively).

Of the 14 marine and estuarine fish species identified from all study sites, 3 species, *Anguilla rostrata, Microgadus tomcod*, and *Morone saxatilis*, were designated as "large fish" due to their three- to eightfold greater length compared to small fish. *Anguilla* occurred in 32% of all samples, and the other two species were rare (5% and 2% of all samples for *M. tomcod* and *M. saxatilis*, respectively). The mean density of large fish across all study sites did not differ between treatment and reference marshes (Figure 9). The same result was found for mean total length (Figure 9), but in this case, there was a trend toward larger mean size for fish captured in the reference marshes.

A comparison of the three reference marshes within a series of linked tidal basins draining into the Piscataqua River revealed significant effects of marsh basin, year, and the interaction of marsh basin and year for the mean density of *Fundulus* and small fish (Figure 10). There was a significant effect of year alone for large fish due to an increase in mean density from $0.002/m^{-2}$ in 1993–$0.010/m^{-2}$ in 1997. Six species were identified from OCC, compared to 4 and 3 species respectively from INMP

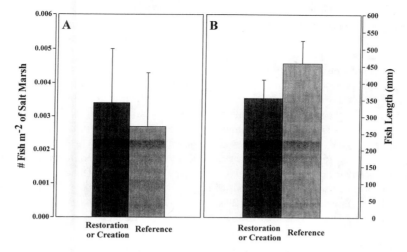

FIGURE 9.—Comparison between reference (n = 29) and treatment (data pooled across all study sites; n = 28) marshes for large fish density (A) and total length (B). There were no significant differences for either variable (p > 0.05 by Kruskal Wallis for fish density). A nonparametric test was used for the density analysis due to the large number of zero values. Vertical bars = 1 standard error of the mean.

and ICC (Table 2). Two of these fishes, *Morone saxatilis* and *Clupea harengus*, were unique to Outer Cutts Cove. There were no significant differences by marsh or year for mean species number, which ranged from 2.5 (ICC) to 3.5 (OCC).

Discussion

In this study we monitored fish utilization of manipulated and reference marshes at six locations within a small geographic area (less than 50 km along the coast from Drakes Island Marsh in Wells, Maine to

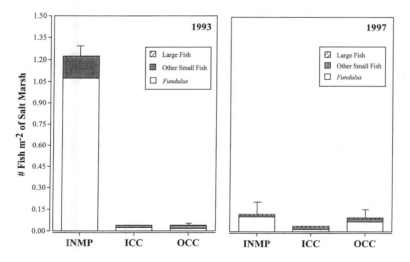

FIGURE 10.—Mean fish densities at three reference marshes in Portsmouth, New Hampshire during 1993 and 1997 (number of samples collected = 4 for each marsh). Both main effects (marsh, year) and their interaction were significant (p < 0.05 by two-way ANOVA) for mean *Fundulus* density and mean small-fish density due to the high densities of fish in the INMP reference marsh in 1993. Vertical bars = 1 standard error of the mean. See Table 1 for full spellings of site names.

Awcomin Marsh in Rye, New Hampshire). We sampled fish populations for one, two, or three years within the initial five-year postrestoration period (eight years in the case of Drakes Island) during the early response phase of marsh creation or restoration. The marsh resident *Fundulus heteroclitus* dominated the fish assemblage and comprised 93% of the mean total fish density. Of the 14 marine and estuarine species identified, more than half were marsh residents (8 species), followed by transients (3 species) that spawn in marine waters and use the marshes as larvae or juveniles, and migratory species (3 species) that use the marshes both as juveniles and adults. This assemblage represents 29% of the 48 fishes known to occur in salt-marsh-dominated estuaries in the Gulf of Maine (Lamborghini 1982; Roman 1987; Murphy 1991; Ayvazian et al. 1992; Doering et al. 1995; Lazzari et al. 1996; Cartwright 1997), including most of the marsh resident species in the Gulf of Maine (Table 3). Elsewhere along the Atlantic coast, marsh residents are known to use the vegetated marsh surface to a much greater degree than other groups of fish that occur in salt-marsh estuaries (Kneib 1984; Talbot and Able 1984; Kneib 1987a, 1987b; McIvor and Odum 1988; Murphy 1991; Rozas 1995; Kneib 1997a).

Overall, we found that fish densities, total length, and species numbers were similar and temporally stable among manipulated and reference marshes. The exception to this pattern was for the INMP created marsh, where fish densities were significantly greater in the reference marsh than the created marsh in 1993 but not in 1997. Sampling error is the parsimonious explanation for this result. Alternatively, the high fish density in the reference marsh could have been an effect of natural annual variation rather than sampling error. The development of the created marsh over five growing seasons could have caused the convergence of fish densities between planted and reference marshes from the initial difference during the first growing season. This interpretation assumes that fish density in the created marsh would have been significantly lower in 1997 if it had been planted in 1996 and 1997 rather than in 1992 and 1993. Fish utilization of the other planted marsh site (SUB) was similar to the reference marsh upon its initial sampling in 1997, but this marsh was sampled during the fourth growing season since its creation, allowing the vegetation to increase in density. Our picture of fish utilization of these created marshes over time would be improved if mitigation plans required that sampling occur at least biannually over the first five years of marsh development (year one, year

three, and year five). Biannual sampling provides the minimum replication necessary for statistical analysis of annual change.

A nonsignificant trend in the data suggested that fish utilize elevated marshes restored by dug channels to a lesser degree than impounded marshes restored by culverts (Figure 8). Even though these data are merely suggestive, it is useful to discuss some potential differences in the restoration of elevated marshes and culverted marshes. Reduced fish densities may persist after hydrologic restoration of marshes elevated by berms because of the inverse relationship between the period of inundation (over the diurnal tidal cycle) and elevation. Channels dug through a raised area of marsh may improve drainage of freshwater from the marsh, and therefore help control *Phragmites*, but the channels will not always restore the pattern of tidal inundation critical for fish access. Depending on their construction, dug channels could provide significant low-marsh fish habitat along their banks or in the lower-elevation area within berms. The channels at Awcomin Marsh and Sandy Point had shallow, vertical banks that did not support plant growth, and adjacent high marsh (especially at Stuart Farm) experienced considerably shorter periods of tidal inundation than reference marsh sites even though flooding was increased during spring tides. Conversely, the restored marshes at Drakes Island and Stuart Farm had lower elevations than the reference sites due to soil subsidence typical of impounded and drained salt-marsh peats. The period of tidal inundation at both of these restored culvert marshes was considerably longer than at the reference marshes due to the lower elevations of the restored marshes. In addition, the period of tidal inundation at the Drakes Island salt marsh was augmented by slow drainage on the ebb tide through the undersized culvert (Burdick et al. 1997). The relationship between marsh elevation and pattern of inundation should be accounted for in designing fish monitoring programs for marsh restoration projects.

At Stuart Farm, the restored marsh area underwent a process of colonization and succession by salt-marsh plants after saltwater from the tidal restoration killed the freshwater marsh vegetation. At Drakes Island, the entire 16–20-ha restored marsh area was dominated by *Spartina alterniflora*, creating an expanse of contiguous low marsh unusual in New England. For marsh resident fishes, prolonged inundation of emergent vegetation can create optimal conditions for feeding, growth, and survival. The dimensions and vertical placement of culverts can also influence the movement of fish to and from restored marshes. At Drakes Island, the small diameter and long traverse of the culvert pipe likely had a negative influence on fish movement compared to the shorter and much wider culvert at Stuart Farm. The significantly higher number of species at the restored marsh at Stuart Farm compared to the reference marsh coupled with a trend toward higher fish densities suggested that there was little interference in the movement of fish by the culvert. The restored and reference marshes at Drakes Island had the same mean number of fish species, although fish density trended lower in the restored marsh in spite of the expansive low-marsh habitat. Tidal movement of the fishes may have been reduced by the long, narrow culvert. Physical and behavioral barriers to fish passage should be considered in the design of marsh restoration and creation projects.

The comparison of manipulated marshes with local reference marshes not only provides an internal standard for the monitoring of each restoration project but also makes it possible (1) to follow changes over time while accounting for natural annual variation and (2) to make valid comparisons of the magnitude and direction of these changes between unrelated restoration projects. If the "appropriate" reference is selected (see below for discussion of reference site selection), this approach will provide a more valid test of the functioning of a manipulated site than the use of fixed benchmarks (Brinson and Rheinhardt 1996; Simenstad and Thom 1996) based on the average performance of undisturbed systems within the region, especially over the short term.

How are the results of monitoring affected by the selection of the reference marsh? Although our study was not specifically designed to investigate this question, we attempted to address it by comparing the variation in fish distributions across three natural fringing marshes in a series of tidally connected basins in Portsmouth Harbor. Inner North Mill Pond (INMP, Figure 1D) is the tidal basin at the head of tide, upstream from Inner Inner Cutts Cove (IICC), Inner Cutts Cove (ICC), and Outer Cutts Cove (OCC) (Figure 1E). Because of the general size, micro-topography, and locality of these latter three marshes, each could have been considered as a reference for the INMP or SUB created marshes. There were significant differences in fish density among the reference marshes due to the much higher density in 1993 of fish in INMP (an urban tidal pond)

than in ICC or OCC. These two downstream sites were in contiguous basins, one in a tidal backwater flanking a major roadway (ICC), the other adjacent to the main stem of the Piscataqua River (OCC). In addition, the species assemblage from OCC contained two fishes (Atlantic herring and striped bass) not found in any other marsh area. The herring entered the marsh as a large school. These species' presence may have been due to the location of the marsh in a narrow, deepwater cove connected to the Piscataqua River mainstem. The movement of water in Gulf of Maine salt-marsh ecosystems is highly directional. At low tide, nearshore water enters from an inlet and progresses upstream so that the marsh is inundated in a sequential pattern. Fish entering the marsh system with the flooding tide will encounter some marsh sites before others depending on marsh size, drainage density (pattern of channels and creeks), and site location. Reference and manipulated sites should be located to minimize the influence of sequential inundation of the marsh surface on fish distribution and abundance, so as not to confound the influence of restoration-specific differences between the sites.

Our study provides the first density estimates for fishes in vegetated salt-marsh habitat in the Gulf of Maine. Most prior studies of fish distribution and abundance in salt marshes of the Gulf of Maine have relied on measures of relative abundance and have been restricted to sampling within intertidal and subtidal waters (Lamborghini 1982; Roman 1987; Murphy 1991; Doering et al. 1995; Lazzari et al. 1996; Cartwright 1997). Ayvazian et al. (1992) used dimension-adjusted (i.e., accounting for the area sampled) seine and trawl data to estimate fish densities in intertidal channels within a Gulf of Maine salt marsh and determined a mean annual fish density of $0.64/m^{-2}$ for channel samples taken adjacent to vegetated marsh. Mean total fish density in this study ranged from $0.05/m^{-2}$ to $0.67/m^{-2}$. The highest mean densities found at our study sites just overlap with some of the lower mean densities measured for vegetated marsh in Virginia ($1.8/m^{-2}$, Varnell and Havens 1995); Georgia ($0.7/m^{-2}$, Kneib and Wagner 1994); Louisiana ($26.0 m^{-2}$, Baltz et al. 1993; $5.3 m^{-2}$, Rozas and Reed 1994); and Texas ($0.3 m^{-2}$ to $7.3 m^{-2}$, Minello et al. 1994). The Virginian, Carolinian, and Louisianan tidal wetlands in the preceding studies are low marsh dominated by *Spartina alterniflora*. The greatest fish densities in our study occurred in the reference sites at Inner North Mill Pond ($0.7 m^{-2}$)

and Sandy Point ($0.5/m^{-2}$). These marsh areas were fringing *Spartina alterniflora* low marsh, as opposed to the *Spartina patens*-dominated high marsh of the Drakes Island, Stuart Farm, and Awcomin Marsh reference areas. Further, the fish assemblages at the low-marsh-only study sites at INMP, SUB, and OCC did not include any of the four stickleback species (Table 2). The data suggest a difference in fish utilization between low- and high-marsh zones that merits further investigation, given that both of these marsh types are important habitats in the Gulf of Maine. The creation of salt marsh on the Atlantic and Gulf of Mexico coasts has focused primarily on low marsh, but most opportunities for marsh restoration in the Northeast occur in marsh systems with both high and low marsh, where the area of low marsh tends to comprise 10–20% of the total marsh area (Nixon 1982).

In this study, we have documented the occurrence of fishes in restored, created, and reference salt-marsh habitats, but we have not determined how these habitats influence fish survival and growth. Salt-marsh estuaries are physically and hydrologically complex systems with a number of different habitats that can be separated or connected depending on tidal stage. Fish can move with the tides to and from open bay waters, subtidal channels, intertidal creeks, rivulets and puddles, low marsh edge, low marsh interior, high marsh edge, high marsh interior, and salt pannes. Recent studies have focused on understanding how life history and developmental stage interact with tides and seasons to determine occurrence and feeding of fish species in these habitats (Kneib 1984, 1987a, 1987b; McIvor and Odum 1988; Rozas et al. 1988; Deegan 1990; Murphy 1991; Rountree and Able 1992a, 1992b; Baltz et al. 1993; Kneib 1994; Kneib and Wagner 1994; Minello et al. 1994; Smith and Able 1994; Miltner et al. 1995; Szedlmayer and Able 1996; Deegan and Garritt 1997; Kneib 1997b). The emerging view is that small marsh residents feed within the vegetated marsh on the high tides and then overlap with and serve as prey for juvenile transient fishes in the intertidal and subtidal habitats as the tides recede. As the juvenile transients grow and mature they move to the open bay areas of the estuary and coastal ocean, finishing the "trophic relay" (Kneib 1997a) of productivity from the vegetated salt marsh to the open marine ecosystem.

The use of marshes by nekton is often considered a criterion of success for salt-marsh mitigation projects (Matthews and Minello 1994). In the present study, it appears that fish will readily visit restored and created marshes in assemblages similar to those found in reference marshes but are subject to the influence of differences in tidal regime, access to marsh habitat, and possibly density of vegetation. This result is not surprising, given the mobility of fish and the general tendency of many littoral fishes to investigate physical structures (e.g., plant stems).

Visitation is necessary but not sufficient evidence for the value of restored and created marsh as fish habitat. From the results of this study, we cannot determine how fish growth and survival in manipulated marshes compares to that in natural marshes. Studies comparing the benthic invertebrate fauna of manipulated and reference marshes indicate that invertebrate prey abundance and availability for fishes can be significantly reduced in created marshes during the first 10–20 years postcreation (Posey et al. 1997). Reduced abundance of benthic invertebrates may be related to the generally low organic content of created marsh soils (Langis et al. 1991; Moy and Levin 1991; Sacco et al. 1994; Scatolini and Zedler 1996). In at least one study, however, densities and diversity of benthic infauna in a created marsh came to resemble the reference marsh within six months (Levin et al. 1996). Moy and Levin (1991) reported lower fish densities but increased feeding in a created marsh due to the increased abundance of polychaetes, which were more accessible to fish than the oligochaetes that characterized the reference marsh. Comparable studies of marsh benthic infauna have not been carried out for restored marshes, but in a study of fish feeding within intertidal ditches in a tidally restored marsh, fish had reduced feeding success compared to fish in a downstream reference marsh (Allen et al. 1994). From the differing results of these studies, it appears that variation in prey availability is an important factor in determining the value of created and restored salt marshes for fish. Measures of fish feeding or growth should be added to the criteria for determining this value.

It appears from our study that both created and restored marshes can be visited by fish assemblages comparable to those found in reference marshes over the short term (1–5 years), as found at Inner North Mill Pond, Stuart Farm, and Awcomin Marsh. Nonsignificant trends in the data also suggest that fish access to vegetated marsh habitat may be restricted by inadequate culvert dimensions as at Drakes Island or inadequate marsh flooding as at Sandy Point. Additional study is needed to further support this interpretation. After they gain access to subtidal marsh channels, the ability of fish to utilize the marsh surface is directly related to the period of marsh inundation. Inundation patterns are primarily a function of tidal restriction and marsh elevation. In the large majority of cases, hydrologic restoration of tidally restricted marshes will improve a much greater area of fish habitat per unit cost than creation of new marsh and will not be subject to many of the constraints that limit the function of created marshes (Zedler 1996).

The primary consideration in tidal restoration projects is not necessarily the cost of construction but the social, economic, and political issues that must be addressed. Often, tidally restricted marshes are in highly developed coastal areas where local residents may perceive the restoration of tidal flow as a threat, even when flood hazard studies show that no such threat exists. This has been the case at Drakes Island Marsh, where property owners in the vicinity of the restored marsh still strongly advocate replacement of a culvert flap gate 10 years after tidal flow was restored. In spite of this caution, hundreds of hectares of coastal fish habitat can be improved through a concerted program to restore the hydrology of tidally restricted marshes in the Gulf of Maine (Dionne et al. 1998).

Acknowledgments

Field assistance was provided by S. Orringer, T. Smith, J. Spicer, K. Schierer, R. Boumans, T. Corneau, A. Bowden, and P. Morgan. Discussions with R. Langton and D. Allen were valuable. In addition, S. Orringer assisted with the production of tables and figures. We thank L. Merril and J. Merril for their cooperation. Funding was provided by the National Estuarine Research Reserve Program of the Estuarine Reserves Division of the National Oceanic and Atmospheric Administration, Department of Commerce (Award # NA57OR0343); The Coastal Program, Office of State Planning, New Hampshire; The Laudholm Trust, Wells, Maine; and the Oak Knoll Foundation, Rowley, Massachusetts. Monitoring of the mitigation sites was supported by the New Hampshire Department of Transportation and New Hampshire Port Authority. New Hampshire–Maine Sea Grant provided support for preparation and presentation of the manuscript. We also acknowledge support from the Wells National Estuarine Research Reserve and Jackson Estuarine Laboratory, Center for Marine Biology, University of New Hampshire. This is JEL contribution number 339.

References

Allen, E. A., P. E. Fell, M. A. Peck, J. A. Gieg, C. R. Guthke, and M. D. Newkirk. 1994. Gut contents of common mummichogs, *Fundulus heteroclitus* L. in a restored impounded marsh and natural reference marshes. Estuaries 2:462–471.

Ayvazian, S. G., L. A. Deegan, and J. T. Finn. 1992. Comparison of habitat use by estuarine fish assemblages in the Acadian and Virginian zoogeographic provinces. Estuaries 15:368–383.

Baltz, D. M., C. Rakocinski, and J. W. Fleeger. 1993. Microhabitat use by marsh-edge fishes in a Louisiana estuary. Environmental Biology of Fishes 36:109–126.

Boesch, D. F., and R. E. Turner. 1984. Dependence of fishery species on salt marshes: the role of food and refuge. Estuaries 7(4A):460–468.

Bosworth, W., and F. T. Short. 1993. Mitigation plan for the New Hampshire Commercial Marine Terminal Development Project in Portsmouth, New Hampshire. Balsam Environmental Consultants, Inc., Jackson Estuarine Laboratory, and Great Meadow Farms, Report to U.S. Army Corps of Engineers, New England Division, Waltham, Massachusetts.

Bozeman, E. L., and J. M. Dean. 1980. The abundance of estuarine larval fish in a South Carolina intertidal creek. Estuaries 3:89–97.

Brinson, M. M., and R. Rheinhardt. 1996. The role of reference wetlands in functional assessment and mitigation. Ecological Applications 6:69–76.

Bryan, R., M. Dionne, R. Cook, J. Jones, and A. Goodspeed. 1997. Maine citizen's guide to evaluating, restoring, and managing tidal marshes. Maine Audubon Society, Falmouth.

Buchsbaum, R., D. Burdick, and M. Chandler. 1997. Challenges of restoring estuarine habitats in the southern Gulf of Maine. Pages 170–182 *in* C. White, editor. Rim of the Gulf: restoring estuaries and resources. Island Institute, Rockland, Maine.

Burdick, D. M., M. Dionne, R. M. Boumans, and F. T. Short. 1997. Ecological responses to tidal restorations of two northern New England salt marshes. Wetlands Ecology and Management 4:129–144.

Cartwright, M. A. 1997. Dietary habits of benthic-feeding fishes in a Southern Maine salt marsh: evaluation of prey availability and feeding selectivity. Doctoral dissertation. University of Maine, Orono.

Chadwick, J. 1997. Shepody Bay and the Petitcodiac River causeway. Pages 112–123 *in* C. White, editor. Rim of the Gulf: restoring estuaries and resources. Island Institute, Rockland, Maine.

Cook, R. A., A. J. L. Stone, and A. P. Ammann. 1993. Method for the evaluation and inventory of vegetated tidal marshes in New Hampshire (coastal method). Audubon Society of New Hampshire, Concord.

Cooper, A. J., and F. Chapleau. 1998. Monophyly and intrarelationships of the family. Pleuronectidae (Pleuronectiformes), with a revised classification. U.S. National Marine Fisheries Service Fishery Bulletin 96:686–726.

Cowardin, L. M., V. Carter, F. C. Golet, and E. T. La Roe. 1979. Classification of wetlands and deepwater habitats of the United States. FWS/OBS-79/31, U.S. Fish and Wildlife Service, Office of Biological Services, Washington, D.C.

Day, J. W., Jr., C. A. S. Hall, W. M. Kemp, A. Yanez-Arancibia, and L. A. Deegan. 1989. Nekton, the free swimming consumers. Pages 377–437 in J. W. Day, C. A. S. Hall, W. M. Kemp, and A. Yanez-Arancibia, editors. Estuarine ecology. John Wiley, New York.

Deegan, L. A. 1990. Effects of estuarine environmental conditions on populations dynamics of young-of-the year Gulf menhaden. Marine Ecology Progress Series 68:195–205.

Deegan, L. A. 1993. Nutrient and energy transport between estuaries and coastal marine ecosystems by fish migration. Canadian Journal of Fisheries and Aquatic Sciences 50:74–79.

Deegan, L. A., and R. H. Garritt. 1997. Evidence for spatial variability in estuarine food webs. Marine Ecology Progress Series 147:31–47.

Deegan, L. A., B. J. Peterson, and R. Portier. 1990. Stable isotopes and cellulase activity as evidence of detritus as a food source for juvenile Gulf menhaden. Estuaries 13:14–19.

Dionne, M. 1994. Coastal habitat alteration. Pages 113–120 in D. Stevenson and E. Braasch, editors. Gulf of Maine habitat: workshop proceedings. Regional Association for Research in the Gulf of Maine Report 94–2. RARGOM, Hanover, New Hampshire.

Dionne, M., D. Burdick, R. Cook, R. Buchsbaum, and S. Fuller. 1998. Physical alterations to water flow and salt marshes: protecting and restoring flow and habitat in Gulf of Maine salt marshes and watersheds. Final draft of working paper for Secretariat of the Commission for Environmental Cooperation. Montreal, Canada.

Doering, P. H., C. T. Roman, L. L. Beatty, A. A. Keller, and C. A. Oviatt. 1995. Water quality and habitat evaluation of Bass Harbor Marsh-Acadia National Park, Maine. Technical Report NPS/NESORNR/NRTR/95-31. U.S. Department of the Interior, National Park Service, New England System Support Office, Boston.

Felley, J. D. 1987. Nekton assemblages of three tributaries to the Calcasieu estuary, Louisiana. Estuaries 10:321–329.

Frenkel, R. E., and J. C. Morlan. 1991. Can we restore our salt marshes? Lessons from the Salmon River, Oregon. The Northwest Environmental Journal 7:119–135.

Gordon, D. C., Jr., and P. J. Cranford. 1994. Export of organic matter from macrotidal salt marshes in the upper Bay of Fundy, Canada. Pages 257–264 in W. J. Mitsch, editor. Global wetlands: old world and new. Elsevier, New York.

Hettler, W. F., Jr. 1989. Nekton use of regularly-flooded saltmarsh cordgrass habitat in North Carolina, USA. Marine Ecology Progress Series 56:111–118.

Irlandi, E. A., and M. K. Crawford. 1997. Habitat linkages: the effect of intertidal saltmarshes and adjacent subtidal habitats on abundance, movement, and growth of an estuarine fish. Oecologia 110:222–230.

Jacobson, H. A, G. L. Jacobson, Jr., and J. T. Kelley. 1987. Distribution and abundance of tidal marshes along the coast of Maine. Estuaries 10:126–131.

Kelley, J. T., D. F. Belknap, G. L. Jacobson, Jr., and H. A. Jacobson. 1988. The morphology and origin of salt marshes along the glaciated coast of Maine, USA. Journal of Coastal Research 4:649–666.

Kneib, R. T. 1984. Patterns in the utilization of the intertidal salt marsh by larvae and juveniles of Fundulus heteroclitus (Linnaeus) and Fundulus luciae (Baird). Journal of Experimental Marine Biology and Ecology 83:41–51.

Kneib, R. T. 1987a. Predation risk and use of intertidal habitats by young fishes and shrimp. Ecology 68:379–386.

Kneib, R. T. 1987b. Seasonal abundance, distribution and growth of postlarval and juvenile grass shrimp (Palaemonetes pugio) in a Georgia, USA, salt marsh. Marine Biology 96:215–223.

Kneib, R. T. 1991. Flume weir for quantitative collection of nekton from vegetated intertidal habitats. Marine Ecology Progress Series 75:29–38.

Kneib, R. T. 1993. Growth and mortality in successive cohorts of fish larvae within an estuarine nursery. Marine Ecology Progress Series 94:115–127.

Kneib, R. T. 1994. Spatial pattern, spatial scale, and feeding in fishes. Pages 171–185 in D. J. Stouder et al. editors. Theory and application in fish feeding ecology. University of South Carolina Press, Columbia.

Kneib, R. T. 1997a. The role of tidal marshes in the ecology of estuarine nekton. Oceanography and Marine Biology 35:163–220.

Kneib, R. T. 1997b. Early life stages of resident nekton in intertidal marshes. Estuaries 20:214–230.

Kneib, R. T., and S. L. Wagner. 1994. Nekton use of vegetated marsh habitats at different stages of tidal inundation. Marine Ecology Progress Series 106:227–238.

Kusler, J. A., and M. E. Kentula, editors. 1990. Wetland creation and restoration: the status of the science. Island Press, Washington D.C.

Lamborghini, P. L. 1982. Seasonal abundance, temporal variation, and food habits of fishes in a Maine salt marsh creek system. Master's thesis. University of Maine, Orono.

Langis, R., M. Zalejko, and J. B. Zedler. 1991. Nitrogen assessments in a constructed and a natural salt marsh of San Diego Bay. Ecological Applications 1:40–51.

Lazzari, M. A., and six coauthors. 1996. Seasonal and annual variation in abundance and species composition of nearshore fish communities in Maine. Maine Department of Marine Resources, West Boothbay Harbor.

Levin, L. A., D. Talley, and G. Thayer. 1996. Succession of macrobenthos in a created salt marsh. Marine Ecology Progress Series 141:67–82.

Matthews, G. A., and T. J. Minello. 1994. Technology and success in restoration, creation, and enhancement of Spartina alterniflora marshes in the United States. Decision Analysis Series No. 2., U.S. Department of Commerce, National Oceanic and Atmospheric Administration, Coastal Ocean Office, Washington, D.C.

McIvor, C. C., and W. E. Odum. 1988. Food, predation risk, and microhabitat selection in a marsh fish assemblage. Ecology 69:1341–1351.

Miltner, R. J., S. W. Ross, and M. H. Posey. 1995. Influence of food and predation on the depth distribution of juvenile spot (*Leiostomus xanthurus*) in tidal nurseries. Canadian Journal of Fisheries and Aquatic Sciences 52:971–982.

Minello, T. J., and J. W. Webb, Jr. 1997. Use of natural and created *Spartina alterniflora* salt marshes by fishery species and other aquatic fauna in Galveston Bay, Texas, USA. Marine Ecology Progress Series 151:165–179.

Minello, T. J., R. J. Zimmerman, and R. Medina. 1994. The importance of edge for natant macrofauna in a created marsh. Wetlands 14:184–198.

Moy, L. D., and L. A. Levin. 1991. Are *Spartina* marshes a replaceable resource? A functional approach to evaluation of marsh creation efforts. Estuaries 14:1–16.

Murphy, S. C. 1991. The ecology of estuarine fishes in southern Maine high salt marshes: access corridors and movement patterns. Master's thesis. University of Massachusetts, Amherst.

Nixon, S. W. 1982. The ecology of New England high salt marshes: a community profile. FWS/OBS-81/55, U.S. Fish and Wildlife Service, Office of Biological Services, Washington, D.C.

Orson, R. A., R. S. Warren, W. A. Niering, and P. Van Patten. 1998. Research in New England marsh-estuarine ecosystems: directions and priorities into the next millennium. Connecticut Sea Grant, University of Connecticut, Groton.

Peterson, G. W., and R. E. Turner. 1994. The value of salt marsh edge vs. interior as a habitat for fish and decapod crustaceans in a Louisiana salt marsh. Estuaries 17(1B):235–262.

Portnoy, J. W., and I. Valiela. 1997. Short-term effects of salinity reduction and drainage on salt-marsh biogeochemical cycling and *Spartina* (cordgrass) production. Estuaries 20:569–578.

Posey, M. H., T. D. Alphin, and C. M. Powell. 1997. Plant and infaunal communities associated with a created marsh. Estuaries 20:42–47.

Reiner, E. L. 1989. The biological aspects of salt marsh protection, restoration and creation in Massachusetts. Master's thesis. Northeastern University, Boston.

Rogers, S. G., T. E. Targett, and S. B. VanZant. 1984. Fish-nursery use in Georgia salt-marsh estuaries: the influence of springtime freshwater conditions. Transactions of the American Fisheries Society 113:595–606.

Roman, C. T. 1987. An evaluation of alternatives for estuarine restoration management: the Herring River ecosystem (Cape Cod National Seashore). Center for Coastal and Environmental Studies, National Park Service Cooperative Research Unit, Rutgers, The State University of New Jersey, New Brunswick.

Roman, C. T., W. A. Niering, and R. S. Warren. 1984. Salt marsh vegetation change in response to tidal restriction. Environmental Management 8:141–150.

Rountree, R. A., and K. W. Able. 1992a. Foraging habits, growth, and temporal patterns of salt-marsh creek habitat use by young-of-year summer flounder in New Jersey. Transactions of the American Fisheries Society 121:765–776.

Rountree, R. A., and K. W. Able. 1992b. Fauna of polyhaline subtidal marsh creeks in southern New Jersey: composition, abundance, and biomass. Estuaries 15:171–185.

Rountree, R. A., and K. W. Able. 1993. Diel variation in decapod crustacean and fish assemblages in New Jersey polyhaline marsh creeks. Estuarine, Coastal and Shelf Science 37:181–201.

Rozas, L. P. 1995. Hydroperiod and its influence on nekton use of the salt marsh: a pulsing ecosystem. Estuaries 18:579–590.

Rozas, L. P., C. C. McIvor, and W. E. Odum. 1988. Intertidal rivulets and creekbanks: corridors between tidal creeks and marshes. Marine Ecology Progress Series 47:303–307.

Rozas, L. P., and T. J. Minello. 1997. Estimating densities of small fishes and decapod crustaceans in shallow estuarine habitats: a review of sampling design with focus on gear selection. Estuaries 20:199–213.

Rozas, L. P., and D. J. Reed. 1994. Comparing nekton assemblages of subtidal habitats in pipeline canals traversing brackish and saline marshes in coastal Louisiana. Wetlands 14:262–275.

Rozsa, R. 1988. An overview of wetland restoration projects of Connecticut. Pages 1–11 *in* M. Lefor and W. Kennard, editors. Proceedings of the IV Wetland Conference. Connecticut Institute of Water Resources, University of Connecticut, Storrs.

Rozsa, R. 1995. Tidal wetland restoration in Connecticut. Pages 51–65 *in* G. D. Dreyer and W. A. Niering, editors. Tidal marshes of Long Island Sound: ecology, history and restoration. Connecticut College Arboretum Bulletin 34. Connecticut College Arboretum, New London.

Sacco, J. N., E. D. Seneca, and T. R. Wentworth. 1994. Infaunal community development of artificially established salt marshes in North Carolina. Estuaries 17:489–500.

Scatolini, S., and J. B. Zedler. 1996. Epibenthic invertebrates of natural and constructed marshes of San Diego Bay. Wetlands 16:24–37.

Shenker, J., and J. M. Dean. 1979. The utilization of an intertidal salt marsh creek by larval and juvenile fishes: abundance, diversity and temporal variation. Estuaries 2:154–163.

Simenstad, C. A., and R. M. Thom. 1996. Functional equivalency trajectories of the restored GOG-LE-HI-TE estuarine wetland. Ecological Applications 6:38–56.

Sinicrope, T. L., P. G. Hine, R. S. Warren, and W. A. Niering. 1990. Restoration of an impounded salt marsh in New England. Estuaries 13:25–30.

Smith, K. J., and K. W. Able. 1994. Salt-marsh tide pools as winter refuges for the mummichog, *Fundulus heteroclitus*, in New Jersey. Estuaries 17:226–234.

Smith, S. M., J. G. Hoff, S. P. O'Neil, and M. P. Weinstein. 1984. Community and trophic organization of nekton utilizing shallow marsh habitats, York River, Virginia. Fishery Bulletin 82:455–467.

Szedlmayer, S. T., and K. W. Able. 1996. Patterns of seasonal availability and habitat use by fishes and decapod crustaceans in a southern New Jersey estuary. Estuaries 19:697–709.

Talbot, C. W., and K. W. Able. 1984. Composition and distribution of larval fishes in New Jersey high marshes. Estuaries 7(4A):434–443.

USDASCS (U.S. Department of Agriculture Soil Conservation Service). 1994. Evaluation of restorable salt marshes in New Hampshire. U.S. Department of Agriculture, Durham, New Hampshire.

Varnell, L. M., and K. J. Havens. 1995. A comparison of dimension-adjusted catch data methods for assessment of fish and crab abundance in intertidal salt marshes. Estuaries 18:319–325.

Weinstein, M. P. 1979. Shallow marsh habitats as primary nursery areas for fish and shellfish, Cape Fear River, North Carolina. Fishery Bulletin 77:339–357.

Weinstein, M. P., J. H. Balletto, J. M. Teal, and D. F. Ludwig. 1997. Success criteria and adaptive management for a large-scale wetland restoration project. Wetlands Ecology and Management 4:111–127.

Weinstein, M. P., and M. F. Walters. 1981. Growth, survival and production in young-of-the-year populations of *Leiostomus xanthurus* Lacepede, residing in tidal creeks. Estuaries 4:185–197.

Zedler, J. B. 1996. Ecological issues in wetland mitigation: an introduction to the forum. Ecological Applications 6:33–37.

Zimmerman, R. J., T. J. Minello, and G. Zamora. 1984. Selection of vegetated habitat by *Penaeus aztecus* in a Galveston Bay salt marsh. Fishery Bulletin 82:325–336.

American Fisheries Society Symposium 22:405–420, 1999
© Copyright by the American Fisheries Society 1999

Coastal Wetland Restoration and Its Potential Impact on Fishery Resources in the Northeastern United States

MARK D. MINTON

Western Pacific Regional Fishery Management Council
1164 Bishop Street, Suite 1405, Honolulu, Hawaii 96814, USA

Abstract.—The importance of coastal wetlands to a large number of commercially important marine fish species for spawning, nursery, and foraging habitat is a commonly held belief. Few studies to substantiate this belief have been conducted in the northeastern United States. This paper examines in detail the life histories and habitat requirements of three species of fish commonly found in salt marshes in the northeastern United States. The results indicate that valuable commercial and recreational species of fish and their prey require coastal wetlands as habitat during their life cycles in New England. Coastal wetland restoration projects will increase the abundance of wetland habitat types required by commercial and recreational species of marine fish. The restoration of the salt marsh within the Galilee Bird Sanctuary in Narragansett, Rhode Island is used as case study. When enhancement of fishery habitat value is a goal of a restoration project, the project should incorporate certain design features. However, the designers of many salt-marsh restoration projects assume that reestablishment of salt-marsh vegetation will result in recolonization by other species of animals.

The restoration of coastal wetlands as a policy of federal and state governments has grown and expanded in recent years. The growing interest in wetlands restoration is a response to the continued loss of coastal wetlands and an increased awareness and understanding of the valuable ecological functions that coastal wetlands serve. The importance of coastal wetlands to a large number of commercially important marine fish species for spawning, nursery, and foraging habitat is a commonly held belief (Day et al. 1989; Mitsch and Gosselink 1993). This function of coastal wetlands is often cited as one of the significant values of coastal wetlands that should be protected, preserved, and restored; both federal and state legislation relating to the preservation, protection, and restoration of coastal wetlands refer to this function.

Few systematic studies of salt-marsh fish communities of the northeastern United States have been conducted to substantiate the importance of salt marshes as spawning, nursery, and foraging habitat (Nixon and Oviatt 1973; Werme 1981; Talbot and Able 1984; Talbot et al. 1986; Murphy 1991; Rountree 1992; Rountree and Able 1992). Many of the studies of nekton use of salt-marsh habitats conducted in the region have focused on the fishery resources of nearshore estuarine waters (Pearcy and Richards 1962; Mulkana 1966; Briggs and O'Conner 1971; Nixon and Oviatt 1973; Stolgitis et al. 1976; Hoff and Ibara 1977; Marteinsdottir 1984; Satchwill and Sisson 1991; Short 1992). Moreover, many of the available studies of fish use of salt marsh focus

on a single species (Chidester 1920; Butner and Brattstrom 1960; Horton 1965; Wright 1972; Lotrich 1975; Valiela et al. 1977; Allen et al. 1994).

Most studies verifying the use of coastal salt marshes as spawning, nursery, and foraging habitat by marine fish and invertebrates have been conducted in the southeastern and Gulf coast regions of the United States (Harrington and Harrington 1961; Subrahmanyam and Drake 1975; Weinstein 1979; Subrahmanyam and Coultas 1980; Weinstein et al. 1980; Rozas and Hackney 1984; Smith et al. 1984; Zimmerman and Minello 1984; McGovern and Wenner 1990; Murphy 1991; Rountree 1992; Peterson and Turner 1994). Marshes are used as primary nursery habitats by numerous valuable commercial and recreational species of fish and invertebrates in these regions (Cain and Dean 1976; Shenker and Dean 1979; Weinstein 1979; Bozeman and Dean 1980; Hettler 1989; Herke et al. 1992; Kneib and Wagner 1994).

This paper draws on the available literature to document the extent to which a link exists between coastal wetlands and valuable species of fish or their prey in the northeastern United States. A detailed analysis of the preferred habitats of the Atlantic silverside *Menidia menidia*, summer flounder *Paralichthys dentatus*, and winter flounder *Pleuronectes americanus* [1] is provided. The paper also discusses design features that salt-marsh restoration projects should incorporate if enhancement of

---

[1] Cooper and Chapleau (1998) have revised the scientific name of winter flounder to *Pseudopleuronectes americanus*.

fisheries habitat value is a goal of a restoration project. In addition, this paper considers the policy aspects of wetland restoration projects and their anticipated beneficial impact on fisheries through examination of the restoration of the salt marsh within the Galilee Bird Sanctuary in Narragansett, Rhode Island.

New England Salt Marshes

Salt marshes in New England comprise only about 3% of the total salt marsh remaining along the east coast of the United States (Spinner 1968, in Reimold 1977). The coastal salt marshes of the east coast of North America can be divided into three subgroups: the Bay of Fundy group, the New England group, and the Coastal Plain group (Chapman 1960). The New England group of salt marshes stretches from Maine to southern New Jersey and includes the salt marshes of Long Island (Chapman 1960).

The salt marshes of the northeastern United States are distinctive from those of the Coastal Plain group, as well as those to the north in the Bay of Fundy region (Johnson 1925; Chapman 1960). The impact of glaciers on the geology of the region distinguishes New England salt marshes from those of the Coastal Plain type (Chapman 1960; Teal and Teal 1969). Past glacial activity in the New England region has had a significant influence on the abundance and extent of coastal salt marshes in the northeastern United States (Teal and Teal 1969).

There are regional variations in the geomorphology of salt marshes found within the New England region. North of Boston, salt marshes generally become much smaller and more isolated than the more extensive coastal marshes found to the south (Shisler 1990). The salt marshes of Maine and New Hampshire display a much higher ratio of high marsh to low marsh than salt marshes found in southern New England (Nixon 1982). The abundance of salt marshes in Maine declines moving northward along the coast (Kelly et al. 1988).

Salt marshes form in sheltered intertidal areas where they are protected from the erosive effects of high wave energy (Redfield 1972; Nixon 1982; Mitsch and Gosselink 1993). The formation of coastal salt marshes requires a source of sediment. Glacial scouring of the northeastern United States during the last ice age greatly reduced the sediment available from upland sources (Teal and Teal 1969). The bedrock of New England itself is resistant to erosion and, as a result, is a poor source of sediment

for salt-marsh formation (Teal and Teal 1969; Mitsch and Gosselink 1993). Therefore, much of the sediment necessary for salt-marsh formation in the northeastern United States is derived from marine sediments (Mitsch and Gosselink 1993), and this limited supply of sediment has resulted in the presence of a relatively low abundance of salt marsh in New England (Nixon and Oviatt 1973; Niering and Warren 1980).

Marsh Habitat and Fish Production

The life histories and habitat utilization patterns of the Atlantic silverside, summer flounder, and winter flounder are examined in the following sections to determine the extent to which these species rely on salt-marsh habitat for foraging, nursery, and spawning habitat in the northeastern United States. This information in turn is used in a later section of this paper to evaluate the probable effects of salt-marsh restoration for the preferred habitats of these species.

Atlantic Silverside

The Atlantic silverside is a small, silvery fish that is commonly found in salt marshes, intertidal creeks, and nearshore estuarine waters along the entire eastern seaboard of the United States (Bayliff 1950; Bigelow and Schroeder 1953; Conover and Murawski 1982). Two subspecies of *Menidia menidia* are found along the east coast, *Menidia menidia menidia* and *Menidia menidia notata* (Bayliff 1950; Bigelow and Schroeder 1953). The northern form of this species, *Menidia menidia notata*, is found from Chesapeake Bay northward to the Gulf of St. Lawrence (Bayliff 1950; Bigelow and Schroeder 1953; Fay et al. 1983). The southern form of the species is found as far north as Cape Cod (Bigelow and Schroeder 1953).

The Atlantic silverside is typically one of the most abundant species collected in surveys of the fishery resources of tidal creeks and estuarine and nearshore coastal waters (Pearcy and Richards 1962; Mulkana 1966; Stolgitis et al. 1976; Hoff and Ibara 1977; Werme 1981; Satchwill et al. 1983; Marteinsdottir 1984; Teal 1986; Satchwill and Sisson 1991; Rountree 1992; Short 1992). Silversides exhibit schooling behavior and are often observed in schools numbering well into the thousands. Werme (1981) found that the Atlantic silverside and the mummichog *Fundulus heteroclitus* together accounted for 90% of the total fish observed in tidal creeks in the Great Sippewisset Marsh on Cape Cod, Massachusetts. In one of the few studies to document the growth, abundance, and biomass of silversides in a tidal-marsh estuarine system, Conover and Ross (1982) calculated a density of 7.8 g/m² wet weight of fish per unit area of marsh.

The silverside is a short-lived species of fish with a life span rarely exceeding one year (Werme 1981; Conover and Ross 1982). Mortality rates for silversides have been reported to be as high as 99.5% (Conover and Ross 1982). The high abundance of the silverside and its high mortality rate suggest that this fish is an important exporter of secondary production from marsh–estuarine systems to offshore waters (Conover and Ross 1982).

The Atlantic silverside spawns several times in a growing season (Bayliff 1950). Silversides exhibit a lunar spawning periodicity that corresponds to the spring high tides that occur during new and full moons (Middaugh et al. 1981). Silversides move into shallow intertidal areas to spawn. Middaugh et al. (1981) found that the silverside spawned exclusively in the upper intertidal zone of their study site at an elevation 1.2–2.4 m above mean low water. *Spartina alterniflora* stems provide an important spawning substrate to which silverside eggs adhere (Bayliff 1950; Middaugh et al. 1981; Fay et al. 1983).

The disappearance of silversides from coastal waters of the northeastern United States during winter months had long puzzled researchers (Bayliff 1950; Bigelow and Schroeder 1953; Conover and Murawski 1982). Conover and Murawski (1982) documented the offshore migration of silversides in late fall from inland coastal waters to the inner continental shelf. This behavior, not observed in the southern subspecies, seems to be in response to declining water temperature (Conover and Murawski 1982). The offshore migration of silversides represents a significant export of secondary energy from coastal salt marshes to the waters of the inner continental shelf (Conover and Murawski 1982).

The silverside is omnivorous, and its diet includes copepods, plant material, and shrimp (Fay et al. 1983; Cadigan and Fell 1985). Research has shown that the silverside feeds almost exclusively during daylight hours (Mulkana 1966; Rountree 1992). One study found that during the day, silversides move out of shallow intertidal and subtidal areas to forage in shallow tidal embayments (Rountree 1992). At night, silversides move into shallow intertidal and subtidal waters to seek refuge from predation (Rountree 1992). Based on these daily foraging movements, Rountree (1992) concluded that silversides do not rely specifically on shallow marsh habitats as foraging habitat (Rountree 1992). However, all studies do not agree on the importance of shallow marsh habitats for foraging. Cadigan and Fell (1985) concluded that silversides rely on shallow, tidal-marsh estuarine systems for spawning, nursery, and feeding habitat. Finally, Werme (1981) found that although silversides occur most frequently in subtidal marsh creeks, 30% of the study population was found in *Spartina alterniflora* during high tide.

Silversides are prey items for several species of commercially and recreationally valuable species of fish. Merriman (1941) found that silversides are one of the most abundant food items in the diet of the striped bass *Morone saxatilis* in Connecticut coastal waters. Silversides are also one of the primary prey items in the diet of summer flounder in tidal creeks in New Jersey (Rountree 1992). Other predators that use silversides as prey items include bluefish *Pomatomus saltatrix,* weakfish *Cynoscion regalis,* Atlantic cod *Gadus morhua,* silver hake *Merluccius bilinearis,* red hake *Urophycis chuss,* Atlantic mackerel *Scomber scombrus,* spotted seatrout *Cynoscion nebulosus,* and Atlantic tomcod *Microgadus tomcod* (Bayliff 1950; Bigelow and Schroeder 1953; Middaugh et al. 1981; Fay et al. 1983; Cadigan and Fell 1985; Rountree 1992).

Summer Flounder

Summer flounder is found from Nova Scotia to south Florida (Rogers and Van Den Avyle 1983). Summer flounder, or fluke as it is commonly known, is found in the greatest abundance in the mid-Atlantic Bight, that is, from Cape Hatteras, North Carolina to Cape Cod, Massachusetts (Bigelow and Schroeder 1953; Rogers and Van Den Avyle 1983; Able and Kaiser 1994; NMFS 1995).

In 1993, approximately 4.5 million kg of summer flounder, valued at US$15.5 million, were landed in the northeastern United States (NMFS 1994). In 1993, reported landings for this species within the mid-Atlantic Bight region reached approximately 4.1 million kg valued at $13.8 million (NMFS 1994). Historically, recreational fishermen have been responsible for 40% of the total annual landings of this species (NMFS 1994).

Spawning occurs during the offshore migration of adult summer flounder from coastal waters to the waters of the outer continental shelf in late fall and winter (Rogers and Van Den Avyle 1983; Able and Kaiser 1994; NMFS 1994). The eggs are buoyant and hatch within two to nine days of fertilization (Clayton et al. 1978; Rogers and Van Den Avyle 1983). The newly hatched summer flounder larvae are carried by the prevailing currents landward to shallow coastal waters (Able and Kaiser 1994; NMFS 1994). The postlarval and juvenile stages of summer flounder develop in coastal embayments and estuaries (Able and Kaiser 1994; NMFS 1994). The juvenile and larval stages of this species have been reported to inhabit intertidal creeks in coastal salt marshes throughout its range (Poole 1966; Cain and Dean 1976; Shenker and Dean 1979; Bozeman and Dean 1980; Weinstein et al. 1980; Rountree 1992; Rountree and Able 1992).

The presence of summer flounder in estuarine waters in southern New England, while rare, has been documented by numerous studies (Pearcy and Richards 1962; Mulkana 1966; Stolgitis et al. 1976; Satchwill et al. 1983; Satchwill and Sisson 1991; F. C. Golet and D. Myshrall, University of Rhode Island, unpublished data; M. D. Minton, Western Pacific Regional Fishery Management Council, personal observations). There is strong evidence that intertidal and subtidal salt-marsh creeks in southern New Jersey are important nursery habitat for young-of-the-year summer flounder (Rountree 1992; Rountree and Able 1992). Rountree and Able (1992) found that summer flounder, one of the 20 most representative species present in a study of faunal composition of a marsh creek, occurred primarily as juveniles. Able and Kaiser (1994) concluded that salt-marsh creeks are critical nursery areas throughout the species' range.

The summer flounder is one of the top-level predators in tidal-marsh estuarine systems (Rogers and Van Den Avyle 1983). It is a voracious eater that feeds on a variety of fish, crustaceans, and invertebrates, including mummichogs, Atlantic silversides, sevenspine bay shrimp *Crangon septemspinosa*, Atlantic menhaden *Brevoortia tyrannus*, blue crab *Callinectes sapidus*, squid, bay anchovy *Anchoa mitchilli*, red hake, weakfish, juvenile winter flounder, and American sand lance *Ammodytes americanus* (Bigelow and Schroeder 1953; Poole 1964; Clayton et al. 1978; Rogers and Van Den Avyle 1983). As mentioned above, Rountree (1992) found Atlantic silversides and mummichogs to be the most abundant fishes in the diet of juvenile summer flounder. The shrimps *Palaemonetes vulgaris* (marsh grass shrimp) and sevenspine bay shrimp were also found to be important prey items of juvenile summer flounder foraging in intertidal and subtidal creeks (Rountree 1992). Rountree (1992) also found that summer flounder entering marsh creeks on the flooding

tide had empty stomachs, while fish leaving marsh creeks during ebb tide had full stomachs. Based on the results of this experiment, he concluded that summer flounder utilize tidal movements in order to move into marsh creeks to feed on the abundant prey present.

Winter Flounder

The winter flounder is found along the east coast of North America from Newfoundland to Georgia (Bigelow and Schroeder 1953; McCracken 1963). Winter flounder is found in greatest abundance from Nova Scotia to New Jersey, where it is an important commercial species (Gray 1991; NMFS 1994). It is also a popular recreational species. Winter flounder is a bottom-dwelling fish that typically resides in shallow inshore waters (Gray 1991). There are three distinct stocks of winter flounder in New England: the Gulf of Maine, Georges Bank, and southern New England–mid-Atlantic stocks (Gray 1991; NMFS 1994). In 1993, commercial landings of winter flounder in the northeastern United States totaled approximately 4.4 million kg valued at $12.6 million (NMFS 1994). The recreational fishing industry landed an additional 0.7 million kg of winter flounder (NMFS 1994).

Adult and juvenile winter flounder are found in shallow tidal embayments and estuaries throughout New England, New York, and New Jersey (Bigelow and Schroeder 1953; Pearcy and Richards 1962; McCracken 1963; Mulkana 1966; Briggs and O'Conner 1971; Nixon and Oviatt 1973; Stolgitis et al. 1976; Hoff and Ibara 1977; Satchwill et al. 1983; Marteinsdottir 1984; Crawford and Carey 1985; Rountree and Able 1992; Short 1992). Stolgitis et al. (1976) found that juvenile winter flounder were abundant in all of Rhode Island's coastal salt ponds during the fall and winter months. Saila (1961b) estimated that two shallow estuaries, Charlestown Pond and Green Hill Pond, contributed 25% of the recruits (i.e., 215,710 fish) necessary to maintain the offshore winter flounder fishery in Rhode Island. The combined area of these two estuaries totaled 824 ha (Saila 1961b).

Winter flounder is a stationary species with very restricted movement patterns (Bigelow and Schroeder 1953). It does, however, undergo small-scale seasonal migrations from shallow coastal waters to deeper offshore waters (McCracken 1963). The migration of winter flounder is thought to be primarily temperature-induced (McCracken 1963). During the warm summer months, winter flounder migrate into cooler, deeper offshore waters (Bigelow and Schroeder 1953; McCracken 1963).

In the late fall and winter, adult winter flounder move into shallow coastal bays and estuaries to spawn (Bigelow and Schroeder 1953; McCracken 1963; Gray 1991). Spawning occurs between January and May (Bigelow and Schroeder 1953). Unlike most species of flatfish, winter flounder eggs are demersal instead of buoyant (Bigelow and Schroeder 1953; Crawford and Carey 1985; Gray 1991). After their release, the eggs sink to the bottom where they are found adhering to one another in clusters (Bigelow and Schroeder 1953). It is thought that this adaptation prevents the eggs from being swept out of estuaries into open water by strong tidal currents (Crawford and Carey 1985; Gray 1991).

After hatching, young winter flounder remain in shallow, coastal waters for the first one to two years of their life (Buckley 1989). Rountree and Able (1992) found that winter flounder, one of the 20 most representative species (along with summer flounder [see above]) present in their study of faunal composition of a marsh creek, occurred primarily as juveniles in their samples. In all of the available studies of salt-marsh fish communities in the northeastern United States, juvenile winter flounder were observed or collected (Werme 1981; Murphy 1991; Rountree 1992; Golet and Myshrall, unpublished data).

Winter flounder feed primarily on benthic invertebrates including polychaetes, isopods, amphipods, clams, and algae (Mulkana 1966; Wells et al. 1973; Gray 1991). Mulkana (1966) found that polychaetes comprised the most important prey item of juvenile winter flounder. Winter flounder feed on food species found in both the subtidal and intertidal zone (Tyler 1971; Wells et al. 1973). Tyler (1971) found that winter flounder preyed heavily on the softshell clam *Mya arenaria*, a species restricted to the intertidal zone. Based on the results of their research, Wells et al. (1973) concluded that the intertidal zone is an important feeding area for winter flounder. Research has documented that winter flounder surge into the intertidal zone during high tide to feed (Tyler 1971; Wells et al. 1973). Tyler (1971) found that winter flounder occupied the intertidal zone for 6–8 h of a 12-h tidal cycle.

Marsh Utilization Factors

Within New England there are two distinct zoogeographic provinces, the Acadian and the Virginian provinces. The Acadian province extends from Cape Cod northward along the Atlantic coast to the Avalon Peninsula; the Virginian province extends from Cape Cod southward to Cape Hatteras (Cowardin et al. 1979). The most prominent zoogeographic boundary that exists within the northeastern United States is Cape Cod. Cape Cod serves as a biogeographic break between fauna of the warmer mid-Atlantic region to the south and the Gulf of Maine to the north (Bigelow and Schroeder 1953; Briggs 1974; Whitlatch 1982; Ayvazian et al. 1992). Cape Cod represents the northern extent of the range of numerous species of migratory fish and macroinvertebrates.

There is a significant difference in water temperature between the Gulf of Maine and the warmer waters south of Cape Cod (Whitlatch 1982). This difference results in a markedly different composition of species in fish populations (Whitlatch 1982). Ayvazian et al. (1992) studied habitat use by estuarine fish in two estuaries, Waquoit Bay located on the south shore of Cape Cod in the Virginian zoogeographic province, and Wells Harbor in southern Maine, which lies in the Acadian zoogeographic province. Ayvazian et al. found that the estuarine fish assemblage in the Virginian zoogeographic province was much more diverse and was composed of species characteristic of warm-temperate waters. The fish assemblage in Wells Harbor was found to be less diverse than that in Waquoit Bay and was dominated by arctic and boreal estuarine resident species (Ayvazian et al. 1992).

The following three subsections describe characteristics of marshes that greatly influence marsh utilization by fishes. The characteristics—tidal amplitude and marsh hydroperiod, marsh access, and marsh edge and creek morphology—also suggest considerations for marsh rehabilitation and restoration projects.

Tidal Amplitude and Marsh Hydroperiod

Tidal amplitude and marsh hydroperiod affect the accessibility of foraging habitat and the amount of time available for foraging on the salt-marsh surface by fish (Kneib and Wagner 1994). The tides of the east coast of the United States are semidiurnal. Moving from the southeastern United States northward along the Atlantic coast, the tidal range increases so that the tidal range found within New England is much greater than that found in the coastal plain region (Chapman 1960; Nixon 1982). Two high tides and two low tides occur daily in intervals of 12 h and 25 min. Regional variations in tidal amplitude exist within New England itself. Tidal amplitude varies greatly on either side of Cape

Cod (Redfield 1972). The average tidal range north of Cape Cod is 3–4 m, while south of the Cape the mean range is 1–1.5 m (Whitlatch 1982). This difference is important in terms of the ability of nektonic organisms (small fish and macroinvertebrates) to use the marsh surface (Nixon 1982; Kneib and Wagner 1994; Rozas 1995).

Marsh hydroperiod—the amount of time that a marsh is flooded by the tide—directly controls the use of the marsh surface by fish and macroinvertebrates. In New England, a seasonal variation in sea level affects marsh hydroperiod (Nixon 1982). This variation is also important in terms of the ability of nektonic organisms to use the marsh surface (Nixon 1982; Kneib and Wagner 1994; Rozas 1995). The marsh surface is a critical foraging habitat for the mummichog, one of the most abundant fishes found in the salt marshes, tidal creeks, and shallow embayments of New England. Weisberg and Lotrich (1986) demonstrated that access to the marsh surface is necessary for the normal high growth rates of the mummichog.

Marsh Access

In a diked salt marsh, which is one of the major causes of coastal wetland loss in the northeastern United States, tidal range is typically much less than that found in an unimpounded natural marsh. Restoration of adequate tidal flow and the subsequent increase in low-marsh habitat would result in, for example, an increase in the preferred foraging habitat of the mummichog. The simple increase of low-marsh area, however, does not ensure that salt-marsh species will have access to this habitat for foraging. Rozas et al. (1988) found that species of fish that are marsh residents such as the mummichog displayed a preference for intertidal rivulets (small intertidal channels draining the marsh surface) as access corridors between subtidal creeks and the marsh surface. Rozas et al. also found that the average number of fish was three times greater in intertidal rivulets accessing the marsh surface than in creek banks. Intertidal rivulets allow fish to begin to move onto the marsh surface earlier and leave later than is possible when access is from the creek bank (Rozas et al. 1988). When fish use intertidal rivulets, they enjoy a prolonged period of access to the abundant prey items of the marsh surface and to greater areas of marsh surface that otherwise would be unavailable. Rozas et al. estimated that the area occupied by intertidal rivulets only accounted for 3% of the total area along the creek bank of their study site. Rozas et al. (1988) also calcu-

lated that when the entrances of intertidal rivulets constituted 19% of the total length along a freshwater tidal marsh creek, most fishes would utilize the rivulets to access the marsh surface. When designing a salt-marsh restoration project, construction of small intertidal rivulets as access corridors for small, resident forage species such as the mummichog would increase the available habitat required by this species for growth.

Studies of salt-marsh and estuarine fish communities frequently categorize species collected as "resident" and "nonresident" species. Resident species depend on a salt marsh for spawning, nursery, and foraging habitat to complete their life cycles. Nonresident species rely on the salt marsh for some portion of their life cycle, whether it be for spawning, nursery, or foraging habitat for juveniles and adults of the species. Resident species include the mummichog, Atlantic silverside, and sheepshead minnow *Cyprinodon variegatus*. Nonresident species are often large migratory piscivores such as bluefish, striped bass, weakfish, and summer flounder. However, Rountree (1992) pointed out that this type of classification system can be misleading. For example, the Atlantic silverside is a year-round marsh resident in salt marshes in the southeastern United States but a seasonal resident in the northeastern United States (Rountree 1992). Conversely, young-of-the-year and juvenile summer flounder are found year-round in New Jersey salt-marsh creeks but are usually considered a seasonal species (Rountree 1992).

Marsh Edge and Creek Morphology

Directly related to the concept of access to the marsh surface is what is known as the "edge effect." According to McIvor and Rozas (1996), marsh edge is the interface between the marsh and open water. The importance and value of the interspersion of different forms of vegetation for a variety of wildlife species in freshwater wetlands is well known (Golet 1976). The boundary between different vegetation types or between vegetation and open water is referred to as edge (Golet 1976). Research has shown that the total abundance of individual species of wildlife in freshwater wetlands is related to the total length of edge present, while species diversity is related to the number of different edge types (Golet 1976).

Studies of the use of intertidal salt marshes by nektonic organisms have produced strong evidence of the importance of edge habitat for wildlife in this environment as well (Kneib and Wagner 1994; Peterson and Turner 1994). Zedler (1990) found that, in regard to salt-marsh restoration and habitat enhancement, increased edge and improved access seemed to increase the secondary productivity of salt marshes.

In a study of nekton use of vegetated marsh habitats, Kneib and Wagner (1994) found that most fishes and macroinvertebrates did not venture very far from intertidal creeks onto the marsh surface. Peterson and Turner (1994) also documented that densities of fish and macroinvertebrates were greatest within 3 m of the marsh–water interface. Peterson and Turner also found that transient fish species primarily used the marsh edge habitat. Several studies have found evidence that the total amount of marsh edge present is a more important factor in determining nekton use of a salt marsh than the total area of the marsh (Turner 1977; Hettler 1989; Peterson and Turner 1994). Hettler (1989) suggested that highly convoluted salt marshes interspersed with numerous small, meandering intertidal creeks and rivulets are potentially more productive for fish and macroinvertebrates than the same area of unbroken marsh. In contrast to the results of such studies, Murphy (1991) reported a greater density of fish in salt-marsh creek samples than marsh-edge samples. The only commercial species collected by Murphy was the winter flounder. This species was only collected by Murphy in tidal creek samples—never in samples of the marsh edge.

Although nekton density has been found to be greatest in marsh-edge habitats, the interior marsh is utilized by resident species of fish and macroinvertebrates, particularly the mummichog and the daggerblade grass shrimp *Palaemonetes pugio*. The presence and abundance of *P. pugio* is not reported in the results of available studies of salt-marsh communities in the northeastern United States. However, *P. pugio* is known to be highly abundant in the salt marshes of this region (Nixon and Oviatt 1973; Welsh 1975; Stone et al. 1994). The daggerblade grass shrimp has been shown to graze on *Spartina alterniflora* detritus, which it breaks down into a more biologically useful form (Welsh 1975; Peterson and Turner 1994). For this reason, as well as its high abundance and biomass and its role as the prey of many species, the daggerblade grass shrimp is potentially a vital link in the exchange of productivity from salt marshes to adjacent waters (Nixon and Oviatt 1973; Welsh 1975; Peterson and Turner 1994).

The ability of fish to utilize and exploit the abundant food of the marsh surface during high tide is restricted by the danger of stranding when waters recede. Kneib and Wagner (1994) suggested that the spatial and temporal distribution patterns of fish and macroinvertebrates in intertidal marshes are directly related to the availability of subtidal habitat at low tide and the amount of time required to move from this habitat onto the marsh surface at high tide.

Creek morphology is an additional factor believed to affect the use of salt-marsh habitat by fishes and macroinvertebrates. Hettler (1989) found that marshes adjacent to rivulets (stream order 1) had higher densities and total biomass present than marshes adjacent to channels (stream order 3). Weinstein (1979) found that juvenile fish and macroinvertebrates actively sought the headwaters of small, shallow salt-marsh creeks and proposed that marshes fill up backwards during recruitment. Rozas and Odum (1987a) also found higher densities of small fish present in low-order streams. It is thought that this distribution pattern is directly related to the reduced presence of large predators in small intertidal streams and rivulets (Rozas and Odum 1987a; Hettler 1989). It is at the head of these small "creeklets" that the rising tide typically first overflows onto the surface of the marsh (Mitsch and Gosselink 1993). In addition, several studies have found that the density and diversity of fish and macroinvertebrate populations are higher along depositional creek banks than along erosional banks (McIvor and Odum 1988; Murphy 1991).

Habitat Use in Restored Marshes

Just as there are many unanswered questions concerning nekton use of natural salt marshes, few studies have attempted to answer questions about the use of restored salt marshes by fish and macroinvertebrates. Wetland restoration has been defined as "the re-establishment of a wetland (on the site of a historical wetland) which has been degraded to such an extent that the site performs little or none of its original wetland functions" (RICRMC 1996). An important distinction must be made between wetland restoration and wetland creation. Wetland creation, another mitigation measure employed to compensate for wetland loss, is the construction of a coastal wetland where one did not previously exist (NRC 1994; RICRMC 1996).

Given current technological and scientific capabilities, it is not always possible to restore a coastal wetland to a fully functional state (NRC 1994). Although it is possible to restore salt marshes, functional equivalency between restored and natural marshes is difficult to demonstrate (Seneca and Broome 1990). Several studies have documented that many of the functions associated with natural marshes are only partially replicated by restored marshes (Cammen 1976; Zedler 1990; Allen et al. 1994). In the case of diked salt marshes, the removal of obstructions restricting tidal exchange may be sufficient to allow recolonization of the marsh by fauna and flora (Seneca and Broome 1990). However, the amount of time required for fauna to recolonize a restored salt marsh to the levels of a natural marsh is not known (Seneca and Broome 1990). Some studies have found that within three to five years, fish utilization of restored or created salt marshes is equal to that of natural marshes (Lewis 1992). This is in contrast to other studies (see below) that have documented significantly lower densities of faunal populations utilizing restored or created marshes. Site-specific environmental factors make it difficult to predict the amount of time required for a restored salt marsh to revert to a more natural state (Zedler 1988; Sacco et al. 1994).

Research has documented significant differences in density and species composition between infaunal invertebrate populations of created and natural marshes. Because of their location near the base of the food chain, these small invertebrates are an important link between the highly productive salt marsh and adjacent coastal waters (Sacco et al. 1994). Sacco et al. (1988) found that after 15 years, the average density and species composition of infaunal invertebrates (primarily oligochaetes and polychaetes) in a planted salt marsh approximated the infaunal populations of a natural salt marsh. Fell et al. (1991) studied the recolonization of a restored, impounded salt marsh in Connecticut by macroinvertebrates, particularly the eastern melampus (salt marsh snail) *Melampus bindentatus*. They reported that 12 years after the reintroduction of tidal flow to the impounded salt marsh, the marsh had developed fauna and flora typical of natural marshes in the region.

Of the few data available concerning the use of restored and created salt marshes by fish and macroinvertebrates, many are from studies of created marshes rather than restored salt marshes. Moy and Levin (1991) found the density of *Fundulus heteroclitus* in a planted marsh in North Carolina to be significantly lower than that found in an adjacent natural marsh. They theorized the difference might be due to reduced suitable spawning sites and in-

creased predation on juvenile mummichogs because of the lower stem density of the created marsh. Due to the complex nature of salt-marsh ecosystems and site-specific environmental factors such as tides and salinity, other possible explanations for differences in fish density cannot be ruled out.

Allen et al. (1994) compared fish utilization of a restored salt marsh in Connecticut to two nearby natural marshes. Although the fish assemblages in the restored and natural marshes were similar, the guts of fish utilizing the restored marsh had little food in them when compared to fish collected in the reference marshes. Allen et al. were unable to explain this finding but suggested that it may be due to quantitative or qualitative differences in food resources. These findings raise the question of whether restored and created salt marshes are functionally equivalent to natural marshes. All the preceding factors have significant implications for the planning, design, and implementation of successful salt-marsh restoration projects, especially projects that include fishery habitat restoration as an intended goal, within the northeastern region of the United States.

Restoration in Practice

The final section of this paper examines the question of whether the implementation of federal coastal wetland restoration projects will increase the abundance of wetland habitat types required by commercial and recreational species of marine fish. The answer to this basic question relates directly to the effectiveness of federal policy in coastal wetland restoration projects that include the enhancement of fish habitat. It is important to remember, as has been stated, that although the restoration of coastal wetlands as a policy of federal and state governments has grown and expanded in recent years, habitat restoration remains a relatively new science (Thayer 1990).

Presently, the designers of many salt-marsh restoration projects assume that reestablishment of salt-marsh plants will result in recolonization by other species of animals (Seneca and Broome 1990). Long-term studies of salt-marsh restoration projects are needed to validate this assumption. A large number of wetland mitigation projects have been undertaken in the northeastern United States, but few evaluations of the success and effectiveness of these projects have been conducted (Shisler 1990). Without adequate baseline data, evaluation of a restoration project's desired impact is impossible. In the case of resource-damage settlements, adequate baseline data and long-term monitoring to evaluate restoration success should be required as part of the settlement. In addition, although the life histories of many species of marsh-dependent fish are reasonably well known, this knowledge has seemingly not been utilized and incorporated into the design of restoration projects. The value of different coastal habitat types for various species of marsh-dependent fish is an important yet neglected component of restoration planning efforts.

When designing a salt-marsh restoration project to create habitat for fish and macroinvertebrates and to enhance fisheries, the construction of numerous intertidal creeks and rivulets would improve access to the marsh surface and interior, increase the total amount of edge present in the restored marsh, and in general help ensure the success of the restoration project (Minello et al. 1994; NRC 1994). The importance of marsh edge has been emphasized by several researchers, including Peterson and Turner (1994), who concluded that if creating habitat that functions as fish habitat is a goal of a salt-marsh restoration project, the amount of edge habitat should be maximized.

The restoration of high marsh is extremely difficult because of its narrow tidal range and salinity requirements (Kusler and Kentula 1990; Shisler 1990). Salt marshes north of Cape Cod are dominated by high-marsh habitat. Not only has research demonstrated the difficulty of restoring high-marsh habitat, studies also have demonstrated that the high stem density of high-marsh vegetation may affect the foraging success of small predaceous fish such as *Fundulus heteroclitus* (Valiela et al. 1977; Van Dolah 1978).

Ensuring that there are adequate subtidal areas remaining at low tide adjacent to, or in close proximity to, the marsh surface also is necessary to enhance the habitat value of a restored salt marsh for nektonic organisms (Kneib and Wagner 1994). Studies of salt-marsh communities have shown that large, predatory fish are rare in intertidal salt-marsh creeks. By increasing the amount of subtidal habitat present in a restored salt marsh, resource managers could enhance the value of the salt marsh as foraging habitat for nektonic organisms.

If the enhancement of commercial and recreational fisheries one of the intended goals of salt-marsh restoration, consideration of the Atlantic silverside's preferred habitat requirements and in-

corporation of these requirements into restoration design would substantially increase the likelihood of fisheries enhancement. As described above, the Atlantic silverside is one of the principal food items for numerous species of commercially and recreationally valuable fish and serves as an important link in the transfer of secondary production and energy from tidal marsh systems to shallow, coastal embayments and offshore waters. One life history characteristic worth considering when designing a salt-marsh restoration project is the Atlantic silverside's preference for subtidal habitats while in the salt marsh. The Atlantic silverside relies on salt marshes as spawning and foraging habitat, and individuals display a preference for areas of vegetation near the water's edge that are covered at high tide at depths of 0–30 cm as spawning sites (Middaugh et al. 1981). As previously mentioned, Middaugh et al. (1981) found that silversides spawn exclusively in the upper intertidal zone at elevations of 1.2–2.4 m above mean low water. Atlantic silversides may occur in such abundance that they exceed the carrying capacity of the available marsh habitat (Conover and Ross 1982).

Past restoration experience has shown that the reintroduction of tidal flow to an impounded salt marsh is often sufficient to restore salt-marsh vegetation (Shisler 1990; Sinicrope et al. 1990; Fell et al. 1991; Allen et al. 1994). Sinicrope et al. (1990), in a study of a restored impounded salt marsh in Stonington, Connecticut, found that low marsh had increased from less than 1% to 45% of the total vegetative cover in the course of a decade after tidal flow had been restored.

Although substantial engineering capabilities exist for the restoration of certain aspects of salt-marsh and intertidal habitats (Kusler and Kentula 1990; NRC 1994), the technology required to restore many of the natural functions of these habitats is less developed (NRC 1994). The construction of habitat edge and channels can present an engineering challenge (Minello et al. 1994). This is especially true for created marshes on dredged material (Minello et al. 1994). Minello et al. (1994) described several methods of creating habitat edge and channels. The creation of habitat edge and channels is expensive and results in increased total project costs (Minello et al. 1994). The creation of edge habitat and numerous intertidal creeks and rivulets also requires the disposal of dredged material, which can be a problem.

Galilee Salt-Marsh Restoration Project

The Galilee salt marsh is located in Narragansett, Rhode Island. In 1955, the state of Rhode Island obtained the area and designated it as the Galilee Bird Sanctuary (USACE 1993). The following year, the state of Rhode Island constructed a four-lane road to serve as an escape route for residents of the Galilee area in the event of coastal flooding during a severe hurricane (USACE 1993). The construction of the escape road, as it is locally known, destroyed approximately 2.8 ha of salt marsh and isolated another 51.8 ha of coastal wetlands south of the road (USACE 1993).

The restoration of the Galilee salt marsh began in the fall of 1996. The restoration was a cooperative effort involving several state and federal agencies including the U.S. Army Corps of Engineers (USACE), the U.S. Fish and Wildlife Service, the U.S. Environmental Protection Agency, the National Oceanic and Atmospheric Administration, the Rhode Island Department of Environmental Management, and the Rhode Island Department of Transportation (RIDOT).

The involvement of the USACE in the Galilee salt-marsh restoration project was based on authority derived from Section 1135(a) of the Water Resource Development Act (WRDA) of 1986. Section 1135(a) grants the USACE the authority to modify water resource projects constructed prior to the passage of the WRDA if doing so would improve environmental quality in the public interest. The USACE's interest in the project was based upon its desire to restore a former dredge spoil disposal site in the northwest portion of the marsh.

In addition, the restoration of the Galilee salt marsh was implemented as part of a Section 404(b)(1) Clean Water Act permit. These restoration efforts, independent of the Section 1135(a) project, were the result of mitigation requirements of a Section 404 permit issued to the RIDOT. When the state of Rhode Island constructed a new bridge (the Jamestown Bridge) spanning a portion of Narragansett Bay, it filled approximately 0.4 ha of freshwater marsh in Jamestown, Rhode Island. The 404(b)(1) permit was issued on the condition that the loss of the wetland would be mitigated by the RIDOT (USACE 1993). The state of Rhode Island took this opportunity to contribute to the restoration of the Galilee salt marsh, a project in which it had long been interested.

Prior to the restoration, one remaining salt-marsh creek and a series of mosquito-control ditches fed by two 77-cm culverts provided all the tidal waters to the 3.8 ha of salt marsh and 4.2 ha of open water remaining within the sanctuary (USACE 1993). Over the years, the existing culverts had gradually silted in, resulting in greatly reduced tidal flow. The tidally restricted salt marsh within the Galilee Bird Sanctuary experienced only a 15–20-cm tidal range, while an adjacent natural marsh experienced a tidal range of 1.1 m (Myshrall 1996). To restore adequate tidal flow, two sets of 1.8-by-6.2-m box culverts equipped with self-regulating tide gates were constructed to replace the two existing 77-cm culverts (USACE 1993). The new culverts provided much greater tidal flushing to the impounded salt marsh than was provided by the two original culverts at the northeast corner of the sanctuary. The new culverts were constructed at two separate locations along the escape road: the first new culvert was constructed at the site of the two existing culverts, and the second culvert was constructed near the northwest end of the escape road. The restoration of tidal flow to the impounded salt marsh within the Galilee Bird Sanctuary is expected to increase the tidal range within the sanctuary to 1.1 m (Myshrall 1996). The increased tidal range will facilitate the use of the marsh surface as a foraging habitat for fish.

As part of the restoration, a major salt-marsh creek that had fed the western portion of the Galilee salt marsh (until the creek was filled by the USACE years ago) was reconstructed. In addition to the reconstruction of the creek bed in its former location, several feeder channels were also constructed (USACE 1993). The purpose of the feeder channels was to provide adequate tidal exchange to interior areas of the marsh. Portions of the Galilee salt marsh were also regraded to elevations necessary for salt-marsh species to recolonize areas dominated by upland species and *Phragmites* (USACE 1993; Myshrall 1996). Beyond the preceding measures, actions to restore estuarine and salt-marsh habitats and their associated values to fish and wildlife were not incorporated into the restoration design.

Prior to the restoration, plant and animal communities within the Galilee salt marsh had been greatly affected by the reduced tidal range of the impounded marsh. Much of the remaining salt marsh within the Galilee Bird Sanctuary was highly disturbed, and much of the salt marsh originally present within the sanctuary had been replaced over the years by dense stands of the reed grass *Phragmites australis*. At the time of the restoration, 39% of the former salt marsh was dominated by *Phragmites* (USACE 1993). This species is of little value to wildlife and is difficult to eradicate once it becomes established. The reintroduction of adequate tidal flushing into the Galilee salt marsh will create salinity levels too high for *Phragmites*. The overall effect will be a reduction of the total area dominated by *Phragmites* and an increase in the amount of salt marsh. Estimates indicate that the elimination of *Phragmites* will take approximately 10 years (USACE 1993).

Another impact of the restoration of increased tidal flow to the impounded marsh will be the reversion of large areas presently dominated by high-marsh vegetation (saltmeadow hay *Spartina patens*, salt grass *Distichilis spicata*, saltmarsh rush *Juncus gerardii*) to low-marsh areas dominated by *Spartina alterniflora* (USACE 1993). It is estimated that the restoration of tidal flow will result in an increase of low marsh from 0.26 to 6.13 ha within the Galilee Bird Sanctuary (USACE 1993). In addition, it is predicted that high-marsh habitat will also increase from 3.30 to 18.22 ha (USACE 1993).

One of the stated goals of the Galilee Bird Sanctuary restoration project was to enhance the sanctuary's value as fish, shellfish, and wildlife habitat. The project will result in the restoration of significant amounts of salt-marsh habitat. This increase in salt-marsh habitat, particularly low-marsh areas, will increase the abundance of wetland habitat required by commercially and recreationally valuable species of fish and their prey.

As part of the Galilee salt marsh restoration project, the fish population present prior to the restoration was sampled over a two-year period to provide baseline data. This sampling program documented large numbers of juvenile winter flounder utilizing the remaining salt-marsh creek within the sanctuary prior to restoration. These baseline data will enable researchers to evaluate the success of the restoration project and its impact on the value of the site for aquatic productivity and finfish production. The identification of funds for evaluations of restoration success and project monitoring remains an important policy challenge.

Conclusion and Discussion

Nixon (1980) theorized that "perhaps estuarine-dependent fish simply do well in shallow protected waters, the same environment that usually favors salt marsh development." To the contrary, there is a growing body of evidence suggesting that salt-marsh habitats and submerged aquatic vegetation in the northeastern United States and other regions do indeed provide important spawning, nursery, and foraging habitat for many species of fish and macroinvertebrates of commercial and recreational interest (Orth et al. 1984; Rozas and Odum 1987b; Sogard and Able 1991; Ayvazian et al. 1992; Rountree 1992). Building upon that evidence, this paper has argued that restoration of coastal wetlands will increase the abundance of wetland habitat types required by commercially and recreationally valuable species of marine fish.

As has been noted, although the life histories of many marsh-dependent fish species are well known, this knowledge has typically not been utilized and incorporated into the design of restoration projects. Integration of scientific understanding of fish habitat requirements with current restoration engineering capabilities in the design and implementation of salt-marsh restoration projects would increase the benefits of such projects to commercially and recreationally valuable species of fish and their prey. If enhancement of fishery habitat value is to be a goal of restoration projects, the projects should be designed to:

- maximize edge habitat,
- increase the total amount of regularly flooded marsh,
- construct intertidal rivulets as marsh access corridors,
- increase the amount of subtidal habitat available for forage and predaceous species of finfish,
- utilize current scientific knowledge and understanding of individual species habitat requirements, and
- consider stream-order influences on nektonic distribution and abundance.

Current federally funded or mandated salt marsh restorations present an excellent opportunity to conduct scientific research concerning the effects of the aforementioned design features on nektonic utilization of salt-marsh habitats in the northeastern United

States. Such research should demonstrate the effects of increased abundance of wetland habitat types required by marine fish resulting from the Galilee salt-marsh restoration project and similar efforts. It is important to remember that although one of the primary goals of the Galilee salt-marsh restoration project was to restore the previously existing estuarine community and its value for fish, the project did not explicitly incorporate specific design features to enhance the fishery habitat value of the restored marsh beyond the reintroduction of tidal flow.

When coastal wetland restoration policy is being formulated and implemented for the New England region, consideration should be given to the biogeographic and physiographic variation present within the region. The two biogeographic provinces in the New England region have distinctively different communities of fish. There is also a distinct variation in salt-marsh geomorphology north and south of Cape Cod.

As stressed in this paper, few systematic studies of fish and macroinvertebrate use of salt-marsh habitats have been conducted in the northeastern United States (Werme 1981; Murphy 1991; Rountree 1992). More research on the use of restored, created, or impounded salt-marsh habitats by fish and macroinvertebrate populations in the northeastern United States is needed. Several studies of nekton use of restored and created salt marshes have found that such marshes support lower densities of fish and macroinvertebrates than natural marshes (Cammen 1976; Moy and Levin 1991; Chamberlain and Barnhart 1994; Sacco et al. 1994) and raise the question of whether restored and created salt marshes are functionally equivalent to natural marshes.

It is difficult to compare the results of the available studies because of the different sampling methodologies employed. It is also difficult to compare the results of the available studies because different microhabitats were sampled within the various marshes analyzed. To facilitate comparisons of data from future studies of salt-marsh community structure, a uniform sampling methodology should be developed. In addition, difficulties associated with sampling vegetated marsh surfaces and shallow intertidal marsh creeks complicate the study of nekton use of these habitats. Various sampling techniques have been developed to facilitate the study of nekton use of salt-marsh habitats. Rozas and Minello (1997) provided a detailed summary of the available sampling techniques that can be employed to sample shallow estuarine habitats. Many techniques selectively sample only portions of the

nekton populations utilizing salt marshes, and if these techniques are used in isolation, they can result in biased data. Kneib and Wagner (1994) and Peterson and Turner (1994) also provided synopses of problems and potential sampling biases associated with various salt-marsh sampling techniques.

The effect of hydroperiod on the utilization of salt-marsh habitats is another area where our understanding is fragmentary. The utilization of microhabitats within salt-marsh systems should be further studied, particularly the use of marsh edge, marsh interior, tidal pools, subtidal areas, and intertidal creeks. As in other regions of the United States, quantitative data are lacking concerning the use of salt-marsh habitats by nektonic organisms in the northeast region. Quantitative data documenting fish and macroinvertebrate per unit area of marsh would be valuable in enhancing our understanding of marsh utilization by nektonic organisms. Research on the food habits of commercially and recreationally valuable fish species is needed to help scientists and managers understand these species' reliance on marsh-dependent fish and macroinvertebrates. An increased understanding of the importance and interplay of the preceding factors and their impact on nekton use of salt-marsh habitats will increase the ability of salt-marsh restoration projects to duplicate the functions and values of natural salt marshes.

Acknowledgments

I express my gratitude to Richard Burroughs, Department of Marine Affairs, University of Rhode Island, whose direction, comments, and enthusiasm for the subject matter were invaluable in the preparation of this paper. I also thank Frank Golet and Dennis Nixon for providing numerous useful comments and insights. I also owe a debt of gratitude to Lee Benaka and the three anonymous reviewers of this work.

References

Able, K. W., and S. C. Kaiser. 1994. Synthesis of summer flounder habitat parameters. National Oceanic and Atmospheric Administration Coastal Ocean Program, Decision Analysis 1. NOAA Coastal Ocean Office, Silver Spring, Maryland.

Allen, E. A., P. E. Fell, M. A. Peck, J. A. Gieg, C. R. Guthke, and M. D. Newkirk. 1994. Gut contents of common mummichogs, Fundulus heteroclitus L., in a restored impounded marsh and natural reference marshes. Estuaries 2:462–471.

Ayvazian, S. G., L. A. Deegan, and J. T. Finn. 1992. Comparison of habitat use by estuarine fish assemblages in the Acadian and Virginian zoogeographic provinces. Estuaries 15(3):368–383.

Bayliff, W. H. 1950. The life history of silverside: *Menidia menidia*. Chesapeake Biological Laboratory, Publication 90, Solomons, Maryland.

Bigelow, H. B., and W. C. Schroeder. 1953. Fishes of the Gulf of Maine. U.S. Fish and Wildlife Service, Fishery Bulletin 53.

Bozeman, E. L., and J. M. Dean. 1980. The abundance of estuarine larval fish in a South Carolina intertidal creek. Estuaries 3:89–97.

Briggs, J. C. 1974. Marine zoogeography. McGraw-Hill, New York.

Briggs, P. T., and J. S. O'Conner. 1971. Comparison of shore-zone fishes over naturally vegetated and sand-filled bottoms in Great South Bay. New York Fish and Game Journal 18:15–41.

Buckley, J. 1989. Species profile: life histories and environmental requirements of coastal fishes and invertebrates (North Atlantic)—winter flounder. U.S. Fish and Wildlife Service Biological Report 82(11.87).

Butner, A., and B. H. Brattstrom. 1960. Local movement in *Menidia* and *Fundulus*. Copeia 2:139–141.

Cadigan, K. M., and P. E. Fell. 1985. Reproduction, growth, and feeding habits of *Menidia menidia* (Atherinidae) in a tidal marsh-estuarine system in southern New England. Copeia 1:21–26.

Cain, R. L., and J. M. Dean. 1976. Annual occurrence, abundance and diversity of fish in a South Carolina intertidal creek. Marine Biology 36:369–379.

Cammen, L. M. 1976. Abundance and production of macroinvertebrates from natural and artificially established salt marshes in North Carolina. American Midland Naturalist 96:244–253.

Chamberlain, R. H., and R. A. Barnhart. 1994. Early use by fish of a mitigation salt marsh, Humbolt Bay, California. Estuaries 16:769–783.

Chapman, V. J. 1960. Salt marshes and salt deserts of the world. Verlag Von J. Cramer, Bremerhaven, Germany.

Chidester, F. E. 1920. The behavior of *Fundulus heteroclitus* on the salt marshes of New Jersey. American Naturalist 54:551–557.

Clayton, G., C. Cole, S. Murawski, and J. Parrish. 1978. Common marine fishes of coastal Massachusetts. Massachusetts Cooperative Extension Service, University of Massachusetts, Amherst.

Conover, D. O., and S. A. Murawski. 1982. Offshore winter migration of the Atlantic silverside. U.S. National Marine Fisheries Service, Fisheries Bulletin 80:145–150.

Conover, D. O., and M. R. Ross. 1982. Patterns in seasonal abundance, growth and biomass of the Atlantic silverside, M*enidia menidia*, in a New England estuary. Estuaries 5(4):275–286.

Cooper, A. J., and F. Chapleau. 1998. Monophyly and intrarelationships of the family Pleuronectidae (Pleuronectiformes), with a revised classification. U.S. National Marine Fisheries Service Fishery Bulletin 96:686–726.

Cowardin, L. M., V. Carter, F. C. Golet, and E. T. LaRoe. 1979. Classification of wetlands and deepwater habitats of the United States. U.S. Fish and Wildlife Service, FWS/OBS-79/31, Washington, D.C.

Crawford, R. E., and C. G. Carey. 1985. Retention of winter flounder larvae within a Rhode Island Salt Pond. Estuaries 2B:217–227.

Day, J. W., C. A. S. Hall, W. M. Kemp, and A. Yanez-Arancibia. 1989. Estuarine ecology. John Wiley and Sons, New York.

Fay, C. W., R. J. Neves, and G. B. Pardue. 1983. Species profiles: life histories and environmental requirements of coastal fishes and invertebrates (Mid-Atlantic)—Atlantic silverside. U.S. Fish and Wildlife Service, Division of Biological Services, FWS/OBS/11.10, U.S. Corps of Engineers, TR EL-82–4.

Fell, P. E., K. A. Murphy, M. A. Peck, and M. L. Recchia. 1991. Re-establishment of Melampus bidentatus (Say) and other macroinvertebrates on a restored impounded tidal marsh: comparison of populations above and below the impoundment dike. Journal of Experimental Marine Biology and Ecology 152:33–48.

Golet, F. C. 1976. Wildlife wetland evaluation model. Pages 13–34 *in* J. S. Larson, editor. Models for assessment of freshwater wetlands. Water Resource Research Center Publication 32, University of Massachusetts, Amherst.

Gray, C. L. 1991. Winter flounder (*Pseudopleuronectes americanus*). Species Profile, Rhode Island Department of Environmental Management, Wickford.

Harrington, R. W., and E. S. Harrington. 1961. Food selection among fish invading a high subtropical salt marsh: from onset of flooding through the progress of a mosquito brood. Ecology 42(4):646–666.

Herke, W. H., E. E. Knudsen, P. A. Knudsen, and B. D. Rogers. 1992. Effects of semi- impoundment of Louisiana marsh on fish and crustacean nursery use and export. North American Journal of Fisheries Management 12:151–160.

Hettler, W. F., Jr. 1989. Nekton use of regularly-flooded saltmarsh cordgrass habitat in North Carolina, USA. Marine Ecology Progress Series 56:111–118.

Hoff, J. G., and R. M. Ibara. 1977. Factors affecting the seasonal abundance, composition and diversity of fishes in a southeastern New England estuary. Estuarine and Coastal Science 5:665–678.

Horton, D. B. 1965. A study population behavior, homing orientation and movement in the common mummichog, *Fundulus heteroclitus*. Doctoral dissertation. University of Rhode Island, Narragansett.

Johnson, D. 1925. The New England-Acadian shoreline. Hafner Publishing Company, New York.

Kelly, J. T., D. F. Belknap, G. L. Jacobson, Jr., and H. A. Jacobson. 1988. The morphology and origin of salt marshes along the glaciated coast of Maine, USA. Journal of Coastal Research 4(4):649–666.

Kneib, R. T., and S. L. Wagner. 1994. Nekton use of vegetated marsh habitats at different stages of tidal inundation. Marine Ecology Progress Series 106:227–238.

Kusler, J. A., and M. E. Kentula, editors. 1990. Wetland creation and restoration: the status of the science. Island Press, Washington D.C.

Lewis, R. R., III. 1992. Coastal habitat restoration as a fishery management tool. Pages 169–174 *in* R. H. Stroud, editor. Stemming the tide of coastal fish habitat loss. National Coalition for Marine Conservation, Savannah, Georgia.

Lotrich, V. A. 1975. Summer home range of *Fundulus heteroclitus* (Pisces: cyprinodontidae) in a tidal creek. Ecology 56:191–198.

Marteinsdottir, G. 1984. Herring River estuary: fish survey, July and September 1984. Rutgers University, Center for Coastal and Environmental Studies, New Brunswick, New Jersey.

McCracken, F. D. 1963. Seasonal movements of the winter flounder, Pseudopleuronectes americanus (Walbaum), on the Atlantic coast. Journal of the Fisheries Research Board of Canada 20(2):551–586.

McGovern, J. C., and C. A. Wenner. 1990. Seasonal recruitment of larval and juvenile fishes into impounded and non-impounded marshes. Wetlands 10:203–221.

McIvor, C. C., and W. E. Odum. 1988. Food, predation risk, and microhabitat selection in a marsh fish assemblage. Ecology 69:1341–1351.

McIvor, C. C., and L. P. Rozas. 1996. Direct nekton use of intertidal saltmarsh habitat and linkage with adjacent habitats: a review from the southeastern United States. Pages 311–334 *in* K. F. Nordstrom and C. T. Roman, editors. Estuarine shores: evolution environments and human alterations. John Wiley and Sons, New York.

Merriman, D. 1941. Studies on the striped bass (Roccus saxatilis) of the Atlantic coast. Fishery Bulletin 50(35):1–77.

Middaugh, D. P., G. I. Scott, and J. M. Dean. 1981. Reproductive behavior of the Atlantic silverside, Menidia menidia (Pisces, Atherinidae). Environmental Biology of Fishes 6(3/4):269–276.

Minello, T. J., R. J. Zimmerman, and R. Medina. 1994. The importance of edge for natant macrofauna in a created marsh. Wetlands 14:184–198.

Mitsch, W. J., and J. G. Gosselink. 1993. Wetlands. Van Nostrand Reinhold, New York.

Moy, L. D., and L. A. Levin. 1991. Are Spartina marshes a replaceable resource? a functional approach to evaluation of marsh creation efforts. Estuaries 14:1–16.

Mulkana, M. S. 1966. The growth and feeding habits of juvenile fishes in two Rhode Island estuaries. Gulf Research Reports 2:97–168.

Murphy, S. C. 1991. The ecology of estuarine fishes in southern Maine high salt marshes: access corridors and movement patterns. Master's thesis. University of Massachusetts, Amherst.

Myshrall, D. 1996. Influence of tidal hydrology on the distribution and structure of salt marsh plant communities at the Galilee Bird Sanctuary, Narragansett, Rhode Island. Master's thesis. University of Rhode Island, Kingston.

Niering, W. A., and R. S. Warren. 1980. Vegetation patterns and processes in New England salt marshes. BioScience 30(5):301–307.

Nixon, S. W. 1980. Between coastal marshes and coastal waters: a review of twenty years of speculation and research on the role of salt marshes in estuarine productivity and water chemistry. Pages 437–525 *in* P. Hamilton and K. MacDonald, editors. Estuarine and wetlands processes. Plenum, New York.

Nixon, S. W. 1982. The ecology of New England high salt marshes: a community profile. U.S. Fish and Wildlife Service, Biological Services Program, FWS/OBS-81/55, Washington, D.C.

Nixon, S. W., and C. A. Oviatt. 1973. Ecology of a New England salt marsh. Ecological Monographs 4:463–498.

NMFS (National Marine Fisheries Service). 1994. Status of fishery resources off the northeastern United States for 1993. National Oceanic and Atmospheric Administration Technical Memorandum NMFS-F/NEC-95.

NMFS (National Marine Fisheries Service). 1995. Status of fishery resources off the northeastern United States for 1994. National Oceanic and Atmospheric Administration Technical Memorandum NMFS-NE-108.

NRC (National Research Council). 1994. Restoring and protecting marine habitat: the role of engineering and technology. Marine Board, Commission on Engineering and Technical Systems, National Academy Press, Washington, D.C.

Orth, R. J., K. L. Heck, and J. van Montfrans. 1984. Faunal communities in seagrass beds: a review of the influence of plant structure and prey characteristics on predator-prey relationships. Estuaries 7:339–350.

Pearcy, W. G., and S. W. Richards. 1962. Distribution and ecology of fishes of the Mystic River estuary, Connecticut. Ecology 43:248–259.

Peterson, G. W., and R. E. Turner. 1994. The value of salt marsh edge vs interior as a habitat for fish and decapod crustaceans in a Louisiana salt marsh. Estuaries 17(1B):235–262.

Poole, J. C. 1964. Feeding habits of the summer flounder in Great South Bay. New York Fish and Game Journal 2(1):28–34.

Poole, J. C. 1966. A review of research concerning summer flounder and needs for further study. New York Fish and Game Journal 13(2):226–232.

Redfield, A. C. 1972. Development of a New England salt marsh. Ecological Monographs 42:201–237.

Reimold, R. J. 1977. Mangals and salt marshes of the eastern United States. Pages 157–166 *in* V. J. Chapman, editor. Wet coastal ecosystems. Elsevier Scientific Publishing, Amsterdam.

RICRMC (Rhode Island Coastal Resource Management Council). 1996. State of Rhode Island Coastal Resource Management Program, as amended. RICRMC, Wakefield, Rhode Island.

Rogers, S. G., and M. J. Van Den Avyle. 1983. Species profiles: life histories and environmental requirements of coastal fishes and invertebrates (south Atlantic)—summer flounder. U.S. Fish and Wildlife Service, FWS/OBS-82/11.15, U.S. Army Corps of Engineers, TR EL-82-4.

Rountree, R. A. 1992. Fish and macroinvertebrate community structure and habitat use patterns in salt marsh creeks of southern New Jersey, with discussion of marsh carbon export. Doctoral dissertation. Rutgers University, New Brunswick, New Jersey.

Rountree, R. A., and K. W. Able. 1992. Fauna of polyhaline subtidal marsh creek creeks in southern New Jersey: composition, abundance and biomass. Estuaries 15:171–185.

Rozas, L. P. 1995. Hydroperiod and its influence on nekton use of the salt marsh: a pulsing ecosystem. Estuaries 18(4):579–590.

Rozas, L. P., and C. T. Hackney. 1984. Use of oligohaline marshes by fishes and macrofaunal crustaceans in North Carolina. Estuaries 7:213–224.

Rozas, L. P., C. C. McIvor, and W. E. Odum. 1988. Intertidal rivulets and creekbanks: corridors between tidal creeks and marshes. Marine Ecology Progress Series 47:303–307.

Rozas, L. P., and T. J. Minello. 1997. Estimating densities of small fishes and decapod crustaceans in shallow estuarine habitats. a review of sampling design with focus on gear selection. Estuaries 20:199–213.

Rozas, L. P., and W. E. Odum. 1987a. Use of tidal freshwater marshes by fishes and macrofaunal crustaceans along a marsh stream-order gradient. Estuaries 10:36–43.

Rozas, L. P., and W. E. Odum. 1987b. Fish and crustacean use of submerged plant beds in tidal freshwater marsh creeks. Marine Ecology Progress Series 38:101–108.

Sacco, J. N., F. L. Booker, and E. D. Seneca. 1988. Comparison of the macrofaunal communities of a human-initiated salt marsh of two and fifteen years of age. Pages 282–285 in J. Zelazny and J. S. Feierabend, editors. Increasing our wetland resources. National Wildlife Federation, Washington, D.C.

Sacco, J. N., E. D. Seneca, and T. R. Wentworth. 1994. Infaunal community development of artificially established salt marshes in North Carolina. Estuaries 17:489–500.

Saila, S. B. 1961a. A study of winter flounder movements. Limnological Oceanography 6(3):292–298.

Saila, S. B. 1961b. The contribution of estuaries to the offshore winter flounder fishery in Rhode Island. Proceedings of the Gulf and Caribbean Fisheries Institute 1961:95–109.

Satchwill, R. J., and R. T. Sisson. 1991. The fisheries resources of Point Judith and Potter Pond, South Kingstown and Narragansett, Rhode Island. Rhode Island Department of Environmental Management, Division of Fish and Wildlife, Federal Aid to Fisheries Project, F-51-R, Rhode Island, Wickford.

Satchwill, R. J., S. P. Turano, and R. T. Sisson. 1983. Preliminary assessment of biological and physical characteristics of the Narragansett Bay Estuarine

Sanctuary. Rhode Island Department of Environmental Management, Division of Fish and Wildlife, Wickford.

Seneca, E. D., and S. W. Broome. 1990. Restoring tidal marshes in North Carolina and France. Pages 53–78 in G. W. Thayer, editor. Restoring the nation's marine environment. Maryland Sea Grant College Program, UM-SG-TS-92-06, College Park, Maryland.

Shenker, J., and J. M. Dean. 1979. The utilization of an intertidal salt marsh creek by larval and juvenile fishes: abundance, diversity and temporal variation. Estuaries 2:154–163.

Shisler, J. K. 1990. Creation and restoration of coastal wetlands in the northeastern United States. In J. A. Kusler and M. E. Kentula, editors. Wetland creation and restoration: the status of the science. Island Press, Washington D.C.

Short, F. T., editor. 1992. The ecology of the Great Bay estuary, New Hampshire and Maine: an estuarine profile and bibliography. National Oceanic and Atmospheric Administration, Coastal Ocean Program, Silver Spring, Maryland.

Sinicrope, T. L., P. G. Hine, R. S. Warren, and W. A. Niering. 1990. Restoration of an impounded salt marsh in New England. Estuaries 13:25–30.

Smith, S. M., J. G. Hoff, S. P. O'Neil, and M. P. Weinstein. 1984. Community and trophic organization of nekton utilizing shallow marsh habitats, York River, Virginia. Fishery Bulletin 82(3):455–467.

Sogard, S. M., and K. W. Able. 1991. A comparison of eelgrass, sea lettuce macroalgae, and marsh creek habitats for epibenthic fishes and decapods. Estuarine Coastal Shelf Science 33(5):501–520.

Spinner, G. P. 1968. The wildlife wetlands and shellfish areas of the Atlantic coastal zone. Folio 18 in Serial Atlas of the Marine Environment. American Geographical Society, Washington D.C.

Stolgitis, J. A., J. F. O'Brien, and M. J. Fogarty. 1976. Rhode Island salt ponds, fisheries inventory. Fisheries Report 2, Rhode Island Division of Fish and Wildlife and Coastal Resources Management Council, Wickford.

Stone, S. L., and seven coauthors. 1994. Distribution and abundance of fishes and invertebrates in Mid-Atlantic estuaries. Estuarine Living Marine Resources Report 12, National Oceanic and Atmospheric Administration, National Ocean Service, Strategic Environmental Assessments Division, Silver Spring, Maryland.

Subrahmanyam, C. B., and C. L. Coultas. 1980. Studies on the animal communities in two north Florida salt marshes, part III, seasonal fluctuations of fish and macroinvertebrates. Bulletin of Marine Science 30:790–818.

Subrahmanyam, C. B., and S. H. Drake. 1975. Studies on the animal communities in two north Florida salt marshes. Bulletin of Marine Science 25(4):445–465.

Talbot, C. W., and K. W. Able. 1984. Composition and distribution of larval fishes in New Jersey high marshes. Estuaries 4A:434–443.

Talbot, C. W., K. W. Able, and J. K. Shisler. 1986. The ecology of regularly flooded salt marshes of New England: a community profile. U.S. Fish and Wildlife Service, Biological Report 85(7.4).

Teal, J. M. 1986. The ecology of regularly flooded salt marshes of New England: a community profile. U.S. Fish and Wildlife Service Biological Report 85(7.4).

Teal, J., and M. Teal. 1969. Life and death of the salt marsh. Ballantine Books, New York.

Thayer, G. W. 1990. The science of restoration: status and directions. Pages 1–5 *in* G. W. Thayer, editor. Restoring the nation's marine environment. Maryland Sea Grant College Program, College Park.

Turner, R. E. 1977. Intertidal vegetation and commercial yields of penaeid shrimp. Transactions of the American Fisheries Society 106:411–416.

Tyler, A. V. 1971. Surges of winter flounder, *Pseudopleuronectes americanus*, into the intertidal zone. Journal of the Fisheries Research Board of Canada 28:1727–1732.

USACE (United States Army Corps of Engineers). 1993. Feasibility (section 1135) report and environmental assessment: Galilee Salt Marsh restoration. Waltham, Massachusetts.

Valiela, I., J. E. Wright, J. M. Teal, and S. B. Volkmann. 1977. Growth, production and energy transformations in the salt-marsh killifish *Fundulus heteroclitus*. Marine Biology 40:135–144.

Van Dolah, R. F. 1978. Factors regulating the distribution and population dynamics of the amphipod Gammarus palustris in an intertidal salt marsh community. Ecological Monographs 48:191–217.

Weinstein, M. P. 1979. Shallow marsh habitats as primary nursery areas for fish and shellfish, Cape Fear River, North Carolina. Fishery Bulletin 77:339–357.

Weinstein, M. P., S. L. Weiss, and M. F. Walters. 1980. Multiple determinants of community structure in shallow marsh habitats, Cape Fear River estuary, North Carolina. Marine Biology 58:227–243.

Weisberg, S. B., and V. A. Lotrich. 1986. Food limitation of a Delaware salt marsh population of the mummichog, *Fundulus heteroclitus* (L.). Oecologia 68:168–173.

Wells, B., D. H. Steele, and A. V. Tyler. 1973. Intertidal feeding of winter flounders (*Pseudopleuronectes americanus*) in the Bay of Fundy. Journal of the Fisheries Research Board of Canada 30:1374–1378.

Welsh, B. L. 1975. The role of grass shrimp, *Palaemonetes pugio*, in a tidal marsh ecosystem. Ecology 56:513–530.

Werme, C. E. 1981. Resource partitioning in a salt marsh fish community. Doctoral dissertation. Boston University, Boston.

Whitlatch, R. B. 1982. The ecology of New England tidal flats: a community profile. U.S. Fish and Wildlife Service, Biological Services Program, FWS/OBS-81/01, Washington, D.C.

Wright, J. H. 1972. Growth, mortality, production and consumption of a population of the salt marsh killifish, *Fundulus heteroclitus* Linnaeus. Master's thesis. Boston University, Boston.

Zedler, J. B. 1988. Salt marsh restoration: lessons from California. Pages 123–138 *in* Cairns, editor. Rehabilitating damaged ecosystems, volume 1. CRC Press, Boca Raton, Florida.

Zedler, J. B. 1990. Restoring cordgrass marshes in southern California. Pages 7–51 *in* G. W. Thayer, editor. Restoring the nation's marine environment. Maryland Sea Grant College Program, College Park.

Zimmerman, R. J., and T. J. Minello. 1984. Densities of *Penaeus aztecus*, *Penaeus setifurus*, and other natant macrofauna in a Texas salt marsh. Estuaries 7(4A):421–433.

American Fisheries Society Symposium 22:421–437, 1999
© Copyright by the American Fisheries Society 1999

A Case for Shelter Replacement in a Disturbed Spiny Lobster Nursery in Florida: Why Basic Research Had to Come First

WILLIAM F. HERRNKIND

Department of Biological Science, Florida State University
Tallahassee, Florida 32306-1100, USA

MARK J. BUTLER, IV

Department of Biological Sciences, Old Dominion University
Norfolk, Virginia 23529-0266, USA

JOHN H. HUNT

Florida Marine Research Institute, Florida Department of Environmental Protection
Marathon, Florida 33050, USA

Abstract.—Basic research on the settlement and postsettlement ecology of spiny lobster *Panulirus argus* has led to an application with the potential to replace lost natural refuge with artificial shelters intended for the vulnerable small juvenile stages. We began investigating ecological processes regulating juvenile spiny lobster recruitment in the Florida nursery in the mid-1980s. An unprecedented massive die-off of sponges in the middle Florida Keys followed cyanobacterial blooms in 1991–1993, ultimately affecting about 300 km^2 of a region providing approximately one-fifth of total juvenile recruitment. Before 1991, crevices in sponges provided diurnal refuge from predators for about 70% of juveniles <50 mm carapace length. On the basis of sampling done before and after sponge loss, we estimated that juvenile abundance declined by 30–50% on spongeless sites without alternative shelter, resulting in a decrease of annual nurserywide potential of up to 10%. Results of a field experiment evaluating the relative influences of the magnitude of settlement and availability of crevice shelter on juvenile recruitment, fortuitously begun before the sponge die-off, showed that juvenile survival and abundance were sustained on small 0.02- to 0.07-ha test sites provided with supplemental artificial shelters (slotted concrete blocks). In the absence of sponges, survival of microwire-tagged juveniles on the shelter-supplemented sites was about six times higher than that on unsupplemented sites. On the basis of our earlier ecological findings, we devised a feasibility study to test whether the artificial shelters could replace lost sponge shelter for juvenile lobsters on a large scale. It took the form of a field experiment using 240 shelters spread over 1-ha sites located amid hard substrate denuded of sponges. The shelters provided substitute crevices, supporting juvenile lobster recruitment approximating that in areas with good sponge cover. This outcome exemplifies the essential value of initial basic research that provides understanding of the ecological processes regulating individual survival and, ultimately, the character and dynamics of the fishery population. Such an approach, and the information it provides, is necessary to successful rehabilitation of essential habitat or restocking of natural populations. Moreover, conducting basic research can help prevent the waste of precious time, funds, income, and human effort that typically has occurred in past failed attempts that were undertaken with insufficient knowledge. We urge the fisheries-ecology discipline and support agencies to promote strongly the primacy of research on basic processes.

Historically, efforts to increase stocks of lobsters (spiny and clawed), as well as other fishable species, have been driven by immediate socioeconomic goals and have constituted either direct, large-scale stocking of small juveniles or habitat enhancement by construction of "reefs" of natural or man-made materials (Conan 1986; Nonaka and Fushimi 1994; Bannister and Addison 1998). The practitioners, whether scientists or entrepreneurial fishers, usually began with limited knowledge of ecological and early life history requirements of the target species. Initial ecological and recruitment research was rarely undertaken, being deemed

too time consuming, too expensive, methodologically unfeasible, or unnecessary. Instead, enhancements or stocking usually proceeded without preliminary field testing and seldom incorporated effective follow-up monitoring designed to evaluate their effect. Most of these costly long-term efforts failed to accomplish the expected outcome, such as a markedly larger catch (Addison and Bannister 1994; Bannister and Addison 1998), or there remained serious questions as to whether an apparent effect was beneficial, for example, whether artificial habitat increased productivity or simply attracted individuals already recruited in the surrounding habitat (Cruz and Phillips 1994). Often, the role of the researcher has been to try, post hoc, to discern the impact of extensive activities in an already altered situation, without undisturbed controls and lacking data on initial conditions (Briones et al. 1994; Phillips and Evans 1997). Present widespread and serious socioeconomic and conservation needs (e.g., to sustain or replenish stocks and ensure availability of essential habitat) demand more effective, anticipatory, and strongly inferential research approaches (Phillips and Evans 1997).

Our research on the settlement and postsettlement ecology of Caribbean spiny lobster *Panulirus argus* in Florida, begun in the 1980s, has led to an application with the potential for artificial replacement of natural refuge lost in an unforeseen, widespread sponge die-off that affected about 20% of the lobster nursery habitat in the early 1990s. The application was a logical extension of knowledge gained during research on factors regulating recruitment of lobsters in the Florida Bay nursery, which sustains the extremely valuable and heavily fished adult population. The basic research we conducted during the decade preceding the sponge die-off was predicated on the rationale that one must know the ecological linkages between juvenile lobsters and those processes and habitat features that determine individual survival and population abundance. This knowledge is essential to solving problems of resource management and conservation. The nature of initially unforeseen linkages, in this case the extreme significance of crevice refuge to survival at a critical juvenile stage and its interaction with postlarval supply, would probably not have emerged without a broad ecological perspective and an initially open-ended research agenda. This is one of a number of recent examples for fished species demonstrating the value of investing in basic research, which alone can provide relevant, applicable knowledge (Caddy 1986; Blankenship and Leber 1995; Cobb 1995).

The first of three sections to follow synopsizes our research on spiny lobsters in south Florida, emphasizing the progression from initially descriptive studies and short-term experiments to developing and testing general hypotheses by large-scale field manipulations that provide inferences at the regional and population level. Amid this work, in 1991–1993, the massive loss of sponges introduced an unplanned "grand" test of hypotheses about the respective effects of variable postlarval supply to the nursery and the abundance of shelters on postsettlement survival. The second section describes and provides an initial assessment of results of a large-scale field test of the effectiveness of replacing lost sponge shelters with artificial structures. The third section reviews and discusses various lobster enhancement efforts, identifies types of research needed to provide baseline data for validly assessing effects of habitat changes, and culminates in a prospectus asserting that basic research on ecological processes must receive the highest priority if we expect to achieve success in habitat rehabilitation in the face of large-scale changes in ecological and populational conditions.

Florida Spiny Lobster Recruitment Research

Life History

The Caribbean spiny lobster supports major commercial fisheries over its range from Brazil to Bermuda. In the Florida Keys it is the focus of both intensive commercial trapping and recreational diving, and it alternates with shrimp as the state's most economically important marine species (Harper 1995). As a large, long-lived, abundant, and widely ranging benthic predator of sedentary mollusks and crustaceans, it is ecologically significant in all the coastal habitats it occupies (Kanciruk 1980). The complex life history of this species requires three distinct habitats (Figure 1; Marx and Herrnkind 1983; Herrnkind et al. 1994; Lipcius and Cobb 1994). Adults potentially can live for several decades, congregating in reef crevices and frequently migrating about the coastal shelf. Mating and spawning occur in spring on oceanic reefs; the phyllosome larva develops as it drifts in the open ocean for an estimated 6–9 months before metamorphosing into the puerulus postlarva. The nonfeeding pueruli move through inlets into Florida Bay every month on nightly flooding tides at new moon phase, then settle within days amid benthic vegetation (Herrnkind et al. 1994).

After metamorphosis, the benthic instars remain within vegetation for several months until attaining about 15–20 mm carapace length (CL), when they take up daytime shelter in sponge crevices or rocky substrate but forage in the open at night. At about 50 mm CL, about one year after settlement, the juveniles leave the initial nursery habitat and move nomadically about the bay for the next year, ultimately migrating offshore to the reefs, where they

Carribbean Spiny Lobster Life Cycle

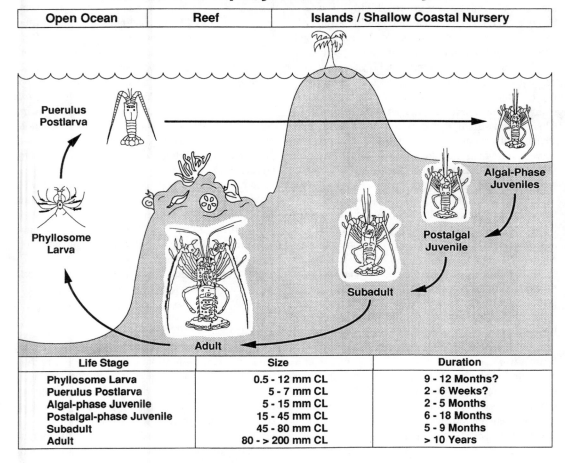

| Open Ocean | Reef | Islands / Shallow Coastal Nursery |

Life Stage	Size	Duration
Phyllosome Larva	0.5 - 12 mm CL	9 - 12 Months?
Puerulus Postlarva	5 - 7 mm CL	2 - 6 Weeks?
Algal-phase Juvenile	5 - 15 mm CL	2 - 5 Months
Postalgal-phase Juvenile	15 - 45 mm CL	6 - 18 Months
Subadult	45 - 80 mm CL	5 - 9 Months
Adult	80 - > 200 mm CL	> 10 Years

FIGURE 1.—Diagram summarizing the stages of the life cycle of the Caribbean spiny lobster *Panulirus argus*, showing size, duration, and habitat of each stage in Florida waters (Butler and Herrnkind 1997). Present evidence suggests that late-stage phyllosome larvae and the subsequent puerulus postlarvae that settle in the region originate from as yet unspecifiable locations in the Caribbean Sea. Florida-born larvae have an unknown fate. (Reprinted from Canadian Journal of Fisheries and Aquatic Sciences with permission of the NRC Research Press, Ottawa, Canada.)

attain sexual maturity (~78 mm CL or "legal" size; Herrnkind 1980). Annual fishing mortality is estimated at >90%, and the removal of the large majority of adults each fishing season, particularly the large fecund females, has reduced the reproductive capacity of the Florida population to approximately 12% of its prefishery level (Kanciruk 1980; Lyons et al. 1981). Because postlarvae settling in the Florida nursery arises from parental stocks at as yet unspecifiable locations elsewhere in the Caribbean basin (Ehrhardt 1994), it is imperative that those recruits be assured appropriate nursery habitat.

The Missing Stage Revealed

In the early 1980s, the descriptive ecology of preadult and reef-dwelling *P. argus* was emerging, but the settlement microhabitat and postsettlement ecology remained unknown (Herrnkind 1980; Kanciruk 1980). Meanwhile, western Australian fisheries ecologists used their growing knowledge of the nursery ecology of *P. cygnus* to predict the fishable population several years into the future (Phillips et al. 1994). Impelled by the Australians' success, an intensified search for the "missing" postsettlement stage of *P. argus* got underway with the support of Florida Sea Grant. James Marx, working in the Florida Keys, discovered highly dispersed, newly settled postlarvae and first benthic instars residing solitarily within and under large, attached clumps of foliose red algae *Laurencia* spp. (Marx 1983; Marx and Herrnkind 1985a). These algal-phase juveniles remain within algae at all times, feeding on abundant small mollusks and crustaceans (Marx and Herrnkind 1985a; Herrnkind et al. 1988). Their outline-disruptive dark and light bands and stripes make them almost invisible to a human observer even when they are exposed atop variegated vegetation. The solitary algal lifestyle gives way to frequent crevice cohabitation with other juveniles at about 15–20 mm CL (i.e., the postalgal stage; Childress and Herrnkind 1996), during which time the banded pattern becomes indistinct and the characteristic benthic-phase spots and coloration appear. Marx's discovery and initial observations made it feasible to undertake simultaneous research efforts to investigate the recruitment process in the nursery and to specify the biological characteristics of the uniquely specialized but poorly understood early benthic stage.

Ecological insights, later leading to recruitment hypotheses, came from early mesocosm and aquarium experiments aimed at elucidating basic behaviors and their probable functions during the early ontogenetic period. Choice tests with presettlement pueruli and first benthic instars showed that both phases strongly, but not exclusively, preferred to reside in algae instead of sea grass *Thalassia testudinum*, long thought to be the predominant settlement microhabitat (Herrnkind and Butler 1986). Substrates with interstices among fibrous structure, whether natural or artificial, were strongly preferred. In mesocosms, algal-phase juveniles avoided exposure but left clumps with (experimentally manipulated) low prey abundance to cross open bottom at night (Marx and Herrnkind 1985b). In the field, however, large contiguous algal patches contained an apparent overabundance of prey for the typically solitary juveniles, which are spaced an average of 1 per 36 m^2 of vegetated substrate (Marx and Herrnkind 1985a; Herrnkind et al. 1988); i.e., food was unlikely to be limiting in typical settlement habitat.

Field experiments showed that juveniles in large, dense algal patches had significantly lower mortality, day and night, than those in small algal clumps or in sea grass, although being in any structure was greatly superior to being in the open (Herrnkind and Butler 1986; Smith and Herrnkind 1992; Childress and Herrnkind 1994). Amid vegetation, the wide spacing and solitary isolation of algal-phase juveniles further promoted evasion of predators (Butler et al. 1997). Despite the refuge afforded by vegetation, numerous predatory species frequented nursery habitat and preyed on juveniles. Predators included snappers *Lutjanus* spp., sting rays *Dasyatis americana*, toadfish *Opsanus tau*, Caribbean reef octopus *Octopus briareus*, and swimming crabs *Portunus* spp. and *Callinectes* spp., among others (Smith and Herrnkind 1992). Larger juveniles that seek crevice refuge still suffered about the same relative predation while foraging away from refuge at night as the smaller algal juveniles experienced while within vegetation. Crevices in a variety of structures such as sponges, rock crevices, and narrow slots in partition concrete blocks offered equal protection (Childress and Herrnkind 1994). Thus, juvenile lobsters are at high risk of predation throughout the early benthic period, especially when they are foraging, seeking shelter, or otherwise exposed.

Settlement: Pattern without Predictability

Two aspects of the above information were directly relevant to questions about crustacean recruitment generally and to the Florida lobster nursery in particular: the highly dispersed spacing of both settling postlarvae and algal-phase instars, and the extreme vulnerability of shelterless, small, postalgal-phase juveniles. The most applicable hypotheses were (1) recruitment success was directly dependent on the numbers of postlarvae entering the nursery (a "supply side"-dominated process; Fairweather 1991; Fogarty et al. 1991), and (2) recruitment was regulated by variable availability of settlement and postsettlement habitat (a "demographic bottleneck"; Caddy 1986; Wahle and Steneck 1991). The applicability of either hypothesis could not be established from data available in the late 1980s (Marx 1986; Herrnkind et al. 1988), so in 1988 we undertook long-term, large-scale experimentation designed to discriminate their respective roles in a productive nursery area of the middle Florida Keys.

To determine the large-scale spatiotemporal pattern of postlarval settlement, we measured numbers of planktonic postlarvae arriving from offshore at four inlets of a 200-km^2 region of the middle Keys while also measuring the numbers settling successively greater distances downstream into the bay (Figure 2); the project ran a total of 6 months over 3

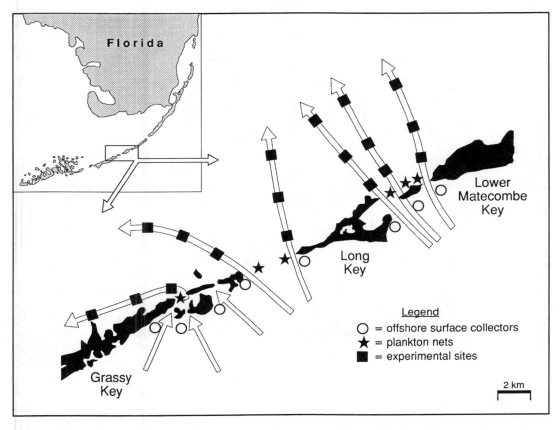

FIGURE 2.—Diagram of the middle Florida Keys showing current paths, postlarval monitoring stations, settlement sites, and adjacent benthic juvenile sampling locations for Caribbean spiny lobster during the summers of 1988–1990. Although overall downstream settlement reflects the relative number of arriving postlarvae, local settlement patterns are unpredictable because of spatiotemporal variability in postlarval abundance and settlement habitat. For more details, see text and Herrnkind and Butler (1994). (Reprinted from Crustaceana with permission of Brill, Leiden, the Netherlands.)

summers from 1988 to 1990 (Herrnkind and Butler 1994). We also compared the magnitude and spatial pattern of settlement on each site to the abundance of small crevice-dwelling juveniles in the surrounding area. Not surprisingly, the numbers of postlarvae settling on our benthic collectors downstream of an inlet reflected the numbers that had just passed through it. Despite this general pattern, the distribution and abundance of settlers was patchy and locally unpredictable from month to month and among the experimental settlement sites. Although areas with abundant, large algal patches, sponges, and other crevice-bearing shelter consistently harbored the highest numbers of small juveniles, algal abundance in most locations fluctuated markedly by season or from year to year. In short, we could identify sites where juvenile recruitment was generally high

or low, on the basis of habitat structure and proximity to inlets supplying postlarvae, but we could not predict short-term or small-scale recruitment patterns. Presumably, variability in both postlarval supply and macroalgal distribution created a continually shifting mosaic of settlement (Butler et al. 1997).

We proposed a conceptual model (Figure 3; Herrnkind and Butler 1994) to explain this spatiotemporally unpredictable pattern of juvenile recruitment on the basis of the relative settlement and survival of arriving postlarvae (support capacity) in a variable system. It was apparent that on poor habitat (sparse algae, few crevice shelters), even large numbers of settling postlarvae cannot yield many juveniles because they suffer very high postsettlement predation. Over time there is unlikely to be any close correspondence between regional

Good Habitat

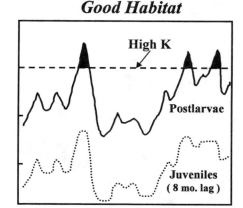

Poor Habitat

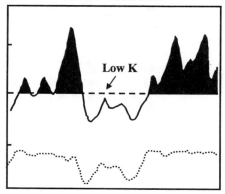

Time

FIGURE 3.—Graphic conceptual model of the relationship between the number of postlarvae settling on "good" (many crevices) and "poor" (sparse crevices) nursery habitat. In good sheltering habitat, with a high carrying capacity (K), mortality crops excess recruits (black area) only when settlement is extremely high, so at other times, settlement is reflected by and closely correlated with later juvenile abundance. However, on habitat of low carrying capacity, there is high mortality after even moderate settlement, so the relationship between numbers of postlarvae and later juvenile abundance is decoupled.

postlarval supply and juvenile recruitment on such sites. Contrarily, numerous settlers on good nursery habitat (abundant algal and crevice refuge) will have comparatively high survival rates through the algal and postalgal period, so juvenile abundance will later be reflected as correspondingly higher compared to periods of low postlarval abundance. However, both postlarval numbers and settlement conditions vary over time and location independently in the Florida nursery. During times when few postlarvae arrive in

an area, even sites with rich nursery habitat will exhibit relatively low juvenile recruitment. Juvenile recruitment will also be reduced at previously productive locations during episodes of low algal production, even when postlarvae are abundant. According to the model, we would expect to see a long-term, high correlation between postlarval abundance and subsequent juvenile abundance only on shelter-rich sites that sustain extensive algal cover. This pattern has been documented on one of our long-term sites that is particularly rich in algae and sponge crevices, which has sustained for a decade the highest juvenile densities of any censused natural site (Forcucci et al. 1994; Butler et al. 1997; Childress and Herrnkind 1997). Nonetheless, predictions of this model needed to be experimentally tested on an appropriate spatial scale.

The importance of both algal condition and postlarval numbers to subsequent juvenile recruitment was demonstrated in a year-long experiment in which, each month, we added differing known numbers of microwire-tagged first benthic instars (total of either 46 or 182 per site) to 18 isolated 200- to 1,000-m² sites (n = 9 sites per density treatment), with naturally varying but known amounts of algal cover (Butler et al. 1997). The number of recovered tagged juveniles gave a direct estimate of survival on each site, whereas the ratio of untagged to recaptured juveniles of the same size (a proxy for age) at each census allowed us to back-calculate the number of natural settlers there. Results showed that postsettlement survival in algae was not strongly density dependent even at our artificially inflated settlement levels. Algal patch size varied nearly threefold over the study period; regional postlarval abundance also varied but independently of algal dynamics. Proportional survival and growth, however, were comparable at the two settlement-density treatments, whereas total juvenile recruitment (tagged plus untagged) was correlated with algal patch size on the site. We concluded from this study that the initial numbers of settlers and condition of the habitat together influenced how many juveniles survive to make the transition into the crevice-dwelling phase.

Crevices: Refuge from the Predator "Gauntlet"

Support for the shelter-bottleneck hypothesis came from an experiment in 1988–1989 designed to test the influence of settlement magnitude and available crevice shelter—for postalgal juveniles—

on recruitment. We added artificial shelters to 6 isolated, 0.05-ha algal and hard-bottom sites and also added algal-phase juveniles to 3 of those sites; 3 other unmanipulated sites served as controls (Butler and Herrnkind 1992, 1997). Twelve artificial shelters (each consisting of two cement partition blocks), each 10 cm W × 20 cm H × 40 cm L, were set haphazardly on each of the six sites. These shelters each provided a total of 6 narrow holes (4 cm W × 2 cm H) and were capable of housing a maximum of about 15 small juveniles (Childress and Herrnkind 1996) up to 50 mm CL. To three of the six isolated sites, we also added an average of 26 postlarvae per site monthly for 6 months. We censused all sites biweekly, counting, measuring, tagging, then releasing all collected juveniles <50 mm CL.

We expected that a substantial number of the added algal-phase juveniles would survive within the algae, thus supplementing the natural settlement and increasing the numbers of postalgal juveniles censused several months later as they moved into crevices. Instead, the numbers of small postalgal juveniles <35 mm CL increased markedly on all shelter-supplemented sites but not on unmanipulated sites (Butler and Herrnkind 1997). Juvenile numbers were statistically similar in the two experimental treatments. The artificial shelters (cement blocks) housed 76% of all juveniles <45 mm CL collected on the manipulated sites; each occupied block housed 1–6 juveniles (mean ~2) of the same size range as those in nearby sponge crevices (mean ~32 mm CL). Tag-recapture data indicated high on-site residency for juveniles <35 mm CL and gradually increasing emigration and immigration thereafter. This outcome suggested that lack of crevice refuge can potentially constrain the number of lobsters in the nursery, given otherwise sufficient numbers of settlers and protective vegetated substrate.

Experimental support of the "bottleneck" hypothesis was significant both to understanding recruitment of obligate crevice-dwelling species generally (Caddy 1986; Wahle and Steneck 1991) and particularly to understanding the processes within the Florida lobster nursery. In addition, the potential to increase the proportion of surviving settlers on vegetated but crevice-poor substrate simply by adding artificial shelter was likely to have appeal to those interested in increasing the fishable population (Fee 1986; Moe 1991).

We believed that the initial study was an insufficient test and that much more needed to be learned about the basic ecological processes involved be-

fore anyone set out to attempt such a large-scale intercession. Therefore, in 1991 we undertook a longer and more extensive experiment incorporating several levels of both available shelter and settler numbers so as to discriminate their respective influences better.

This study included three levels each of added settlers and shelter blocks. We also used microwire tags to mark the introduced algal-phase juveniles so we could assess survival, growth, and natural settlement. The study incorporated 27 isolated sites (each ~200–1,000 m²) in a completely crossed 3 × 3 factorial design potentially allowing interpretation of main effects and interactions. Algal cover could not be effectively regulated but was measured monthly along with number, size, and gender of crevice-dwelling juveniles; identification of juvenile shelter and number of conspecifics in each shelter also occurred monthly.

Small postalgal juveniles were initially few on all the test sites but increased in number and grew in size between June and October 1991 (Figure 4a). This is a characteristic seasonal pattern in the Florida nursery, probably caused by the acceleration of growth rates with rising temperatures, so many of the winter and early spring settlers make the transition into the crevice-dwelling stage over summer and early fall (Lellis and Russell 1990; Forcucci et al. 1994; Herrnkind et al. 1997b). Recapture of sphyrion-tagged postalgal juveniles demonstrated site fidelity until ~45 mm CL and negligible movement between sites (W. Herrnkind, M. Butler, and J. Hunt, unpublished data). Recovery of microwire-tagged juveniles indicated a survival rate during the first benthic year of ~1–4% (Herrnkind and Butler 1994; Butler et al. 1997).

Housing Shortage in the Nursery

The preceding experiment, started in June 1991, was disrupted the following November by an unprecedented massive bloom of cyanobacteria, which reduced visibility to <1 m and curtailed assessment of the sites until February 1992 (Figure 5). In the wake of the bloom, we found that approximately half of the marked sponge dens had disappeared from the study sites and throughout hundreds of square kilometers of the surrounding region; sponge crevices formerly had housed >60% of all postalgal juveniles (Butler et al. 1995; Herrnkind et al. 1997b) but afterward housed only 25%. The total number of juveniles on the experimental sites did not decrease, but the proportion in shel-

428 HERRNKIND ET AL.

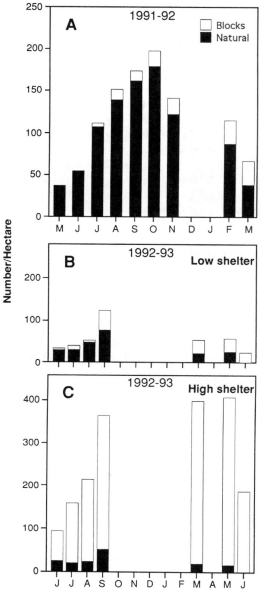

FIGURE 4.—(A) Mean numbers per hectare of juvenile spiny lobster <35 mm carapace length (CL) on 9 sites in the middle Florida Keys with primary sponge or other natural crevices between May 1991 and March 1992. Numbers increase through early fall as algal juveniles grow and leave the settlement vegetation to become crevice dwellers. A sponge-killing cyanobacterial bloom lasted from November 1991 through January 1992; about one-half of sponge dens were obliterated. (B) Numbers of juveniles <35 mm CL on 8 sites, affected by the 1991–1992 bloom, with mainly natural crevices between June 1992 and June 1993. A second bloom from October 1992 through February 1993 destroyed all sponges on the sites. (C) Numbers of lobsters during the same period as (B) on eight sites supplemented with concrete shelter blocks.

ter blocks, 24% before sponge loss, increased to 49% following this first bloom. We began a revised experiment incorporating 24 sites in June 1992, only to have it curtailed by an even larger, longer-lasting bloom from October 1992 through February 1993. This time all large, lobster-sheltering sponges died. We found only small numbers of postalgal juveniles on spongeless test sites without artificial shelters; those few individuals occupied rock crevices and occasional coral heads.

The extreme sponge loss across hundreds of square kilometers of a productive nursery region raised the specter that a refuge shortage might cause increased juvenile mortality and a subsequent decline in the adult population. Eventual repercussions to the fishery became a primary concern. In spring 1993, we set out to assess the change in the juvenile distribution, abundance, and shelter within the affected area. Our field studies in the bloom-swept region for the previous five years (e.g., Herrnkind and Butler 1994; Field and Butler 1994; Forcucci et al. 1994) provided data for before-and-after comparisons of algal and sponge cover, juvenile abundance, age structure, and types of shelter occupied.

Regionally, spongeless hard-bottom patches with few alternative crevice-bearing shelters harbored only about half the number of juveniles (<50 mm CL) they had housed in their previous, sponge-rich condition (Herrnkind et al. 1997b). On sites that retained some sheltering sponges or had numerous rock or coral crevices, juvenile abundances were actually about 40% higher than during the several-year period before the blooms, although some of this increase probably came from local immigration by larger, nomadic juveniles. Nevertheless, the presence of the entire juvenile size range showed that settlement and recruitment had continued across the affected region throughout the bloom period. The use of den structures reflected the available housing choices; for example, rock and coral crevices accounted for about 70% of dens, and sponges accounted for <20%. This pattern was echoed by conditions on the experimental sites provided with supplemental artificial shelter. There, juvenile numbers were as high as or higher than prebloom levels, but the vast majority of juveniles occupied shelter blocks (Butler et al. 1995; Herrnkind et al. 1997a).

The age structure of newly emerged postalgal juveniles (<35 mm CL) in the 1992 experiment repeated the typical seasonal pattern for the period June through September, but abundances strongly reflected the amount of shelter available on each site. That is, few juveniles were present in the natural (spongeless) treatment, substantially more in the intermediate treatment,

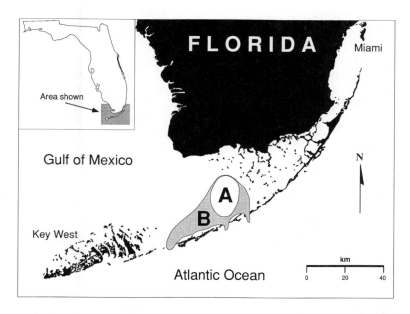

FIGURE 5.—Map of south Florida showing the approximate extent of cyanobacterial blooms in (A) fall 1991 and winter 1992 and (B) fall 1992 and spring 1993. One-half of large sponges used as dens by small juvenile spiny lobsters through the affected region were obliterated in the first bloom, and the remaining sponges were killed by the second bloom. The affected area accounts for approximately 20% of the total productivity of the main Florida nursery. Figure redrawn from Butler et al. (1995). (Reprinted from Marine Ecology Progress Series with permission of Inter-Research, Oldendorf/Luhe, Germany.)

and even higher numbers on sites with the highest shelter supplementation (Figure 4b,c; Herrnkind et al. 1997b). The same abundance pattern was present in spring 1993 after total sponge loss. Postbloom juvenile abundances on shelter-block sites in fall 1992 and spring 1993 equaled the highest levels recorded on natural unaffected sites in 1991 and approached the maximum recorded at any location (~400 juveniles <50 mm CL per ha; Forcucci et al. 1994).

The differences in abundances of small juveniles (<35 mm CL) among the sites were due to the corresponding availability of artificial shelters because the numbers occupying sparse natural crevices were similar in all treatments. Moreover, microwire tag-recovery data also indicated survival rates corresponding to shelter availability. Although an equal number of tagged early instars were released into each of the three shelter conditions, approximately six times as many were recovered as postalgal juveniles from the high-shelter (block) as from the low-shelter (natural) condition. Neither algal abundance, local variation in settlement, nor immigration of older juveniles explained the above pattern. These results extended the interpretation of the initial shelter experiment. The paucity of crevice refuge can present a "bottleneck" for small juvenile P.

argus over a large area of nursery as Caddy (1986) hypothesized. Observations of a high rate of occupancy of artificial crevices by small postalgal juveniles also suggested potential shelter limitation in a Mexican spiny lobster nursery (Arce et al. 1997).

Artificial Shelter on a Large Scale: The Acid Test

Rationale

The artificial shelters we had deployed for experimental purposes appeared to compensate for the lost natural sponge crevices by providing refuge for the vulnerable small juveniles as they emerged from the initial postsettlement algal microhabitat (Herrnkind et al. 1997a). From these results, a new question arose. Could the shelter blocks that served as substitute refuge on small patches in one area be effective over the range of conditions across the larger affected region?

Most nursery habitat in the Keys is distributed as large, discontinuous stretches across many hectares interrupted or separated by large sea grass meadows (Herrnkind, Butler, and Hunt, unpublished data), yet for experimental manipulations we had deliberately selected small (0.05–0.10-ha) patches isolated in large and otherwise contiguous sea grass meadows. The two types of sites might differ with respect to settlement, survival, or movement of juvenile lobsters. For example, in the small corral-like patches, the effect of enhanced shelter on survival might be increased, whereas immigration might be lower than at open sites.

For a large-scale test of shelter replacement, we chose to use 1-ha arrays of the cement-block shelters at a density of 240/ha, estimated to approximate the housing capacity of crevices in regional sponge habitat. Past studies indicated that a 1-ha patch (100 m × 100 m) is sufficiently large that postlarvae settling within the array would grow through the juvenile period there until the onset of the nomadic stage (~40–50 mm CL; Forcucci et al. 1994). That is, newly emerging postalgal individuals entering the artificial shelters would be those originally recruited as postlarval settlers on that 1-ha site.

We confine the presentation below to an assessment of two key hypothetical predictions based on the postsettlement recruitment processes reviewed above (a detailed analysis of the project is being prepared). Prediction 1: numbers of small postalgal juveniles would recruit to the artificial shelter sites consistent with seasonal patterns of settlement and growth, as well as to sponge sites, but not to spongeless sites. Prediction 2: because each hectare with artificial shelters was surrounded by a much larger spongeless area of sparse crevice shelter, where larger, mobile postalgal juveniles should wander about seeking shelter, older nomadic juveniles would rapidly immigrate to and remain in residence primarily on the artificial-shelter sites and, to a lesser extent, on large, sponge-dominated sites, but not at all on spongeless sites.

Methods

We applied methods and procedures used in previous experiments (details in Butler and Herrnkind 1997; Butler et al. 1997; Herrnkind et al. 1997b). As experimental comparisons to the 1-ha, 240-block treatment, we chose patches on spongeless substrate about 0.5 km from the block arrays and on sponge-rich sites that were relatively untouched by the 1991–1992 blooms (Butler et al. 1995; Herrnkind et al. 1997b).

In June 1995, study sites were established within widely separated about 0.5- to >1.0-km² patches of algal hard bottom. We marked 500-m² sampling plots

on the sponge-rich and spongeless sites and in the centers of 1-ha areas, which later received artificial shelters. Divers then surveyed each plot, using three parallel 25-m line (measuring tape) and belt transects (2 m wide) spaced about 5 m apart to characterize algal cover (percent cover) and potential den structures (sponges, corals, etc. >20 cm diameter). We also captured and measured all crevice-dwelling juvenile lobsters present there (<50 cm CL). During the following week, 240 artificial shelters (2 stacked, 3-slot partition blocks) were placed about 8 m apart throughout the 1-ha plots; the 12 blocks in the center plot were marked by numbered tags. The 500-m² plots on all sites were recensused for juvenile lobsters and resurveyed for algal cover in September 1995 and in February, May, and July 1996.

Results

Figure 6 shows the mean abundances (as per-hectare density) of small postalgal juveniles (Figure 6a, <25 mm CL) and larger, more mobile juveniles (Figure 6b, 35–50 mm CL) for each site type through the project period. In June 1995, numbers of postalgal juveniles were similarly low on all the sites (20–30/ha), as is common in that season (Herrnkind et al. 1997b). Over the next 2 quarters, the abundances of new crevice dwellers (<25 mm CL) doubled or tripled on the shelter-supplemented and sponge sites but not on the spongeless plots (20/ha in September 1995; 0/ha in February 1996). Diver reconnaissance and supplemental censusing showed juveniles were also present throughout the sponge areas and among artificial shelters outside the sampled plots on all three sites. In May 1996, abundances of juveniles <25 mm CL were again seasonally low on all site categories (0–33/ha), but by July 1996 they increased to similarly high levels on sponge (100/ha) and block (93/ha) sites. Meanwhile, spongeless sites had 0/ha and 33/ha (i.e., no change from the previous year). Mean overall abundances of juveniles <25 mm CL were remarkably congruent on the natural sponge sites and on those on which we placed artificial shelters as substitutes for lost sponge crevices. These data affirm the hypothetical prediction that numbers of locally recruited, newly emerged postalgal juveniles on the shelter-supplemented as well as sponge sites should increase and exceed the numbers on spongeless sites.

The second prediction was also upheld, i.e., that larger, more nomadic juveniles from the surrounding low-shelter areas should quickly immigrate and

a. <25 mm Carapace Length

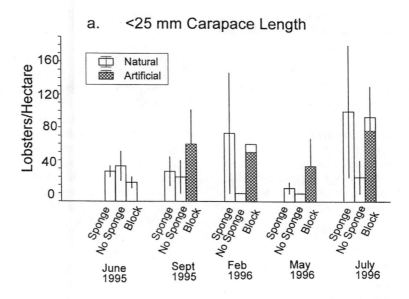

b. 35-50 mm Carapace Length

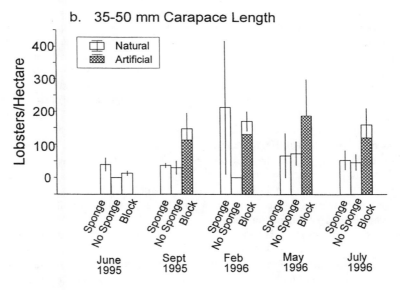

FIGURE 6.—Histogram comparison of abundances of small postalgal juvenile lobsters (a, <25 mm carapace length [CL]) and older, mobile juveniles (b, 35–50 mm CL) on sponge-dominated natural sites, natural sites with no sponges, and spongeless sites on which we arrayed 240 concrete shelter blocks. The initial lobster census (June 1995) was taken just before addition of the concrete blocks to the artificial shelter sites. There were 3 replicate sites in each category; means of census counts on 0.05-ha plots on the 3 sites in each category are scaled up to 1.00 ha. Bars represent 1 standard error. (6a, Feb 1996, includes only one Block site.)

markedly inflate numbers on the shelter-supplemented sites (Figure 6b). Between June and September 1995, the mean number of juveniles 35–50 mm CL increased from 20/ha in June 1995 to 146/ha in September 1995 on the shelter-supplemented sites. The intervening period (~2.5 months) was too

short for growth of sufficient numbers of algal juveniles to the larger size range (35–50 mm CL; Forcucci et al. 1994; W. Sharp, Florida Marine Research Institute, unpublished data), so the surge of older juveniles there had to be mostly immigrants. Shelter-supplemented sites had the highest abundances of 35–50 mm CL juveniles for three of the four sampling periods after the shelters were added, suggesting continuous immigration and long residency.

Data from short-term antenna tagging of postalgal juveniles, done in conjunction with a separate study, are presently being analyzed and may establish the relative migration rates into and out of different kinds of sites (Butler, unpublished data). Although we set out microwire-tagged algal-phase juveniles, we recovered very few, possibly indicating movement out of the unbounded 0.05-ha plots or especially high mortality.

Discussion

The close match between recruitment patterns of young postalgal juveniles (<25 mm CL) observed on the 1-ha sites supplemented with cement-block shelters and their abundance and seasonal pattern on natural sponge sites resembles prior results from small, confined sites (Herrnkind et al. 1997a) and suggests that artificial shelters can effectively substitute for lost sponge refuge on a large scale. Because each shelter block has several crevices of appropriate size, relatively few are needed as compared to natural sponges, only a small fraction of which have suitable interstices; e.g., the mean density of sponges is >2,000 per ha in the undisturbed portion of the nursery (Herrnkind et al. 1997b). Large predatory fishes such as groupers and snappers are not strongly attracted to these small isolated structures, which are about the size of sponges. Spacing the blocks several meters apart yields juvenile spatial distributions typically observed in natural sponge habitat in the Florida nursery (Childress and Herrnkind 1997). Separation by at least 2 m additionally prevents close proximity of early postalgal juveniles (~15 mm CL), which potentially increases their vulnerability to predators (Butler et al. 1997).

Until they attain substantially larger size, aggregated postalgal juveniles in a den probably gain little or no advantage in cooperative defense over solitary individuals (Childress 1995; Childress and Herrnkind 1997). Large objects like the "casitas" used by fishers to attract subadult and adult lobsters often attract large snappers and groupers that prey on smaller juveniles (Cruz and Phillips 1994; Mintz et al. 1994). For this reason, it seems unnecessary, or possibly counterproductive, to build large artificial structures for small postalgal juveniles (Cruz et al. 1986; Lozano-Alvarez

et al. 1994; Arce et al. 1997). There is evidence, however, that larger nomadic juveniles (>50 mm CL) and subadults benefit from group dens (Eggleston et al. 1992; Mintz et al. 1994; M. Butler, and A. McDiarmid, unpublished data). The great majority of older juveniles in the Florida nursery do not use sponges but instead occupy large rock crevices and undercuts (Butler and Herrnkind 1997). Although they sometimes den singly, 50–75-mm CL lobsters more commonly reside in groups; e.g., we have seen over 100 lobsters in a large natural crevice (Herrnkind, personal observation).

The comparison of abundances between our sites with artificial shelters and the sponge-dominated areas should be applied strictly to the newly emerged postalgal recruits and not to the largest juveniles. That is, the present data show that many mobile lobsters 35–50 mm CL immigrated to the 1-ha shelter-supplemented area from the large shelter-poor surrounding region. At first glance, mean total juvenile abundance (all juveniles <50 mm CL) for the study period appears substantially higher on sites with artificial shelter (387 per ha versus 211 per ha); that result is caused largely by the inflated numbers of older immigrants and is not a valid reflection of on-site recruitment. The present situation for 35–50-mm CL juveniles in spongeless areas seems analogous to the attraction and retention of large numbers of similar-aged juveniles to casitas set in sea grass and other crevice-poor habitat. Ontogenetic changes in mobility as well as sociality, vulnerability to predators, and other age-related features must be distinguished and separately evaluated for accurate assessment of the ecology of "juveniles" because effects differ markedly in the nursery depending on age and size (Childress and Herrnkind 1994, 1996).

The small-slot cement blocks we used may not be the most attractive or protective artificial shelter possible. Rather, they serve juveniles <50 mm CL analogously to the range of natural crevice-bearing structures in Florida nursery habitat. Small P. argus respond to the features of a crevice rather than to the structure bearing it (Herrnkind et al. 1997b). Our artificial shelters, like some natural crevices, allow for either solitary or communal denning. Across the nursery, about half of juveniles <50 mm CL shared a den with conspecifics, usually with one (45%) or two (27%) but up to nine (Childress and Herrnkind 1997). Space for several individuals to be close together, whether or not in the same den, may be an important attribute of both artificial shelters and large or closely spaced natural crevices because postalgal juveniles are attracted to (or can find) other denned individuals from an as yet unspecified distance (probably exceeding several meters) away at night, presumably in response to chemical cues from conspecifics in the den (Zimmer-Faust and Spanier 1987; Childress 1995). Rapidly locating a den by homing to a resident individual shortens the exposure time of a shelter-seeking juvenile, thus reducing its probability of being intercepted by a predator (Childress 1995; Childress and Herrnkind 1997).

As a rehabilitation device, the small artificial shelters seem particularly appropriate because they match the sheltering qualities of the missing natural structures, even though other artificial objects may attract and hold more juveniles. The number of experimental blocks (240/ha) supported roughly the same juvenile recruitment rate as the sponge-rich habitat, although all shelters were not used simultaneously, and all slots were not filled to capacity. That is, an array of 240 shelters/ha may be sufficient to replace lost sponges in this region. Adding more seems unnecessary for rehabilitation, and adding many more would be unlikely to produce a corresponding increase in recruitment because of upper limits placed by episodically low settlement and crevice-independent mortality both during the algal phase and while postalgal juveniles forage in the open (Butler and Herrnkind 1997).

We have concentrated research on processes specifically applying to the early juvenile phases because they suffer the highest natural mortality and consequently exert the greatest influence on recruitment to the fishable population (Smith and Herrnkind 1992; Butler and Herrnkind 1997). Nevertheless, older juveniles suffer predation and benefit from refuge in the habitats they traverse, including large areas of sea grass where prey can be plentiful but shelter is scarce. The ecology of late juvenile *P. argus* has been extensively studied in the Bahamas, Mexico, and Florida with respect to the impact of lobster-attracting casitas (or "pesqueros") by R. Lipcius, D. Eggleston, and their colleagues (Briones et al. 1994) and in Cuba by Cruz and others (Cruz and Philips 1994). Although these devices can reduce predation and provide access to abundant food for large numbers of nomadic lobsters (Briones et al. 1994; Cruz and Phillips 1994), they have not been employed to replace lost natural shelters (but see Davis 1985), and there is not yet compelling evidence that the devices promote recruitment of juveniles making the transition to crevice-dwelling.

We refrain from advocating the large-scale deployment of artificial shelters for shelter rehabilitation (or for enhancement) in Florida although they seem suitable (innocuous, inexpensive, nonpolluting), and there is as yet no apparent sign of sponge recovery to pre-1991 levels. Such decisions need to be made by other agencies of the body politic. In addition, estimates of the lobster catch in the past several years have been about the same as those in years before the sponge loss, although this result may be attributable to several years of especially high postlarval supply to the unaffected portion of the nursery. Moreover, some important concerns about mass deployment of artificial structures remain worthy of further research. Because we expect that new sponges will eventually recruit, the artificial shelters would become redundant but remain a permanent part of the underwater landscape. Perhaps similar structures could be made of natural oolitic rock fragments and be weakly bonded so that they disintegrate into harmless substrate after 10–20 years. We do not know how long the structures will remain effective before silt and epibiota clog the crevices (some we set out in 1988 still house juveniles, but many slots have filled and become inaccessible). It is not certain how the massive presence of artificial structures would affect juvenile lobster-den competitors (stone crabs, small toadfish) and predators (octopus, portunid crabs). To this point, no one has performed an adequate cost–benefit economic projection. Also, much of the spongeless region lies within Everglades National Park and the rest within the Florida Keys National Marine Sanctuary, thus raising concerns about preservation and environmental impact. Irrespective of whether or where artificial shelters are deployed for shelter rehabilitation, we believe their performance as juvenile lobster refuge has been ecologically demonstrated at a relevant scale.

Basic Research for Applied Information Needs: A Retrospective

Both clawed and spiny lobsters have been the focus of long-term, intense efforts to enhance fished populations (see recent reviews by Conan 1986 [clawed]; Briones et al. 1994; Cruz and Phillips 1994; Nonaka and Fushimi 1994 [spiny]; Hunt and Scheibling 1997 [general]; Pickering and Whitmarsh 1997; Bannister and Addison 1998). The enhancement literature chronicles a long history of direct attempts to stock or add habitat on a large scale to increase the catch or to improve harvesting efficiency, usually with good public support and sometimes initiated by the fishers. For example, once it became feasible to raise American clawed lobsters *Homarus americanus* through the egg and larval stage in the late 19th century, stocking efforts began and have continued since; restocking of *H. gammarus* (and *H. gammarus* × *H. americanus* hybrids) got underway in Europe around 1970 (Addison and Bannister 1994). Spiny lobsters have only recently been successfully cultured (see Kittaka 1994), but in the 1930s Japanese workers attempted to use artificial reefs to create new sites for lobster fishing, and in the 1970s they deployed arrays of large stone beds (5 m × 200 m) to improve recruitment of postlarval *Panulirus japonicus* (Nonaka and Fushimi 1994). Sometime around World War II, Cuban lobster fishers began to deploy shallow roofed structures of about 2 m^2 on shallow, open substrate to attract and concentrate *P. argus*, a fishing practice so effective that now at least 250,000 of these pesqueros account for half of the Cuban commercial catch—the largest for spiny lobster in the western hemisphere (Cruz and Phillips 1994). Analogous deployment of similar casitas has more recently taken place in eastern Mexico and in the Bahamas (Briones et al. 1994). Although the fishers argue that the structures are also refugia promoting survival of recruits, population-level evidence from which to make a valid determination has not yet been fully reported (Lipcius and Cobb 1994).

Nearly all recent reviewers and researchers have pointed out that most of these projects have yielded no discernable, documented increase in population recruitment. What is scientifically discordant is that the actual implementation of these practices each constituted a large-scale, expensive trial-and-error exercise, not a valid experiment. Researchers typically have had to try to evaluate impacts after the fact rather than initially evaluating important ecological processes or performing feasibility experiments. Instead, what researchers learn about ecological regulating processes emerges from their attempt to understand the effects that an extensive practice has already caused (Addison and Bannister 1994; Briones et al. 1994). It seems unreasonable to criticize the lack of appropriate science in past enhancement attempts before the relatively recent advent (since ~1960) of certain powerful technologies (scuba, microwire tags, telemetry, molecular-genetic identification) and sophisticated field experimental

designs and quantitative statistical methods for ecology. In addition, neither the strong theoretical framework nor the rigorous hypothesis-testing approach of contemporary ecology existed then, but those tools are available now, so we should integrate them into scientifically and economically sound research programs (Cobb 1995).

Our own experience, in retrospect, and lessons learned from other recent workers make a strong case for immediately beginning extensive, rigorous basic research leading to field experiments at an appropriate scale, even if doing so means deferring an important project with a large potential payoff. The answers needed for either a proposed new application or to assess the impact of an ongoing one (shelter rehabilitation, restocking, etc.) must ultimately come from an understanding of the natural mechanisms and processes operating on the focal population and region.

An apparent criticism of the basic-research-first approach is the unknown duration of studies, during which the stock or habitat is not being enhanced, and uncertainty that the knowledge gained will be sufficient. However, historical information shows that years of full-scale, direct applications without solid understanding of natural processes have rarely been successful. Our recruitment research reported here took over a decade to accomplish largely because large-scale experiments necessary for population-level inferences required years to perform and replicate. Our work to understand the dynamics of postlarval delivery and integrate a decade of research findings to develop a predictive individual-based model continues today. In addition, our recognition of the need to scale up each subsequent step was partly serendipitous, so the rate of progress varied. That is, we did not conceive a structured research track from the outset, but others to follow can do better. The important nursery and recruitment studies on western Australian *P. cygnus* took about two decades (1970–1990), but the knowledge gained has served as the framework for what is widely recognized as a model of spiny-lobster fishery management. Yet the time invested in the above projects is not particularly long compared to that for other approaches. For example, Norwegian scientists recently carried out an eight-year program to restock *Homarus gammarus*, involving release of >130,000 small tagged juveniles (van der Meeren 1994) with the aim of eventually replenishing a severely depleted population. However, because postrelease mortality was so extreme and so few were recovered, a three-year intensive ecological study is now underway to assess predation, habitat requirements, and settlement density (Phillips and Evans 1997)—basic questions that emerged early as the focus of the Florida juvenile-recruitment study. Answers about ecological processes will be needed sooner or later, and we recommend seeking that information sooner.

That more intensive and thorough basic research presently is not being done, particularly in the United States, seems to be the result of a production-oriented economic mind-set of the public, commerce, and politicians and the granting agencies they control. Our research has been sponsored largely by the Florida Sea Grant College Program and the Florida Department of Environmental Protection (FDEP), primarily through personnel and logistical support by the Florida Marine Research Institute (FMRI). We view the dynamic cross-linkage between the applied goals and information needs of management and the tenets and research protocols of basic ecology as a central reason for our successes. The collaboration and logistical contributions by the FDEP and FMRI have been essential both to the conduct of the study and, more pragmatically, to meeting granting-agency matching requirements. Although research for fisheries management has been a priority of Sea Grant and some other agencies, such research usually has no immediately specifiable monetary benefit. It is both little valued by fishers or related private enterprise (i.e., "users") and poorly understood by the general public, so it is difficult to gain popular or special-interest backing and to meet fund-matching requirements. As is the case with most government granting agencies intended to support university-based and other nonagency researchers, funds must be obtained competitively every two years. The short term of such grants and frequent priority shifts to new areas of emphasis create a situation nearly irreconcilable with conducting ecological research on fisheries species. To achieve effective research in fisheries ecology, fishery agencies, as well as granting entities, must put in place programs that promote, foster, and better support closely linked basic and applied collaborative research among scientists in academia and government.

Acknowledgments

We recognize Florida Sea Grant for funding our work through a series of research grants to W. Herrnkind and M. Butler from 1981 to the present, as well as agency initiatives to engage scientists and managers to pursue research on spiny lobster and fishery-relevant issues such as recruitment and artificial reefs. The Florida Department of Environmental Protection, through the Florida Marine Research Institute, has provided invaluable logistical support, personnel, and contracts for studies of concern to both basic science and management. Other important support came from the Center for Field Studies (Earthwatch), the Keys Marine Laboratory and Florida Institute of Oceanography, and our respective institutions. We particularly thank the many field personnel, students, and volunteers without whose help this long-term program could not have operated.

References

Addison, J. T., and R. C. A. Bannister. 1994. Re-stocking and enhancing clawed lobster stocks: a review. Crustaceana 67:131–155.

Arce, A. M., W. Aguilar-Davila, E. Sosa-Cordero, and J. F. Caddy. 1997. Artificial shelters (casitas) as habitat for juvenile spiny lobsters *Panulirus argus* in the Mexican Caribbean. Marine Ecology Progress Series 158:217–224.

Bannister, R. C. A., and J. T. Addison. 1998. Enhancing lobster stocks: a review of recent European methods, results, and future prospects. Bulletin of Marine Science 67:369–387.

Blankenship, H. L., and K. M. Leber. 1995. A responsible approach to marine stock enhancement. Pages 165–175 *in* H. L. Schramm, Jr., and R. G. Piper, editors. Uses and effects of cultured fish in aquatic ecosystems. American Fisheries Society, Symposium 15, Bethesda, Maryland.

Briones, P., E. Lozano, and D. B. Eggleston. 1994. The use of artificial shelters (casitas) in research and harvesting of Caribbean spiny lobsters in Mexico. Pages 340–362 *in* B. F. Phillips, J. S. Cobb, and J. Kittaka, editors. Spiny lobster management. Blackwell Scientific Publications, Oxford.

Butler, M. J., IV, and eight coauthors. 1995. Cascading disturbances in Florida Bay, USA: cyanobacteria blooms, sponge mortality, and implications for juvenile spiny lobsters, *Panulirus argus*. Marine Ecology Progress Series 129:119–125.

Butler, M., and W. Herrnkind. 1992. Spiny lobster recruitment in South Florida. Proceedings of the Gulf and Caribbean Fisheries Institute 42:508–515.

Butler, M. J., IV, and W. F. Herrnkind. 1997. A test of recruitment limitation and the potential for artificial enhancement of spiny lobster (*Panulirus argus*) populations in Florida. Canadian Journal of Fisheries and Aquatic Sciences 54:452–463.

Butler, M. J., W. F. Herrnkind, and J. H. Hunt. 1997. Factors affecting the recruitment of juvenile caribbean spiny lobsters dwelling in macroalgae. Bulletin of Marine Science 61:3–19.

Caddy, J. F. 1986. Modelling stock-recruitment processes in Crustacea: some practical and theoretical perspectives. Canadian Journal of Fisheries and Aquatic Sciences 43:2330–2344.

Childress, M. J. 1995. The ontogeny and evolution of gregarious behavior in juvenile Caribbean spiny lobster, *Panulirus argus*. Doctoral dissertation, Florida State University, Tallahassee.

Childress, M., and W. F. Herrnkind. 1994. The behavior of juvenile Caribbean spiny lobsters in Florida Bay: seasonality, ontogeny, and sociality. Bulletin of Marine Science 54:819–827.

Childress, M. J., and W. F. Herrnkind. 1996. The ontogeny of social behavior among juvenile Caribbean spiny lobsters. Animal Behaviour 51:675–687.

Childress, M. J., and W. F. Herrnkind. 1997. Den sharing by juvenile caribbean spiny lobsters (*Panulirus argus*) in nursery habitat: cooperation or coincidence. Marine and Freshwater Research 48:751–758.

Cobb, J. S. 1995. Interface of ecology, behavior, and fisheries. Pages 139–151 *in* J. R. Factor, editor. Biology of the lobster *Homarus americanus*. Academic Press, New York.

Conan, G. Y. 1986. Summary of session 5: recruitment enhancement. Canadian Journal of Fisheries and Aquatic Sciences 43:2384–2388.

Cruz, R., R. Brito, E. Diaz, and R. Lalana. 1986. Ecologia de la langosta (*Panulirus argus*) al SE de la isla de la Juventad. I. Colonizacion de arrecifes artificiales. Revista de Investigaciones Marinas 8:3–17.

Cruz, R., and B. F. Phillips. 1994. The artificial shelters (pesqueros) used for the spiny lobster (*Panulirus argus*) fisheries in Cuba. Pages 323–339 *in* B. F. Phillips, J. S. Cobb, and J. Kittaka, editors. Spiny lobster management. Blackwell Scientific Publications, Oxford.

Davis, G. E. 1985. Artificial structures to mitigate marina construction impacts on spiny lobster *Panulirus argus*. Bulletin of Marine Science 37:151–156.

Eggleston, D. B., R. N. Lipcius, and D. L. Miller. 1992. Artificial shelters and survival of juvenile Caribbean spiny lobster *Panulirus argus*: spatial, habitat, and lobster size effects. Fishery Bulletin 90:691–702.

Ehrhardt, N. M. 1994. The lobster fisheries off the Caribbean coast of Central America. Pages 133–143 *in* B. F. Phillips, J. S. Cobb, and J. Kittaka, editors. Spiny lobster management. Blackwell Scientific Publications, Oxford.

Fairweather, P. G. 1991. Implications of supply side ecology for environmental assessment and management. Trends in Ecology and Evolution 6:60–63.

Fee, R. 1986. Artificial habitats could hike crab and lobster catches. National Fisherman 67(8):10–12, 64.

Field, J. M., and M. J. Butler, IV. 1994. The influence of temperature, salinity, and postlarval transport on the distribution of juvenile spiny lobsters, *Panulirus argus* (Latreille, 1804) in Florida Bay. Crustaceana 67:26–45.

Fogarty, M. J., M. P. Sissenwine, and E. B. Cohen. 1991. Recruitment variability and the dynamics of exploited marine populations. Trends in Ecology and Evolution 6:241–246.

Forcucci, D., M. J. Butler, IV, and J. H. Hunt. 1994. Population dynamics of juvenile Caribbean spiny lobster, *Panulirus argus*, in Florida Bay. Bulletin of Marine Science 54:805–818.

Harper, D. E. 1995. The 1995 spiny lobster update of trends in landings, CPUE, and size of harvested lobster. Technical Report, National Oceanic and Atmospheric Administration, Miami.

Herrnkind, W. F. 1980. Spiny lobsters: patterns of movement. Pages 349–407 *in* J. S. Cobb and B. F. Phillips, editors. The biology and management of lobsters, volume 1. Academic Press, New York.

Herrnkind, W., and M. Butler. 1986. Factors regulating postlarval settlement and juvenile microhabitat use by spiny lobsters, *Panulirus argus*. Marine Ecology Progress Series 34:23–30.

Herrnkind, W., and M. Butler. 1994. Spiny lobster settlement in Florida: pattern without predictability? Crustaceana 67:46–64.

Herrnkind, W. F., M. J. Butler, IV, and J. H. Hunt. 1997a. Can artificial habitats that mimic natural structures enhance recruitment of Caribbean spiny lobster. Fisheries 22(4):24–27.

Herrnkind, W. F., M. J. Butler, J. H. Hunt, and M. Childress. 1997b. Role of physical refugia: implications from a mass sponge die-off in a lobster nursery in Florida. Marine and Freshwater Research 48:759–769.

Herrnkind, W. F., M. J. Butler, IV, and R. A. Tankersley. 1988. The effects of siltation on recruitment of spiny lobsters, *Panulirus argus*. Fishery Bulletin 86:331–338.

Herrnkind, W., P. Jernakoff, and M. Butler. 1994. Puerulus and post-puerulus ecology. Pages 213–226 *in* B. F. Phillips, J. S. Cobb, and J. Kittaka, editors. Spiny lobster management: current situation and perspectives. Blackwell Scientific Publications Scientific, Oxford.

Hunt, H. L., and R. E. Scheibling. 1997. Role of early post-settlement mortality in recruitment of benthic marine invertebrates. Marine Ecology Progress Series 155:269–301.

Kanciruk, P. 1980. Ecology of juvenile and adult Palinuridae (spiny lobsters). Pages 59–92 *in* J. S. Cobb and B. F. Phillips, editors. The biology and management of lobsters, volume 2. Academic Press, New York.

Kittaka, J. 1994. Culture of phyllosomas of spiny lobster and its application to studies of larval recruitment and aquaculture. Crustaceana 66:258–270.

Lellis, W. A., and J. A. Russell. 1990. Effect of temperature on survival, growth and feed intake of postlarval spiny lobsters, *Panulirus argus*. Aquaculture 90:1–9.

Lipcius, R. N., and J. S. Cobb. 1994. Introduction: ecology and fishery biology of spiny lobsters. Pages 1–30 *in* B. F. Phillips, J. S. Cobb, and J. Kittaka, editors. Spiny lobster management. Blackwell Scientific Publications, Oxford.

Lozano-Alvarez, E., P. Briones-Fourzan, and F. Negrete-Soto. 1994. An evaluation of concrete block structures as shelter for juvenile Caribbean spiny lobsters *Panulirus argus*. Bulletin of Marine Science 55:351–362.

Lyons, W. G., D. G. Barber, S. M. Foster, F. S Kennedy, and G. R. Milano. 1981. The spiny lobster, *Panulirus argus*, in the middle and upper Florida Keys: population structure, seasonal dynamics, and reproduction. Florida Marine Research Publication 38, St. Petersburg, Florida.

Marx, J. M. 1983. Aspects of microhabitat use by young juvenile spiny lobsters, *Panulirus argus*. Master's thesis., Florida State University, Tallahassee.

Marx, J. M. 1986. Recruitment and settlement of spiny lobster pueruli in south Florida. Canadian Journal of Fisheries and Aquatic Sciences 43:2221–2227.

Marx, J. M., and W. F. Herrnkind. 1983. Species profiles: life histories and environmental requirements of coastal fishes and invertebrates (south Florida): spiny lobster. U.S. Fish and Wildlife Service Biological Report 82:1–22.

Marx, J. M., and W. F. Herrnkind. 1985a. Factors regulating microhabitat use by young juvenile spiny lobsters, *Panulirus argus*: food and shelter. Journal of Crustacean Biology 5:650–657.

Marx, J. M., and W. F. Herrnkind. 1985b. Macroalgae (Rhodophyta: *Laurencia* spp.) as habitat for juvenile spiny lobsters, *Panulirus argus*. Bulletin of Marine Science 36:423–431.

Mintz, J. D., R. N. Lipcius, D. B. Eggleston, and M. S. Seebo. 1994. Survival of juvenile Caribbean spiny lobster: effects of shelter size, geographic location and conspecific abundance. Marine Ecology Progress Series 112:255–266.

Moe, M. A. 1991. Lobsters: Florida, Bahamas, the Caribbean. Green Turtle Publications, Plantation, Florida.

Nonaka, M., and H. Fushimi. 1994. Restocking. Pages 446–460 *in* B. F. Phillips, J. S. Cobb, and J. Kittaka, editors. Spiny lobster management. Blackwell Scientific Publications, Oxford.

Phillips, B. F., R. Cruz, R. S. Brown, and N. Caputi. 1994. Predicting the catch of spiny lobster fisheries. Pages 285–301 *in* B. F. Phillips, J. S. Cobb, and J. Kittaka, editors. Spiny lobster management. Blackwell Scientific Publications, Oxford.

Phillips, B. F., and L. H. Evans. 1997. Aquaculture and stock enhancement of lobsters: report from a workshop. Marine and Freshwater Research 48:899–903.

Pickering, H., and D. Whitmarsh. 1997. Artificial reefs and fisheries exploitation: a review of the "attraction versus production" debate, the influence of design and its significance for policy. Fisheries Research 31:39–59.

Smith, K. N., and W. F. Herrnkind. 1992. Predation on juvenile spiny lobsters, *Panulirus argus*: influence of size, shelter, and activity period. Journal of Experimental Marine Biology and Ecology 157:3–18.

van der Meeren, G. I. 1994. Lobster stock enhancement in Norway. Pages 131–139 *in* ICES workshop to evaluate the potential of stock enhancement as an approach to fisheries management. Charlottenlund, Denmark, 19-24 May 1994. ICES CM 1994/F:9 (mimeo.). International Council for the Exploration of the Sea, Copenhagen.

Wahle, R., and R. S. Steneck. 1991. Recruitment habitats and nursery grounds of the American lobster *Homarus americanus*: a demographic bottleneck? Marine Ecology Progress Series 69:231–243.

Zimmer-Faust, R. K., and E. Spanier. 1987. Gregariousness and sociality in spiny lobsters: implications for den habitation. Journal of Experimental Marine Biology and Ecology 105:57–71.

American Fisheries Society Symposium 22:438–454, 1999

The Role of Oyster Reefs as Essential Fish Habitat:
A Review of Current Knowledge and Some New Perspectives

LOREN D. COEN

South Carolina Department of Natural Resources, Marine Resources Research Institute
Post Office Box 12559, Charleston, South Carolina 29422-2559, USA

MARK W. LUCKENBACH

Eastern Shore Laboratory, Virginia Institute of Marine Science
College of William and Mary, Post Office Box 350
Wachapreague, Virginia 23480, USA

DENISE L. BREITBURG

The Academy of Natural Sciences, Estuarine Research Center
10545 Mackall Road, St. Leonard, Maryland 20685, USA

Abstract.—The importance of molluscan-dominated systems (e.g., oysters reefs, mussel beds, vermetid gastropods) to the maintenance of commercially and ecologically important species has not been as broadly recognized as has been the importance of other structurally complex estuarine habitats such as sea grass beds and salt marshes. As a consequence, these systems have often been unappreciated and understudied. Important ecosystem services of molluscan-dominated systems include: (1) filtering capacity; (2) benthic–pelagic coupling; (3) creation of refugia from predation; (4) creation of feeding habitat for juvenile and adult mobile species as well as sessile stages of species that attach directly to molluscan shells; and (5) provision of nesting habitat. Destructive harvesting and overfishing can reduce habitat extent and impair habitat functioning. Only recently have ecosystem services been incorporated into the management of these systems. The role of oyster reefs as "essential fish habitat" falls into two principal categories: (1) reefs as habitat for oysters and (2) reefs as habitat for resident and transient species. Although the former role has received some attention as part of efforts to restore oyster resources, the latter role remains largely unexplored. The role of oyster reefs as critical habitat for other species is suggested by the diverse fauna associated with them; however, the factors that control the development of these reef-associated assemblages are generally unknown, and enumeration of specific habitat services using replicated field experiments is just beginning. Using data summarized from studies in Maryland, Virginia, North Carolina, South Carolina, and Texas, we classify finfish assemblages associated with reefs based upon the degree of their association and include an extensive finfish and decapod species list. We conclude, within the context of the current state of knowledge, that (1) the construction of reef bases using materials that provide adequate vertical relief and interstitial space and (2) the establishment of broodstock sanctuaries protected from harvesting pressure are important for restoring oyster populations. Utilization of reef habitats by numerous commercially, recreationally, and ecologically important species across a wide geographic range likely portends the reef habitats' importance as essential fish habitat, but many functional relationships remain to be evaluated. Future oyster habitat research needs include (1) defining the morphological and spatial reef characteristics that support enhanced oyster growth and survival; (2) improving understanding of how harvest methods affect reef integrity and function; (3) determining the critical services provided by reef habitats in the life cycles of important species; and (4) further clarifying the trophic links between the resident fauna on oyster reefs and transient species.

Approximately 75% of the commercial fish and shellfish species of the United States depend on estuaries at some stage in their life cycles (Chambers 1992), and the continued health and productivity of these finfish, mollusc, and crustacean populations are in large part dependent on the quantity and quality of appropriate nursery and adult habitats (e.g., Heck and Wetstone 1977; Heck and Orth 1980; Nixon 1980; Boesch and Turner 1984; Heck and Thoman 1984; Orth et al. 1984; Orth and Van

Montfrans 1987; Zimmerman et al. 1989; Wilson et al. 1990; Barshaw et al. 1994; Haywood et al. 1995; Peterson and Lubchenco 1997). Plants such as submerged aquatic vegetation (SAV) or emergent vegetation (marshes and mangroves) typically dominate critical habitats within estuaries. The 1996 reauthorization of the Magnuson-Stevens Fishery Conservation and Management Act (Public Law 104–208) included an explicit goal to protect, restore, and enhance all "essential fish habitats" (henceforth referred to as EFH). The law defined EFH as "those waters and substrate necessary to fish for spawning, breeding, feeding, and or growth to maturity," and "fish" was defined to include "finfish, molluscs, crustaceans, and all other forms of marine animal and plant life other than marine mammals and birds" (USDOC 1997). The ability of fishery managers to identify EFH depends on the availability of information on various habitats. For many habitats, a wealth of information is available, but for other habitats information is scarce. Therefore, as part of the habitat information-gathering process, it is important to understand the extent to which estuaries and specific estuarine habitats serve as EFH and what estuarine habitat characteristics are most important to EFH-related processes.

There is no question that oyster reefs qualify as EFH because of the importance of reefs to the oysters themselves. However, we are just beginning to understand what precise characteristics of oyster reefs enhance oyster recruitment, growth, and survival. In addition, recent research has highlighted the importance of oyster reefs to ecosystem-level processes and as habitat for fishes and macroinvertebrates other than oysters. In this paper we summarize the current state of our knowledge of oyster (specifically the eastern oyster *Crassostrea virginica*) reefs as (1) important to ecosystem-level processes in estuaries; (2) essential habitat for oysters; and (3) important habitat for ecologically, commercially, and recreationally important finfish and crustacean species. We include in this study existing descriptive data on oyster-reef habitat ecology and recent and ongoing experimental investigations that are relevant to understanding how the structure and ecological function of oyster reefs may be incorporated into an EFH framework. We also discuss issues relating to tradeoffs between habitat and resource management and protection, the value of areas closed to harvesting due to poor water quality, and habitat restoration and enhancement (see Coen and Luckenbach, in press, for more information on habitat enhancement).

Decline of the Oyster Fishery and Reef Habitat

The range of the eastern oyster *Crassostrea virginica* (Gmelin) extends from the Saint Lawrence River in Canada to the Atlantic coast of Argentina (Carriker and Gaffney 1996), with introductions into the northwest Pacific region of the United States.

The eastern oyster is a reef-forming organism, but it varies throughout its range in habitat and growth form. Eastern oyster reefs may be intertidal or subtidal, fringing or patch reefs, and may vary in size from a few square meters to many hectares. Greatest abundances are found in areas where a partial predation refuge exists, such as low-salinity (<15 ppt) waters or in the intertidal zone (e.g., MacKenzie 1983, 1996a, 1996b; Burrell 1986; Kennedy et al. 1996).

Although intensive, hatchery-based aquaculture of oysters is increasing in the United States, the oyster fishery historically has been based upon wild stocks. Some areas in the United States still have wild oyster stocks supporting valuable fisheries (see MacKenzie et al. 1997a, 1997b), but most stocks are in decline owing to the following factors (Gross and Smyth 1946; MacKenzie 1983, 1996a, 1996b; Rothschild et al. 1994; Kennedy et al. 1996; NOAA 1997; Lenihan and Peterson 1998; Hargis and Haven, in press; Luckenbach et al., in press):

- overfishing and associated habitat destruction;
- shortages of oyster cultch (i.e., shell or other hard substrate);
- disturbance (e.g., dredging, boating, storms);
- reduced water and habitat quality;
- alteration of natural flow and salinity patterns;
- natural and introduced predators and competitors; and
- oyster disease pressures.

Between 1880 and 1910, the oyster fishery peaked at more than 72.7 million kg of meat per year (Brooks 1891; MacKenzie 1996a), but by 1995, U.S. landings had declined to 18.4 million kg (MacKenzie 1996a). The once highly productive fisheries of the Chesapeake and Delaware Bays and North Carolina (Frankenberg 1995) have virtually collapsed. Although diseases are often cited as the reason for recent declines, overharvesting and resultant habitat destruction with little shell replacement (considered analogous to strip mining by some [see Hargis and Haven, in press]) have certainly been major causes for the dramatic declines throughout much of the mid-Atlantic region (see Brooks 1891; Gross and Smyth 1946; Rothschild et al. 1994; Lenihan and Peterson 1998; H. Lenihan and F. Micheli, University of North Carolina, unpublished data).

Oyster fishing methodologies, such as hand- and hydraulically operated tongs, dredges pulled by sailing and motor-powered vessels, and hand-harvesting on intertidal reefs, have been particularly destructive to the reef matrix (reviewed in Hargis and Haven 1995, in press; MacKenzie 1996a; MacKenzie et al. 1997a, 1997b; Lenihan and Peterson 1998; Lenihan and Micheli, unpublished data). In addition, size restrictions placed by fisheries managers as well as market demand may result in small oysters being culled from the catch and returned to the water. In these situations, the oysters are no longer attached to the reef, and the damage to the reef may be significant (see Burrell et al. 1991; L. Coen, South Carolina Department of Natural Resources, personal observations; Lenihan and Micheli, unpublished data). Relaying—the practice of moving attached juvenile oysters on shell (also called "cultch") to other areas—is commonly utilized to reduce mortality due to disease or to achieve better growth, but little information is available on the relative survival of these "redeployed" oysters for different system configurations around the United States. For example, Klemanowicz (1985) and Burrell et al. (1991) evaluated impacts of relaying intertidal oysters and found significant impacts on survival that were strongly influenced by when harvesting occurred.

Two oyster protozoan parasites *Perkinsus marinus* and *Haplosporidium nelsoni* are now endemic in *C. virginica* throughout much of its range, causing epizootics in many but not all areas (Ford and Tripp 1996; but see Bobo et al. 1997). Specifically, *P. marinus*, the causative agent of "Dermo," can be found from Maine to Mexico, and *H. nelsoni*, the cause of "MSX," infects oysters from Maine to the Atlantic coast of Florida (Ewart and Ford 1993; Ford and Tripp 1996). Both diseases cause significant mortality, especially in oysters greater than two years of age, and often have been given too much credit as the primary cause of the collapse of the northeastern oyster fisheries (see Rothschild et al. 1994; Paynter foreword in Brooks 1891, 1996 revised edition).

Efforts to sustain and enhance oyster fisheries have included (e.g., MacKenzie 1983, 1996a, 1996b; Leonard 1993; Kennedy et al. 1996; Andrews et al. 1997; Powell et al. 1997; Lenihan and Peterson 1998; Hayward et al. in press; Luckenbach et al., in press):

- developing broodstock sanctuaries;
- supplementing hard substrate with either natural or alternative materials (or cultch);
- relaying (defined above) seed and adult broodstock;
- improving water quality; and
- attempting in a limited manner to supplement natural populations with hatchery-reared stocks.

For example, Connecticut's Long Island Sound oyster industry has recently seen a resurgence in landings from only 33,000 bushels in 1972 to a peak of nearly 900,000 bushels in 1992. Here resource restoration was successful due to improved water quality and unusual industry circumstances, including extensive bottom leases by a single major company and intensive bed manipulations (MacKenzie et al. 1997a; Goddard 1998; J. Volk, Connecticut Department of Agriculture, personal communication). However, in 1998, both Dermo and MSX, previously rare in Long Island Sound, significantly impacted these beds.

Oyster Reefs as EFH for Oysters: Critical Characteristics

Reef environments have generally been recognized as essential for oysters for aggregation of spawning stock, chemical induction of gregarious settlement, and predator refugia. Reef environments also provide oysters with a means of coping with siltation. Re-shelling programs conducted by most oyster-producing states point to the critical importance of reef habitat in supporting oyster population growth. Recent research has highlighted the contribution of particular reef characteristics to the recruitment, growth, and survival of oysters, and thus the EFH value of reefs to the oysters themselves. Among these characteristics are reef height (Lenihan and Peterson 1998) and the quality and quantity of interstitial spaces for recruiting oysters (Bartol and Mann, in press). Lenihan (1996), Lenihan and Peterson (1998), and Lenihan et al. (in press) constructed experimental subtidal reefs varying in morphology, water depth, and location within North Carolina's Pamlico River estuary. To date these studies have demonstrated that subtidal oyster growth, survival (Lenihan and Peterson 1998), and disease dynamics (Lenihan et al., in press) vary with position on reefs in relation to flow velocity, sedimentation rate, and dissolved oxygen regimes. In addition, these studies, especially for stratified estuaries, indicate that placement of materials for subtidal reef habitats requires prior knowledge of local hydrographic conditions (i.e., current velocities, sedimentation rates, temperature and density stratification, and oxygen levels).

Bartol and Mann (in press) have reported the importance of interstitial space within a reef for oyster recruitment and survival. On a large, constructed intertidal reef with a small tidal amplitude in the Piankatank River, Virginia, Bartol and Mann observed that survival of oysters was greater below the reef surface, in the interstices between shells, than on the reef surface itself. Interstitial spaces presumably provide settlement sites with adequate water flow for spat growth and survival while providing a partial refuge from predation. These findings have implications for the types of substrates and planting configurations needed to support the development of oyster populations and epifaunal assemblages on constructed reefs.

Ecosystem Services of Oyster Reefs

Molluscan-dominated assemblages (e.g., oyster and vermetid gastropod reefs, mussel beds, and clam beds) can have significant impacts on population, community, and landscape-level processes (e.g., Cloern 1982; Safriel and Ben-Eliahu 1991; Paine 1994; Dame 1996). The importance of these assemblages stems both from their ability to filter large quantities of water (e.g., Newell 1988; Dame 1996) and the fact that some of these molluscs (including oysters) generate the primary structural habitat where they are common and thus act as ecosystem engineers (sensu Jones et al. 1994; Lenihan and Peterson 1998). In addition, much of our knowledge of marine communities derives from research on rocky shores, and these communities often are dominated by mussels (e.g., reviewed in Paine 1994; see also Petraitis 1987, 1995; Witman 1987).

There is good evidence that large numbers of suspension-feeding bivalves (or their absence) can have a significant impact on basinwide ecosystem attributes (Cloern 1982; Cohen et al. 1984; Dame 1996). Numerous studies point to the vast filtration capacity of dense bivalve populations as contributing to the control of water column phytoplankton dynamics. Specifically, these studies have focused on:

- clams in San Francisco Bay (Cloern 1982);
- cockles and mussels in the Oosterchelde estuary, Netherlands (Smaal and Haas 1997);
- asiatic clams in the Potomac River, United States (Cohen et al. 1984);
- zebra mussels in the Hudson River, United States (Roditi et al. 1996); and

- oysters in tidal creeks, South Carolina (Dame et al. 1992).

For example, intertidal oysters in South Carolina alter phytoplankton concentrations and energy flow rates in overlying waters (Dame et al. 1984, 1992; recently reviewed by Dame 1996). Similarly, Newell (1988) calculated that, before 1870, the Chesapeake Bay's oysters could filter the entire volume of the bay in 3.3 d. In contrast, the estimate for the same activity by reduced oyster populations in 1988 was 325 d. Recent ecosystem mass-action models have indicated that a return of significant oyster biomass could greatly decrease planktonic primary productivity and secondary gelatinous consumers to historically low levels and increase benthic primary and secondary productivity, thus potentially reducing Chesapeake Bay eutrophication (e.g., Ulanowicz and Tuttle 1992 and references therein). (See also Dame 1996 for a review of shellfish impacts on materials fluxes.)

Are Oyster Reefs EFH for Finfish and Other Macroinvertebrates?

Descriptive studies and reviews indicate that oyster reef communities along the Atlantic and Gulf coasts are highly diverse and include numerous species rare or absent in adjacent soft-bottom habitats (e.g., Wells 1961; Dame 1979; Bahr and Lanier 1981; Klemanowicz 1985; Burrell 1986; Stanley and Sellers 1986; Zimmerman et al. 1989). However, research including experimental manipulations is required to determine relationships among the different ecological functions of reefs (e.g., materials fluxes, provision of habitat, and trophic dynamics); the structural characteristics of reefs (e.g., oyster density, spatial extent, elevation, construction material); and the use and importance of oyster reefs to finfish and macroinvertebrate species other than oysters. Because of their large spatial scale, manipulations created by management and restoration activities will be an important tool in attempts to determine the importance of oyster reefs to species other than oysters (see recent reviews by Coen and Luckenbach, in press; Luckenbach et al., in press).

Finfish associated with oyster reefs can be divided into three categories: (1) reef residents, which use oyster reefs as their primary habitat; (2) facultative residents, which are generally associated with structured habitats and utilize oyster reefs as well as other habitat with vertical relief or shelter sites (e.g.,

TABLE 1.—Fishes and decapod crustaceans found on oyster reefs or in waters directly overlying reefs at Flag Pond (MD1; Breitburg, in press, unpublished data); the Patuxent River (MD2; D. Breitburg, the Academy of Natural Sciences, and T. Miller, University of Maryland, unpublished data); Piankatank River (VA1; J. Harding, Virginia Institute of Marine Science, unpublished data); Fisherman's Island (VA2; M. Luckenbach and J. Nestlerode, Virginia Institute of Marine Science, unpublished data); Neuse River and Pamlico Sound (NC; Lenihan et al. 1998); Inlet Creek and Toler's Cove (SC; Wenner et al. 1996; Coen et al. 1997, 1998; Coen and Luckenbach 1998, unpublished data) and West Bay (TX; Zimmerman et al. 1989).

Common name (scientific name)	MD1 [a]	MD2	VA1 [b]	VA2 [c]	NC	SC [d]	TX [e]
Oyster reef resident fishes							
gulf toadfish (*Opsanus beta*)							X
oyster toadfish (*Opsanus tau*)	X	X	X	X	X	X	
skilletfish (*Gobiesox strumosus*)	X	X	X	X	X		X
striped blenny (*Chasmodes bosquianus*)	X	X	X	X	X	X	X
feather blenny (*Hypsoblennius hentz*)	X	X		X	X		
freckled blenny (*Hypsoblennius ionthas*)							X
naked goby (*Gobiosoma bosc*)	X	X	X	X	X	X	X
Facultative resident fishes							
northern pipefish (*Syngnathus fuscus*)	X			X		X	
black sea bass (*Centropristis striata*)	X		X	X	X		
Atlantic spadefish (*Chaetodipterus faber*)	X		X		X		
darter goby (*Gobionellus boleosoma*)						X	
seaboard goby (*Gobiosoma ginsburgi*)				X			
Transient fishes							
Atlantic stingray (*Dasyatis sabina*)						X	
cownose ray (*Rhinoptera bonasus*)	X		X		X		
American eel (*Anguilla rostrata*)	X	X	X		X		
speckled worm eel (*Myrophis punctatus*)						X	X
glass eel (*Conger oceanicus*)				X			
blueback herring (*Alosa aestivalis*)			X				
gulf menhaden (*Brevoortia patronus*)							X
Atlantic menhaden (*Brevoortia tyrannus*)		X	X		X	X	
Atlantic herring (*Clupea harengus*)				X			
bay anchovy (*Anchoa mitchilli*)			X	X		X	X
striped anchovy (*Anchoa hepsetus*)				X		X	
carp (*Cyprinis carpio*)			X				
brown bullhead (*Ameiurus nebulosus*)		X					
channel catfish (*Ictalurus punctatus*)		X					
inshore lizardfish (*Synodus foetens*)	X				X		
spotted hake (*Urophycis regia*)			X				
sheepshead minow (*Cyprinodon variegatus*)						X	
mummichog (*Fundulus heteroclitus*)				X		X	
rainwater killifish (*Lucania parva*)				X			
rough silverside (*Membras martinica*)				X			
inland silverside (*Menidia beryllina*)						X	X
Atlantic silverside (*Menidia menidia*)	X					X	
fourspine stickleback (*Apeltes quadracus*)				X			
lined seahorse (*Hippocampus erectus*)			X	X			
chain pipefish (*Syngnathus louisianae*)						X	
northern sea robin (*Prionotus carolinus*)			X	X			
bighead searobin (*Prionotus tribulus*)					X	X	X

Common name (scientific name)	MD1 [a]	MD2	VA1 [b]	VA2 [c]	NC	SC [d]	TX [e]
white perch (*Morone americana*)		X		X			
striped bass (*Morone saxatilis*)	X	X	X	X	X		
gag (*Mycteroptera microlepis*)				X	X		
green sunfish (*Lepomis cyanellus*)							X
bluefish (*Pomatomus saltatrix*)		X	X	X	X		
cobia (*Rachycentron canadum*)			X				
lookdown (*Selene vomer*)				X	X		
gray snapper (*Lutjanus griseus*)					X	X	
mahogany snapper (*Lutjanus mahogoni*)						X	
spotfin mojarra (*Eucinostomus argenteus*)				X		X	
pigfish (*Orthopristis chrysoptera*)			X	X	X	X	
sheepshead (*Archosargus probatocephalus*)				X	X	X	X
pinfish (*Lagodon rhomboides*)	X		X		X	X	X
silver perch (*Bairdiella chrysoura*)			X	X	X	X	
spotted seatrout (*Cynoscion nebulosus*)			X		X		
weakfish (*Cynoscion regalis*)			X	X	X		
spot (*Leiostomus xanthurus*)	X	X	X	X	X	X	
Atlantic croaker (*Micropogonias undulatus*)		X	X	X	X	X	
black drum (*Pogonias cromis*)				X	X		
red drum (*Sciaenops ocellatus*)						X	
spotfin butterflyfish (*Chaetodon ocellatus*)				X			
striped mullet (*Mugil cephalus*)						X	X
white mullet (*Mugil curema*)						X	
tautog (*Tautoga onitis*)			X	X			
lyre goby (*Evorthodus lyricus*)						X	
Atlantic cutlassfish (*Trichiurus lepturus*)				X			
Spanish mackerel (*Scomberomorus maculatus*)			X		X		
harvestfish (*Peprilus alepidotus*)			X		X		
butterfish (*Peprilus triacanthus*)			X		X		
bay whiff (*Citharicthys spilopterus*)						X	
summer flounder (*Paralichthys dentatus*)	X		X	X	X	X	
southern flounder (*Paralichthys lethostigma*)					X	X	
winter flounder (*Pleuronectes americanus*)	X			X			
blackcheek tonguefish (*Symphurus plagiusa*)				X		X	
hogchoker (*Trinectes maculatus*)		X	X				
orange filefish (*Aluterus schoepfi*)						X	
planehead filefish (*Stephanolepis hispidus*)						X	
pygmy filefish (*Monacanthus setifer*)					X		
striped burrfish (*Chilomycterus schoepfi*)	X						
northern puffer (*Sphoeroides maculatus*)			X				

Transient Decapod Crustaceans

Common name (scientific name)	MD1	MD2	VA1	VA2	NC	SC	TX
brown shrimp (*Penaeus aztecus*)						X	
pink shrimp (*Penaeus duorarum*)						X	X
white shrimp (*Penaeus setiferus*)						X	
daggerblade grass shrimp (*Palaemontes pugio*)	X	X		X	X	X	X
marsh grass shrimp (*Palaemontes vulgaris*)	X	X		X	X	X	X
lesser blue crab (*Callinectes similis*)						X	
blue crab (*Callinectes sapidus*)	X	X	X	X	X	X	X

Common name (scientific name)	MD1 [a]	MD2	VA1 [b]	VA2 [c]	NC	SC [d]	TX [e]
Number of oyster reef resident fishes	5	5	4	5	5	3	5
Number of facultative resident fishes	3		2	3	2	2	0
Number of transient fishes	10	10	26	29	25	30	9
Number of transient decapod crustaceans	3	3	1	3	3	7	4
Total number of species	21	18	33	40	35	42	18

[a] Flag Pond data are from dive surveys only.

[b] Piankatank data are from trawls along the reef base.

[c] Fisherman's Island data are from gill nets, drop nets, and trawling, as well as from diver surveys.

[d] South Carolina data are from replicate (24-m^2 of oyster habitat) lift nets triggered at high slack tide and fished at low tide.

[e] Texas data are from 2.6-m^2 drop-trap samples.

beds of SAV); and (3) transient species, which may forage on or near the reef but are wide-ranging (Breitburg, in press). Of the 79 finfish species found in surveys of oyster reefs in Maryland, Virginia, North Carolina, South Carolina, and Texas (Table 1), seven species (naked goby *Gobiosoma bosc,* striped blenny *Chasmodes bosquianus,* feather blenny *Hypsoblennius hentz,* freckled blenny *H. ionthas,* skilletfish *Gobiesox strumosus,* oyster toadfish *Opsanus tau,* and gulf toadfish *O. beta*) can be clearly identified as oyster reef residents. For these species, oyster reef habitat can be considered "essential" with a high degree of certainty. These resident gobies, blennies, toadfish, and clingfish use oyster reefs as breeding and feeding habitat and as shelter from predators. Oyster and gulf toadfish attach eggs to the underside of consolidated masses of oyster shells, while the smaller gobies, blennies, and clingfish lay eggs on the inside of recently dead oyster shells that are still articulated (Breitburg, in press). Size-based competition exists for oyster shells as nest sites, and small oyster reef residents need shells whose inner surfaces have not yet become covered with sessile invertebrates. Because of these factors, well-developed oyster reefs with natural and continuous levels of oyster mortality in all size classes are likely to provide the best supply of new nesting sites (i.e., clean, still-articulated oyster shells in a variety of sizes, including large oysters) to accommodate reproduction by high densities of all resident species (Breitburg, in press). Unconsolidated small cultch material (e.g., coal ash), large rocks, and rubble are likely to be poor substitutes for the natural reef shell matrix. In addition to the seven species listed as oyster reef residents in Table

1, descriptions of breeding habitat indicate that the seaboard goby *G. ginsburgi,* green goby *Microgobius thalassinus,* longhorn sculpin *Myoxocephalus octodecemspinosus,* Atlantic midshipman *Porichthys plectrodon,* and northern pipefish *Syngnathus fuscus* also use oyster reefs as habitat for reproduction (Hardy 1978a, 1978b; Johnson 1978; Jones et al. 1978; Martin and Drewry 1978).

In addition to the above-mentioned species that breed on oyster reefs, a much larger number of fish species (including many that are important to recreational and commercial fisheries) facultatively utilize oyster reefs and the waters directly overlying them as feeding and refuge sites. (The numbers below include only facultative residents and transients.) Studies in Chesapeake Bay (Maryland and Virginia), the Neuse River and Pamlico Sound (North Carolina), the Charleston Harbor area (Inlet Creek and Toler's Cove sites in South Carolina), and West Bay (Galveston, Texas) have identified 72 facultative resident and transient fish species in close proximity to oyster reefs through diver observations and the use of trawls, drop samplers, lift and gill nets, and fish trays and traps (Table 1, Figure 1). Species listed in Table 1 as facultative residents appear to be represented by at least some individuals that remain on the oyster reef for several months. Some species listed as transients may actually be facultative residents (exclusive of South Carolina intertidal species). However, these species are highly mobile within the reefs, and the duration of residency of individuals has not been studied. Differences in species richness (Figure 1) and composition among sites in Table 1 likely reflect differences in collection methods (see Table 1 footnotes), as well as true differences in the fish and crustacean assemblages.

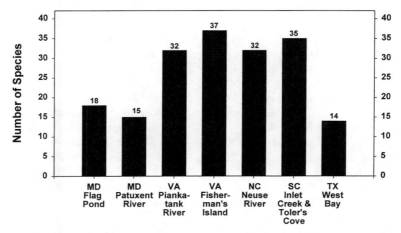

FIGURE 1.—Cumulative number of finfish species (resident, facultative resident, and transient combined) collected by site and study in association with oyster reef sampling. Overall taxonomic composition and species numbers among studies (bars) reflect sample sizes and gear type differences, in addition to biogeographic diversity and local hydrographic conditions (i.e., intertidal and subtidal conditions, tidal range, salinity, depth) from Maryland to Texas. (See Table 1 for specific site information and collection methods.)

For example, 13 species of finfish (see Table 1 for additional macroinvertebrates) were observed within 1 m of the reef surface during late spring to summer at the Flag Pond Oyster Reef in the mesohaline Maryland portion of Chesapeake Bay (D. Breitburg, the Academy of Natural Sciences, personal observations), and 10 finfish species were identified on Patuxent River oyster reefs during preliminary diving (Breitburg, personal observations), gill-net, and crab-pot surveys (Breitburg and T. Miller, University of Maryland, unpublished data). J. Harding (Virginia Institute of Marine Science, unpublished data) found 28 finfish species on Piankatank River oyster reefs in Virginia, and M. Luckenbach and J. Nestlerode (Virginia Institute of Marine Science, unpublished data) found 32 finfish species on oyster reefs at Fisherman's Island near the mouth of the Chesapeake Bay. In North Carolina, H. Lenihan (unpublished data) identified 27 fish species at oyster reefs in the Neuse River, and Coen et al. (1997, unpublished data) found 32 finfish species at two South Carolina reef sites (Table 1, Figure 1). A study in the Gulf of Mexico that quantified macroinvertebrates and finfish associated with oyster reefs identified nine finfish species from 2.6-m² drop-trap samples taken in West Bay, Galveston, Texas (Zimmerman et al. 1989; Minello 1999, this volume) (Table 1, Figure 1).

Numerous macroinvertebrates, including penaeid and caridean shrimp (primarily members of the genus *Palaemonetes* spp.) and portunid crabs also are found on Atlantic coast oyster reefs (Table 1; Zimmerman et al. 1989; Wenner et al. 1996; Coen et al. 1997). It is clear from numerous estuarine studies that grass shrimp in Atlantic and Gulf estuaries serve as a critical trophic link in both detrital and higher food webs (e.g., Adams and Angelovic 1970; Bell and Coull 1978; Morgan 1980; Anderson 1985; Kneib 1997). In Texas, as in South Carolina, stone crabs *Menippe* spp. are often collected in association with oyster habitat (Wenner and Stokes 1984; Zimmerman et al. 1989; Coen et al. 1997).

As a caveat, variability in the species list and species numbers generated from these ongoing studies is reflective of large differences in sampling intensity and sampling gear (from diver observations to seines, trawls, and lift or drop nets), in addition to biogeographic (Maryland to Texas) and local system characteristics (e.g., tidal range, position, flow, depth, salinity) among sites (see Table 1, Figure 1). More important, results of these studies illustrate the wide range of species that utilize oyster reefs and highlight the importance of determining whether reef area and other characteristics influence the size and health of fish populations other than oyster reef residents. It is a given that this preliminary list of species will grow significantly with time and additional studies.

As has been seen for oysters themselves, modification of flow by high-relief oyster reefs may be important to both resident fishes and to those transient fish species using reefs as feeding habitat. Large numbers of late-stage larvae of resident fish species (particularly those of the naked goby) can be found on the down-current side of high-relief structures within oysters reefs, where reduced flow velocity allows larvae to maintain their position during high-flow portions of the tidal cycle (Breitburg et al. 1995). The heterogeneity in the flow environment created by vertical relief within reefs influences the spatial pattern of settlement of fish onto oyster reefs (Breitburg et al. 1995), the spatial pattern of predation by fish larvae, and the distribution and likely the feeding success of their predators (Breitburg, in press). Larval and juvenile naked gobies and other resident fishes are significant zooplankton predators (Breitburg, in press). These fish are also, in turn, prey for larger transient fishes including striped bass *Morone saxatilis*, which can occur in high densities within 1 m of oyster reef substrate (Breitburg, in press). For example, Breitburg (in press) observed juvenile striped bass at a density of 15.4 individuals per m² of "reef" surface in diver surveys over artificial structures (33 cm x 33 cm x 33 cm concrete cubes). The juvenile striped bass were aggregating a few centimeters over the reef surface and actively feeding on naked goby larvae congregating on the down-current side of the miniature reefs.

The interstitial spaces within the oyster reef matrix may also provide a refuge from predation for small resident fishes as they do for small oyster spat. The typical behavior observed for gobies, blennies, clingfish, and small juvenile toadfish in the presence of either a predatory fish or a sudden move by a diver is to dart into the shell matrix rather than to flee along the substrate surface or rise in the water column. Although the efficiency of this escape response has not been tested experimentally, field observations indicate that the spaces within the shell matrix of a well-developed oyster reef allow small fish to escape piscivores such as striped bass and pinfish that capture prey directly from the reef surface. Similarly, mesocosm experiments have indicated that the grass shrimp *Palaemonetes pugio* seeks refuge in a simulated oyster reef when threatened by finfish predators (Posey et al., in press). The results of Posey et al. (in press) also suggest that some decapod and finfish species, in addition to those listed in Table 1, may be facultative reef residents, moving onto reefs in response to tidal stage and predator abundance.

Differentiating between habitat that is simply utilized by facultative resident and transient finfish and crustaceans and habitat that falls under the EFH definition is important to truly determine the role oyster reefs play in the ecology of coastal systems. A number of studies are addressing this need by better defining the specific habitat requirements for resident and transient species associated with oyster reefs and examining trophic links between transient finfish and the resident fish and invertebrate assemblages. For example, studies by Coen and others and Dame and others in South Carolina, Breitburg and Miller in Maryland, and Luckenbach and others in Virginia are being conducted as of this writing (see also Coen et al. 1997, in press; Dame et al. 1997; Meyer et al. 1997; Harding and Mann, in press; Lenihan and G. W. Thayer, National Marine Fisheries Service, unpublished data; D. Meyer, National Marine Fisheries Service, personal communication).

Parallels with Artificial Reefs

Another critical issue to address in determining whether oyster reefs can be considered EFH on the basis of their use by fish is the extent to which oyster reefs result in the production of additional fish biomass rather than simply concentrating existing fish biomass. The question of concentrating biomass versus increasing regional production may be especially critical for constructed reefs and for finfish species that are targeted by commercial or recreational fisheries. As Grossman et al. (1997) pointed out, artificial reefs that concentrate biomass, but do not increase production, may be detrimental to fish populations because such reefs also concentrate fishing pressure and can increase total fishing mortality of targeted stocks. Although it may seem logical that the concentrating effect of reefs is due to their attractiveness as feeding habitat and that better feeding habitat will result in greater fish production, Grossman et al. (1997) suggested that for the majority of cases there are insufficient data to determine whether the net effect of reef construction is beneficial to finfish populations and further suggested that the effect of reef construction will depend on the factors that currently limit local fish abundance. Regional assessments of the effects of reef construction will be needed because of the open (i.e., mobile) nature of many fish populations (Carr and Hixon 1997).

Of paramount importance for determining the value of constructed reefs as EFH for reef-associated estuarine species is distinguishing between the habitat value of reefs with viable oyster populations and more traditional artificial fishing reefs (e.g., wrecks, concrete rubble, and constructed concrete structures). The distinction here is likely to be one of degree, as virtually any hard substrate appropriately placed within Atlantic and Gulf coast estuaries will develop epifaunal assemblages that include some *C. virginica*. However, we hypothesize that fully functional oyster reef habitats will provide ecosystem services and EFH benefits that have the potential to increase regional fish production beyond increases provided by artificial reef habitats for at least three reasons:

1. In high-sedimentation environments typical of many estuaries inhabited by *C. virginica*, growth of the entire reef, via growth of individual oysters and annual recruitment, provides a mechanism for maintaining the reef in the face of sedimentation. As discussed elsewhere (Coen and Luckenbach, in press), it is doubtful that any other species within the oyster reef assemblage, including mussels (primarily *Mytilus edulis* and *Geukensia demissa*), is capable of providing sufficient structural integrity and vertical relief to overcome natural sediment deposition rates and near-bottom hypoxia (see Lenihan and Peterson 1998).
2. Living oyster reefs provide a diversity of microhabitats—both for support of oyster survival (Bartol and Mann, in press) and for nesting sites and shelter sites for resident finfish (see preceding discussion and Breitburg, in press)—that are not necessarily provided by artificial reef structures lacking high densities of oysters.
3. In some mid- and south-Atlantic coastlines with tidal ranges in excess of 1–2 m, oyster reefs provide extensive intertidal habitat that cannot be mimicked with traditional artificial fishing reefs.

Oysters are capable of growing in dense vertical clusters or hummocks (cf. Bertness et al. 1998), extending above the surrounding soft sediments and forming reefs where other epifaunal species would quickly be buried. Reef bases constructed as part of restoration efforts of materials other than oyster shell (e.g., fly or coal ash, sludge bricks, construction rubble, etc.) need to mimic both the vertical relief and interstitial space provided by mounded oyster shell to ensure that viable oyster populations can persist and that natural reef communities can exist.

Linkages with Other Types of EFH

Estuaries have long been recognized as the most productive ecosystems in the world (Peterson and Lubchenco 1997). They provide critical feeding, spawning, and nursery habitats for numerous species, including commercially and recreationally important fish, shellfish, and waterfowl. Most of these organisms are dependent upon one or more estuarine habitats (e.g., SAV, mud flats, salt marshes, oyster reefs) that are being lost or degraded at an ever-increasing rate as a result of coastal population increases and associated industrial, residential, and recreational development.

Management practices that protect habitats or mitigate for losses are often based on the assumption or recognition that key habitats are critical to nearshore ecological processes such as nutrient cycling, nursery habitat functions, and trophic stability and are important, for example, in maintaining coastal fisheries (Costanza et al. 1997; Peterson and Lubchenco 1997). The question of relative habitat value is important given the frequent legal mandate to protect or restore coastal habitats that have undergone significant changes as a result of development. Throughout most estuaries, multiple habitats (e.g., mud, SAV and emergent vegetation, oysters) exist in a mosaic, providing a complex environment for associated mobile species (Bell et al. 1991 and papers therein) and recruiting sessile flora and fauna. However, the relative ranking in value and contribution of each different nearshore habitat to ecosystem functions and overall biodiversity remain largely undetermined (e.g., Heck and Wetstone 1977; Weinstein and Brooks 1983; Wilson et al. 1987, 1990; Thomas et al. 1990; Rozas and Minello 1997). In addition to these landscape issues, mobile organisms typically occupy a suite of habitats during their life cycles, and we are just beginning to evaluate these linkages (e.g., Abele 1974; Bray et al. 1981; Parrish 1989; Zimmerman et al. 1989; Ambrose and Anderson 1990; Fitz and Wiegert 1991; Barshaw et al. 1994; Posey and Ambrose 1994; Heck and Coen 1995; Heck et al. 1997; Irlandi and Crawford; 1997; Posey et al., in press).

For oyster reef habitat, whether intertidal or subtidal, we have little comparative data with which to examine linkages with other habitats. For example, in South Carolina, sea grasses are absent, but there is abundant salt-marsh habitat interspersed with extensive tidal mud flats and oyster reefs. The importance of each of these dominant intertidal habitats has been indicated through independent efforts using very different sampling gear. Which habitats are utilized or required by which species is unclear. Anecdotal information and recent quantitative studies (Table 1; Wenner et al. 1996; Coen and Luckenbach, in press; Coen, unpublished data) for South Carolina indicate that many fishes (e.g., anchovy and silversides) are attracted to oyster reefs because the reefs' habitat structure provides a refuge from ecologically and commercially important fish predators (e.g., spotted seatrout *Cynoscion nebulosus* and flounders). These large predators, along with sheepshead *Archosargus probatocephalus*, black drum *Pogonias cromis*, and red drum *Sciaenops ocellatus* (see Table 1), migrate into creeks on flood tides to feed on small crabs and shrimp that reside in and around reef structure in large numbers (Coen, unpublished data). Quantitative sampling on the vegetated intertidal areas has shown that penaeid shrimps, flounders, blue crabs *Callinectes sapidus*, and other important species make regular tidal excursions across the flooded vegetated salt marsh (Hettler 1989; Rozas 1993; Kneib and Wagner 1994; Peterson and Turner 1994; Irlandi and Crawford 1997; Minello 1999; D. Allen, University of South Carolina, unpublished data; M. Posey, University of North Carolina Wilmington, unpublished data). Clearly, intertidal oyster reefs and salt marshes together provide a valuable set of structured habitats for juveniles of many important fish species such as sheepshead, gag grouper, and snapper, as well as stone and blue crabs and penaeid shrimps (Table 1; Wenner et al. 1996; Coen, unpublished data).

Similarly, sampling on subtidal and intertidal Chesapeake Bay oyster reefs and adjacent habitats has begun to elucidate transient utilization patterns by both finfish and decapod crustaceans (Table 1; Nestlerode, unpublished data). At Fisherman's Island, Virginia, the development of extensive sea grass beds (*Zostera marina* and *Ruppia maritima*) adjacent to experimental reefs is providing an opportunity to track community development in both habitat types (Luckenbach et al. 1997). Underwater video is currently being used to characterize movements of transient species between reefs and adjacent habitats (Nestlerode, unpublished data). In a coastal lagoon in Magothy Bay, Virginia, J. Wesson with the Virginia Marine Resources Commission and R. Orth and colleagues from the Virginia Institute of Marine Science have recently initiated a project involving experimental construction of oyster reefs and eel-

grass habitats individually and in combination to evaluate community development and utilization of these structured habitats.

Finally, few studies and associated models have incorporated the contribution of oyster larvae to zooplankton biomass. The effects of significant ecosystem shifts (for example, in Chesapeake Bay) from oyster-dominated systems with enormous numbers of oyster larvae as a food source to present conditions dominated by gelatinous secondary consumers are unclear (Newell 1988; Ulanowicz and Tuttle 1992; Dame 1996). Future research needs to evaluate the potential linkage between oyster larvae and zooplankton biomass.

Current and Future Management of Oyster Habitat

Historically, oyster habitat management has not been one of the primary goals of resource managers attempting to maintain oyster harvests (Lenihan and Peterson 1998; Lenihan and Micheli, unpublished data). However, with improved understanding of the added ecosystem services derived from these biogenic habitats (see above and Daily 1997; Peterson and Lubchenco 1997), we sense that a shift is beginning to occur in how we view, manage, and restore molluscan-dominated systems (Frankenberg 1995; Lenihan and Peterson 1998; C. Peterson, University of North Carolina, personal communication).

Three basic management and restoration approaches are available to resource managers: (1) fisheries restrictions on existing reefs; (2) substrate additions; and (3) stock enhancement through active transplanting of oysters. The first of these approaches has generally not proven to be sufficient to maintain either oyster standing stocks or reef integrity. Recent closure of the oyster fishery throughout most of the Virginia portion of Chesapeake Bay has resulted in increases in oyster standing stocks in the area, but the closure has not been sufficient, at least in duration, for the development of reefs with significant three-dimensional relief (J. A. Wesson, Virginia Marine Resources Commission, personal communication).

The addition of oyster shell and (occasionally) alternative substrates is a widespread management tool designed to replace substrate extracted as part of the fishery or to extend oyster recruitment into new areas (reviewed in Luckenbach et al., in press).

This approach has generally been associated with a put-and-take fishery. In the absence of harvest restrictions, it makes little economic sense to restore oyster reef habitat by adding substrate beyond that necessary to achieve market-size, 2-to-3-year-old oysters.

In some areas such as Connecticut's Long Island Sound, the transplanting of wild oysters to enhance oyster resources has been successful, but the emphasis has been on improved growth to market size rather than reef habitat restoration (Volk, personal communication). Hatchery-produced oysters, set onto bags of shell and planted in the field, are being used to supplement natural recruitment of oysters in Maryland and Louisiana (Supan et al., in press; D. Merritt, University of Maryland, personal communication). Again, this transplanting effort has been directed toward a short-term put-and-take fishery. Current management approaches in Virginia involve all three of the above elements, including broodstock enhancement programs using both wild and hatchery-reared stocks. These enhancement programs concentrate broodstock with desirable traits (disease tolerance and rapid growth) onto reef bases with adequate three-dimensional relief (constructed from shell plantings) and protect them from harvest as broodstock sanctuaries. This strategy is intended to restore viable oyster populations and functioning reef habitats while supporting oyster fisheries in adjacent areas through enhanced oyster recruitment.

Areas where shellfish harvesting is prohibited or restricted owing to public health concerns may provide an opportunity to create refuge areas for both oysters and reef-associated species. We contend that protecting and restoring shellfish habitat in these areas may be desirable due to the habitat's intrinsic worth as both habitat and larval and broodstock reserves (cf. Whitlach and Osman, in press). Recent research also suggests that many areas that are closed due to human health concerns support resident and transient finfish and crustacean associations equivalent to those of open areas (Coen et al. 1997; Coen and Luckenbach, in press; Coen et al., unpublished data).

Our expectation is that establishing reef sanctuaries, whether in areas closed to harvesting (see above) or in areas classified as either open or restricted, may, among other benefits, serve as sources of oyster larvae for surrounding exploited areas. This activity has recently been suggested for Virginia

waters (Wesson, personal communication; see also Whitlach and Osman, in press). However, the establishment of sanctuaries raises difficult questions. Ultimately, we will have to weigh derived ecosystem services against the resource's economic value (Costanza et al. 1997; Daily 1997; Kaufman and Dayton 1997; Lenihan and Micheli, unpublished data). Fisheries interests have considerable political support in some regions (e.g., Chesapeake Bay) and in most cases are the principal source of funding for oyster reef restoration efforts (cf. New Chesapeake Bay Reef Programs). Balancing short-term exploitation against the need to establish sustainable and functioning reefs poses a formidable challenge.

Future Needs

Manipulative studies of the types described in this chapter will be required to evaluate the individual and linked contributions of various estuarine habitat types to the maintenance of ecosystem services and to establish the relative importance of oyster reef habitat in these systems. Results from our work in South Carolina, Virginia, and Maryland and by others in North Carolina make it clear that considerable work must still be done to establish appropriate metrics for evaluating the value of oyster habitat as EFH and associated links with other estuarine habitats that may also serve as EFH. Such evaluations will require further research on natural reefs to clarify ecological functions, critical species, functional groups, and trophic structure interactions. Continued characterization of the development of "restored" reefs to establish successional trajectories and appropriate time scales will also be required. The identification of critical habitat components for other target species must be a focal point of these efforts. Currently we have very little data for natural reef systems. Detailed analyses of trophic links to transient finfish species are currently underway in several studies (e.g., Harding and Mann, in press; Coen, unpublished data; Lenihan and Thayer, unpublished data; Luckenbach, unpublished data; Miller and Breitburg, unpublished data) and should provide critical information on the value of oyster reef habitats to commercially exploited finfish.

Achieving a working balance between resource extraction and habitat function will require the development and testing of alternative harvest practices that permit extraction of oysters after some developmental period while maintaining habitat services as discussed above. Currently, we do not know whether extraction and habitat function are compatible (Burrell et al. 1991; Kaufman and Dayton 1997; Lenihan and Micheli, unpublished data). Implicit in this uncertainty is the need for adaptive management approaches that incorporate monitoring and research-based information into restoration efforts and management decisions (Grumbine 1994; Christensen et al. 1996; ESA 1998; Lenihan and Peterson 1998).

Acknowledgments

We thank Lee Benaka and Kamille Hammerstrom for significant interactions throughout the preparation of this paper. We also thank Hunter Lenihan, Julie Harding, and Roger Mann for sharing their unpublished data. For the South Carolina (SC) work presented in this chapter (L. D. Coen), many individuals were involved in the development of the ongoing Oyster Research Program and the collection of the data included here, and these individuals are too numerous to mention, but we are especially grateful to Rachel Giotta, Bruce Stender, David Knott, Betty Wenner, Will Hegler, Mark Thompson, and Bill Post for laboratory and field assistance. The SC portion of this research was funded by grants from the National Oceanic and Atmospheric Administration's SC Sea Grant Consortium (#NA46RG0484), the SC Marine Recreational Fisheries Stamp Program, and the SC Department of Natural Resources (SCDNR) through its Marine Resources Research Institute. This is Contribution #421 from the Marine Resources Research Institute, SCDNR. The Virginia work (M. W. Luckenbach) presented in this chapter was supported by grants from the U.S. Environmental Protection Agency Chesapeake Bay Program and Virginia Electric and Power Company. We wish to acknowledge Francis O'Beirn and Janet Nestlerode for assistance in all phases of the work, Greg Coates, and the many others who have assisted in the field. This is contribution #2,177 from the Virginia Institute of Marine Science. Funding from the Chesapeake Bay Program to D. Breitburg and T. Miller supported the Maryland work presented in this chapter. This manuscript was greatly improved by the reviewers' comments.

References

Abele, L. G. 1974. Species diversity of decapod crustaceans in marine habitats. Ecology 55:156–161.

Adams, S. M., and J. W. Angelovic. 1970. Assimilation of detritus and its associated bacteria by three species of estuarine animals. Chesapeake Science 11:249–254.

Ambrose, R. F., and T. W. Anderson. 1990. Influence of an artificial reef on the surrounding infaunal community. Marine Biology 107:41–52.

Anderson, G. 1985. Species profiles: life histories and environmental requirements of coastal fishes and invertebrates (Gulf of Mexico)—grass shrimp. Biological Report 82(11.35), March 1985 TR EL-82–4, U.S. Fish and Wildlife Service, U.S. Department of the Interior.

Andrews, R. S., R. W. Alden, III, M. W. Luckenbach, and J. A. Wesson. 1997. The use of coal combustion by-product as substrate for oyster reef development. Pages 363–375 in B. A. Sakkestad, editor. Proceedings of the 22nd International Technical Conference on Coal Utilization and Fuel Systems. Coal and Slurry Technology Association of America, Washington, D.C.

Bahr, L. M., and W. P. Lanier. 1981. The ecology of intertidal oyster reefs of the South Atlantic Coast: a community profile. U.S. Fish and Wildlife Service Program FWS/OBS/-81/15.

Barshaw, D. E., K. W. Able, and K. L. Heck, Jr. 1994. Salt marsh peat reefs as protection for postlarval lobsters *Homarus americanus* from fish and crab predators: comparisons with other substrates. Marine Ecology Progress Series 106:203–206.

Bartol, I., and R. Mann. In press. Small-scale patterns of recruitment on a constructed intertidal reef: the role of spatial refugia. In M. W. Luckenbach, R. Mann, and J. A Wesson, editors. Oyster reef habitat restoration: a synopsis, and synthesis of approaches. Virginia Institute of Marine Science Press, Gloucester Point, Virginia.

Bell, S. S., and B. C. Coull. 1978. Field evidence that shrimp predation regulates meiofauna. Oecologia (Berlin) 35:141–148.

Bell, S. S., E. D. McCoy, and H. R. Mushinsky. 1991. Habitat structure: the physical arrangement of objects in space. Chapman and Hall, London.

Bertness, D., S. D. Gaines, and S. M. Yeh. 1998. Making mountains out of barnacles: the dynamics of acorn barnacle hummocking. Ecology 79:1382–1394.

Bobo, M. Y., D. L. Richardson, L. D. Coen, and V. G. Burrell. 1997. A report on the protozoan pathogens *Perkinsus marinus* (Dermo) and *Haplosporidium nelsoni* (MSX) in South Carolina shellfish populations, with an overview of these shellfish pathogens. SCDNR (South Carolina Department of Natural Resources)-MRD-MRRI Technical Report, Charleston, South Carolina.

Boesch, D. F., and R. E. Turner. 1984. Dependence of fishery species on salt marshes: the role of food and refuge. Estuaries 7:460–468.

Bray, R. N., A. C. Miller, and G. C. Gessey. 1981. The fish connection: a trophic linkage between the planktonic and rocky reef communities. Science 215:204–205.

Breitburg, D. L. In press. Are three-dimensional structure, and healthy oyster populations the keys to an ecologically interesting, and important fish community? *in* M. W. Luckenbach, R. Mann, and J. A. Wesson, editors. Oyster reef habitat restoration: a synopsis, and synthesis of approaches, Virginia Institute of Marine Science Press, Gloucester Point, Virginia.

Breitburg, D. L., M. A. Palmer, and T. Loher. 1995. Larval distributions and the spatial patterns of settlement of an oyster reef fish: responses to flow and structure. Marine Ecology Progress Series 125:45–60.

Brooks, W. K. 1891. The oyster, re-issued. 1996. edition with a foreword by K. T. Paynter, Jr. Johns Hopkins University Press, Baltimore, Maryland.

Burrell, V. G., Jr. 1986. Species profiles: life histories and environmental requirements of coastal fishes and invertebrates (South Atlantic)—American oyster. U.S. Fish and Wildlife Service Biological Report 82 (11.57), U.S. Army Corps of Engineers TR EL-82–4.

Burrell, V. G., Jr., J. J. Manzi, and C. B. O'Rourke. 1991. Assessment of mechanical transplanting as a means of rehabilitating intertidal oyster beds. Proceedings of the Gulf and Caribbean Fisheries Institute 40:228–240.

Carr, M. H., and M. A. Hixon. 1997. Artificial reefs: the importance of comparisons with natural reefs. Fisheries 22(4):28–35.

Carriker, M. R., and P. M. Gaffney. 1996. A catalogue of selected species of living oysters (Ostreacea) of the world. Pages 1–18 *in* V. S. Kennedy, R. I. E. Newell, and A. F. Eble, editors. The eastern oyster, *Crassostrea virginica*. Maryland Sea Grant College Program, University of Maryland, College Park.

Chambers, J. R. 1992. Coastal degradation and fish population losses. Pages 45–51 *in* R. H. Stroud, editor. Stemming the tide of coastal fish habitat loss. National Coalition for Marine Conservation, Savannah, Georgia.

Christensen, N. L., and 12 coauthors. 1996. The report of the Ecological Society of America committee on the scientific basis for ecosystem management. Ecological Applications 6:665–691.

Cloern, J. E. 1982. Does the benthos control phytoplankton biomass in South San Francisco Bay? Marine Ecology Progress Series 9:191–202.

Coen, L. D., D. M. Knott, E. L. Wenner, N. H. Hadley, and M. Y. Bobo. 1997. Functional role of oyster reefs as "critical" estuarine habitats. Annual Report to SC Sea Grant Consortium, 1996-97, Charleston, South Carolina.

Coen, L. D., D. M. Knott, E. L. Wenner, N. H. Hadley, and A. H. Ringwood. In press. Intertidal oyster reef studies in South Carolina: design, sampling, and experimental focus for evaluating habitat value, and function. *In* M. W. Luckenbach, R. Mann, and J. A. Wesson, editors. Oyster reef habitat restoration: a synopsis, and synthesis of approaches. Virginia Institute of Marine Science Press, Gloucester Point, Virginia.

Coen, L. D., and M. Luckenbach. In press. Developing success criteria, and goals for evaluating shellfish habitat restoration: ecological function or resource exploitation? Ecological Engineering.

Cohen, R. R. H., P. V. Dresler, E. J. P. Phillips, and R. L. Cory. 1984. The effect of the Asiatic clam, *Corbicula fluminea*, on phytoplankton of the Potomac River, Maryland. Limnology and Oceanography 29:170–180.

Costanza, R., and 12 coauthors. 1997. The value of the world's ecosystem services and natural capital. Nature (London) 387:253–260.

Daily, G. C., editor. 1997. Nature's services: societal dependence on natural ecosystems. Island Press, Washington, D.C.

Dame, R. F. 1979. The abundance, diversity and biomass of macrobenthos on North Inlet, South Carolina, intertidal oyster reefs. Proceedings of the National Shellfish. Association 68:6–10.

Dame, R. F. 1996. Ecology of bivalves: an ecosystem approach. CRC Press, Boca Raton, Florida.

Dame, R. F., and 10 coauthors. 1997. Oyster reefs as structural and functional components of tidal creeks: an ongoing ecosystem experiment. Journal of Shellfish Research 16:260.

Dame, R. F., J. D. Spurrier, and R. G. Zingmark. 1992. In situ metabolism of an oyster reef. Journal Experimental Marine Biology and Ecology 164:147–159.

Dame, R. F., R. G. Zingmark, and E. Haskin. 1984. Oyster reefs as processors of estuarine materials. Journal Experimental Marine Biology and Ecology 83:239–247.

ESA (Ecological Society of America). 1998. Sustainable marine fisheries. Ecological Applications 8(Supplement 1):S1–S174.

Ewart, J. W., and S. E. Ford. 1993. History and impact of MSX and Dermo diseases on oyster stocks in the Northeastern region. Northeastern Regional Aquaculture Center Fact Sheet 200, NRAC, University of Massachusetts, Dartmouth.

Fitz, H. C., and R. G. Wiegert. 1991. Utilization of the intertidal zone of a salt marsh by the blue crab *Callinectes sapidus*: density, return frequency, and feeding habitats. Marine Ecology Progress Series 76:249–260.

Ford, S. E., and M. R. Tripp. 1996. Diseases and defense mechanisms. Pages 585–660 *in* V. S. Kennedy, R. I. E. Newell, and A. F. Eble, editors. The eastern oyster, *Crassostrea virginica*. Maryland Sea Grant College Program, University of Maryland, College Park.

Frankenberg, D. 1995. North Carolina Blue Ribbon Advisory Council on Oysters: final report on studies and recommendations. Raleigh, North Carolina.

Goddard, J. W. 1998. On Long Island Sound, a strong comeback. Soundings 36(1):55–57.

Gross, F., and J. C. Smyth. 1946. The decline of oyster populations. Nature (London) 157:540–542.

Grossman, G. D., G. P. Jones, and W. J. Seaman, Jr. 1997. Do artificial reefs increase regional fish production? a review of existing data. Fisheries 22(4):17–23.

Grumbine, R. E. 1994. What is ecosystem management? Conservation Biology 8:27–38.

Hardy, J. D., Jr. 1978a. Development of fishes of the mid-Atlantic Bight. Volume II. U.S. Fish and Wildlife Service, U.S. Department of the Interior, Washington, D.C.

Hardy, J. D., Jr. 1978b. Development of fishes of the mid-Atlantic Bight. Volume III. U.S. Fish and Wildlife Service, U.S. Department of the Interior, Washington, D.C.

Hargis, W. J., Jr., and D. S. Haven. 1995. The precarious state of the Chesapeake public oyster resource. Pages 559–584 in P. L. Hill and S. Nelson, editors. Toward a sustainable coastal watershed: the Chesapeake experiment. Chesapeake Research Consortium Publication 149, Solomons, Maryland.

Hargis, W. J., Jr., and D. S. Haven. In press. Chesapeake oyster reefs, their importance, destruction, and guidelines for restoring them. in M. W. Luckenbach, R. Mann, and J. A. Wesson, editors. Oyster reef habitat restoration: a synopsis, and synthesis of approaches. Virginia Institute of Marine Science Press, Gloucester Point, Virginia.

Hayward, E. L., III, T. M. Soniat, and R. C. Broadhurst, III. In press. Alternative to clam, and oyster shell as cultch for eastern oysters. in M. W. Luckenbach, R. Mann, and J. A. Wesson, editors. Oyster reef habitat restoration: a synopsis, and synthesis of approaches. Virginia Institute of Marine Science Press, Gloucester Point, Virginia.

Haywood, M. D. E., D. J. Vance, and N. R. Loneragan. 1995. Seagrass and algal beds as nursery habitats for tiger prawns (Penaeus semisulcatus and P. esculentus) in a tropical Australian estuary. Marine Biology 122:213–223.

Heck, K. L., Jr., and L. D. Coen. 1995. Predation and the abundance of juvenile blue crabs: a comparison of selected East and Gulf Coast (USA) studies. Bulletin of Marine Science 57:877–883.

Heck, K. L., Jr., D. A. Nadeau, and R. Thomas. 1997. The nursery role of seagrass beds—commentary. Gulf of Mexico Science 15:50–54.

Heck, K. L., Jr., and R. J. Orth. 1980. Seagrass habitats: the roles of habitat complexity, competition, and predation in structuring associated fish and motile macro-invertebrate assemblages. Pages 449–461 in V. S. Kennedy, editor. Estuarine perspectives. Academic Press, New York.

Heck, K. L., Jr., and T. A. Thoman. 1984. The nursery role of seagrass meadows in the upper and lower reaches of the Chesapeake bay. Estuaries 7:70–92.

Heck, K. L., Jr., and G. S. Wetstone. 1977. Habitat complexity and invertebrate species richness and abundance in tropical seagrass meadows. Journal of Biogeography 4:135–142.

Hettler, W. F. 1989. Nekton use of regularly flooded salt marsh cordgrass habitat in North Carolina, USA. Marine Ecology Progress Series 56:111–118.

Irlandi, E. A., and M. K. Crawford. 1997. Habitat linkages: the effect of intertidal saltmarshes and adjacent subtidal habitats on abundance, movement, and growth of an estuarine fish. Oecologia 110:222–230.

Johnson, G. D. 1978. Development of fishes of the mid-Atlantic Bight. Volume IV. U.S. Fish and Wildlife Service, U.S. Department of the Interior, Washington, D.C.

Jones, C. G., J. H. Lawton, and M. Shachak. 1994. Organisms as ecosystem engineers. Oikos 69:373–386.

Jones, P. W., F. D. Martin, and J. D. Hardy Jr. 1978. Development of fishes of the mid-Atlantic Bight. Volume I. U.S. Fish and Wildlife Service, U.S. Department of the Interior, Washington, D.C.

Kaufman, L., and P. Dayton. 1997. Impacts of marine resource extraction on ecosystem services and sustainability. Pages 275–293 in G. C. Daily, editor. Nature's services: societal dependence on natural ecosystems. Island Press, Washington, D.C.

Kennedy, V. S., R. I. E. Newell, and A. F. Eble, editors. 1996. The eastern oyster, Crassostrea virginica. Maryland Sea Grant College Program, University of Maryland, College Park.

Klemanowicz, K. J. 1985. Effects of a mechanical oyster harvester on macrofaunal community structure. Master's thesis. College of Charleston, Charleston, South Carolina.

Kneib, R. T. 1997. Early life stages of resident nekton in intertidal marshes. Estuaries 20:214–230.

Kneib, R. T., and S. L. Wagner. 1994. Nekton use of vegetated marsh habitats at different stages of tidal inundation. Marine Ecology Progress Series 106:227–238.

Lenihan, H. S. 1996. Physical-biological coupling on oyster reefs: hydrodynamics, sedimentation, and the production of oysters. Doctoral dissertation. University of North Carolina at Chapel Hill.

Lenihan, H. S., F. Micheli, S. W. Shelton, and C. H. Peterson. In press. The influence of multiple environmental stressors on susceptibility to parasites: an experimental determination with oysters. Limnology and Oceanography.

Lenihan, H. S., and C. H. Peterson. 1998. How habitat degradation through fishery disturbance enhances impacts of hypoxia on oyster reefs. Ecological Applications 8:128–140.

Leonard, D. L. 1993. Turning the tides on water quality on declining shellfish resources. World Aquaculture 24:56–64.

Luckenbach, M. W., R. Mann, and J. A Wesson, editors. In press. Oyster reef habitat restoration: a synopsis, and synthesis of approaches. Virginia Institute of Marine Science Press, Gloucester Point, Virginia.

Luckenbach, M. W., J. Nestlerode, T. Hurlock, and G. Coates. 1997. Characterization of resident and transient assemblages associated with constructed oyster reef habitats: beginning to relate structure and function. Final report, year 1. Aquatic Reef Habitat Program, Chesapeake Bay Program, Wachapreague, Virginia.

MacKenzie, C. L., Jr. 1983. To increase oyster production in the northeastern United States. Marine Fisheries Review 45:1–22.

MacKenzie, C. L., Jr. 1996a. History of oystering in the United States and Canada, featuring the eight greatest oyster estuaries. Marine Fisheries Review 58:1–87.

MacKenzie, C. L., Jr. 1996b. Management of natural populations. Pages 707–721 in Kennedy, V. S., R. I. E. Newell, and A. F. Eble, editors. The eastern oyster, Crassostrea virginica. Maryland Sea Grant College Program, University of Maryland, College Park.

MacKenzie, C. L., Jr., V. G. Burrell, Jr., A. Rosenfield, and W. L. Hobart, editors. 1997a. The history, present condition, and future of the molluscan fisheries of North and Central America and Europe. Volume 1, Atlantic and Gulf coasts. U.S. Department of Commerce, National Oceanic and Atmospheric Administration Technical Report NMFS 127, Seattle.

MacKenzie, C. L., Jr., V. G. Burrell, Jr., A. Rosenfield, and W. L. Hobart, editors. 1997b. The history, present condition, and future of the molluscan fisheries of North and Central America and Europe. Volume 2, Pacific coast and supplemental topics. U.S. Department of Commerce, National Oceanic and Atmospheric Administration Technical Report NMFS 128, Seattle.

Martin, F. D., and G. E. Drewry. 1978. Development of fishes of the mid-Atlantic Bight. Volume V. U.S. Fish and Wildlife Service, U.S. Department of the Interior, Washington, D.C.

Meyer, D. L., E. C. Townsend, and G. W. Thayer. 1997. Stabilization and erosion control value of oyster cultch for intertidal marsh. Restoration Ecology 5:93–99.

Minello, T. J. 1999. Nekton densities in shallow estuarine habitats of Texas and Louisiana and the identification of essential fish habitat. Pages 43–75 in L. R. Benaka, editor. Fish habitat: essential fish habitat and rehabilitation. American Fisheries Society, Symposium 22, Bethesda, Maryland.

Morgan, M. D. 1980. Grazing and predation of the grass shrimp Palaemonetes pugio. Limnology and Oceanography 25:896–902.

Newell, R. I. E. 1988. Ecological changes in Chesapeake Bay: are they the result of overharvesting the American oyster, Crassostrea virginica? Pages 536–546 in M. P. Lynch and E. C. Krome, editors. Understanding the estuary: advances in Chesapeake Bay research. Chesapeake Research Consortium, Publication 129 CBP/TRS 24/88, Gloucester Point, Virginia.

Nixon, S. W. 1980. Between coastal marshes and coastal waters: a review of twenty years of speculation and research on the role of salt marshes in estuarine productivity and water chemistry. Pages 437–525 in P. Hamilton and K. MacDonald, editors. Estuarine and wetland processes. Plenum, New York.

NOAA (National Oceanic, and Atmospheric Administration). 1997. The 1995 National Shellfish Register of Classified Growing Waters. Office of Ocean Resources Conservation and Assessment, Silver Spring, Maryland.

Orth, R. J., K. L. Heck, Jr., and J. Van Montfrans. 1984. Faunal communities in seagrass beds: a review of the influence of plant structure and prey characteristics on predator–prey relationships. Estuaries 7:339–350.

Orth, R. J., and J. Van Montfrans. 1987. Utilization of a seagrass meadow and tidal marsh creek by blue crabs Callinectes sapidus. I. seasonal and annual variations in abundance with emphasis on postsettlement juveniles. Marine Ecology Progress Series 41:283–294.

Paine, R. T. 1994. Marine rocky shores and community ecology: an experimentalist's perspective. Ecology Institute, D-21385, Oldendorf/Luhe, Germany.

Parrish, J. D. 1989. Fish communities of interacting shallow-water habitats in tropical oceanic regions. Marine Ecology Progress Series 58:143–160.

Peterson, C. H., and J. Lubchenco. 1997. Marine ecosystem services. Pages 177–194 in G. C. Daily, editor. Nature's services: societal dependence on natural ecosystems. Island Press, Washington, D.C.

Peterson, G. W., and R. E. Turner. 1994. The value of salt marsh edge vs interior as a habitat for fish and decapod crustaceans in a Louisiana tidal marsh. Estuaries 17:235–262.

Petraitis, P. S. 1987. Factors organizing rocky intertidal communities of New England: herbivory and predation in sheltered bays. Journal Experimental Marine Biology and Ecology 109:117–136.

Petraitis, P. S. 1995. The role of growth in maintaining spatial dominance by mussels (Mytilus edulis). Ecology 76:1337–1346.

Posey, M. H., T. D. Alphin, C. M. Powell, and E. Townsend. In press. Oyster reefs as habitat for fish, and decapods. In M. Luckenbach, R. Mann, and J. A. Wesson, editors. Oyster reef habitat restoration: a synopsis of approaches. Virginia Institute of Marine Science Press, Gloucester Point, Virginia.

Posey, M., and W. G. Ambrose, Jr. 1994. Effects of proximity to an offshore hard-bottom reef on infaunal abundances. Marine Biology 118:745–753.

Powell, E. N., J. M. Klinck, E. E. Hoffman, and S. Ford. 1997. Varying the timing of oyster transplant: implications for management from simulation studies. Fisheries Oceanography 6:213–237.

Roditi, H., N. F. Caraco, J. J. Cole, and D. L. Strayer. 1996. Filtration of Hudson River water by the zebra mussel (Dreissena polymorpha). Estuaries 19:824–832.

Rothschild, B. J., J. S. Ault, P. Goulletquer, and M. Héral. 1994. Decline of the Chesapeake Bay oyster population: a century of habitat destruction and overfishing. Marine Ecology Progress Series 111:29–39.

Rozas, L. P. 1993. Nekton use of salt marshes of the southeast region of the United States. Pages 528–537 in O. T. Magoon, W. S. Wilson, H. Converse, and L. T. Hobin, editors. Proceedings of the Coastal Zone 1993 Conference. American Society of Civil Engineers, New York.

Rozas, L. P., and T. J. Minello. 1997. Estimating densities of small fishes and decapod crustaceans in shallow estuarine habitats: a review of sampling design with focus on gear selection. Estuaries 20:199–213.

Safriel, U. N., and M. N. Ben-Eliahu. 1991. The influences of habitat structure and environmental stability on the species diversity of polychaetes in vermetid reefs. Pages 349–363 *in* S. S. Bell, E. D. McCoy, and H. R. Mushinsky, editors. Habitat structure: the physical arrangement of objects in space. Chapman and Hall, London.

Smaal, A. C., and H. A. Haas. 1997. Seston dynamics and food availability on mussel and cockle beds. Estuarine Coastal Shelf Science 45:247–259.

Stanley, D. W., and M. A. Sellers. 1986. Species profile: life histories and environmental requirements of coastal fishes and invertebrates (Gulf of Mexico)—American oyster. U.S. Fish and Wildlife Service Biological Report 82(11.64), U.S. Army Corps of Engineers, TR EL-82-4.

Supan, J. A., C. A. Wilson, and K. J. Roberts. In press. Economics of augmentation of natural production using hatchery techniques. *In* M. Luckenbach, R. Mann, and J. A. Wesson, editors. Oyster reef habitat restoration: a synopsis of approaches. Virginia Institute of Marine Science Press, Gloucester Point, Virginia.

Thomas, J. L., R. J. Zimmerman, and T. J. Minello. 1990. Abundance patterns of juvenile blue crabs (*Callinectes sapidus*) in nursery habitats of two Texas bays. Bulletin of Marine Science 46:115–125.

Ulanowicz, R. E., and J. H. Tuttle. 1992. The trophic consequences of oyster stock rehabilitation in Chesapeake Bay. Estuaries 15:298–306.

USDOC (U.S. Department of Commerce). 1997. Magnuson-Stevens Fishery Conservation and Management Act, as amended through October 11, 1996. National Oceanic and Atmospheric Administration Technical Memorandum NMFS-F/SPO-23. U.S. Government Printing Office, Washington, D.C.

Weinstein, M. P., and H. A. Brooks. 1983. Comparative ecology of nekton residing in a tidal creek and adjacent seagrass meadow: community composition and structure. Marine Ecology Progress Series 12:15–27.

Wells, H. W. 1961. The fauna of oyster beds, with special reference to the salinity factor. Ecological Monographs 31:266–329.

Wenner, E., H. R. Beatty, and L. D. Coen. 1996. Method for quantitatively sampling nekton on intertidal oyster reefs. Journal of Shellfish Research 115:769–775.

Wenner, E. L., and A. D. Stokes. 1984. Observations on the fishable population of the stone crab *Menippe mercenaria* (Say) in South Carolina waters. Journal of Shellfish Research 4:145–153.

Whitlach, R. B., and R. W. Osman. In press. Oyster reefs as metapopulations: approaches for restoring, and managing spatially fragmented habitats. *In* M. Luckenbach, R. Mann, and J. A. Wesson, editors. Oyster reef habitat restoration: a synopsis of approaches. Virginia Institute of Marine Science Press, Gloucester Point, Virginia.

Wilson, K. A., K. W. Able, and K. L. Heck, Jr. 1987. Juvenile blue crab (*Callinectes sapidus*) survival: an evaluation of eelgrass as refuge. Fishery Bulletin 85:53–58.

Wilson, K. A., K. W. Able, and K. L. Heck, Jr. 1990. Habitat use by juvenile blue crabs: a comparison among habitats in southern New Jersey. Bulletin of Marine Science 46:105–114.

Witman, J. D. 1987. Subtidal coexistence: storms, grazing, mutualism, and the zonation of kelps and mussels. Ecological Monographs 57:167–187.

Zimmerman, R., T. J. Minello, T. Baumer, and M. Castiglione. 1989. Oyster reef as habitat for estuarine macrofauna. National Oceanic and Atmospheric Administration Technical Memorandum NMFS-SEFC-249.

American Fisheries Society Symposium 22:455–459, 1999

Summary of Panel Discussions and Steps toward an Agenda for Habitat Policy and Science

LEE R. BENAKA

Sea Grant, American Fisheries Society
5410 Grosvenor Lane, Suite 110, Bethesda, Maryland 20814-2199, USA

The Sea Grant symposium on fish habitat that took place at the 1998 Annual Meeting of the American Fisheries Society (AFS) included six panel discussions covering a range of topics from the need for outreach to the need for prioritization of essential fish habitat (EFH). This chapter describes in a general manner the comments made in each panel discussion and identifies an agenda for future habitat policy and research based on the issues raised at the Sea Grant symposium.

Essential Fish Habitat Perspectives

The first session of the symposium was made up of presentations that expressed differing views on the efficacy of the EFH policy created through the 1996 reauthorization of the Magnuson-Stevens Fishery Conservation and Management Act (Magnuson-Stevens Act, also called the Sustainable Fisheries Act). Although all presenters agreed that healthy levels of fish production were related to healthy habitat, some presenters suggested that the EFH policy represented an onerous burden to the fishing industry and was a weak regulatory tool that would be unable to effectively protect fish habitat from nonfishing pressures. The range of opinions expressed would have been wider had a greater variety of stakeholders—including numerous interest groups that until recently have been uninterested in fish habitat—been involved in the panel discussion. In addition to representatives of federal fishery management agencies, conservation organizations, and fishing industry groups, representatives of homebuilders associations, agricultural interests, ports, timber companies, universities, and other institutions have contrasting and thought-provoking perspectives on EFH. Future symposia and books on fish habitat and EFH should involve as large a variety of stakeholders as possible so that a wide range of viewpoints can be shared. Such forums should lead to greater understanding and cooperation among groups and interests that may be suspicious of each other's motives.

The need to encourage participation and seek input from nonfishing interests was highlighted by one of the panel members in this first discussion. Conducting educational and outreach activities and setting clear policy priorities were cited as crucial to the EFH policy's success. Another panel member asserted that public education can lead to public and political support of policies. According to this panel member, people need to learn where their seafood comes from, especially if they do not live in a coastal community with a vibrant fishing culture. One audience member stated the need for a habitat constituency to ensure funding. One possible large source of funding for habitat research could take the form of a Living Marine Resources Trust Fund (Brouha 1998), according to the audience member.

The third panel member cautioned that the rules to implement the EFH policy dwell on ecosystem-level issues rather than focusing on threats to fish habitat from coastal development. As a result of this ecosystem focus, the need for control of coastal development is ignored and the fishing industry suffers from overregulation of fishing gear. The general issue of where to focus management and research resources was echoed by an audience member, who perceived that research on estuarine habitats was being emphasized at the expense of research on offshore habitats. According to this audience member, estuarine habitats are not of primary importance in all regions of the United States.

An audience member questioned how the importance of habitat could be best communicated to the public at large, and a panel member in response suggested that extension and communication professionals within the National Sea Grant College Program (Sea Grant) could serve as valuable educational resources because of their close working relationships with coastal and inland natural resources stakeholders. Finally, one audience member stressed the need for the AFS to continue its leadership role in the area of fish habitat and EFH and praised Paul Brouha for making habitat a top priority during his tenure as Executive Director of the AFS.

Essential Fish Habitat Identification

The second session of the symposium consisted of presentations by fisheries professionals who have taken various approaches to identifying EFH for a variety of fish species. In general, the presenters felt that the acquisition of additional data on habitat parameters of fish species through the use of appropriate sampling techniques and predictive models—as well as the funding of additional habitat research—would lead to identification of EFH areas more discrete than the seemingly broad areas of EFH initially proposed for some species. Indeed, presenters and audience members expressed strong feelings (both positive and negative) about the methodology used to initially identify EFH.

One panel member led off the discussion by asking who would coordinate future research requirements and determine how research should be prioritized so that EFH identification progress can be made rapidly. Another panel member, bringing up a view that would be expressed several times during the symposium, suggested that EFH designations may not be taken seriously because they are so broad. This panel member suggested that three criteria should be used to determine whether habitat is truly essential for a species: (1) the degree of utilization, (2) availability, and (3) vulnerability of the habitat. A member of the audience stated that it is important in estuarine areas to examine how habitat gradients are being used, although such specific research would require significantly more funding than had been allocated thus far for EFH identification. A panel member stated that EFH guidelines issued by the National Marine Fisheries Service (NMFS) needed to provide stronger direction in narrowing down the initial designations.

The critique that initial EFH designations were overly broad was countered by an audience member who pointed out that broad designations were necessary due to the precautionary principle and time constraints imposed by the U.S. Congress for the identification of EFH. In addition, the audience member cited the policy's provisions for the identification of habitat areas of particular concern (HAPCs), which serve to narrow the scope of EFH designations and perhaps indicate what is the "essential" EFH. Finally, the audience member suggested that the EFH consultation process to be carried out by the NMFS would allow managers to prioritize which activities have the most impact on which types of habitat. The broad-brush approach to EFH identification had other supporters on the

panel and in the audience. One audience member stressed the need to address marginal rather than gross changes in habitat quantity and quality and argued that the best way to do this is through large-scale EFH designations. A panel member added that initial broad EFH designations were being used as management tools already.

An audience member from Alaska described the precautionary approach used for EFH identification in the North Pacific region, which was necessitated due to a severe lack of species-specific data and the large scale of fish habitat in Alaska (i.e., approximately 26,000 anadromous fish streams). This audience member suggested that EFH identification needs to be connected to fishery abundance levels and that seafloor habitat needs to be mapped. Another audience member suggested that, using geographic information system technology, it would be instructive to superimpose EFH and HAPC designations to more effectively identify EFH.

One audience member commented that state fishery and natural resource management agencies need to be involved in the EFH identification process because estuarine areas that have been identified as EFH are within state waters. Another audience member questioned whether the NMFS had allocated sufficient fiscal year 1999 funding for research needed to better identify EFH. Also on the subject of funding, a panel member wondered whether funding from the Wallop-Breaux Act could be given to state agencies for individual EFH-related programs.

As of this writing, the 11 October 1998 deadline for the regional fishery management councils to identify EFH is three months past, and it remains to be seen whether EFH identification will lead to effective consultation practices and the additional protection of fish habitat. Consistent leadership for habitat management activities in the NMFS's headquarters in Silver Spring, Maryland will be needed to ensure EFH success. The EFH consultation process will be time-consuming and politically sensitive, requiring numerous professionals with expertise in habitat management.

Fishing Impacts on Fish Habitat

Presenters in the third session of the symposium discussed impacts of fishing activities and natural processes and the importance of involving commercial fishermen in habitat management. Most of the abbreviated panel discussion that followed the presentations revolved around the relationship between impacts on habitat due to natural processes and impacts due to gear. One panel member argued that although fishing gear clearly has impacts on habitat, impacts due to gear such as trawls or dredges should not be extrapolated to all habitats because such gears are only used in certain areas of the ocean. In addition, particular parts of the ocean are more resilient than others to gear impacts. Another panel member stated that the effects of fishing gear on soft sediments should not be minimized because many ecological processes that enhance juvenile fish survivorship take place in soft sediments. An audience member questioned whether the natural mobility of benthic sediments could truly be equated with trawling-induced sediment disturbance. A panel member replied that the effects of waves on bottom sediments are dynamic and that a large range of effects of waves on bottom sediments have been documented.

The number of published studies of fishing-gear impacts on fish habitat has grown substantially over the past few years. In addition to studies of gear impacts presented in this volume, the December 1998 issue of *Conservation Biology* contained seven papers on the effects of trawls and dredges on the seafloor. An entire book published in 1998 was devoted to the effects of fishing gear on the seafloor of New England (Dorsey and Pederson 1998). Similar books and dedicated journal issues examining gear impacts in other regions of the United States and around the world should be published. It must be recognized that the study of fishing-gear impacts on habitat is a politically sensitive issue because the results of such studies, due to the EFH provisions, could possibly restrict the use of certain types of gear beyond already-stringent restrictions in areas such as New England and result in economic hardship for coastal fishing communities. The study and management of fishing-gear impacts on fish habitat can, like many other aspects of fisheries science and management, serve to pit gear types against one another (e.g., fixed gear versus mobile gear). However, when strong evidence is available that particular fishing activities may harm areas of the seafloor that are important to certain life stages of fishes, managers must act decisively to protect such habitat through gear restrictions or the creation of marine reserves.

Nonfishing Impacts on Fish Habitat

The number and variety of impacts on fish habitat and EFH from sources other than fishing activity are considerable and difficult to prioritize. The fourth session of the Sea Grant fish habitat symposium, which was devoted to nonfishing impacts, barely plumbed the depths of such impacts, although it did include thought-provoking presentations on climate, water diversions, oil spills, and riparian habitat alterations. Many other nonfishing threats loom large in the habitat management arena, however, including gravel mining, port and marina operations, coastal development, and agricultural practices. Effective habitat management will require comprehensive literature reviews for each possible nonfishing impact and, resulting from such literature reviews, guidance and procedures that fisheries managers can use in swiftly responding to proposals for activities that may impact fish habitat. One model for the creation of science-based management tools for fisheries managers is the "Habitat Synthesis Document" collaboration between the NMFS and Sea Grant, which is still in a formative stage as of this writing but has the potential to provide helpful guidance to fisheries managers (Benaka 1998).

The panel discussion during this fourth session of the symposium revolved around the critical issue of outreach, that is, how to make people care about fish habitat. One panel member pointed out that long-term public-education efforts about habitat and small, habitat-related demonstration projects were crucial to obtaining substantial funding to carry out habitat restoration work. The panel member stressed the importance of involving children and students in projects such as habitat monitoring programs that are perceived as worthwhile. An audience member mentioned course work that had been developed in Florida to help the public understand the functioning of estuarine environments.

Effective fish habitat conservation will not occur unless the public finds value in such efforts. Local, grassroots habitat-restoration efforts need to be brought to the attention of and supported by federal and state fisheries-management agencies. The habitat observations of trained volunteers could help fill gaps in science when government funding is not available to hire professionals. The importance of fish habitat is being recognized more often than ever due to the EFH policy, and reports on EFH and fish habitat are being published more frequently than ever in scientific publications that are not exclusively focused on fisheries and that are aimed at a general readership (e.g., Schmidt 1998; Hiney 1999; Merriman-Clarke 1999). Continued innovative approaches to outreach, such as those used routinely by Sea Grant extension agents, are required to build on this recognition of habitat and to ensure that people buying fish at the supermarket in Kansas know what conditions are required for healthy fish to end up on their dinner plates.

Fish Habitat Rehabilitation and Socioeconomic Issues—Focus on the Great Lakes

When discussing marine fish habitat, one should not ignore the important fish habitat research that has been conducted in the Great Lakes by Canadian and U.S. scientists. Marine fisheries scientists and managers have much to learn from their Great Lakes counterparts and vice versa because they both deal with the same problems: habitat degradation, nonindigenous species, pollution, etc. In this fifth session of the symposium, two presenters discussed habitat management and the assessment of fish habitat parameters, and two presenters described the economic and ecological effects of the construction of a large artificial fish habitat in Lake Erie.

During the following panel discussion, one panelist stated that the greatest challenges for Great Lakes fish habitat management and research were decreased funding and declines in human resources. The panelist further stated that strong habitat policy statements and habitat inventories would be crucial for improved management. An audience member asked whether improvements in Great Lakes water clarity due to the explosion of the zebra mussel *Dreissena polymorpha* population had led to improved habitat mapping and growth of submerged aquatic vegetation (SAV). One panelist answered affirmatively and added that improvements in water clarity may be especially helpful to smallmouth bass *Micropterus dolomieu* populations. Another panelist agreed that the zebra mussels had especially improved water quality in embayments, which in turn benefitted largemouth bass *Micropterus salmoides* and pike *Esox lucius* populations, as well as anglers. However, another panelist reminded the audience that the preceding "benefits" were caused by an exotic species and that some of the newly abundant SAV can become uprooted during storms and dam waste in bodies of water.

One panelist asked a simple but thought-provoking question: why can't the Great Lakes be covered by the EFH policy? Although the EFH provisions contained in the 1996 reauthorization of the Magnuson-Stevens Fishery Conservation and Management Act do not focus on Great Lakes fisheries, it may be useful for Great Lakes fisheries

managers to ask themselves, "Which kinds of habitats would be identified as EFH for the fish we manage?" According to one panelist, Great Lakes fisheries managers and researchers have been asking this type of question, without using the EFH acronym, for many years by setting fish community objectives and other activities. As Sea Grant continues to work closely with the NMFS on EFH issues, Great Lakes researchers affiliated with the Sea Grant network will be involved, speculated another panelist. Another panelist reiterated that habitat capacity-building was needed for fisheries managers in the Great Lakes because many Great Lakes fisheries management plans do not yet include components that resemble the EFH provisions.

Marine Fish Habitat Rehabilitation and Socioeconomic Issues

In the sixth and final session of the symposium, presenters discussed habitat rehabilitation issues related to New England salt marshes and spiny lobster and oyster populations. In the panel discussion, when it came to acknowledging the role of Sea Grant funding in the success of their habitat research, two panelists had differing viewpoints. One panelist stated that Sea Grant's long-term support had greatly enhanced the success of the research conducted. Another panelist argued that long-term research efforts had been hampered by Sea Grant's short-term grant cycles. The importance of educational and outreach efforts was again raised by a panelist who stated that the biggest challenge to habitat rehabilitation was a lack of appreciation by local populations for habitat projects and resulting changes and improvements. Another panel member commented that habitat rehabilitation in New England salt marshes is hard to measure due to the few salt-marsh studies that have been conducted in the region. Finally, a panelist speculated that restored marsh habitats in New England could result in the restoration of coastal fisheries.

Conclusion

The Sea Grant fish habitat symposium held at the 1998 AFS Annual Meeting set a benchmark for the early stages of the new EFH policy and suggested an agenda for future fish habitat policy and science. The short time-frame for EFH identification, lack of fisheries life history data, and four-tier identification process adopted by the NMFS (see Minello

1999, this volume) led to initial EFH identifications that seemed overly broad to some observers. However, the EFH policy should focus future fish habitat research by governmental and nongovernmental biologists so that habitat-related gaps in life history data can be filled and EFH designations can be narrowed. Overall, the EFH policy has brought a high profile to fish habitat considerations, which should lead to greater habitat conservation in the long term.

Future efforts toward fish habitat identification, conservation, and rehabilitation should include three crucial components. First, increased education and outreach will be necessary to communicate the importance of fish habitat quality and ensure political support for habitat activities. Popular support for habitat activities will contribute to the second component of future successful habitat work—increased funding. Filling the gaps in fish habitat science and fully utilizing the management tools provided by the EFH provisions will only be possible through the dedication of additional trained professionals around the United States. Third, partnerships and collaboration will be essential to manage fish habitat in the best possible manner. The partnership between the AFS, NMFS, and Sea Grant that led to the fish habitat symposium and this book is one example of a collaboration designed to help raise the profile and enhance understanding of fish habitat issues. Other collaborations and partnerships should be forged between Great Lakes and marine fisheries managers and scientists, as well as between the diverse stakeholders affected by fish habitat considerations, ranging from fishermen to real estate developers. Education and outreach, funding, and partnerships and collaboration will help fulfill the promise of the EFH policy and should lead to even more effective efforts to protect fish habitat and restore fisheries.

References

Benaka, L. R. 1998. Fish habitat takes center stage, but collaboration is needed to keep it there. Fisheries 23(8):4.

Brouha, P. 1998. A Living Marine Resources Trust Fund: its time has come. Fisheries 23(7):4.

Dorsey, E. M., and J. Pederson. 1998. Effects of fishing gear on the sea floor of New England. Conservation Law Foundation, Boston.

Hiney, T. 1999. Home is where the essential habitat is. Texas Shores 31(4):2–21.

Merriman-Clarke, K. 1999. The Sustainable Fisheries Act: reversing the decline of America's marine fisheries. Conservation Sciences (Winter 1999):17–20.

Minello, T. J. 1999. Nekton densities in shallow estuarine habitats of Texas and Louisiana and the identification of essential fish habitat. Pages 43–75 in L. R. Benaka, editor. Fish habitat: essential fish habitat and rehabilitation. American Fisheries Society, Symposium 22, Bethesda, Maryland.

Schmidt, K. 1998. Ecology's catch of the day. Science 281:192–193.